The Great Ideas

President Wilson, France's Clemenceau, England's Lloyd George at the Versailles peace negotiations, 1919. Detail of painting by Sir William Orpen.

"....a universal dominion of right by such a concert of free peoples as shall bring peace and safety to all nations and make the world itself at last free...." Woodrow Wilson

The
Great Ideas
Today

1971

William Benton, *Publisher*

Encyclopaedia Britannica, Inc.

Chicago • London • Toronto • Geneva • Sydney • Tokyo • Manila

The Great Ideas Today 1971

Printed in the U.S.A. Library of Congress Catalog Number: 61-65561
International Standard Book Number: 0-85229-167-1

"The Problem of World Government" from *Man and the State*
by Jacques Maritain is reprinted by permission of University
of Chicago Press, copyright 1951 by the University of Chicago.

The Time Machine by H. G. Wells is reprinted by permission of
William Heinemann Limited, Publishers.

Distributed to the trade by Praeger Publishers, Inc., New York, Washington

Contents

A NOTE ON REFERENCE STYLE

In the following pages, passages in *Great Books of the Western World* are referred to by the initials '*GBWW*,' followed by volume, page number, and page section. Thus, '*GBWW*, Vol. 39, p. 210b' refers to page 210 in Adam Smith's *The Wealth of Nations,* which is Volume 39 in *Great Books of the Western World.* The small letter 'b' indicates the page section. In books printed in single column, 'a' and 'b' refer to the upper and lower halves of the page. In books printed in double column, 'a' and 'b' refer to the upper and lower halves of the left column, 'c' and 'd' to the upper and lower halves of the right column. For example, 'Vol. 53, p. 210b' refers to the lower half of page 210, since Volume 53, James's *Principles of Psychology,* is printed in single column. On the other hand, 'Vol. 7, p. 210b' refers to the lower left quarter of the page, since Volume 7, Plato's *Dialogues,* is printed in double column.

Gateway to the Great Books is referred to by the initials '*GGB*,' followed by volume and page number. Thus, '*GGB*, Vol. 10, pp. 39-57' refers to pages 39 through 57 of Volume 10 of *Gateway to the Great Books,* which is James's essay, "The Will to Believe."

The Great Ideas Today is referred to by the initials '*GIT*,' followed by the year and page number. Thus '*GIT* 1968, p. 510' refers to page 510 of the 1968 edition of *The Great Ideas Today.*

PART ONE

The World Community

A Symposium

Introduction

When the Second World War was drawing to a close more than a quarter of a century ago, and even before its end was in sight, men began to consider how further wars of the same kind might be prevented. It was believed by at least some people that this would require a world government, but among the difficulties that were foreseen there was disagreement as to whether such a government can ever be created before a world community has come to exist, or whether a world community can have reality only through the operation of a world government.

As matters fell out, this question was avoided by the representatives of forty-six countries who met at San Francisco in the spring of 1945 to adopt what became the Charter of the United Nations. These representatives did not even attempt to create a world government, which most of them regarded as a visionary idea. Instead, they established a vaguer and looser thing called a "world organization," which took no governmental authority upon itself, and which did not recognize the existence of any world community. The burden of proof thus fell upon those who claimed that such a community could come about in the absence of governmental powers, and indeed that it would have to before they could be assumed.

Our contributors to this year's symposium discuss the extent to which this has actually happened since that time and express themselves as to the likelihood of such a development in the future. While they perceive some gains during the twenty-five years that the UN has survived, and some hopeful signs, they are not overly optimistic about the prospects for a true world community, which they consider from various points of view.

Among the obstacles is the lack of definition or protection of fundamental human rights and liberties in many parts of the world, as the French jurist René Cassin, the principal author of the UN Universal Declaration of Human Rights (1948), points out. Then, too, there are still profound cultural and religious differences that divide mankind, though Arthur Lall, India's former ambassador to the UN, believes that UN-sponsored efforts to build a world university may help to overcome these.

Perhaps the most encouraging news is in the field of ecology, where the threat to the biosphere caused by pollution has lately brought men together from many countries; so we learn from Dr. Henry J. Kellermann of the National Academy of Sciences. Yet the problems are not yet recognized everywhere, Dr. Kellermann makes clear, and while much is being done to meet them, there is much more to do and not much time left in which to do it. Nor can it be done at all without revising our ideas

Final session of the League of Nations General Assembly, April 18, 1946

about world economic development, we are told by the British economist E. J. Mishan, who goes on to note serious anticommunal tendencies in the postwar economics of abundance and consumption.

It is therefore not surprising that former U.S. Senator Joseph S. Clark, who is now president of World Federalists, USA, asserts the need for world government. We need it, he says, not only to forestall a third world war but also to deal with worldwide problems of poverty and population —problems that are not likely to be solved until a world government exists.

The idea of a world community occurs at many points in the Great Books. How it does so, and where, is discussed in a separate essay at the end of the symposium.

René Cassin

René Cassin, jurist, academician, and
winner of the Nobel Prize for Peace (1968),
has for half a century served France and
the world in the field of international affairs
and the cause of human rights. A delegate
to the League of Nations (1924–38) and
the United Nations (1946–58), he was one
of the founders of UNESCO, on which he
served between 1945 and 1962, took part

in the formation of the UN Commission on
Human Rights (1946), on which he served
until 1968, and was the principal author
of the Universal Declaration of Human
Rights (1948). From 1959 to 1968 he was
judge and later president of the European
Court of Human Rights. In 1968 he established the International Institute of Human
Rights at Strasbourg, over which he still
presides. He is the author of several books
and innumerable articles on civil, public,
and international law.

Human Rights Since 1945:
An Appraisal

For all who may be willing to profit by self-examination, the twenty-fifth anniversary of the founding of the United Nations, recently celebrated in New York and the capitals of its member states, provides an opportunity to appraise candidly the efforts that have been made since 1945 to promote and protect the rights of man.

Broadly speaking, accomplishments have been positive in terms of international organizations and world opinion, significantly less so in terms of individual states. World developments with respect to human rights and individual liberties are genuinely hopeful and at the same time threatening in ways that are not exclusively political. All who shape public opinion, as well as those who lead nations, must share grave responsibilities.

In July 1970, at the opening of the first academic session of the International Institute of Human Rights in Strasbourg, man's basic rights were defined as "the sum of all the rights, privileges and freedoms that every human being in society must enjoy to insure both his dignity and the full development of his personality."

Several points are involved here that require further clarification. First, human rights can never be permanently defined or fixed once and for all, since their evolution is a constant, dynamic process. Second, the "leaps forward" that these rights have made have almost invariably come as the result of historical upheavals of worldwide significance. Third, in the modern era the internationalization of human rights has become a controlling fact.

To take the first point: it is not because man's physical characteristics have changed little since the beginning of verifiable time that the list of his fundamental rights and freedoms has been thought to be forever fixed, but because of the belief that such rights and freedoms are themselves natural and innate. This belief has merit insofar as it places value on those traits that distinguish man from other species, notably his sense of

Translated from the French by Phyllis Nauts Ott.

individual worth based on conscience and reason, but it is inadequate, even dangerous, if it does not reckon with new demands, equally conscientious and reasonable, which arise from changes both in his moral or social ideas and in the material conditions of his life.

The second point, a corollary of the first, is that the evolution of human rights through the centuries has always been strongly influenced by great events in history, whether of a moral, economic, or political nature.

Although for a long time the individual was considered to be merely a unit in his immediate social group, whether family, tribe, or town, from the beginning his individual personality and responsibility were defined in moral and religious terms. The Ten Commandments constituted his first moral code, and Christianity was a religion of individual salvation based on the equality of all men before God. The Renaissance and Reformation were progressions for the individual toward freedom of thought and creativity in science and art, on the one hand, and on the other, toward freedom of conscience.

The course of events has been less smooth for political rights. Originally set down in Greek and Roman law, then temporarily suppressed, men's personal liberties and civic rights have been reaffirmed with increasing forcefulness since *Magna Carta* and establishment of the free towns of the Middle Ages, despite the opposition of absolute monarchs: these liberties have been incorporated in such documents as the British Declaration of Rights of 1689, the State of Virginia's Bill of Rights and the Declaration of Independence (1776), the Constitution of the United States (1787), and the French Declaration of the Rights of Man (1789).

The movement to abolish slavery, begun in the late eighteenth century, was of crucial importance in buttressing the universal principles of liberty and equality. In spite of the fact that the institution of slavery had been considered both natural and economically imperative for thousands of years, and that Christianity had been unable to loosen its hold for eighteen centuries, it was all but gone in a century and a half.

In the last two centuries, the evolution of human rights has been closely related to the liberation of increasing numbers of peoples and also to the economic changes based on technological achievements that have transformed the world, reducing it in size and creating the industrial system. The freedom to own individual property and to draw up contractual agreements acted as an extremely powerful stimulus to population mobility, increased individual initiative, and the creation of new wealth. At the same time, however, it also facilitated the exploitation of labor in the cities and colonies and enabled a few to monopolize the goods needed by all. This in turn was counterbalanced by the growth of powerful labor unions and the rebirth of the concept of public ownership, even in nations not affected by the Soviet Revolution. In addition, new rights for man, both as a person and as a social being, began to be recognized as worthy of attention and protection: rights of education, health, free choice of work and its conditions, of social security, association, information, freedom to speak and to teach, and so forth.

As for the third point mentioned above, the end of the First World War signaled a new and decisive era in the internationalization of human rights. Until that time the question of human rights had been considered as in effect the province of each separate country, and international humanitarian agreements had confined themselves to slavery, problems concerning the Red Cross, and efforts to control epidemic diseases. After the war, however, through the International Labor Organization (ILO) agreements were reached that transcended frontiers, and international organizations were established to protect the rights of workers, both men and women, without compromising the principles of free trade. On the other hand, although the Covenant of the League of Nations did not contain a general discussion of human rights, it included provisions to protect specific groups: the national minorities in Europe, and peoples falling under the mandate system outside Europe.

Such, then, was the general situation of human rights in the world—progress had been slow but unquestionable, even in the colonies—when nazism, heralded by fascism and based on principles (racism, the annihilation of entire groups of people, the glorification and practice of domination by force, and the debasement of the human being) negating all humanity, undertook the most appalling counterrevolution against the rights of individuals and peoples that has ever been attempted. It was finally overcome, after unparalleled human losses in a war lasting five years that became something of a "crusade for human rights" on the part of the Allied nations.

*   *   *   *   *

Viewing in this way the victory gained over nazism in 1945, we must ask what has been made of it by the victors in the last twenty-five years. To what extent have the promises of emancipation, particularly those made by the wartime leaders, been kept?

When the delegations met at the San Francisco Conference in the spring of 1945, during the very period when Allied troops were uncovering the horrors of the death camps, there was widespread evidence of goodwill. Not only was "respect for all without distinction as to race, sex, language, or religion" placed among the basic purposes of the Charter (Art. 1), alongside peace through cooperation, but special responsibilities in this area, to go beyond those of the principal organs (General Assembly, Security Council, Trusteeship Council, and Economic and Social Council), were assigned to a proposed Commission to promote human rights (Art. 68), and the member nations pledged themselves to "take joint and separate action in cooperation with the Organization" for the same purpose (Arts. 55 and 56).

In order that this might be achieved, it was decided to have an ad hoc commission prepare a draft document on human rights to be submitted to a vote of the General Assembly. The first part of the task was accomplished within a short period. Under the chairmanship of Mrs. Roosevelt, the commission in three sessions prepared a Universal Declaration of principles, which was contained in thirty articles and adopted, with several modifications—after three months of impassioned debate by the Paris session of the General Assembly—on December 10, 1948. This absolutely unprecedented document proclaimed, first, certain fundamental principles of a universal nature: liberty, equality, the outlawing of all discrimination, brotherhood. It then formulated four groups of basic rights and liberties, namely: (1) the classic rights and freedoms, both personal and civil (life, security, etc.); (2) the relations of the individual with members of various groups in society and with the external world (spouse, family, domicile, nationality, property); (3) rights of conscience, thought, information, expression, and political action (vote, peaceful association, trade unions, assembly); (4) economic, social, and cultural rights (work, free choice of work, favorable working conditions, rest and leisure, social security, health, standard of living, education, participation in cultural life and intellectual and artistic endeavor). It concluded with a section on the duties and responsibilities of men toward each other and toward society.

Although the Universal Declaration was a manifesto of general principles and, unlike a convention, was not strictly binding on the signatories, the balance it struck between common civil rights and freedoms, on the one hand, and on the other, the economic, social, and cultural rights that each nation must define for itself, aided when necessary by the international community, constituted a dynamic response to the needs not of a privileged few but of all men of all races. The declaration did not rule differently for human beings on a particular continent, or from a particular bloc of nations, but ruled for all members of the human family considered as equally worthy of respect.

It immediately raised great hopes for justice among oppressed peoples throughout the world. It became a guide to many leaders pursuing policies of reform and was signed by every nation, old or new, that became independent during the decolonization period and obtained admission to the United Nations. Pope John XXIII gave it his seal of approval in the papal encyclical *Pacem in Terris*. By now it has become far more than a simple adjunct to the United Nations Charter and is a permanent part of the common heritage of mankind.

Yet despite the great wave of enthusiasm the Declaration inspired, the fact that nations were not legally required to conform to its tenets in their laws and policies left room for serious abuses. For this very reason, the Commission on Human Rights began even before 1948 to lay the groundwork for a covenant on human rights in which more precise definitions of such rights would be incorporated into a treaty legally binding on the signatories; it would also define the legal machinery required to prevent, and when necessary to correct, violations of the obligations undertaken by the signatories.

The preparatory study was a long and arduous task, partly because the General Assembly, which followed the work closely in the course of its own annual sessions, finally instructed the commission in 1950/51 to divide the project into two separate parts—a covenant on civil and political rights, and a covenant on economic, social, and cultural rights—each of which would define the rights in question and set forth measures to implement and protect them.

Beyond the difficulty of separating the work into two covenants, the commission's job was further impeded by the fact that two great tasks being pursued simultaneously by the United Nations presented closely parallel and even interlocking problems: implementing the "right of peoples to self-determination," and the drafting of the World Bill of Rights.

Even after the possibility had been accepted that the principle of the right of self-determination, as a binding rule, could be placed at the beginning of the two covenants, another obstacle delayed ratification for some time. This was the unwillingness of most authoritarian governments, and even the majority of the great powers, to accept the concept of an international authority interfering in the relations between a government and its citizens or subjects. We touch here on the most sensitive point in all efforts at internationalization.

The authors of the Bill of Rights did not dare to make a frank exception of human rights, traditionally considered to be domestic matters, by removing them from the jurisdiction of the famous Article 2, section 7, which enjoins the United Nations from interfering in questions falling essentially within the domestic affairs of a country. They did so indirectly by giving organs of the United Nations—the General Assembly and the Economic and Social Council—and pledges of the members (Arts. 55 and 56) a scope that is incompatible, as far as human rights are concerned, with Article 2, section 7. Unlike the ILO statutes, the United Nations Charter also contains no provision for regulating the manner in which international control would operate to insure that countries respect human rights, in particular those covered by conventions.

This intentional restraint created a great many problems. For a long time, certain powerful nations refused to allow the United Nations to initiate any measures to implement the conventions drawn up under their auspices. Their rigid stand could not be maintained indefinitely, but concessions came slowly and were difficult to obtain.

In 1956, since the covenants were still not ready to be voted on, the Commission on Human Rights initiated a system, based on a 1950 French proposal and an American proposal of 1953, whereby the member nations were all invited to make periodic reports on progress made and obstacles encountered in the areas covered by the Universal Declaration.

Finally, certain countries such as the U.S.S.R., which had been particularly outspoken and persistent in its proposals to supervise the implementation of the Convention Against Racial Discrimination voted in December 1965, were invited to make a final decision about the two covenants, in anticipation of the twentieth anniversary of the Universal Declaration in 1968. The U.S.S.R. agreed to vote for the texts, but on condition that the measures of implementation proposed by the Commission on Human Rights for the covenant on civil and political rights—which were even less strong than those contained in the 1965 discrimination covenant—be considerably weakened. In the end, every country against which a claim was made was given the *option* of whether or not to consider it, whether it emanated from another country or, in exceptional cases, from an individual citizen.

It was thus at a very high price that a unanimous vote was finally obtained in December 1966 on the two covenants to implement the Universal Declaration, which complete and perfect the World Bill of Rights promised at the time of the first General Assembly meeting of the United Nations. The fact that the drafting of the two covenants dragged on for nineteen years had at least one valuable compensation: all the nations that became independent and joined the United Nations after the declaration of 1948 were able to be associated with it in a more active and positive manner than would have been the case had they simply ratified it, because they participated in the preliminary discussions and the final vote on the two covenants.

However, the story of the covenants is not yet, alas, complete. Four years after their adoption, they have still only been ratified by nine states, instead of the thirty-five necessary for the covenants to become operative. The World Bill of Rights thus still exists only on paper, for although the United Nations has accomplished its task, the same is not true of its member states.

As long as significant numbers of nations do not ratify, we cannot say that the second, and technically the more important part, of the promises made to the peoples of the world at the San Francisco Conference—to "take joint and separate action" on civil rights—has been kept. Looking back at certain important political events, or at certain trials that have taken place in the last four years, we may well ask if they would have occurred in the same manner, or have had the same outcome, if the World Bill of Rights had been in force.

*   *   *   *   *

Certainly, the patience of the world would have worn thin if the United Nations had concentrated all its efforts since the war on drafting universal covenants. Fortunately, this has not been the case. A sustained flow of work has enabled international organizations to become involved in matters of a less general nature.

Chronologically, the Convention on the Prevention and Punishment of the Crime of Genocide was the first; unanimously adopted on December 9, 1948, it has since been ratified by seventy-five states. Yet despite the numerous mass killings which would have justified its application, it has never functioned, because nations have not yet been willing to create the international penal tribunal and the international prosecutor without which it can never function in practice.

The agreements drawn up by international organizations in the past twenty-five years may be divided into several groups, which can only be briefly listed here.

The first group includes a 1956 convention supplementing an earlier one of the United Nations against slavery, and a convention drawn up under ILO auspices against forced labor. However, the reports required from nations by the former convention have not been forthcoming, and the Sub-Commission on Prevention of Discrimination and Protection of Minorities has only just recently begun to carry out its work.

The second group is comprised of all the conventions against various kinds of discrimination that have been initiated by the Commission on Human Rights since 1954. The ILO adopted a Convention Concerning Discrimination in Employment and Occupation in 1958, and in 1960 UNESCO adopted a convention on matters of education, paired with a regulatory protocol. The Commission on Human Rights drew up a convention on the elimination of all forms of racial discrimination, adopted in December 1965 and ratified by a sufficient number of states to enter into force. A committee of experts elected to insure that its provisions are carried out has met three times and submitted a first report to the General Assembly in September 1970.

The list of conventions and declarations concerning the rights of women and children is an imposing one. It includes a Convention on the Political Rights of Women, a Convention on Nationality of Married Women, a third, emanating from the ILO, to impose the principle of "equal pay for equal work"; there is also a 1962 Convention on Consent to Marriage, followed by a 1965 recommendation on the minimum age for marriage (fifteen years); and lastly, there exists an important declaration of 1967 on the rights and status of women. The Declaration of the Rights of the Child was adopted by the General Assembly in 1959, and a further declaration in 1965 concerns the promotion of the ideals of peace among the young.

In addition, the powers of the High Commissioner for Refugees have been extended, and in 1967 a declaration was passed concerning the right of asylum. Along the same line, the Commission on Human Rights itself has begun in the last few years to affirm its right, particularly where apartheid is concerned, to be notified of specific cases involving serious violations of human rights.

Conversely, on certain key issues that are considered particularly sensitive by totalitarian countries and their allies, no progress whatsoever has been made. Efforts to pass conventions on freedom of information, a crucial right in democratic countries, have all been abortive. Only one, the Convention on the International Right of Correction, dealing with the rights of a country allegedly victimized by distortions in the press of another country, has come to fruition.

Similarly, the convention prepared by the Commission on Human Rights against intolerance in religious matters and discrimination based on religion, originally designed to complement the convention against racial discrimination, has met with skillful and effective opposition in the General Assembly.

Among the other failures indicative, at least for the present, of the general mood is the vote against the Costa Rican proposal for a High Commissioner for Human Rights, during the most recent General Assembly session. This vote, as well as the delaying tactics that, contrary to the wishes of most ECOSOC members, have prevented the Sub-Commission on Prevention of Discrimination from following through on procedures to examine "communications" (*i.e.,* complaints from private individuals sent to the United Nations), augurs ill for the future and demonstrates that opportunities for legal progress, at least on the international level, have been narrowed down. For the immediate future we cannot afford to strive for perfection or place undue emphasis on international controls but must put existing international mechanisms to the test in practice, so that nations become accustomed to already established institutions, before attempting to go further.

*   *   *   *   *

In conclusion, let us try to establish a balance between the dangers threatening human rights and liberties, and the expectations that, after twenty-five years of effort, we may reasonably hope to realize.

Of all the dangers facing mankind, jeopardizing not only future progress but the very existence of man and all human rights, the most serious is war—not only worldwide nuclear war, but all armed conflict, foreign or domestic, and even limited warfare. The Geneva Convention and other humanitarian agreements on the laws of warfare are of inestimable value, and we must constantly seek to perfect them. Yet they have only a palliative effect. The fact that normal protection of human rights can no longer be guaranteed in wartime has been borne out by experience, and even by clauses in the most forward-looking agreements on human rights. The European Convention for the Protection of Human

Rights and Fundamental Freedoms, Article 15, and the Covenant on Civil and Political Rights, Article 4, allow the governments of the signatory nations to suspend all their obligations in wartime, with the exception of an extreme few related to barbaric practices (slavery, summary execution, torture). The World Bill of Rights was adopted only a few years after man learned to master atomic power; as a guide to moral conduct, it should prove superior to the balance of terror in preventing world leaders from continuing on the fatal path toward the destruction of their fellow men.

The second grave threat to human rights is that the doctrine of the sovereignty of the state, as opposed to that of a community of nations or of individuals, continues to hold sway. Even after the experience of Hitler, a large number of countries still claim exclusive and arbitrary jurisdiction over their nationals and are unwilling to admit the supreme right of the international community to intervene in the fate of human beings who are members of it as well. The non-ratification of the two covenants of the World Bill of Rights is an ominous indication of this tendency.

The future of human rights is further, and doubly, jeopardized by the undernourishment and grossly inadequate economic development of huge areas of the world, in contrast to others better provided for in every sense. How can we expect members of these communities to benefit from man's inalienable rights and freedoms if they suffer from hunger, disease, extreme poverty, ignorance, and disorganization, or if they must bear the burdens of a tyranny or a caste system? And how can we expect them to remain eternally passive if other, more fortunate peoples offer them only token or inadequate help? Pope Paul, after his recent visit to the Far East, voiced his concerns in this matter quite openly.

A fourth danger to human rights, more serious in developed nations, is the increasingly inhuman nature of individual life. The adverse effects of environmental pollution of the air and water are already danger signals. Even worse, perhaps, are the harmful influences of certain scientific and technological discoveries, involving the evaluation and manipulation of young children, and infringing also upon the basic freedoms of the adult. National and eventually international regulations will be necessary to protect the individual from invasions of privacy or oppression by technological devices; the computer alone poses extremely serious problems.

Thus the issue is no longer simply one of extending human rights but also of facing the danger that they may be curtailed. Men must make a concerted effort, in small local groups and in international organizations transcending frontiers, to anticipate and avert the most dangerous threats to human rights.

Yet the work that needs to be done should not be construed in a negative light, for it is positive efforts to promote human rights, in as many and as diverse forms as possible, that we must engage in. This will entail, first, the kind of direct pressure that public opinion and legislative bodies can bring to bear on their governments to ratify the 1966 human rights covenants.

In conjunction with work on the international level, initiatives can be made on a regional scale, inspired by the European example. It has already been seventeen years since the Human Rights Convention, drawn up in 1950, became operative, and since the institutions created to carry out its basic provisions began to function: the European Commission of Human Rights, the Commmittee of Ministers of the Council of Europe, and the European Court of Human Rights. Of the seventeen signatory nations, eleven have agreed to have the Commission examine complaints brought against them by individual citizens, and eleven have also agreed to be brought before the European Court by the Commission or by another signatory nation. More than four thousand suits have been examined by the commission, and since 1960 the court has pronounced judgments, generally well received, in ten important cases. The actual mechanisms of these organizations have not yet been perfected, but the results achieved by the Council of Europe have been thought worthy of emulation. Twelve Latin American countries drew up a convention inspired by very similar ideas—the Inter-American Convention on the Protection of Human Rights—on November 22, 1969. It is to be hoped that, despite the far greater problems they face, Africa and other continents will make comparable efforts, even if on a more modest scale.

In actual fact, however, efforts to safeguard respect for human rights in the underdeveloped areas of the world will be far more fruitful after technical assistance has first raised the general standard of living and improved economic conditions.

Even more important, as the authors of the World Bill of Rights made clear, is education; it is through education on all levels, concentrating on youth but including adults, that men and women will come first to appreciate human rights, and then to insure that they are respected by individuals as well as by authorities. Whether or not people achieve these two objectives, and also understand the international nature of the struggle for human rights, will depend on the intensity and effectiveness of their education.

In order to reinforce the overall work of UNESCO in this field, the International Institute of Human Rights has been formed in Strasbourg, to coordinate and support efforts being made by universities and institutes throughout the world. A new science, that of the rights of man, which has existed for only twenty-five years, now claims its place alongside the others. It is inconceivable that in the near future the long, hard struggle for basic rights and liberties, drawing encouragement from all mankind and now armed with a scientific method, will not build on the steps taken since 1945 and make decisive progress.

Phyllis Nauts Ott, translator of the above article, has been a writer for Columbia University's Urban Center, which studies urban and minority problems in New York City. She has translated several books about emerging African peoples, among them *False Start in Africa* (1966) by René Dumont, *Education in Africa* (1968) by Abdou Moumouni, and *East Africa: The Past in Chains, the Future in Pawn* (1969) by Albert Meister.

Henry J. Kellermann

Henry J. Kellermann maintains that he is not an expert in ecology, if such a thing exists, but he probably knows as much as anyone does about the worldwide threat to the environment, and he clearly knows more than most people do about world efforts to preserve the biosphere. A career government official who has held many posts, notably in the U.S. Foreign Service,

he was among other things a Special Assistant for Environmental Affairs in the Department of State at the time of his retirement from government service in 1970. He is now executive director of the Committee for International Environmental Programs of the National Academy of Sciences, which serves also as the American committee of SCOPE, the international scientific body formed in 1968 to advise governments everywhere as to what the environmental problems are and what steps can be taken to meet them.

Ecology: A World Concern

Ecology is the science of the mutual relations of organisms with their environment and with one another. Only when we get it into our collective head that the basic problem confronting twentieth-century man is an ecological problem, will our politics improve and become realistic.

Aldous Huxley

The clinical picture

On Tuesday, October 26, 1948, the people in Donora, a small industrial town in Pennsylvania, woke up to discover that they were trapped in a dense pall of smog drenched with odoriferous chemicals. When the smog lifted several days later, half of the population had been taken ill and twenty-one persons were dead or dying. Four years later, on Friday, December 5, 1952, about four thousand persons perished in London, England, victims of a massive dose of sulfur dioxide that had infiltrated the thick layers of London's black fog.

Experts have predicted similar disasters for other metropolitan areas, which could take a toll of human lives exceeding many times that of the London kill. Many of the world's industrial centers remain enveloped in so-called inversion layers created by factory emissions and combustion products. From Los Angeles to Ankara to Seoul, our skies are littered with chemicals and particles keeping out the sunlight; at the same time, airplane travelers passing over industrial regions have occasionally been treated to the spectacle of two suns: the real sun and the "under sun," which is the reflection of the sun in a thick carpet of floating pollutants below the flight level. So far, the rate of fatalities resulting from air pollution has been modest. But death rates from heart disease are increasing, as are cases of lung cancer, chronic bronchitis, and emphysema.

Lakes and rivers are dying. Lake Erie is not dead yet, but it is being gradually poisoned by enormous quantities of waste dumped into it day and night by the lakeside industries and municipalities that drain its water of life-sustaining oxygen. Nor is the phenomenon of "water-kill" limited to the United States. Lake Baikal in the Soviet Union, one of the world's largest reservoirs of fresh water, and one of nature's most prolific sanctuaries for more than a thousand different species of plants, fish, and other animals, has reportedly become a sink for millions of cubic meters

of waste pumped into it by the rapidly expanding paper and pulp industries along its shores. Within a few months, animal and plant life
within the dumping zone has decreased by one-third to one-half. Rivers
have turned into fire hazards. In 1966 the oil covering Islet River near
Sverdlovsk (U.S.S.R.) was ignited by a cigarette butt. Three years later
the totally polluted Cuyahoga River in Cleveland, Ohio, burst into
flames.

The worst of it is that pollution is compounding the damage inflicted
by "normal" use. Diversion of river and lake water for industrial purposes
is drying out some of the earth's largest water reservoirs. Within less than
ten years the water level of the Aral Sea has dropped by three to six feet,
that of the Caspian Sea by more than seven feet during the last twenty
years.

Loss and pollution of water produce chain reactions. The drop in the
water level of the Caspian Sea has produced a dramatic drop in the fish
catch. In Egypt the Aswan Dam now stores in Lake Nassar an estimated
total of thirty million tons of sediments containing nutrients essential
for the sustenance of marine life. The fish catch has critically suffered
off the mouths of the Nile River, resulting in a net loss of seven million
dollars to the fish industry of the U.A.R. As fish disappear, mosquitoes,
snails, and other disease vectors reenter the ecosystems. As a result of new
techniques providing year-round irrigation of larger areas, an estimated
two million people in Egypt are exposed to schistosomiasis, a disease of

Chemist analyzing the air in Donora, Pennsylvania, where a dense smog killed twenty-
one persons and made hundreds of others ill

Donora, Pennsylvania, a few days after the poisonous smog had lifted

the liver brought on by snails, which is expected to affect 55 percent of the population.

Pollutants introduced into water also enter the food chain. Japan reports new types of health hazards caused by ingestion of fish containing toxic chemicals. Fishermen struck by the "Minamata disease," a form of methyl-mercury poisoning, after eating fish caught in the Minamata area, developed numbness in their extremities, loss of balance, slurred speech, constriction of visual fields, and deafness, symptoms of cerebellar ataxia and dysarthria. Between 1953 and 1961, a total of 121 cases were reported in Minamata, 46 of which ended in death. Niigata had 30 cases in 1965, 5 of which were fatal. The Jintsu River Valley contributed the "Itai-Itai disease," an extremely painful sickness caused by cadmium, which induces an increasing brittleness of the human bone structure. The mortality rate is estimated to reach 50 percent. Finally, the so-called Yok-kaichi asthma, a type of severe bronchial infection, originated in a town that has been described as one of the worst polluted places in Japan.

19

Compounding the picture is the high degree of mobility, and consequently the wide diffusion of contaminants, facilitated by the currents of nature's most common carriers, air and water, and by their cycles of interaction. Pollutants become migratory and travel long distances. Sweden has complained for many years about its "acid rain," *i.e.*, the presence of obnoxious chemicals in precipitation. Some may be of local origin, but much is suspected to be imported by winds crossing the Baltic from Great Britain and the continent. Penguins in the Antarctic regions, according to some reports, are carrying residues of DDT in their tissues.

Most frequently cited, and by all accounts the most visible and dramatic illustration of decay, is the degradation of our oceans into gigantic sinks for the disposal of global wastes. Ocean travelers have noticed what the Norwegian Thor Heyerdahl, who crossed the waters in a papyrus boat, described as "a continuous stretch of at least four thousand miles of the Atlantic polluted by floating lumps of solidified asphalt-like oil." Oil and other wastes may be found thousands of miles from their point of origin. Some of the pollution, such as the *Torrey Canyon* or Santa Barbara oil spill, is accidental; much of it is deliberate, or the side effect of day-by-day operations, such as loading or unloading of ships, normal rates of leakage, and the like. Whatever the cause, estimates have it that an average of 7,422,000 million tons per year has been dumped in U.S. coastal areas alone in the period 1964–68, not including dredge spoils, radioactive wastes, and military explosives.[1] There is no way of telling with any degree of accuracy how much of the waste has accumulated below the surface, how much of it has been absorbed or dissolved, or what the total effect has been on marine life, although it is estimated that there has been a substantial loss of life among marine organisms. Recently we have become aware of the indirect effects of ocean pollution on human health. Mercury has been found in quantities exceeding tolerable levels in tuna, kingfish, and swordfish. Shellfish has been discovered to contain hepatitis, polio virus, and other pathogens. One-fifth of U.S. commercial shellfish beds have had to be closed. Many beaches are no longer accessible for recreational purposes. The trend is continuing; in fact, it is increasing.

The historical perspective

So much for the clinical picture. The diagnosis is not complete, and the prognosis is uncertain. The sum total of the symptoms is commonly referred to as our "environmental crisis." Its extent and gravity are not fully known and cannot be accurately assessed with existing tools of measurement. One hundred fifty animal species are estimated to have vanished. More are threatened with extinction. The danger to human life is even more difficult to gauge. For the immediate future it seems that it is the quality of life rather than life itself that is at stake. But the question of survival has arisen on the assumption that present trends will continue and that there is a limit to human capacity for tolerating sustained attacks on physical and social well-being.

How did this situation come about? Why is humanity, all of a sudden, threatened by the specter of attrition, pollution, and conceivably of ultimate extinction?

The answer is, of course, that there is nothing "sudden" about the threat nor about its multiple symptoms. They are merely contemporary manifestations of a conflict between man and nature that has raged for most of the last million years. What has changed are the rationale, the instruments of combat, and, as a result, the intensity of the struggle and the size of the battlefield. Long before smog descended upon Los Angeles, the people of London executed a man for fouling the city air by burning coal. That was in the Middle Ages. Evidently it did not help improve conditions. In the beginning of the nineteenth century, Shelley complained that "Hell is a city much like London, a populous and smoky city." Then came the catastrophe of 1952.

Originally at the mercy of nature's forces, man for reasons of self-protection sought to pacify, even to deify nature. Man feared and accepted nature's dominance. Prudently he took no more of nature's bounty than he needed, which was little enough, and nature could spare it. As man grew in number and in aspirations, and as he increased his power to satisfy his ambitions, his demands on nature increased proportionately. Judeo-Christian religion provided the rationale: it subordinated nature to man. Contemporary critics have accused Christianity, and with it the anthropocentric orientation of Western religion, of having created the antagonistic dualism between man and nature, which, some claim, laid the groundwork for the concept of nature's preordained servitude to man.[2] This may sound extreme, and it is. Religion as practised by Western man may not have prescribed effective rules for the protection of nature, but disrespect and exploitation of nature on secular grounds long preceded religion's influence. The history of civilization could be described, at least to a degree, as a relentless effort by man to impose, extend, and enforce his controls over nature. While he has not succeeded in establishing unchallenged supremacy—and, as the recent Bay of Bengal disaster has served to remind us, probably never will—man has managed with increasing skill and experience to broaden and strengthen his network of controls. As a result, many of nature's resources have been depleted, its cycles deranged, and its processes disrupted. "Man," George Perkins Marsh wrote more than a hundred years ago, "is everywhere a disturbing agent. Wherever he plants his foot, the harmonies of nature are turned to discord. The proportions and accommodations which insured the stability of existing arrangements are overthrown. . . . Of all organic beings, man alone is to be regarded as essentially a destructive power. . . ."

George Perkins Marsh, lawyer, scholar, diplomat, and, according to some, America's first ecologist, reached this conclusion during extensive travels through Europe, and especially after intensive study of those Mediterranean regions that once formed the core of the Roman Empire. He was shocked to discover that countries that in ancient times reportedly were blessed with an abundance of flora and fauna, now lay prostrate in barren abandon. They were, as he describes it, "either deserted by civilized man and surrendered to hopeless desolation or at least greatly reduced in both productiveness and population." In what has become a classic treatise of ecology, *Man and Nature* (1864), Marsh attributed the decay of the countries he visited in part to geological causes but also to "the direct violence of hostile human forces," and above all to "the brutal and exhausting despotism which Rome herself exercised over her conquered kingdoms and even over her Italian territory."

The history of American civilization bears ample testimony to the ravages committed by man on nature, of which Marsh said that they have "subverted the relations and destroyed the balance which nature has established between her organized and her organic creations." Eighteenth-

and nineteenth-century America was a huge battleground of man's war against nature. Indeed the very concept of the frontier provided a new rationale. Daniel Boone considered himself "an instrument ordained to settle the wilderness." Chabot's "Little Giant"—a canvas hose and nozzle that gouged out Western lands for the benefit of gold diggers—the massacre of the buffalo, the cattle invasion of the grasslands, the "Big Raids" of the forests, were all weapons in man's growing arsenal, and part of his strategy of uncontrolled expansion adapted to the political, social, and economic conditions of his time.[3]

Industrialization and technology increased the means of conquest to satisfy the demands of a growing number of consumers. But it remained for political ideology to brutalize the conflict to the point of absurdity. Taking its cue from the Soviet doctrine of ecological control through economic planning, Communist China tried to improve the Soviet model by turning nature from a prostrate victim into a deadly opponent. Man declared war on nature. Nature was exposed as the enemy who must be utterly defeated and forever kept in chains.[4] In Communist Chinese dialectics, environmental cleanups become battles fought not for nature's protection but against nature's intrusion of man's eminent domain. The following "battle report" appeared in a Chinese paper:

The "under sun," a reflection of the sun in layers of pollutants

> *Nine thousand persons were mobilized on the industrial and agricultural fronts in Shanghai to form muck-dredging and muck-transporting teams, waging a vehement people's war to dredge muck from the Suchow River. After a hundred days of turbulent fighting, more than 403,600 tons of malodorous organic mire had been dug out.*

The turning point: crisis

From conservationism to environmentalism

Marsh was not the first to raise his voice in protest. Eighteenth-century philosophers had postulated the inviolability and even the divinity of nature. Shaftesbury considered nature "a vast system of interconnected and interdependent parts of which we see little, but enough to be convinced that it is an admirable Cosmos moving majestically according to unalterable laws."

The United States produced some of the earliest and most passionate partisans of nature's cause. Emerson, Audubon, and, above all, Thoreau paved the way for coming generations of conservationists, insisting that there must be "national preserves, in which the bear, and the panther, and some even of the hunter race may still exist, and not be civilized off the face of the earth. . . ."

Under the administrations of John Quincy Adams, Hayes, Harrison, Cleveland, and Theodore Roosevelt, conservation became first a legitimate, then a respectable, and eventually a significant platform of national policy. It became institutionalized in the Department of the Interior and other federal agencies. The conservation movement was born. The National Wildlife Federation, the National Audubon Society, the Sierra Club, and the Conservation Foundation were created—to name a few of the most prominent activist groups. The movement surfaced in other countries. It became international and produced worldwide organizations such as the International Union for Conservation of Nature and Natural Resources (IUCN).

The conservationists were the classical defenders of nature. They were naturalists with a mission: to save the rare and the weak and to come to the rescue of species under attack. Their rationale was religious, moral, aesthetic, social, scientific; above all, they were ecological protectionists. They wished to conserve nature for nature's sake. During the romantic so-called period of conservation they insisted that man should be "kept out" and nature be "left to look after itself."[5] They opposed interference with nature because such conduct violated the ordained or the natural order of things, because it blighted and shortened life, because it destroyed harmony and beauty—but not because destruction and defilement were final or fatal. To men like Marsh, the effects of man's action were not irreversible. Alternative options and remedies were available, including an abundance of untapped resources. True, Marsh warned that nature may avenge herself upon the intruder, but nowhere in his writing are to be found visions of ultimate vengeance or of inescapable apocalyptic doom.

It is only recently that conservationists have begun to revise their objectives. John F. Kennedy, who defined conservation as "the wise use of our natural environment," was among the first to recognize that the abuse of the nation's resources with the help of modern technology was fast approaching the dimensions of a national dilemma, and to demand that the concept of conservation be expanded to meet the imperious problems of the new age. The crisis, in Kennedy's view, was still a quiet one, but it was now engulfing the entire national community. Its effect, as he put it, "will not only degrade the quality of the national life but . . . weaken the foundation of national power."

Global alert

In late spring of 1970, United Nations Secretary-General U Thant delivered a speech in Texas in which he said:

> *This is the first time in its history that mankind faces not merely a threat, but an actual worldwide crisis involving all living creatures, all vegetable life, the entire system in which we live, and all nations large or small, advanced or developing. It is a crisis which concerns literally everyone, and involves, directly or indirectly, almost everything. It underlines, as no other phenomenon can, the fact that ours is the first global civilization and that, as such, it can make global mistakes which can wreck not just one nation or society, but the very earth itself.*

Thant's statement added a new dimension to previous definitions. It implied first and foremost that the problem had reached *crisis* proportions, which meant in clinical terms that a level of climactic intensity had been attained that dwarfed all previous threats, and that the hour of decision was near. Secondly, the crisis was *global,* which meant that it was no longer confined, as in Marsh's days, to certain countries or regions, but that it actually or potentially threatened the totality of our biosphere. Thirdly, the man-made crisis had *finally turned on man himself,* which meant it was no longer only a question of preserving the forests, the grasslands or other biomes, or of saving rare species, but that it was now posed in terms of human survival. Man's interference with nature had boomeranged; he himself had become the target.

Thant's thesis has been acclaimed and challenged. The challengers contend that it is too sweeping or at least premature, that while there is evidence of hazards, they are isolated instances that are controllable, and that there is as yet no conclusive proof of their lethal effect on man nor indeed of the precise nature of their impact in general. As far as their effect on life-sustaining resources is concerned, Thant's critics insist, first, that man's innovative genius will in time provide proper substitutes or "technological fixes" to slow down or altogether stop attrition and degradation, and, second, that man's adaptive capability will permit gradual adjustment to environmental stresses.

The critics are not entirely wrong. Forty scientists, who assembled recently to undertake, under the auspices of the Massachusetts Institute of Technology, a study of critical environmental problems, concluded after a month of deliberation that the data needed to form conclusive judgments about the nature of the problem under study were fragmentary, contradictory, and in some cases completely unavailable. This was true in particular of data on important physical, chemical, and ecological phenomena and parameters, which were to provide the scientific basis for assessing environmental effects. The participants therefore recommended "the development of new methods for gathering and compiling global economic and statistical information."

There are indeed countless blind spots in our scientific knowledge. We know for a fact that pollutants have infiltrated our water, air, and soil. We know that almost nothing gets lost in nature. But while we have reasons to assume that 25 percent of all DDT produced to date has sunk into the oceans and is affecting marine life, we do not know what has happened to the rest, nor do we know for certain what the long-range cumulative effects of the floating and migrant compounds will be on plant, animal, and human life.

Take carbon dioxide (CO_2), which is produced by the combustion of fossil fuels. We know that its quantities in the atmosphere are steadily increasing.[6] But while we know that 50 percent of it remains in the atmosphere, we have as yet not been able to trace the routes and destinations of the other 50 percent; that is to say, we do not know how much of it enters the oceans and how much filters into other parts of our biosphere. Nor do we know for certain how the accumulation of CO_2 in the atmosphere will eventually affect our climate. Scientific opinion, in fact, is sharply divided on whether the layers of carbon dioxide will increase the surface temperature of the earth by intercepting the infrared radiation of the earth and radiating it back—the so-called greenhouse effect—or whether, by absorbing sun radiation, it is likely to start a cooling-off process.

Finally, we do not know how close we are to the threshold where nuisance turns into acute danger and where human resistance will simply collapse under the cumulative assault of the invading pollutants.

But while there are serious gaps in our knowledge, there exists nevertheless a substantial consensus among scientists on a number of propositions that are fundamental to an understanding of the nature of the environmental crisis, its causes and effects. They can be roughly identified as follows:

First proposition: The resources of the world that make up our bio-sphere, that is, the thin mantle of sunlight, air, water, soil, and minerals that sustain human, plant, and animal life, are finite; yet they are exposed to mounting, seemingly unlimited demands by a steadily growing number of consumers. If the increase of the demands continues at present rates, the end of some resources, such as fossil fuels and minerals, can be predicted in a not too distant future.

Second proposition: Attrition of resources through normal or excessive use is being further accelerated through pollution. This occurs through the infusion of extraneous, often toxic bodies into the biosphere, which changes the complexion, corrupts the quality, and reduces the utility of nonrenewable as well as renewable resources on which life depends.

Third proposition: Since the biosphere forms a single balanced global system of interdependent and interacting elements, significant changes in the quality or quantity of any of these elements cannot be kept isolated in airtight or watertight compartments but are bound to upset the total balance.

Fourth proposition: While man has tried with varying success to regu-late his relations with his fellowman, his relations with nature are still largely in a state of anarchy. In the absence of international agreements, resources remain subject to national sovereignty; in the absence of na-tional legislation, they remain under the control of those claiming owner-ship or physical access. The result is that resources essential to all or to many may be monopolized, manipulated, and even abused by a few. On the other hand, resources such as the oceans or the airspace above them, which are under the sovereignty or control of none, may be tampered with by all.

Fifth proposition: Inasmuch as attrition and pollution are substantially the results of man's direct and arbitrary interference with the environ-ment in an effort to satisfy his ever increasing needs, management of the crisis becomes a matter of social strategy, and ultimately of political control.

Causes and symptoms

Among the factors normally listed as causes of the environmental crisis, the following rank highest: population growth, modern economics, and technology.

The population factor. There is no gainsaying that growth and expan-sion of the human race have provided spaceship earth with a critical bal-last. There is still space left, but it is mainly deck space and the deck is getting crowded. More seriously, the provisions are limited. Still more importantly, it is not so much the total number as the rate of increase that creates problems. According to generally accepted estimates, the human population totaled 5 million in 8000 B.C. Within the next ten thousand years it grew to 500 million. It took mankind another two hun-

dred years to double its number. Less than half the time, scarcely eighty years, was needed to reach 2 billion. Thereafter it took only forty years to grow to the current total of 3.5 billion. At the present rate of growth, the so-called doubling time is about thirty-five to thirty-seven years.

Each of the 3.5 billion now alive has his claim on nature's resources, and his appetite is growing. The food potential of our planet is calculated to be adequate for 30 billion people but only at a level of chronic near-starvation.[7] Accepting a doubling time of about thirty-five years, the limit would be reached approximately in the year 2075.

These estimates are valid if we assume that the population explosion will continue on the present scale. This assumption may be wrong. In the absence of a universally enforceable population policy, no present predictions are reliable. Optimists have it that the increase may level off at a total of 10 billion. But a gradual slowdown and even a stagnation will not necessarily lessen the stress on the earth's resources, because the environmental crisis is not simply a numbers game. In terms of its ecological impact, notably its effects on resources, the population problem is an important factor, but it is only one of several. Moreover, its importance has often been overestimated, or, more correctly, it has not been properly related to other factors of equal if not surmounting significance. The point is that the environmental crisis may persist and even worsen, regardless of minor or even major drops in the rates of population growth, and, indeed, may reach intolerable levels long before the prognosticated saturation date of 2075 is anywhere near.

The economic factor. A reciprocal relationship between population growth and economic development is undeniable. More people simply means more consumers; more consumers means increased production and larger markets; more production and more consumption mean more drainage of resources, more waste, and more pollution. Yet it does not follow that the rates of economic growth parallel faithfully those of population growth or that the latter provide a reliable index to calculate the former. This may be true of countries living on a bare subsistence level. It is wholly inapplicable in industrial societies where affluence has caused quantum jumps of prosperity and where, as a result, economic growth has left population growth far behind. Take the United States. Between 1940 and 1965 the population increased by 47 percent, but the gross national product almost tripled. The U.S. example is not a typical one as far as the order of magnitude is concerned. Growth rates in other developed countries may be more modest, each following its local laws of supply and demand and the dictates of national policy. Comparisons of population and production figures show surprising degrees of variation, confirming the fact that population size alone is not a reliable indicator of ecological change and that economic growth is not a fixed proportional adjunct of population growth.[8] In assessing their cumulative effect on the environment, we must examine each of them within its own terms of reference.

As a rule, the economic factor seems to outweigh the demographic one. Economic growth has reached a temporary climax in the developed countries, where affluence has become a reality in some and a desired social objective in most, and where, as a result, mass production, with its built-in stimulants of planned obsolescence, technological improvements, and easier purchase conditions, has cut deep into available resources. Moreover, all-out competition for internal and external markets has placed a premium on ever faster, bigger, and cheaper production, with little regard for harmful side effects such as the emission of millions of tons of pollutants into air, water, and soil. Costs and benefits are calculated and balanced to assure a profit margin for the marketed product, but no adequate allowance is made for the prevention of societal damages or diseconomies caused by the so-called externalities of the mass-production process. Changes in the system by "internalizing the externalities" (*i.e.*, by installing proper safeguards to minimize the side effects) are being resisted on grounds that the costs of such safeguards would have to be charged to the customer, with the result that whole industries would price themselves out of the domestic or international market.

In developing countries, where affluence is still a distant goal, the argument assumes political overtones. Here, economic growth is regarded as a question of national survival. Development planning and aid have attained the status of an overriding national priority that must not be tampered with. The installation of ecological safeguards to protect the beauty of the landscape or even the health of the native population is a matter of secondary importance to countries with explosive birthrates, which live at the brink of starvation. In countries where quality is measured by standards quite different from ours, pollution, far from being a blight, is often welcomed as a symptom of economic growth. While ecologists in those countries recognize the danger signs, political leaders and planners insist that in societies where food, not health, and survival, not prosperity, are the national priorities, governments cannot afford to place long-range ecological objectives promising uncertain benefits or warding off uncertain risks before short-range economic goals promising immediate relief. The recent obsession of the developed countries with environmental problems is highly suspect in many of the new nations, and attempts by the former to introduce environmental controls in development planning are being resisted on grounds that they are apt, if not indeed intended, to stifle economic growth. Arguments have been heard to the effect that the environmental fad is a trick on the part of industrialized societies to fence off economic competition and to maintain their monopoly over the world markets.

The technological factor. In advanced societies, technology is now being made a scapegoat for most of our predicament and especially for the rising level of present-day pollution. While it is recognized that antiquity and the Middle Ages had their own pollution problems, modern technology is regarded as the principal factor in accelerating ecological chaos. In actual fact, technology is no more than the instrument of its users. As a means of modern warfare, technology can be wholly destructive. In the service of science it has expanded immensely the frontiers of human knowledge. Under the tutelage of modern economics, technology has provided the tools for the most thorough exploitation of natural resources yet.[9] Unfortunately, it has produced secondary effects that at

Polluted Cuyahoga River (Ohio) in flames

times have reduced and in some cases have offset the primary benefits.

Fertilizers and pesticides have helped increase agricultural production manifold. But overfertilization has caused eutrophication of lakes, rivers, and estuaries, reducing the oxygen content of water and killing fish and plant life. Pesticides, notably DDT, have left residues in plants, animals, and, through the food chain, in humans, for instance in the milk of nursing mothers. DDT has reduced the reproductive capabilities of fish and birds and in some instances has exceeded established tolerance levels for human consumption. Certain species have all but disappeared; others are nearing the point of extinction.

Fossil fuels have been the lifeblood of our industry, of our transportation system, of our energy-generating plants. We take great pride in the fact that we have multiplied our gross national product, that we have nearly doubled the number of automobiles per family, that we have expanded the number of electric utilities. But we keep forgetting that the increase results in a yearly output of 33.2 million tons of sulfur oxides, 20.6 million tons of nitrogen oxides, 32 million tons of hydrocarbon compounds, 100.1 million tons of carbon monoxide, and 28.3 million tons of particulate matter—all of which equal more than one ton of air pollution per person per year.

We have already mentioned the deleterious effects of mercury on plant and marine life. Other heavy metals have caused similar damages.

Trace gases, such as carbon dioxide (CO_2), again present a different kind of threat. The danger here is not toxicity but turbidity. CO_2 is an industrial by-product. But while CO_2 is not toxic, its ever increasing concentration and long residence in the atmosphere are expected eventually to affect the heat balance and with it the climate on earth.

31

The common characteristic of all these pollutants is that their negative effect is secondary and incidental. Most of them are waste products; that is, as in the case of mercury or carbon monoxide, they are the unused and relinquished leftover of production and consumption.[10] The continued existence and circulation of such residues thus attests to the imperfection of present-day technology and to failure to use or perfect the use of existing technologies. The result is the ejection of ever increasing mountains of waste in all forms—vaporous, liquid, and solid.[11]

Such, then, is the price we pay for the services of technology in a growth-oriented economy.

Toward a global initiative

It has taken us dangerously long to recognize that the crisis we face is a global one, that the threats to our resources and to the quality of our life are not isolated thrusts with fixed and narrow targets, of limited duration and with transitory effects. We now know that by its rapid and continuing increase, its mobility, and the interaction of its components, the danger has achieved a range of penetration, a virulence, and, above all, a cumulative impact that threaten life, health, and safety everywhere. It has taken us even longer to admit that ironically the crisis is the by-product of social, economic, and technological progress, and that to overcome it means no more and no less than to question some of the most cherished values of Western civilization, such as indiscriminate growth and prosperity. But it is only very recently that we have concluded that a global crisis calls for global action; that national capabilities and even such international instruments as do exist no longer suffice to meet and to manage it effectively and decisively; and that, in fact, a new and wholly different approach is needed—an approach that requires not merely new forms of international cooperation but also the systematic and coordinated engagement of all pertinent scientific disciplines, professional expertise, and technical skills.

The first breakthrough came in 1964 when the International Council of Scientific Unions (ICSU), comprising fifty-seven nations, organized multidisciplinary teams of scientists under the auspices of the International Biological Programme (IBP) to study "the biological basis of productivity in human welfare," with special emphasis on the interaction between man and his environment.

The second international initiative of major significance was taken by UNESCO, the United Nations Educational, Scientific and Cultural Organization. In the fall of 1968 UNESCO convened an Inter-governmental Conference of Experts on the Scientific Basis for Rational Use and Conservation of the Resources of the Biosphere. This conference, which adopted twenty major recommendations, recognized explicitly that many of the man-induced global changes in the biosphere require attention on a global scale, and that the multidisciplinary nature of the problems, which involve not only biological and physical but also social sciences, makes it necessary to call on the various disciplines of the scientific community to concentrate on environmental problems. The conference recommended that a plan for an international and interdisciplinary program on the rational utilization and conservation of the resources of the biosphere be prepared for the good of mankind—a program that should be carried out on an intergovernmental basis, with the participation of nongovernmental organizations as required.

On December 3, 1968, the United Nations General Assembly at its twenty-third session passed a resolution that may yet turn out to be the most important milestone on the road toward responsible international action on behalf of the world's environment. Resolution 2398, which was initiated by the government of Sweden and adopted unanimously, called for the convening of a United Nations Conference on Human Environment, in the belief that it was desirable

> *to provide a framework for comprehensive consideration within the United Nations of the problems of human environment in order to focus the attention of Governments and public opinion on the importance and urgency of this question and also to identify those aspects of it that can only or best be solved through international co-operation and agreement.*

Subsequently, the secretary-general and the preparatory committee tentatively identified the problems to be considered as "Environmental Aspects of Human Settlements," "Rational Management of Natural Resources," and "Environmental Degradation from Pollution and Nuisances." These headings must unhappily be regarded as in many ways equivalent. To maintain clear divisions between them will present a formidable task for the organizers and leaders of the conference. Considering the fluidity of the problems they describe and their constant interpenetration, there will be considerable overlap between agenda items. This, however, is not decisive. What is important is the explicit recognition of the environmental crisis as a matter of universal concern calling for concerted international initiatives. The emphasis is clearly on action. The conference, which will be held in 1972 in Stockholm, is conceived as a meeting not of scientists but of governmental officials, capable by virtue of the rank and nature of the positions they hold nationally of taking action on the international as well as on the national level. In addition, there will be representatives of international organizations, both intergovernmental and nongovernmental, who will provide much of the substantive input and some of the needed instruments of action.

The world science community is getting organized. The International Council of Scientific Unions has created a Special Committee on Problems of the Environment (SCOPE) to serve as a nongovernmental resource and as an interdisciplinary council of scientists for the benefit of governments and intergovernmental organizations.

Partly as a result of the UN initiative, partly independently, environmental organizations and conferences have begun to mushroom everywhere. Among the most important meetings to date has been the European Conservation Conference held in February 1970 at Strasbourg, France, under the auspices of the Council of Europe. In a formal declaration, the conference proposed, among other things, that the Council of Europe be charged to draw up a protocol to the European Convention on Human Rights guaranteeing "the right of every individual to enjoy a healthy and unspoiled environment." Among recent important conference meetings is the Conference on Problems Related to the Environment, held in May 1971 at Prague, Czechoslovakia, under the auspices of the Economic Commission for Europe (ECE). This addressed environmental problems of industrialized nations in Eastern and Western Europe and in the United States. One of the major objectives of the conference was to stimulate "a new approach to economic thinking and theory by which due account could be taken of the cost and profitability of projects, not only in purely economic terms but also in terms of environmental effect."

Possibly none of these conferences will produce a panacea for the environment. Some may fall short of their purposes and especially of the expectations set upon their agendas. Some, in fact, may only serve to cast the difficulties into sharper relief and may surface points of conflict, obstructing rather than producing solutions. There may be retreats from current objectives and a lowering of sights. Nevertheless, in spite of such possibilities, it is unlikely that partial failure or temporary setbacks will be able to reduce substantially the momentum that has been generated by manifest worldwide concern. It is far more likely that the conferences will act as an incentive to governments, scientists, and citizens everywhere to translate their apprehensions into specific, if perhaps limited, initiatives.

There are three priority areas where action must be taken without delay if governments, scientists, and citizens are to be believed when they say that they are in earnest with their declarations of intent to meet the crisis.

The first priority is the maintenance of a global alert. That does not mean an appeal to public hysteria through horror stories or sensational predictions of impending disaster. It means a sustained effort by informed and reliable sources to educate the authorities and the citizenry on the nature and the implications of the crisis. This can be done by public media having access to scientific facts, by conferences and workshops attended by scientists, public officials, and opinion makers, and by grass-roots campaigns. A special effort may be needed in the developing countries where, for reasons indicated above, public concern is lagging, and where much of the basic information may have to be developed from zero level.

The second priority is the systematic development of the scientific basis for action. This will require the preparation of studies, such as the MIT study, of situations in which action is needed but in which critical gaps in our knowledge still exist. It furthermore calls for the exchange of information, and for the collection, storage, analysis, and dissemination of data now available and yet to be developed. It will necessitate the early establishment of a network of base-line and impact stations to monitor, on a continuing basis, significant parameters and the changes occurring within each of them. It will finally require the organization of research facilities to study specific problems in depth, but on an interdisciplinary scale, to evaluate the monitored data and to define the criteria needed for standard setting.

The third priority is the establishment of systems of controls. It involves the organization of the institutional apparatus needed to plan and review policies and programs and to determine priorities for action. Something must be done, further, to formulate standards and to issue regulations for their enforcement, to coordinate existing operational facilities, to authorize the adaptation of existing facilities or the installation of new ones, and to set up machinery for arbitration and enforcement.

It is not likely that action on all priorities will be initiated at once or even in rapid succession. Prospects are brightest on the national level, where the organizational and technical prerequisites and, above all, the authority for action exist. Even here, however, there will remain formidable pockets of resistance. The "now or never" stance of the Nixon policy, and legislation sponsored by Senators Jackson, Muskie, and Magnuson, may help break down some of the resistance in the United States and may set an example for others to follow. But the contest will be long and hard.

On the international level the difficulties will be even greater, and progress may be considerably slower. Of the three priorities, the third one—establishment of controls—will provoke the most stubborn opposition. It will be resisted on grounds of national sovereignty, national interest, and political and economic security. It may be opposed in the name of free enterprise and free market competition. It may be denounced as an invasion of privacy and an infringement on personal liberty and the pursuit of happiness. Governments of closed societies may reject cooperative research and monitoring as "ecological espionage."

Nevertheless, initiatives in the first and second areas of priority are possible now and may be set in motion at some of the forthcoming con-

ferences. In a way, these conferences, in particular the UN conference at Stockholm, may perform the function of a world-wide alert. Moreover, if present plans are followed, the preparations may produce the most comprehensive and authentic record of the state of our environment yet assembled. Beyond this, if the Stockholm conference were to constitute itself as the first in a series of world initiatives to assess and to report periodically on the state of the world environment, it would implicitly institute a permanent alert. Furthermore, the conference may issue a "Global Declaration"—such as is now being prepared by governments for submission to the conference—which, in the form of an international Jackson law,[12] would declare the protection of the environment an international obligation of governments and citizens everywhere and recommend that it be made an integral part of national policies.

The establishment of a global monitoring network, consisting of a series of stations to record the present rates of critical phenomena, to

trace their routes, and to measure changes, has been widely discussed and even demanded as an essential tool for the assessment of the problems that require action. A number of international organizations are already engaged, with the help of governments, in monitoring selected phenomena falling within their areas of competence. What is needed, however, is the development of a comprehensive system permitting a far broader coverage of phenomena than has been heretofore observed, including the tracing of certain phenomena, such as pollutants, in parameters falling within the competence of more than one agency. Such a system would make use of existing installations, but it would also provide for coordination between them and, in addition, would establish new stations. The design of such a system has been under way for some time, and the plan is expected to be completed in time for submission to the UN conference.

Another, equally important priority is the development of an international research capability, which would be at the disposal of international agencies as well as governments. It would be one of the tasks of such an institute to evaluate the data produced by the monitoring system and to make appropriate recommendations for action. While such research capabilities exist in advanced countries, most of the smaller and new nations lack the funds, and many the necessary know-how. The in-house capabilities of international agencies, such as they are, are often too limited to serve more than the immediate purposes of the agency. Proposals for the creation of an international research institute have come from international and national quarters.[13] Its exact purpose, functions, auspices (i.e., whether intergovernmental or nongovernmental), and its relationship to the UN system of agencies, remain to be defined. An institute of this kind may start modestly, for instance as a data bank and clearance center. It could gradually expand to a full-fledged research institute with an international and interdisciplinary staff and with the requisite sophisticated equipment for long-range research, model building, and so forth. Plans for such an institute are now under study and, if they are sufficiently matured, may also be placed on the agenda of the UN conference.

Finally, the time has come for formalized international agreement on such priorities as the prevention of ocean dumping. This is one of the few problems where international concern may have reached a level permitting direct action. If the Stockholm conference could agree on a draft, the UN General Assembly may be ready to accept it.

The above proposals by no means exhaust the list of possible initiatives. Other, more ambitious proposals have been advanced, perhaps the most far-reaching by UN Secretary-General Thant, who has urged the creation of "global authority . . . to police and enforce its decisions," supported by governments and relying on experts, scientists, and scholars who would be true international servants. "Do the sovereign nations of the world," asks Thant, "have the courage and the vision to set up and support such an agency *now,* and thus, in the interest of future generations of life on earth, depart radically from the hitherto sacred paths of national sovereignty?"

Thant's proposal may be premature; his question, on the other hand, is quite to the point. It is not addressed to the official authorities alone. It is directed to those who have entrusted their political leaders with the mandate to protect their freedom to produce, regardless of their real needs; to consume and to dispose of the unconsumed residue as they may think convenient; to sweep their waste under the rug; to bury, to burn, or to drown it; to dump it onto public streets, into their neighbor's garden, or into our great commons, the air and the oceans. It is aimed at us.

It is at this point that the ecological crisis becomes a social and a moral one.

We shall not solve one without the other.

1 For details *see* "Ocean Dumping—A National Policy," Report to the President prepared by the Council on Environmental Quality.

2 "By destroying pagan animism," Lynn White, Jr., writes in "The Historical Roots of Our Ecological Crisis," (*Science*, March 10, 1967), "Christianity made it possible to exploit nature in a mood of indifference to the feelings of natural objects. . . . Man's effective monopoly on spirit in this world was confirmed, and the old inhibitions to the exploitation of nature crumbled."

3 For further details *see* Stewart Udall's *The Quiet Crisis* (New York: Holt, Rinehart, & Winston, 1963).

4 Rhoads Murphy in *Modern Asian Studies* I (1967): 313–33, offers a graphic list of titles of articles and publications typifying Communist Chinese dialectics, such as "The Desert Surrenders," "We Bend Nature to Our Will," "How We Defeated Nature's Worst," "Chairman Mao's Struggle Against Nature," etc.

5 *See* V. Westhoff in *New Scientist*, April 16, 1970.

6 The MIT study estimated a rate of 0.2 percent per year since 1958.

7 For further details *see* "Resources and Man," a study published by the National Academy of Sciences—National Research Council.

8 In their introduction to *America's Changing Environment* (Boston: Houghton Mifflin Co., 1970), Roger Revelle and Hans Landsberg develop this thesis more extensively. They point out that of a total of twenty-six developed countries in Europe, North Africa, and Japan, thirteen with a population increase of 0.8 percent had an economic growth rate of 7.2 percent, while the remaining thirteen countries had population growth rates of 3.4 percent but only a 1.1 percent economic growth rate.

9 The MIT study of critical environmental problems estimated that man is using these materials now at rates greater than the global rates of geological erosion and disposition, that more than 40 percent of the total land surface is in use, and that the total amount of organic matter in land vegetation has been reduced by one-third.

10 The evaporated and unburned gasoline emitted by automobiles is estimated to be 10 to 15 percent of the total fuel used.

11 Exact estimates for the sum total of wastes generated by the various segments of society are not available. In the United States the total of all major air pollutant emissions has been estimated to amount to 214.2 million tons per year. Water pollution is more difficult to calculate. The volume of waste water from industries has been estimated to total 13,100 billion gallons, and suspended solids 18,000 million pounds; these figures do not include animal wastes or oil spills. More reliable figures have been computed for solid wastes. The total of solid wastes produced from all major sources in 1969 was 4,340 million tons, of which 250 million were residential, commercial, and industrial wastes, 110 million were industrial wastes, 1,700 million were mineral wastes, and 2,280 million were agricultural wastes. Each person thus generates 7 pounds per day from residential, commercial, and municipal sources, which adds up to 30 million tons of paper and paper products, 4 million tons of plastics, 100 million tires, 30 billion bottles, 60 billion cans, and further millions of tons of demolition debris, grass and tree trimmings, food wastes, and sewage sludge. These figures do not include the millions of discarded automobiles and major appliances. The above statistics are recorded in the First Annual Report of the Council on Environmental Quality, as transmitted to the Congress of the United States in August 1970.

12 The National Environmental Policy Act of 1969, sponsored by Henry M. Jackson, senator from Washington, established the protection and enhancement of the quality of the environment as a matter of national policy and made it incumbent on all agencies of the federal government to assure in their policies and programs full compliance with the purposes and provisions of the act.

13 An ad hoc committee of ICSU has suggested the establishment of an "International Center for the Environment," which would operate a "monitoring service," a "research and planning service," and an "intelligence (information) service." Senate Resolution 399, which was sponsored by Warren Magnuson, senator from Washington, and which was passed unanimously, proposed the establishment of a "World Environmental Institute" to act as a global research center.

Arthur Lall

Arthur Lall, a native of India, was born in Lahore and educated at the University of the Punjab as well as at Oxford (Balliol) and Grenoble. A specialist in international affairs, he has represented the Indian government at many international conferences, was its consul general at New York from 1951 to 1954, has been ambassador to Austria (1959–62), and was ambassador

and permanent representative to the United Nations (1954–59). Since 1965 he has been Adjunct Professor of International Affairs at Columbia University and a consultant to the UN, for which he recently prepared a study exploring the possibilities for an international university. He is the author of several books on diplomatic subjects and has published two novels, a number of short stories, and some verse.

Toward a World University

The culture of peoples finds expression in their art and literature, whether secular or religious; it appears also in the variety of material forms they develop, from their apparel and other artifacts to their architecture and engineering constructions; it may even be seen in their social behavior and actions. But these things also reflect what may be called the soul of a people and are often religious manifestations as well as culture symbols. In such cases, religion and culture are connected, indicative of a common source in the human spirit.

In some societies, the line between the religious and the secular is indistinct, because religion is neither so awesome nor so dogmatic—and therefore not so clearly separable—as it may be elsewhere. This is especially true in those societies that either give expression to the Godhead as immanent and universal, or that, like Buddhism, ignore the whole notion of God as irrelevant, having no conception of the Almighty as a separate, exalted Being, authoritative and dominant.

> *Thou art the dusky butterfly,*
> *The green parrot red-eyed.*
> . . . .
> . . . .
> *Filled with Brahman are all things seen,*
> *Filled with Brahman is the whole unseen.*

These are the words, in translation from the Sanskrit, of one of the Vedas, the religious books of the early Indo-Aryans (c. 1750 B.C.). Clearly, a culture in which a person, from his young and impressionable years onward, is taught to see God in a flitting butterfly and the flying birds, is not setting up a Supreme Being that is awesome, and approachable only through communal or personal ritual as the Almighty and Supreme Judge.

The emperor of Japan is regarded as an embodiment of God. While this is so, the Japanese, who mostly profess a view of the Deity as immanent and universal, do not include among the emperor's divine attributes the qualities of omniscience and omnipotence. Therefore the secular fortunes and misfortunes of Japan as a state, and of the emperor as the ruler of the state, do not affect either the concept of the emperor as the Godhead or the related system of beliefs of the Japanese people in the way that could happen, and indeed has happened, with certain primitive societies.

In those societies in which the concept of God is formulated as immanent and universal, or is altogether absent, the divine may be an interplaying ever-presence and copresence but is not a dominance. Indeed, in such societies man dominates the divine as much as he is dominated. He is thus in some ways spiritually more on his own, a freer agent, than he is in societies where a normative concept of the divine as the Supreme Law Giver, the Merciful, the unswervingly Just, and so on, prevails.

At the same time, inspired by the concepts of perfection, omniscience, and justice, man in the latter kind of society may be more active in seeking to attain his goals. The freer agent is not necessarily the more highly motivated and active in the mundane sphere. Eventually the achievements scored through such activity may herald man's emergence from the dominance of religious concepts into secularly conceived and actualized forms of existence. Even when a society is moving into secularism, however, it will in some respects continue to be influenced by the religious background of the people. Barely a generation ago, T. S. Eliot could write: "An individual European may not believe that the Christian faith is true, and yet what he says, and makes, and does, will all spring out of his heritage of Christian culture and depend upon that culture for its meaning" (*Notes Towards the Definition of Culture* [1948]). In 1971 it would be inaccurate to assert that a strongly religious background motivates the individual European. But the religious past makes a continuous aesthetic impact on him through the quality of religious writing, through beautiful cathedrals, temples, monasteries, and other religious buildings, and through canonical music, painting, and sculpture.

In those parts of the world where the concept of the nonimmanent and authoritarian, albeit merciful, God has remained dominant, such dominance may still significantly influence cultural expression, keeping this largely within the framework of doctrinal precepts. Cases in point are parts of the Islamic world where man has not emerged from under the dominant concept of the divine.

Our own era has witnessed the rise of secular doctrines that likewise impose conditions upon cultural expression and that, though not religious —indeed, they may claim to be antireligious—operate in ways that recall eras of divine dominance at its uncompromising zenith. This is the case, in different degrees, with such doctrinal systems as Marxism-Leninism, Stalinism, fascism, and Maoism—and their variants. But the culture of people thus governed remains a true expression of them, in art and literature, in material forms, in social patterns and behavior.

Had different human communities always maintained their doctrine and ideology as their cultures developed, much deeper chasms than now exist must have opened among them. Fortunately, it has mostly happened otherwise. For example, while doctrinally Islam did not permit the creation of representations of the human form or of portraits, and while this interdiction has been widely adhered to in the public and religious art and architecture of many Islamic countries, nevertheless, lively and expressive paintings of the human form as well as portraits have long been a feature of Persian art and of Mogul art on the Indian subcontinent. Nor has fine secular music been lacking in Islamic societies, though it too is frowned upon in Islamic doctrine.

In much the same way, strict ideological directives in certain materialist societies have been circumvented from time to time. During the Stalinist era the works of Dostoevsky were not available in his homeland, but recently some of them have been published there. Similarly, directives as to Soviet painting have been relaxed, and painters other than those of the school of socialist realism have created striking canvases—those of Oskar Rabin, Tischler, and Ilya Kabakov come to mind. It is even said that Pasternak's *Dr. Zhivago* (1957), the publication of which outside the Soviet Union created so great a furor in the U.S.S.R., may soon be published in Moscow.

It may be inferred from these examples, drawn as they are from various parts of the world and reflecting different kinds of cultural restrictions, that there exist manifestations of the spirit of man so characteristically human that, in time, though frequently after a long struggle, they will sprout, whatever the state of the cultural soil. Yet we cannot lull ourselves with the assumption that a steady erosion of the rules that cramp man's urges for creative cultural expression is taking place. The present condition of man, his hopes and fears, his problems of nourishment and well-being and even survival are too complex, especially in the prevailing context of "independent" sovereign states, to permit of too facile expectations in this direction.

There is ample evidence that man has not yet reached the stage of full and peaceful flowering of all his cultural capacities. This achievement will have to await the discovery of some means by which each person may do his or her "thing" without diminishing the operative right of all others to do *their* things. Man's sociological ingenuity may eventually produce a formula for this. Meanwhile, as we have noted, even in unpropitious circumstances the urge to cultural freedom continues to wear down opposition. Though expressed in distinctive national and regional idioms, these urges are positive factors in the advance toward a world community.

Particular idioms of cultural expression have not in themselves constituted barriers to cross-cultural understanding and universal appreciation. Written in Russian about the lives of Russians in their own distinctive habitat, Tolstoy's *War and Peace* (1863–69)* and Dostoevsky's *The Brothers Karamazov* (1879–80)† are, even in translation, among the greatest novels available to the reading public in English-speaking countries, as they are in France, in Germany, and elsewhere. In the same way, the works of Shakespeare, Lorca, Rilke, Kalidasa, Balzac, Tu Fu, and others are universal. So too is there spontaneous and universal response to the architectural and sculptural languages of Kyōto, Greece, Ellora, the Nile Valley, Angkor Wat, Agra, Paris, Córdoba, Rome, Peking, and the Incas. Whatever the idiom and the cultural context, the creative capacity of man seems able to build an exquisitely beautiful overarching dome under which all men everywhere can live richer and more fulfilled lives.

The cultural achievements that constitute the peaks of man's artistic and intellectual endeavor, though expressed in a variety of idioms, are a universal means of communication and in no way impede the development of a world community. It is rather the secular and religious constraints on cultural expression in a community, often acceptable to elements in the population that have so far been denied full educational and cultural opportunities or have been unable to take advantage of these, that impede the advance of a world community.

Frequently such restrictions and constraints may be declared by institutionalized or traditional authority to be necessary for the preservation of the community, as well as for its vitality, well-being, and further development. There is, nevertheless, impressive evidence to suggest that such pronouncements are largely unfounded rhetoric, however appealing they may sound. Every society comes sooner or later to realize that its truly great cultural achievements are those that express fully and freely and with utmost intensity the aesthetic experiences, the imaginative perceptions, the intellectual insights, and the social ideas of its creative geniuses. In time it becomes clear that those who succumb to cramping rhetoric and regulations, to aesthetic and intellectual straitjackets, do not produce cultural creations that generation after generation of human beings, both within that society and around the world, are able to look upon with continuing satisfaction, pride, and joy.

At the same time, cultural constraints do exist and, as they become welded into the cultural and religious traditions of various societies, may promote separatist attitudes among communities and nations, accompanied by assertions of superiority or uniqueness. Worst of all, they may promote fears that the ethos of a community will be overwhelmed or undermined if cultural intermingling is permitted. Once these fears become dominant, it comes to seem that defensive measures of a military kind are needed to protect the community. This leads in turn to counter-defensive steps by other communities. In our time this process has been carried to the point where two states now deploy "defensive" weapons that could easily destroy the world. In the foreseeable future a number of other states may well do likewise. Meanwhile, other states are armed with less spectacular but equally terrible devices such as lethal gases and germ preparations that could rival nuclear weapons in their powers of destruction.

There is irony in the cultural and religious contribution to this state of affairs. We have already observed that the greatest aesthetic works in all cultures are universally admired and acclaimed, and that this universal response adds to, rather than in any way diminishes, each individual culture. Similarly, all major religions regard mankind as one family, at least potentially. All major ideologies, too, claim a universal applicability. In this sense, all major religions and ideologies are universal, in spite of the competitiveness of their creeds, which paradoxically breed exclusivity. It is the element of universality that has given strength to the current movement of ecumenism: in a few generations (though it may be doubted whether we have that much time allotted to us, unless other measures are also taken in the meanwhile) this movement is likely to set the tone of man's future religious consciousness, providing much greater tolerance and cooperation. Nevertheless, in the name of nearly every religion, ideology, and culture extant in the world today, it continues to be possible to keep people apart, to teach them to fear, and to make them retreat behind barriers buttressed by the weaker and less widely appreciated aspects of their traditions—aspects that they themselves, with the passage of time, do not highly prize.

The confrontations of cultural and religious traditions, springing out of the fears they generate and not from their own best achievements— at which level they are able to communicate and understand each other almost perfectly—remain with us. Brutal experience in this century has forced man to begin to respond to this fact by efforts to replace confrontation by negotiation in the political relations of states. This movement has led to the creation of continuously available machinery, such as the Security Council of the United Nations and the system of consultation among the representatives of more than 120 states at United Nations headquarters, to deal with the various abrasive aspects of political and economic relations. Confrontations have not ended, but at least the rudiments of arrangements to promote alternative and corrective relationships now exist. There are also regional bodies such as the Organization of American States, the Organization of African Unity, and the Arab League, which provide machinery for dealing with disputes within their regions, but the very regionalism of these groups may promote negative reactions to other regional systems, and their validity in a shrinking world is open to serious questioning.

There is not yet available to mankind any universal organization that

---

* *GBWW*, Vol. 51.
† *GBWW*, Vol. 52.

draws together all of the world's cultures and religions in a continuous process of analysis. Such analysis might make it possible to rethink and resolve the fears that cause people to recede from their faith in themselves, their creative capacities, and their desire to relate and to love, into attitudes of defensiveness, suspicion, and strife.

In times past, when at least certain areas of the world were in close relationship, there were institutions to bring together, through study and reflection, religious and cultural trends. Thus in ancient India, commencing some centuries before the Christian era, universities such as those at Taxila, and a little later at Nalanda, conducted religious and cultural dialogues that brought together Hindus, Buddhists, Taoists, Jains, and others drawn from communities that stretched from Asia Minor through central Asia to China. Artistic counterparts of these intellectual endeavors were also created, for example, in the amazing array of temples and monasteries of the three religious traditions of Hinduism, Buddhism, and Jainism, standing side by side in their extraordinary sculptural beauty at Ellora in west central India. In the next historical era, the lesser diversities of tradition among the smaller European communities were knit together at such centers of learning as Bologna, Oxford, and Paris. The Indian experiments were destroyed by the rise of later dogmatisms, and the European centers too were often at the mercy of political events affecting ducal, regal, and imperial fortunes. Their effectiveness rose and fell over the decades and centuries. With the rise and consolidation of the nation-state in Europe, what had been truly European centers became primarily national institutions.

In our own era, men and women of concern have begun to realize that in order to be able to resolve the multifaceted problems that stand in the way of the emergence of a peaceful and friendly world, more must be done than to create political institutions to deal with disputes and conflicts. This conviction has been expressed to some extent by the creation of such UN bodies as UNESCO, the Human Rights Commission, the Development Programme, and the Industrial Development Organization. Thus the foundations on which the structure of a world community could arise are being extended, though they remain incomplete and weak. The vast area of cultural traditions has been given only slight consideration on a global basis. These traditions will have to be brought directly into the planning of the world community, for they form the matrices in which are born the deep inchoate fears of communities that manifest themselves ultimately in political strife and military conflict.

No truly viable, habitable structure containing a peaceful and increasingly fulfilled world community can be built without including in the foundations a spacious provision for the cultural and ideological aspects of the life of peoples. After the end of the First World War, and with the setting up of the League of Nations, there appeared the first glimmerings of realization that the world needed centers of study, discussion, analysis, and reflection that would bring people together from different places and traditions. From the early days of the league, proposals began to come in for the establishment of a world university, indicative of a desire to reinstitute, this time on a worldwide basis, the transparochial outlook of the ancient and medieval schools of learning to which we have drawn attention. The League of Nations considered more than a dozen such proposals. For several reasons it was unable to implement them. First and the most important, the league itself was not a world body. Great parts of the world remained in colonial status, and even the member-states of the British Commonwealth were still tied to the apron strings of the mother country. Furthermore, the United States had decided to remain outside the league. A worldwide proposal was thus beyond its capacity to enact. Then, too, the idea of internationalizing the terms of humanity's existence was a novel one. The politically oriented organs of the league were hardly capable of coping with their own responsibilities, let alone of taking steps to internationalize the culture of Frenchmen, Germans, British, and Japanese (most other people hardly counted in the affairs of the league). What was not realized was that the first steps were shaky precisely because they were steps on only one leg—a political leg. It would have added to the firmness of those first steps, and perhaps been of crucial significance to the peace of the world, if there had been another foot to plant firmly on the earth. The other limb was not created, and the league limped finally into oblivion.

Since the Second World War, in the time of the United Nations, there have been many new proposals for a world university. Indeed, the total number of these communications in this era is computed at a thousand. More than two hundred of them have been addressed to the UN and its agencies, but till recently it has been outside the UN organization that practical efforts have been made to assemble transnational scholars and thinkers on a continuing basis. And in these efforts the educational establishment has not been in the forefront. Commenting on this fact, Dr. Abdus Salam, himself a distinguished educationist, a leading high-energy physicist, and director of the recently established International Centre for Theoretical Physics at Trieste (which is sponsored by the International Atomic Energy Agency, a UN body), has observed:

> *That at least one such [international] university did not come into existence at the same time as the United Nations Organization in 1945 is something of which the world's academic and scientific communities cannot feel proud. It is imperative that practical steps be taken in the nearest future to ensure that we see one or more truly international universities taking shape during the next twenty years.*

There exist a few, for the most part modestly conceived, institutions that have tried to function as truly world universities. The earliest of these still recent ventures dates from 1923, when the Nobel laureate poet Rabindranath Tagore set up an international university at Santiniketan in eastern India. Now known as the Rabindra Bharati University, this institution has a strong transnational cultural emphasis and draws scholars and faculty from most parts of the world. Nearby, at Calcutta, an Institute of Culture is being transformed into a School of World Civilization specifically to promote international cultural cooperation within the world community.

In the Western world, a transnational pilot project at university level was conducted near New York City in 1963 under the direction of Dr. Harold Taylor, formerly president of Sarah Lawrence College, with the assistance of an international faculty. It was attended by students from about twenty countries. From that experiment has developed the Friends World College at Westbury, N.Y., with a present enrollment of about 150 students, mostly Americans, offering transnational courses of study that are partly conducted in countries round the world.

Meanwhile at Auroville, in southern India, a farsighted and carefully planned university city is taking shape with national and regional pavilions of culture. Symbolizing its comprehensive transnational focus, fistfuls of earth from 120 countries were deposited by representatives of those countries in an urn placed in the center of the city. Persons from some twenty countries are at work at Auroville, building, according to the university's charter, "a place of unending education, of constant progress . . . the bridge between the past and the future . . . a living embodiment of an actual human unity."

It has come to seem important that the collective will of the nations express itself as to the relevance of institutions for continuing international cultural studies, considered in the light of mankind's increasingly urgent and fateful struggle to build a world at peace. Sensitive to the needs of the era, U Thant, secretary-general of the United Nations, has taken a personal initiative with respect to a world university. Acknowledging the efforts of individuals and groups in various parts of the world, he stated in his report to the UN General Assembly of 1969:

> *I feel that the time has come when serious thought may be given to the establishment of a United Nations university, truly international in character and devoted to the Charter objectives of peace and progress. . . . Working and living together in an international atmosphere, these students from various parts of the world would be better able to understand one another. Even in their formative years they would be able to break down the barriers between nations and cultures which create only misunderstanding and mistrust.*

The UN General Assembly showed its interest in U Thant's suggestion by asking him for a feasibility study on an international university. The preparation of this study served to heighten interest in the matter, and at the end of 1970 at its twenty-fifth session, the General Assembly, without a single country casting a negative vote, authorized the secretary-general and UNESCO to advance further explorations. Though the old fears of certain politicians and diplomats still retard progress toward an international understanding on this subject, which would clearly be conducive to the basic objectives of the United Nations itself—"peace and progress," as U Thant succinctly described them—it would appear that the international community has made its view sufficiently clear so that we can say that we are now approaching the era when truly international institutes of higher learning will be a reality.

The premise on which we are proceeding is that world universities would counteract the influence of the essentially weaker but nevertheless widespread aspects of cultural and religious traditions that impede the growth of the world community. Let us carefully scrutinize this premise.

The first step is to observe that a world university, as conceived in the UN study and as likely to develop, would be transnational in the following five respects, which do not characterize existing major universities. First, scholars and faculty (or resource persons, to use an alternative name for the senior scholars on a campus) would be drawn from all parts of the world, without a preponderance from any one of them. Second, the study of the cultures of the world, including religions, would be obligatory. Third, global problems having to do with economic development and the environment would be studied from the points of view of all regions of the world. Fourth, in order to ensure world participation, the world university would be located in a number of scattered campuses, at least one in each of the major world regions. Finally, though regionally based, each campus would be global in its scholars and resource persons. Each campus would be bilingual. Scholars would be fluent in one of the campus languages and acquire a working knowledge of the other.

Scholars attending the international university should be such as have already acquired one or more university degrees in their own university systems, or who have in the pursuit of their vocations developed sufficient interest in learning to be able to engage in transnational studies at the graduate level. These requirements for admission would ensure that scholars had a sound grasp of their own traditions. The starting point of the university's work would be where the world situation actually finds itself: in the hands of societies that have become entities in confrontation, indrawn on account of fears, nurturing the separateness of their traditions.

Course work might be envisaged in groups of ten to twelve scholars from as many countries, each group being assisted by several—or more—resource persons, no two being from the same country. The very nature

of these groups would ensure that the needs of humanity as a whole became the subject of discussion and research. All the great streams of
knowledge would for the first time begin to merge in the confluence
of the world university. At the same time, the characteristic riches of the
various cultures of the world would probably have a better chance of surviving and growing than they do at present, when the favorably placed
cultures tend to overwhelm other less aggressive ones, whose potential
contributions and intrinsic human values are largely ignored.

To the end that such a university might have an immediate as well as
a long-range effect upon the world, there would also be short-term global
culture courses, lasting from a few weeks to a couple of months each,
for persons in public affairs—government personnel, legislators, economic
planners, business executives, and opinion molders of all kinds—in short,
the decision makers of the world. Having lived together in a microcosm
of the whole world, discussing and learning together, these men and
women, on returning home, could give added strength to moves for
developing a cooperative world community.

The governance of the university would be entrusted to an international board that would include women and youth. All the relevant aspects of human society would be represented, without any one of them
being allowed to dominate. The deliberations of this board would in
themselves be a new chapter in international cultural understanding.

The sites for campuses would be made available—and a high proportion of their cost would be met in local currencies—by host countries or
host regions. For the sake of such a truly global enterprise in education, it
is thought that transoceanic air and sea passengers might be very willing
to accept a surcharge of one dollar per fare, to help defray expenses. This
insignificant individual effort alone would probably cover the balance of
costs at a half-dozen campuses of modest size. Host countries would also
assist with computer, library, and other technical facilities.

Taking advantage of the speed of travel in our era, arrangements are
entirely feasible that would bring frequent visits from leading authorities
in their fields to the world university campuses, without requiring such
persons to cut themselves off from their work at their own universities,
institutes, or other organizations.

Now envisage seven or eight—and after a generation, perhaps twelve
or fifteen—such campuses functioning in as many regions of the world,
each one globally representative. The mutual understanding and appreciation of diverse cultural achievements that would be generated at these
campuses would be disseminated to the countries and regions of the world.
As a result of this refreshing radiation, would there not begin to appear,
at first tentatively but with increasing vigor, a desire in all parts of the
world to apprehend the higher levels of cultural achievements all over
our globe? There would also be rising dividends in peace, mutual appreciation and syncretism, and an easier flow of cooperative development

to end the indignities of poverty. Moreover, these campuses would soon begin to affect the work programs in national university systems, encouraging truly transnational studies among them.

The highest cultural and religious achievements are not impediments to the development of the world community. It is at other levels that culture and religion engender fears and lead to separatist and aggressive attitudes. A network of world university campuses is needed to assist in lifting us above these lower levels. It is such institutions that could fill the gaping hole in the still incomplete foundations that are being laid in our era, and upon which in due time the world community must grow and thrive.

E. J. Mishan

Of the economists who have appeared on
the scene over the past decade or so, one
of the most trenchant, not to say acerbic,
is E. J. Mishan, whose writings have been
widely noted and discussed. A former
student of Milton Friedman at the University of Chicago, Professor Mishan teaches
at the London School of Economics. The

titles of certain of the books and articles he
has published suggest the direction of his
thought. Among them are *Technology and
Growth: the Price We Pay* (1970), *Welfare
Economics: An Assessment* (1969), "Abyss
of Progress" (*Nation,* November 1968),
and "Futurism and the Worse That Is Yet
to Come" (*Encounter,* March 1971). In
these and other works he has consistently
questioned the idea of economic growth,
of which he says the motto should be
"Enough Does Not Suffice," and which, as
the following essay indicates, he regards
as potentially destructive of every real
human and social good.

Economic Growth:
Some Pessimistic Reflections

Introduction

More so than with the physical sciences, the development of economics tends to reflect the contemporary problems of society.
Adam Smith's *Wealth of Nations** was among other things an eloquent
protest against the constraints placed by the old mercantilist system on
the emerging industrial enterprises of the second half of the eighteenth
century. Ricardo's theory of rent, with its recourse to the crucial notion
of *marginal* land, is believed to have arisen directly from the attempt to
explain the high price of corn during the Napoleonic wars. Not surprisingly, the period between the two world wars gave impetus to prolonged theorizing on the causes of mass unemployment, which theorizing
could be said to have culminated in Keynes's *General Theory of Employment* of 1936. As for the current preoccupation of economists with increasingly sophisticated models of economic growth, there is no difficulty
in tracing its genesis to the unprecedented postwar economic expansion
and, through modern news media, to our increasing awareness of this
phenomenon. It may be added in passing that the sustained growth in
the West was not foreseen by economists in the immediate postwar years.
Indeed, they were still thinking in terms of fiscal policies and other
measures designed to prevent large-scale unemployment. In the event,
some years elapsed before economists began to recognize that chronic
inflation had replaced chronic unemployment as perhaps the major
economic malaise of the West. Today, however, there is no doubt that
the focus of interest has shifted to inflation, and that the study of money,
and its relation to aggregate expenditure and the price level, is absorbing
the energies of a large number of professional economists.

One might continue to speculate, though with less confidence, about
the relation between other theoretical developments—including the growing popularity of quasi-mathematical techniques—and contemporaneous
social and economic events. But I shall resist the temptation here in order

---

* *GBWW*, Vol. 39.

to turn to a yet more fascinating inquiry—one that is the reverse of the causal relationship just touched upon—that of the effects of economic ideas upon society itself; in particular, the impact on postwar society of the idea of economic growth.

The widest scope for conjecture and interpretation is provided by the events of the past five years, but before concentrating on this short period let us recall first some of the broad developments leading up to it.

As in the years immediately following the First World War, so just after the Second there was an intense desire to return to "normalcy" and, inevitably also, intense hope verging on expectation of a new era of greater international understanding as a precondition for world peace. The hope was short-lived. Barely a year had passed before the term *Iron Curtain* became an essential part of the political vocabulary of the West. Until the mid-fifties the two superpowers, the United States and the Soviet Union, appeared to dominate the international arena. But soon after the rise of Red China, the cracks in the once-monolithic Communist bloc were visible to all. Moreover, it was gradually recognized that the threat of a nuclear holocaust was too dangerous a game to play. Following the experiences of Vietnam and the Middle East, the United States and the Soviet Union are both placing increased emphasis on more conventional methods of warfare and diplomacy. The return to greater flexibility in dealing with international conflicts has allowed the lesser great powers, in particular Britain and France, to play a more active part in international affairs.

Turning to the economic scene, until the last five years at least, the atmosphere has been one of optimism. Within a few years after the war, aided initially by the Marshall Plan, Western Europe completely recovered from the material devastation of the war. An almost miraculous economic recovery followed the West German monetary reform of 1948. By 1954 the German mark was one of the most respectable currencies in Europe. Thus all the elaborate intellectual preparations made by economists to combat "cyclical" and "secular" unemployment were left to molder. For a secular boom had begun that has not yet ended. Employment remained high—by prewar norms, incredibly high. International trade, at least among Western countries, grew rapidly despite an armory of trade restrictions. Only the economic plight of the poorer countries of the world remained to nag the conscience of the West.

During the last decade, the continuous postwar material prosperity came to be accepted by people, and certainly by the younger generation, as one of the more mundane facts of economic life. At the same time, two related phenomena began to impinge on their consciousness and to grow into something like an obsession. On the one hand was the index of economic growth, which inevitably was compared with the growth indexes of other countries. The imaginary growth race was under way, producing from time to time in each country torrents of exhortation, plus much

impatience, self-examination, and anxiety. On the other hand was the inescapable fact of inflation—a slow, creeping inflation to start with in countries such as Britain, France, the Scandinavian countries, and the United States, but gathering pace and in the last decade encompassing West Germany also.

The postwar inflation

Some brief comments on this postwar inflation provide a fitting preface to the more extended treatment of economic growth that follows.

In their analysis of the postwar inflation, economists have for the most part confined themselves to two issues. Concerning the cause, the question has been whether the inflation is principally the result of excessive wage demands or of excessive demand for goods. As to remedies, the specialists are divided roughly between those who favor fiscal policies operating directly upon aggregate demand as the chief weapon of attack, and those who favor stricter control of the supply of money. Whatever the respective merits of the opposing arguments, too little has been said by economists generally of the social and political factors that have aggravated if not actively promoted the forces of inflation. For, since the war, there has been a strong political, indeed electoral, emphasis on material growth in the Western world. With the spread of television and news media, the public has been deluged with an uninterrupted flow of invidious statistical information bearing on changing differentials in pay as between occupations, on annual advances in aggregate and per capita real income, and on differences in growth rates as between regions and countries. Taken together with the intermittent forecasts of economic advance, of new growth targets, of plans for faster growth, and of institutional re-arrangements for raising productivity, these developments have created in society at large expectations of material improvements that are both exaggerated and possibly unrealizable. At the same time, as an ancillary effect among individuals and occupations, there has been engendered a hypersensitivity to the question of their share in the national dividend. A revealing instance in this connection was the setting up in Britain (1968) of a Prices and Incomes Board to control the rise in wages, salaries, and prices. The event was soon followed by a round of exorbitant wage claims, each labor union apparently anxious to submit its claims before "the doors closed" and to allow itself plenty of margin for bargaining with the board. Strike action, especially by those engaged in "essential" services—transport, post office, garbage collection, schools, nursing, fuel and power—amounts to an as-yet legitimate and apparently effective form of blackmail of the public. Since democratic governments depend upon popular support, they are more likely than not to make concessions and, being seen to make concessions, to strengthen the appeal of such tactics to other labor unions and professional bodies who see themselves as having slipped behind in the scramble for more. To put the matter crudely, governments fanning the flames of greed for electoral advantage are belatedly discovering that the flames are burning the edges of the economy and are stubbornly resisting attempts to extinguish them.

In the decade immediately after the war it may well have been true, as asserted by many economists, that rates of unemployment between 2.5 percent and 4 percent—depending on the composition of the unemployed—would have sufficed to ensure overall price stability. Today it is no longer true. Since 1940 there has been no experience in the West of a major economic depression. A generation has grown to maturity in an atmosphere in which governments are held responsible for every random shift in the economic weather, and in which people expect, as a matter of right, not simply employment opportunities but also a progressive improvement in the pecuniary opportunities open to them. The experience of two or three decades of continually rising prices adds to these complacent aspirations a general confidence that prices will continue to move upward no matter what governments may do. In order to break the back of this expectational momentum, which sustains and powers the current inflation, it may be necessary to create a rate of unemployment of 10 percent or more for a two- to three-year period. No democratic government, however, is likely to try the experiment or to remain long in power if it does so. We may conclude tentatively that the persistent inflation we are experiencing has political origins in the political aggravation of men's avarice and also that, for political reasons, the monetary and fiscal pressures necessary to bring it to a halt are unlikely to be exerted. The only alternative measure remaining to us—distasteful to economists but nevertheless conceivable to undertake in recognition of a national emergency—is that of imposing, for not-too-short a period, rigid price controls over the main sectors of economy.

Economic growth and pollution

In the last five years the postwar obsession with economic growth has been under attack by ecologists, by sociologists, by a number of economists, and by scientists in many fields. There is more than just a doubt that the genie of "progress" may not be a good genie after all: there is a growing alarm in the West, especially in the United States, at what is happening to our environment and to our civilization. In the recent speculation about the causes and consequences of a number of distasteful developments, the role played by economic growth in the context of a liberal and commercial society has not been accorded its due. I propose therefore to adopt it as the leitmotiv of the remainder of the article. For this purpose the social phenomena to be treated will be grouped under two main headings—pollution and social disintegration, in that order.

Over the last two decades, and particularly over the last five years, there has been a growing awareness of the reckless pollution by man of his planetary home. The notion of the earth as a finite body of matter having limited resources of air, water, earth, and minerals for sustaining life is rapidly supplanting in men's consciousness the older idea of an endless frontier of material opportunities. The image that has taken shape over the last few years is that of the spaceship earth, man's only refuge, a tiny green and blue planet warmed by a dwarf star, fanned by breezes, floating alone in a cold, dark, and inhospitable universe. But this glimmer of truth is slow in asserting itself. The new concern over our unique heritage, the fear that in our unbounded rapacity we are irrevocably destroying it, expresses itself in words rather than in action. The issues raised by this new concern are as yet relegated to the periphery of political power. At the center of power there remains an apparently immovable complex of business and bureaucracy allied with and reinforced by the new technology, one inspired yet by the boundless visions of science. Official priority is still accorded to economic indexes, to per capita real income, to rates of expansion, export performance, industrial disputes, market-sharing arrangements, and to research, development, and innovation. Primary concern with these familiar and mundane issues, it is still believed, must somehow promote the general well-being. And if, contrary to these articles of faith, one observes increasing air and noise pollution, incipient ecological disturbances, the continued spread of steel and concrete over once-beautiful landscape—if one remarks the proliferation of protest movements, the contempt for authority in the young, the intensification of racial conflicts, the rise in divorce rates, the upward trend of all forms of nervous disease, the rising tide of crime and insensate violence— the remedies proposed by men in high places almost invariably place the greatest emphasis on faster economic growth and more research.

We need say very little about population trends, as this is one aspect of modern ecology that is continually and forcibly brought to people's attention. While before the war, fears of a declining population were voiced in Europe and America, today with more justification it is the nightmare of "population explosion" that transfixes our imagination. If current trends continue, we are to anticipate a world population of some seven billion souls before the century is out.

This jetport in Florida was left unfinished because of protests by environmental scientists and conservationists contending that its use would virtually destroy wildlife in nearby Everglades National Park

In the Malthusian scheme of things, population pressed against the limited means of subsistence. Even today economists and scientists can be found who see the problem of an expanding population largely in terms of available food supplies and in terms of improved medicines, pesticides, and disinfectants. And if such people are not altogether complacent, it is to some extent because of a fear that Darwinian adaptations to pesticides may release upon us vast insect populations, and that new strains of more resistant bacteria are emerging in response to widespread application of "miracle" drugs and serums.

But survival of larger populations is a questionable goal of policy. The continuing pressure of population on this small planet can destroy all hope of being able to realize the good life that above all depends on space and leisure. Already in the ever-expanding metropolises and suburbs we are getting in each other's way, treading on each other's toes, getting on each other's nerves, repeatedly delayed in endless traffic jams, waiting in interminable queues. And this mutual frustration is not to be eased by existing developments in transport, by producing higher powered cars, faster aircraft, larger airports, more private planes and helicopters. Quite the contrary: just as an increase in the speed of the molecules of a given volume of gas increases the pressure, so will attempts to increase individual mobility aggravate the existing congestion.

In these circumstances, the hope of some minuscule increases in productivity arising from further economies of large-scale production is hardly worthy of consideration. Yet we have seemingly responsible statesmen in a number of countries, including Britain, talking of the desirability of a larger population than the existing one. This larger population goal is reinforced by the old-fashioned belief that since an expanding population is apparently good for business, it must also be so for the nation at large. Of course businessmen prefer an expanding population to a static one, in that the former entails an expanding market. Moreover, the faster population expands, the greater is the tendency of rents and profits to rise relative to wages. But this conflict of interest as between capitalists and property-owners on the one hand, and the rest of society on the other, is of a purely distributional nature. The nation as a whole is not thereby made better off. And what are suffered by the citizens of the nation as a whole, irrespective of the distribution of income, are the congestion effects referred to.

Yet assurance of a stable population, or even of a declining population, would not by itself serve to calm our apprehensions of the future. For today's generation, it is a fact of experience that within the span of a few years, and without any appreciable population increase, the unchecked production and marketing of new technological products has resulted in a cumulative deterioration of the environment and consequently in a reduction of the ordinary pleasures of living. The private enterprise system and the profit motive, on which we have depended for economic

Rush hour in New York City

guidance for the best part of two centuries, can do wonders under certain conditions—briefly, under those conditions that ensure that the impact on the welfares of all people arising from producing or using economic goods is largely captured by the pricing system. Such conditions never quite prevailed, but they are certainly absent today. One of the consequences is that we have built cities fit only for machines to navigate and have crammed them with towered structures that are fitting monuments only to the commercial spirit. The offense to the eyes, ears, nostrils, the blight on a man's spirits and risk to his health are social costs that under existing institutions are wholly omitted in the pricing of modern office blocks, and in the pricing of airline and automobile travel. So such things multiply unchecked, and in quantity far beyond that which could be justified on any rational economic criterion, to produce for us monster

cities such as a New York, which is bursting at the seams in the attempt to keep the traffic moving, or a Los Angeles, the nemesis of the automobile era, a non-city buried under the tentacles of its freeway system.

Other disagreeable features may be mentioned in passing, many of them the result either of wide-eyed private enterprise or of myopic municipalities, such as postwar suburban "development," the erosion of the countryside, the "uglification" of coastal towns, the pollution of air and water with chemical wastes, the accumulation of thick oils upon our beaches, the sewage poisoning of rivers, the destruction of wildlife by the indiscriminate use of pesticides, the changeover from animal farming to animal factories, and, visible to all who have eyes to see, the wanton destruction of a rich heritage of natural beauty—a heritage that cannot be restored in our lifetime.

The economist is aware of these phenomena, for they fit comfortably into his broad concept of adverse "spillover effects"—the harmful effects, imposed on innocent members of society, regarded as the by-products of the pursuit by others of pleasure or profits. Yet despite his familiarity with the spillover concept, and the growing economic literature on solutions to spillover problems, very little has been done to curb these problems. Indeed, it is the unprecedented speed and scale of such developments that have caught us off our guard. Such is the thrust of modern technology, such is the opportunism of man's enterprise, that the disposal of the waste products of industry, which for thousands of years were absorbed into the life cycle of nature, has suddenly, it seems, broken all ecological bounds. And the general public, its attention continually distracted by technological wonders, has only just begun to take measure of the gravity of the situation. We have only begun to calculate the generations it would take to undo the damage wrought over the last thirty years alone: to regrow forests on the hundreds of thousands of acres stripped of timber, to remove some of the thousands of square miles of concrete laid over the green earth, to purify lakes and rivers reeking of eutrophication, to revive the wildlife of Africa and Asia, to restore to original magnificence many hundreds of miles of Mediterranean coastline ruined in the postwar tourist spree, to cleanse the atmosphere of millions of tons of floating pollutants and of an uncertain but steadily growing amount of radioactive matter.

Such has been the scale of destruction, and such is the current state of alarm among ecologists and conservationist societies, that one detects both an "eat, drink, and be merry" spirit among the young, on the one hand, and on the other, a frigid reaction by some well-known historians and scientists whose cultivated detachment forbids them to be ruffled by the mere proximity of current events. Rather than project uncouth magnitudes into the future, they find it more satisfying to respond to present dangers by observing patiently that similar alarms were sounded in ages gone by—and withal humanity survived.

Economic growth and social disintegration

Economic growth with stable population, and under conditions in which adverse environmental effects are contained by legislation and by new institutional mechanisms, is feasible enough and obviously to be preferred to the existing indiscriminate scramble for increased material product. Yet economic growth based chiefly on technological innovation carries with it other consequences that are likely to be inimical to any acceptable vision of the good life. And though some of these consequences operate independently of the form of social organization, it is worth distinguishing those consequences more overtly connected with the com-

". . . and a Chargey Card for Freddie and a Chargey Card for Sissy."

mercial ethos that continues to guide the economic destiny of the more affluent West.

First, there is the erosion of tastes and standards. The opportunities for quick profits, the result of the successful marketing of novelties and gimmicks, are magnified in a prosperous private enterprise system by the formation of a volatile consuming public—one that has gradually been severed from the sobering influences of tradition. Indeed, the growthman's chief hope of maintaining the economic momentum in the West lies precisely in the creation of such a consuming public. Success achieved in producing high levels of expenditure in a rich society requires the continuous re-creation of new dissatisfactions that are made to rise phoenixlike from the ashes of old satisfactions—a process that is facilitated by a consuming public just described, whose tastes are free of traditional notions of excellence and whose acquisitive impulses are unrestrained by any norms of propriety.

Thus the ideal consuming public for the wealthy competitive economics of the West is one that is free-floating, untethered to any values, one that can be molded and segmented, and pulled hither and thither, by bright-eyed admen who are subject to no moral restraints. And if this ideal public has in fact so conveniently come into being in economic

conditions of near surfeit,[1] some thanks are due also to the pronounce-
ment of those technocrats who bid us seek emancipation by embracing the
novel idea that perpetual and accelerating change is the essence of our
future civilization, a civilization in which social norms will have no time
to form and in which, indeed, concepts of right and wrong, vice and
virtue, can only be functional and ephemeral.

Second, and closely connected with this development, is the growing
moral vacuum, especially among the young. The attitude of so many of
the young is no longer to be explained by the familiar sort of tension
between parent and growing child in older and more stable societies. The
unconcealed contempt for the Establishment of the world of adults is but
a by-product of the dissolution of a common ethical frame of reference.
True, the secularization that comes with the growing prestige and power
of science is manifestly the fundamental factor in this collapse of an
ethical consensus once rooted in traditional religions. But the nature of
the reaction and its extremity cannot be divorced from the economic
and social institutions. In a commercial society in which money is seen
to be made by fanning the flames of envy, lust, vanity, and greed—a society
in which status and success are the overt rewards of sustained and ruthless
self-seeking—it is no great wonder that utter cynicism is in vogue among
the young. Yet insofar as this cynicism breeds among the young a complete rejection of what they imagine to be adult values, they are themselves the more readily exploitable as consumers by the commercial
purveyors of baubles, frippery, and feathers. Only the exacting demands
of a competitive and technically sophisticated civilization stand between
them—or rather some of them—and their surrender to the amoral arcadia
where nothing matters but the instant.

In such a milieu, no one need wonder long that crime, robbery with
violence in particular, is one of the West's fastest growing industries.
To the uncluttered conscience of the young, the only considerations are
the rewards and the risks, and it so happens that the rewards are larger
and the chances of being caught and punished smaller than they used
to be. At the same time as the deterrents to crime are weaker, the in-
centives are stronger. The visions portrayed by glossy magazines and
tourist brochures of a perpetual *dolce vita,* to be enjoyed by young, smart,
cool, fast-moving, freely spending cliques, act as a standing temptation to
impressionable youths to make good their deficiencies of talent or fortune
by crime rather than by industry.

Third, there is the perversion of the ideals of a liberal education. In
the West today this ideal has a distinctly nostalgic flavor. Adult education is quite openly regarded as a means to material ends. The greater
part of university education today is unadulterated vocational training,
the degree associated with it aptly dubbed the meal ticket. Of course, it
may be protested that this feverish postwar expansion of vocational train-

ing at least brings us closer to the ideal of universal equality of opportunity. Yet, according as we realize this ideal, the closer we approach a fully working "meritocracy." That is, we approach a system of society in which the resulting inequality of rewards is closely related to unalterable inequalities of intellectual and artistic endowment—or, in effect, to pure accident of birth. The culmination of such trends will issue, perhaps, in a yet more efficient economy, but it will hardly result in a more egalitarian society. On the contrary, the society toward which it tends, if fully realized, is likely to be a good deal more irksome and mortifying to ordinary people than a hierarchical society based on aristocratic privilege.

Fourth, there is the upsurge over the last five years of overtly aphrodisiac art. That there has always been a market for such things is not to be denied. What is unique is the present scale and ubiquity of the phenomenon. And the lack of effective protest at its forest-fire spread is to be explained, not in terms of the growth of tolerance in a mature society, but rather in terms of that same helpless bewilderment of an age that is witnessing the collapse of all norms of taste and propriety. People may feel uneasy about these developments, but they remain timid before journalistic sophistry about the value of erotic art forms. Indeed, to be in tune with the times one is expected to respond with an outward show of coolness, suppressing excitement or oral-aggressive feelings aroused by highly salacious "art forms," suppressing also any feelings of anxiety. For to express misgivings is to open oneself to charges of being illiberal if not obscene. It appears but a matter of time before the public succumbs to the pressure of interested groups—well-meaning liberals as well as congenital voyeurs, neurotic artists, enterprising publishers and impresarios—for the removal of all legal censorship and restraint.

The rapid economic growth of the West over the postwar period has not been accomplished without traumatic effects on its populations. Tension is everywhere more evident than harmony, disproportion more evident than proportion. The gross overdevelopment of man's acquisitive instinct has its genesis in the industrial free-enterprise system beloved of many economists. The growing obsession with sex and with sexual display masquerading as fashion, the technique of distilling the carnality of sex as a titillating essence to be poured slyly into modern forms of advertising and entertainment—these too owe much to private enterprise. The consequences of this commercially powered irruption of aphrodisiac interest in an already morally fragile and edgy society are likely, on balance, to accelerate the forces of social disintegration.

---

1 With the *existing* distribution of disposable purchasing power, the United States is a near-surfeit economy in the sense that sales pressure and created obsolescence are necessary to maintain the consumers' propensity to spend. It is not impossible that it would continue to be a near-surfeit economy, even with a much more egalitarian structure of disposable income.

Summer of 1970, New York City: compensation for the unemployed

Technological growth in any society

As indicated earlier, there are other consequences for society of technological growth, which are independent of the particular form of social organization. Chief of these are the consequences flowing from changes in productive methods. The loss of aesthetic and instinctual gratification suffered by workingmen over two centuries of technological innovation, which changed them from artisans and craftsmen into machine-minders and dial-readers, must remain a matter of speculation. It need not be supposed, however, that every phase of this historical transformation produced a change for the worse. From some period in the first half of the nineteenth century, conditions of work may well have been improving. Yet the conditions of work, including the social facilities provided, may not be among the chief factors contributing to the satisfaction that men derive from their daily tasks. Two centuries ago, before the "industrial revolution" was properly launched, a skilled workman was a craftsman. Whether he worked in wood, leather, clay, metal, stone, or glass, he was the master of his material, and the thing he created grew in his hands from

the substance of the earth to the finished article. He was mindful also that he was a member of an honored craft, having reached his status after a long apprenticeship, and he took legitimate pride in the excellence of his work. But it is not merely the act of creating things with his hand and brain. A man today can divert himself with such hobbies if he has a mind to. What mattered to the preindustrial craftsman was that his work was needed by the community he dwelt in, as evinced by their readiness to pay for his skill as a master craftsman. There was also then the feeling of belonging, of being an indispensable part of the daily life of his community. From this sprang his unassailable self-respect and that abiding sense of security that is no common thing in the feverish jostling world of today.

There are other sources of human gratification that elude the economist's yardstick. Some of the features incidental to the mode of production, irrelevant to any modern index of "real" income, may yet be vital to the human condition. An open, easy, and full-hearted relationship with one's fellows, for instance, is not something that can be bought on the market or willed into being. The indispensable ingredient of such a re-

lationship is mutual trust, a quality nurtured in the small agrarian society, and one of the first casualties when such a society is uprooted from
the soil and sucked into the vortex of modern capitalism.

With this crucial factor in mind, one may appreciate the difficulty of
giving impetus in the newly built suburbs and towns to something resembling a community spirit—something that was not uncommon in
yesterday's slums that, for all the dirt and distress, had in them much that
was warmly human. Today's new suburbs, in contrast, are apt to degenerate rapidly into so-called dormitory areas in which people of similar
pecuniary circumstances occupy all the houses or blocks of flats within
a precinct. Each family, each member of the family, has his own television
set and private car, the elegant instruments of his estrangement from his
fellows. Is it even conceivable for a community to take root in a neighborhood teeming with cars, transistors, television sets—in which people have
no need or care to know the names of their itinerant neighbors?

It would seem, on reflection, that every step forward in technological
progress, and particularly in those things most eagerly anticipated—swifter
travel, push-button comforts, labor-saving devices, and round-the-clock
synthetic entertainment—effectively transfers our dependence upon other
human beings to dependence upon machines, and therefore unavoidably
constricts further the direct flow of understanding and sympathy between
people.

Future options

Although on the whole the outlook is bleak, there are a number of ways open to us by which the present and the future can be made less intolerable. Let us consider three areas.

Living conditions

In order to strengthen the impulse toward a radical replanning of our cities, we should consider the advantages, even under existing laws, of introducing *separate areas* embodying environmental features different from those in the country at large. The larger the proportion of the population desirous of environmental characteristics that are different from those universally prevalent, the more practical and allocatively superior is the separate-areas solution to any one plan for the area as a whole.

The size of these separate areas can range from enclaves of quiet and repose, within existing cities, to large and viable amenity areas connected by rail to one or more of the large towns or cities. Two sorts of decisions are called for, one with respect to features, the other with respect to size.

First, the main features to be adopted in such areas may be (1) at the extreme, a complete ban on all motorized vehicles and implements, and all aircraft flying over the area; (2) a dependence upon public transport only, preferably electrically powered and possibly supplemented by a taxi service; (3) tolerance of commercial vehicles, which would be confined, however, to certain lanes and within certain hours, and which would be severely limited in respect to size, speed, and type of engine.

Second, there have to be decisions about the size of the areas themselves over which any of the above features, or combination of such features, is to be established. For example, (1) the minimum nonmotoring area could be no smaller than a conventional pedestrian precinct found within certain towns or suburbs; (2) in addition, ancient, winding, narrow streets, or secluded squares, could be set aside purely for the convenience of pedestrians; (3) central parts of some cities and towns, and the more picturesque and historic parts, could be cleared of all motorized traffic; (4) some town and city centers entire could be freed of all private and commercial traffic; (5) some cities, towns, and suburbs may be freed wholly of all private motoring; (6) select regions, districts, and whole counties might be made available for all those wishing to escape the proximity and consequences of private motoring and air travel.

A number of auxiliary decisions concerning compensation, public utilities, schooling, and the like will come up in arranging the transition from the present unrelieved traffic nightmare to any one of a variety of separate areas, in addition to decisions about the number, size, characteristics, and location of such areas. But a beginning has to be made. Once the principle is accepted, there should be no political difficulty in setting aside several areas in an experimental spirit. From what is learned, over the months, of the response of people to one feature or another, one can move on to plan other areas with increasing skill and confidence.

People will then come to realize that there is a wide range of possibilities in the area of choice most critical to their welfare, the physical environment in which they dwell and work.

Leisure

Average family income in the United States is today about fifteen thousand dollars per annum; in an unautomobiled, nonadvertising community, a family could live comfortably, and to spare, on a third of this. But if the resulting increased leisure is economically feasible, its desirability for the mass of humanity is far from being self-evident. The innocent vision of the workingman, freed from the tedium of work, spending joyful hours in museums and picture galleries, visiting ballet and opera, avidly reading the classics of literature and poetry, discovering history and music, voracious for education and self-betterment, is altogether nineteenth century in its iridescence. It is worlds removed from the round of television-viewing, bowling, package tours, and grooming the family car on Sundays—the standard leisure activities of today's working-class family. What they would do with additional leisure if they were obliged to accept it is uncertain. Labor unions appear to have little interest in reducing hours, save for the purpose of increasing the proportion of overtime worked, so increasing earnings for about the same length of working week.

If, however, people were to become satisfied with good food, clothing, and shelter (which, under the existing commercial system, they are never allowed to be); and if the environment in which they live and work were to become pleasant (which, at present, it is not); and if, under these conditions, they could adjust their lives to a significant extension of leisure without becoming either restless or depressed (which is not too likely) —then increasing leisure would be one of the finer fruits of technological advance. If the former two conditions were met—and there is no economic reason why they should not be—there remains the problem of teaching people how to enjoy their increased leisure. Else they might find themselves in a familiar American predicament: that of trying to spend their way out of boredom and, eventually, finding themselves working harder for the "leisure goods" they have little time to use. One need not doubt that troops of social workers would offer themselves as instructors in the arts of leisure usage. But one cannot feel too optimistic about the outcome of so anomalous a situation.

Work

It is perhaps more profitable to consider, instead, the possibilities of making the work itself more satisfactory to the worker—though we do so at a time when we are moving into an era in which intellectual incapacity, as much as monotony of the job in hand, will pose a problem.

With some initiative by the government, and by existing cooperative societies that would undertake to arrange training and marketing facilities, it would be economically feasible to make provision for the production of a wide range of goods in traditional materials—wood, metal, glass, clay, wool, leather—in which men might once more take on the role of creative craftsmen rather than machine-minders specialized on narrow-range processes.

Although as society increases in wealth there is likely to be a growing market for individually produced goods made from traditional materials, it may be doubted whether it will expand fast enough to maintain more than a small fraction of the existing labor force in craft industries at incomes comparable with those to be earned in modern corporations. As more than this fraction opt for work in the craft industries, incomes there will decline relative to those paid in modern industry. Nonetheless the experiment should be encouraged, for it offers men a significant extension of choice in activities that intimately affect their welfare. Many thousands of men may be willing to sacrifice income for the satisfaction of working as craftsmen and for the creative pride of watching the raw materials take shape in their hands.

However, not only may the new craftsmen have to forgo something in the way of pecuniary rewards in exchange for increased pleasure in their occupation; Western society as a whole may have to forgo something. For it should be obvious that many such goods could be imported more cheaply from poorer countries. Unless restrictions were placed on the import of such goods, the nationals of the Western countries would find little scope in this option. If one regards this as too crucial an option for the West to be sacrificed to conventional international trade policies, the losses suffered by the poorer countries will have to be made good in any of a number of practical ways.

Aside from such meliorating proposals, the small hope that remains for the better life we aspire to resides in the dawning recognition that what is significant for humanity is not the conventional growth race but the race within each nation, or within the West as a whole, between on the one hand the powerful momentum toward technological advance regardless of consequences and, on the other hand, the slowly gathering forces of sanity and understanding. The struggle is an uneven one, if only because of the uncertainties that beset the more sober critics of technological progress. They are aware of the immense productive power at the disposal of the West, and of the almost unnerving technological and scientific possibilities we are stumbling upon. Most of all they are aware that whatever the outcome of the struggle, painful choices will soon have to be made in a state of knowledge bordering on ignorance.

Joseph S. Clark

One of the encouraging postwar events in American politics was the election in 1951 of an enlightened progressive named Joseph S. Clark as mayor of Philadelphia, a city that for more than sixty years had been in the grip of a party machine. In 1956 Clark ran for and was elected to the United

States Senate from Pennsylvania, serving for two terms. As a member of the Senate Foreign Relations Committee he called for the creation of an international organization based upon law and was known as one of the few Congressional figures who were genuinely interested in the idea of world government. He left the Senate in 1968 and the following year was chosen President of World Federalists, USA, the principal American body working to bring about a world government.

The Prospects for
World Government

I The concept of world government

World government may be defined as an international institution authorized to enforce its decisions with respect to war prevention and other critical problems that are soluble only on a global basis. The goal of world government is a world without war, in which such world-wide concerns as pollution, poverty, and the population explosion can be dealt with effectively. World government is a means to this end, not the end itself.

World government should have only those powers that are necessary to perform its mission. This, in turn, would require a limited yielding of sovereignty to a world authority by the nation-states. Most of the models for world government contemplate a bicameral legislature, perhaps a reformed Security Council and General Assembly, of the sort that the United Nations now has. They also call for an executive with substantially greater powers than those now exercised by the secretary-general of the United Nations.[1]

There would be a judiciary system modeled on the present World Court but with broader jurisdiction, to deal with mediation, arbitration, and conciliation, as well as justiciable controversies. For the judiciary system to work effectively, the Connally Amendment and all other reservations on the court's authority would have to be repealed.

The judgments, decrees, and awards of the World Court, and the laws passed by the international legislature, would be enforced by a world police force modeled on some of the proposals that have recently been

---

[1] The most explicit and probably the best-known plan for world government was written by the Americans Grenville Clark and Louis Sohn in 1958 under the title *World Peace Through World Law* (Cambridge: Harvard University Press). This work includes a comprehensive revision of the charter of the United Nations to bring it into line with the concepts outlined here. Clark and Sohn dealt largely with war prevention, although they also provided for a world development authority to attempt to ameliorate the gross inequities in economic conditions between the nation-states of the Northern and Southern hemispheres.

made for the creation of a United Nations police force. This force would be under the command of the world executive.

There would be general and complete disarmament of the nation-states under a system of strict international control. Authority would be given to the world government and its agencies to monitor the disarmament process and to assure that none of the nation-states rearmed themselves thereafter.

None of this would require the elimination of the nation-states. On the contrary, the world government that is envisaged would be a federation of such states. Within the federation, the states would retain their domestic authority. Even their foreign policy would be affected only to the extent that such policy would be required to stop at the verge of war. So long as the guns were not shooting and the bombs not falling, there would be no need for the world government to interfere in any except a diplomatic sense. Of course there should be powers to enforce financial contributions from the nation-states, both to prevent war and to finance the solution of other critical problems. But each nation-state would retain the right to have a lightly armed police force to maintain law and order and social justice within its boundaries—but one incapable of opposing the international police force equipped with sophisticated weapons.

In these terms—the terms, that is, of a federation of limited powers—the idea of world government is no more radical than the Constitution of the United States. Of course, the complexities of the twentieth-century world are far greater than the problems that confronted the framers of the Constitution. Nevertheless, the basic principle of a federation of independent states can be adapted to our needs and must be.

II The need for world government

There is very little possibility of attaining world peace, or of enforcing world law in a nuclear age, unless some such form of limited world government is created through the relinquishment of partial sovereignty by the present nation-states. Throughout history, sovereign countries have proved themselves incapable of keeping the peace. Sooner or later diplomacy has always failed to solve quarrels between the nations, the military has taken over, and the shooting has begun. Our present precarious balance of terror results from the possession of nuclear weapons by the two superpowers, the United States and the Soviet Union, as well as by France, Britain, and China. This peril appears to have accelerated in almost geometric proportion since 1945. The prospect of present-day nuclear or, for that matter, chemical, biological, and radiological warfare threatens the very existence of civilization.

A world government that would monitor general and complete disarmament, and would amicably police it through an international

Street scene in Belfast

authority, could prevent such a catastrophe. Although the practical difficulties of achieving such a government are enormous, there seems no
feasible alternative to its creation. The pertinent question is not whether
world government is needed—it obviously is—but whether fallible mankind and particularly present-day political leaders are ready to turn to
the solution before it is too late. World government is not an idea that
has arrived before its time. It is the most timely of all solutions to our
present frightening difficulties. Unless enforceable law can be created
through international institutions, there is little hope for this, the twenty-
first identifiable civilization since man came down from the trees.

Secretary-General U Thant of the United Nations put the question
succinctly in a speech he delivered at the Fourteenth World Congress of
the World Association of World Federalists in Ottawa, Canada, on
August 23, 1970. He said in part:

> A world under law is realistic and attainable. I think I have some
> sense of the obstacles—in fact, they are my constant companions—
> but I have an even stronger sense of the prospects opening out
> before us.

75

> *The ultimate crisis before the United Nations, therefore, is the crisis of authority. Management of problems which are global in scope requires extension of authority to world agencies.*
>
> *First and foremost, the decisions of the United Nations, particularly of the Security Council, must be enforceable.*
>
> *Are there any short-cuts to constructing the needed world order and the code of enforceable world law together with the necessary executive, legislative and judicial functions? I do not think so.*

The consensus of informed global opinion is in accord with the foregoing comments by U Thant. As Arnold Toynbee put it in his latest book, *Experiences:*

> *Living when and where I have lived, and having had the education that I have had, I have been concerned above all, since August 1914, to do what I can in my lifetime towards bringing about the abolition of war. This is the wickedest of all living human institutions, and it is also an institution to which human beings cling with obstinate tenacity. In 1914, war could take lives only by the million. Since 6 August, 1945, it has been on the way towards becoming deadly enough to wipe out the human race and perhaps even to make the surface of our planet no longer habitable for any form of life.*
>
> *We do have the freedom to abolish war by a pacific political act. The institution of war between states is a parasite on the institution of local sovereignty; a parasite cannot survive without its host; and we can abolish local sovereignty pacifically by voluntarily entering into a world-wide federal union in which the local states would surrender their sovereignty while continuing to exist as subordinate parts of the whole. This is the positive solution of the problem of war. One need not, and should not, be dogmatic about the details of a federal constitution for the World. But one should work for the achievement of this in some form or another. In the Atomic Age, this looks as if it were mankind's only alternative to mass-suicide.*

III Brief history of thought on world government

From the prophet Isaiah, who spoke of beating swords into ploughshares, down through history the ancients talked much about the desirability of peace; but a supranational worldwide government with power to keep the peace between antagonistic tribes or nation-states does not seem to have occurred to them. Probably this is because it was not until quite recently—not perhaps till 1943, when Wendell Willkie wrote a popular book called *One World*—that the unity of the world came to be recognized by most intelligent people.

Prior to the enormous technological and scientific advances of the nineteenth and twentieth centuries, the mobility of man was so limited that the concept of a government of the entire world seemed quite impractical. Nonetheless, the thought was advanced more than 650 years ago by Dante in his chapter on world government in *De Monarchia*.* However, Dante's concept was of a world ruled by the pope with the Holy Roman Emperor enforcing the church's decrees and being the secular leader of the world.

Immanuel Kant in the eighteenth century wrote of world government in the modern sense but acknowledged that it was a transcendent ideal.† Nevertheless, Kant believed that men of good will should work for it as they work for any form of right.

Up to a point, such visions suggest what Toynbee, in his *Study of History*, calls the universal state. He writes of a rhythm in history that carries identifiable civilizations through periods of genesis, growth, decay, and dissolution. Preceding dissolution, but part of decay, is often the universal state. This occurs when one civilization, having come to be ruled by a dominant minority that is no longer capable of creative activity, has conquered all its enemies and reigns supreme in the world. Such civilizations include, among others, the Egyptiac and the Sinic, and the Roman Empire. In each instance there were no more wars to fight. The trouble was that the effort of achieving the universal state had so exhausted the creative ability of the conquering nation that it was left without any remaining desire to improve the state of its civilization. In the end, the universal state was brought down by a discontented internal proletariat or was overrun by barbarians from beyond the frontier.

These universal states could be termed world governments, but as invariably their authority was based upon their conquest of the world rather than upon its consent, they could not long maintain themselves and are not true precedents for the kind of world government that is required today.

The League of Nations, formed at the Treaty of Versailles at the end of World War I, was the first serious effort to keep world peace through the creation of an international institution. But the League was a group of sovereign states with no power to enforce its judgments other than to call on its members for appropriate action. The controversial Article XIV of the covenant of the League, which called for action against an aggressor, was never capable of being enforced. The unwillingness of the United States to become a member was a crippling blow. The League withered

---

* *GGB*, Vol. 7, pp. 379–99.
† *Perpetual Peace; GGB*, Vol. 7, pp. 437–75.

and disappeared at the end of the precarious peace between the two
world wars. While it was in existence it proved incapable of acting on the
aggressive invasion of Manchuria by Japan in 1931 and on the equally
deplorable invasion of Ethopia by Italy just before World War II
broke out.

While great hopes were held for the League, its inherent weakness was
that it had no capability for enforcing common action against an obvious
aggressor. It could merely call on the individual nation-states to supply
troops that would carry its decisions into effect. There was never any
question of yielding national sovereignty to a supranational institution.

After World War II, in 1945, came the United Nations organization,
which has just passed its twenty-fifth anniversary. It is an improved
version of the League of Nations, but it can hardly as yet be called a
world government.

Its charter is brave. The preamble refers to "the peoples of the United
Nations," whereas the League of Nations referred to the nation-states.
The preamble continues with an eloquent determination to save succeeding generations from the scourge of war, to reaffirm faith in fundamental
human rights, to establish conditions under which justice and respect for

The war in Vietnam continues: Saigon again under fire

the obligations arising from treaties and other sources of international law can be maintained, and to promote social progress and better standards of life in greater freedom. In later articles, the signers commit themselves to unite their strength to maintain international peace and security and to ensure that armed force shall not be used, save in the common interest, and further, to employ international machinery for the promotion of the economic and social advancement of all peoples. But the end result is not a world government; it is merely a stronger union of states than was the case with the League of Nations for dealing with problems of war and peace.

The United Nations has some very significant achievements to its credit during the last twenty-five years, largely achievements in the economic and social field but also in matters dealing with war and peace such as the Antarctica treaty, the Nuclear Test Ban Treaty, the Space Treaty, and the Nuclear Nonproliferation Treaty. Nevertheless, these accomplishments are all in the form of international treaties, which no international institution is given effective authority to enforce.

Such successes as the UN has had have been the result of persuasion, by which interested powers have agreed that they would join together in a certain course of action. While this is, of course, valuable, it is not a world government, which assumes a supranational federation over the sovereign states in the limited sense discussed above.

It seems highly unlikely that such an organization, under its present charter and with the body of procedures that has been developed over the last twenty-five years, can really be an effective instrument to keep the peace, or even deal adequately with international aspects of problems such as pollution, poverty, and population control.

Since 1945, most efforts looking toward the eventual creation of a limited form of federated world government have come through the disarmament approach. Thus we had the abortive Baruch Plan, where the United States endeavored to internationalize nuclear weapons. We had the efforts that President Eisenhower made with Premier Khrushchev at Paris to achieve an agreement leading to disarmament. In this connection, the action of Christian Herter, Eisenhower's last secretary of state, in committing the United States in 1960 for the first time to general and complete disarmament under enforceable world law, has been almost overlooked.

The strongest official American effort to achieve world government was made by President John F. Kennedy, in the context of disarmament negotiations with the Soviet Union. In a speech at the United Nations in 1961, he called for an end to the arms race, and for an "advance together step by step, stage by stage until general and complete disarmament has been achieved." And he added: "To destroy arms, however, is not enough. We must create even as we destroy, creating worldwide law and law enforcement as we outlaw worldwide war and weapons."

Later, in 1963, President Kennedy said:

> *The UN cannot survive as a static organization. Its obligations are increasing as well as its size. Its charter must be changed as well as its customs. The authors of the charter did not intend it to be forever frozen. The science of weapons and war has made us all . . . one world and one human race with one common destiny. In such a world absolute sovereignty no longer assures us of absolute security. The conventions of peace must pull abreast and then ahead of the conventions of war. The United Nations must be developed into a genuine world security system.*

Two treaties of general and complete disarmament under strict international control were filed in Geneva in 1962, one by the United States

and one by the U.S.S.R. The United States Arms Control and Disarmament Agency was created by the Congress at the president's request. Serious negotiations then took place at the 17-nation Disarmament Conference in Geneva. They broke down largely over the issue of on-site inspection, an issue that is no longer critical. Progress in the art of detection by satellite, photographic, electronic, and seismographic intelligence has made on-site inspection unnecessary to prevent cheating on a scale massive enough to endanger an agreement.

The assassin's bullet killed this last significant American effort in November 1963. Neither President Johnson nor President Nixon has shown any interest in resuming negotiations, although the Soviet Union has occasionally suggested resuming talks. The two treaties lie on the table at Geneva gathering dust despite the resolutions passed annually

West Berlin street adjoining a section of the Berlin Wall; behind the wall are guards, mines, electrified fences— the borderland

by the General Assembly of the United Nations urging the major military powers to proceed with negotiations for disarmament.

The United States and the U.S.S.R. are currently engaged in the Strategic Arms Limitation Talks, but this is merely a bilateral effort to stabilize the nuclear arms race. Arms control is a very different thing from disarmament. It has no implications for world government.

China has recently expressed an interest in comprehensive disarmament. The Chinese asked on November 1, 1970, for the elimination of all nuclear weapons. Whether they could be persuaded to join the United Nations and even discuss world government presently is dubious. More recently, in June 1971, the Soviet Union called for a conference of all the nuclear powers to eliminate strategic nuclear weapons.

The proponents of world government today are largely citizen groups within the United States, Canada, Japan, and, to a limited extent, some of the other countries of the world. The World Association of World Federalists, of which World Federalists, USA, is the United States branch, has considerable strength in the Scandinavian countries, particularly Denmark and Norway; it has also a scattering of members in 30 of the 126 countries that belong to the United Nations, among them England, France, Ethiopia, India, Pakistan, and Nigeria. There are no official groups in any of the Communist countries except Yugoslavia, where Marshal Tito has expressed interest in the movement.

Many members of these World Federalists groups sit in their respective parliaments. This is especially true in Japan, the Scandinavian countries, Great Britain, and France. There are at present three members of the United States Senate who are World Federalists. Members of Congress for Peace Through Law, a bicameral bipartisan group, number 110, but their devotion to world government is slight.

These citizen groups continue to agitate for world government. Thus the Center for the Study of Democratic Institutions has sponsored two widely attended *Pacem in Terris* conferences, in 1965 in New York and 1967 in Geneva, to advocate peace through the medium of disarmament and world government. The name comes from a papal encyclical issued by Pope John XXIII in 1963. The United States government played no significant role in these meetings.

The World Peace Through Law Center has held several worldwide conferences in New Delhi, Washington, and Bangkok. Another is planned for Yugoslavia in the summer of 1971. But this distinguished organization of lawyers and judges has never actively advocated world government. It is more of an international bar association than a group interested in international political action for peace.

In the United States today there are several hundred citizen organizations, each with a "piece of peace." They exercise little influence on the present government of their country.

Semantics plays an important part in advocacy of or opposition to world government. Everybody is, in theory, in favor of "peace." Most people are in favor of "world law"—as long as it is not enforceable. But if the concept is expressed in terms of "world government" or "yielding national sovereignty," most of these groups who think of themselves as having "a piece of peace" tend to shy away. The term "world order" tends to attract more supporters, until its necessary connection with world government is explained.

An important research and educational program sponsored by the World Law Fund, a tax-exempt group with headquarters in New York, is the World Order Models Project designed by international law professor Saul H. Mendlovitz, who, with Professor Richard A. Falk, was co-author in 1966 of a four-volume textbook entitled *The Strategy of World Order*—in effect a treatise on world government founded on the Clark-Sohn study, *World Peace Through World Law*.

The World Order Models Project has organized eight regional research teams whose task is to formulate fully developed models of the world in 1990. The teams are located in Europe, Latin America, North America, India, Russia, Africa, and Japan, and a transnational group is centered in Oslo, Norway. Efforts are being made to organize a team in mainland China.

Since the three basic assumptions guiding the deliberations of all eight teams are that there must be (1) arms control and disarmament, (2) pacific settlement of disputes, and (3) cognizance of the "scientific-technological revolution"—a comprehensive phrase encompassing population, pollution, resource depletion, food production, economic development, and human rights—it is inconceivable that the end product will not include some form of world government.

Useful studies looking toward achievement of world government by small steps have been prepared under the auspices of the United Nations Association. Thus "Controlling Conflicts in the 1970s" is the proposal of a panel chaired by Kingman Brewster, Jr., president of Yale, to create an adequately financed UN Peace-Keeping Force. And the Commission for the Organization of Peace chaired by Professor Louis Sohn has proposed 106 changes in the procedures and charter of the UN to make it an effective instrument of world government.

IV Obstacles to world government

The principal human obstacle to world government is the dual nature of man. It is perhaps best defined by the Chinese as *Yin* and *Yang*—*Yin* roughly translated as the spirit of love, *Yang* the spirit of hate. Stated differently, man has two built-in moods—the desire for cooperation and the desire for conflict. Sometimes one predominates, sometimes the other.

''Tiger Cubs'' train at a camp in Jordan

There have always been those who glorify war. There have always been those who strive for peace. The leaders of powerful nations are sometimes for one, sometimes for the other. It has never yet happened that they were all for peace, and for the steps necessary to achieve peace, at the same time. Moreover, leaders respond to what their peoples feel, and there is as yet no overwhelming popular support for world government.

But given the threat of the imminent destruction of the human race by nuclear war, or by its chemical, biological, and radiological equivalent, this would not seem to condemn world government for the future. Surely the people would follow if their leaders told them that for civilization to be preserved there is no alternative to disarmament and world government. Perhaps, as the late Grenville Clark thought shortly before he died, things will have to get worse before they get better—even to the extent of a few nuclear bombs being dropped and the deaths of several million people.

Apathy, a feeling of individual helplessness, and a lack of understanding of the personal nature of the threat hanging over us are great obstacles to the coming of world government. Men return to their vineyards on the slopes of Etna and Vesuvius as soon as the lava from the latest eruption has cooled. It is now twenty-five years since Hiroshima and Nagasaki. More than half the present population of the world was not alive at the time of those disasters. Very few people still living were there in person to experience them. Hardly a few hundred thousand have seen the films of the horror, only recently released.

That inadequate understanding of the threat to existence is a big obstacle to world government, seems clear. The peace movement itself has never acquired staunch adherents in minority groups or in the third world. World government as the necessary condition of peace is an idea little appreciated outside the intelligentsia. And even among social scientists in the universities there are still plenty of skeptics. For world government has never become stylish. It has few supporters among the "establishments" here or abroad, save in a few small powers such as Denmark, Norway, and Canada.

Old-fashioned patriotism is surely an obstacle to world government. Dr. Johnson's view that "patriotism is the last refuge of a scoundrel" has fewer adherents than those who proclaim with Stephen Decatur, "Our country! . . . may she always be in the right; but our country, right or wrong."

When the flag flies and the band plays and the drums beat and the troops march and the Veterans of Foreign Wars and the American Legion parade, the "silent majority," at least in the United States, still tends to respond. This would be particularly true with blue-collar workers, hard-hats, white-collar engineers, and scientists in the military-industrial field if world government became a practical threat to their jobs. It is true today with many of them in this country and abroad when it comes to winding up the arms race and the war in Vietnam, or bringing a peace to the Middle East that might inhibit the manufacture and sale of arms. And of course one could count on the opposition of the military forces of all of the nation-states.

The former colonial nations in Africa and Asia tend to oppose world government on the ground that it would return them to a colonial status that would threaten their hard-earned freedom. Another obstacle is the attitude of the media all over the world. The present Soviet government, although favoring general and complete disarmament, is opposed to the concept of world government, fearing, with typical Russian suspicion, that the U.S.S.R. would be outnumbered in the voting. So *Pravda, Izvestia,* and the rest of the Soviet press and radio make no effort to explain world government objectively to the citizens. The same is true of mainland China and its media. In the "free" world, the media consistently play to the prejudices of the masses rather than to their latent idealism. Reports of conflict rather than cooperation set the standard for news. Education of the media should be an early step in bringing popular support for world government.

A final obstacle affecting the totalitarian states is that all models for a world government assume a democratic form of decision, as, for instance, in requiring within the international institution a majority or perhaps a two-thirds vote to authorize action. This concept is anathema to the Soviet Union. Hence the veto in the Security Council. It will take a great deal of persuasion to bring the totalitarian states around to agree to a democratic form of decision. The reverse side of the coin is that many in the democratic countries fear that world government would threaten civil liberties.

V   Prospects for world government

Faced with these formidable obstacles, it would take an incorrigible optimist to contend that world government is just around the corner. Indeed it is not. Yet perhaps the tide is beginning to turn away from a preoccupation with nationalism toward the formation of international institutions with power to keep the peace, toward a form of world order to deal with worldwide problems—in short, toward a limited form of world government. A straw in the wind appeared in the *New York Times* on June 19, 1971, in the form of a short article by Richard J. Barnet entitled "Farewell to the Nation-State."

There would appear to be three major approaches to the desired end. One is through developing within the United Nations the support of small and middle-sized nations for a drastic revision of the UN charter.

Several countries have asked that charter revision be placed on the agenda at the General Assembly. The charter itself requires in Article 109 a charter-review conference to be called on a vote of the majority of the General Assembly and seven members of the Security Council at any time after the tenth annual session of the General Assembly.

Among the major changes in the charter that would be required to create a limited world government with power to keep the peace are (1) elimination of the veto in the Security Council; (2) substitution for the "one nation, one vote" rule in the General Assembly of a more realistic system that recognizes the vast disparity of both population and economic power of the nation-states; (3) a self-operating system of financing the UN, such as a license fee on concessions in the seabed, or a small tax, payable directly to the UN treasury, on transactions in international trade; (4) a strong United Nations Peace-Keeping and Peace-Making Force, subject to the control of the secretary-general acting under instructions of the Security Council; (5) general and complete disarmament; and (6) compulsory jurisdiction over disputes between nations, whether justiciable or not, by the World Court, (i.e., repeal of the Connally Amendment).

A seventh reform, closely allied to charter revision, is the admission of all nation-states to the UN. Thus we would have the possibility of creating a universal federation of all the nation-states in a limited world government with power to keep the peace.

At the same time, and by the same steps, the specialized agencies of the UN—UNESCO, ILO, WHO, FAO, and others—would acquire the power to deal with the problems of pollution, poverty, and population.

A second method would be to bring about a limited world government with power to keep the peace out of the 26-nation Conference of the Committee on Disarmament that sits periodically in Geneva. This procedure would at least avoid the many crippling disabilities in the UN charter—for example, there is no legal veto at CCD, nor do the "mini nations" have a vote. Most of the major military and economically strong nations are members of the CCD. There is adequate representation from the underdeveloped world. Agreement between them might well be easier to achieve than in a 126-member UN. Of course, mainland China would have to come in as an active participant, and France would have to take up its currently vacant seat in the committee.

The third approach, however, presents perhaps the most pragmatic solution.

Prime Minister Trudeau of Canada remarked early in 1970 that whenever he thought of his country's relations with the United States he was reminded of a small boy in bed with an elephant. Every time the elephant kicked or squirmed the boy was in danger of falling out of bed.

In truth there are three rogue elephants in the world today, determined not to be trained to acknowledge the necessity for world government. They are the United States, the U.S.S.R., and the People's Republic of China.

We citizens in the United States can do little to train the Chinese elephant. But we can take it into the United Nations and start training it by example.

We citizens in the United States can do little to train the Russian elephant. But at least our government can talk to the Russians, and the contacts between knowledgeable private citizens, such as the Pugwash conferences, are increasing year by year. And the Russians have been committed to general and complete disarmament ever since Czar Nicholas's day, a commitment that Lenin adopted.

But we citizens in the United States *can* do something about our own government, for we are still a free country where *demos* at least still makes a stab at *kratioing*. By persistent educational effort, accompanied by continuing political action, it is quite possible that, before the present decade ends, we can establish in Washington a Congress and a president committed to yielding enough sovereignty to an international organization to make peace through enforceable world law a priority national objective, as it was in President Kennedy's day.

Once this is done, we will be well on the road to civilizing the other two rogue elephants and making human survival a probability instead of a pretty bad bet.

For, to reiterate, world government is not an idea that has arrived before its time. There is in truth no logical alternative. Its time is now, before it is too late.

The Idea of World Community In Great Books of the Western World

In 1953, G. A. Borgese suggested that the "myth of World Government" was self-evidently "the myth of this generation . . . the missionary fervor of this idea-force being such . . . that its dignity as a categorical imperative has already found a formulation in Julian Huxley's dogma that 'present-day men and nations will be judged by history as moral or immoral as to whether they have helped or hindered that unification.'"[1]

That statement arose, of course, in response to historical events—to the appearance of the bomb at the close of two *world* wars. It may be thought, therefore, that the idea of world community is preeminently an example of an idea that had to wait its time in history until historical experience would suggest it to political philosophy as something possible and necessary.[2] As regards its attaining ineluctable historical force, it may be true that its time is our time.

However, it is not true that the idea of world community was born in our time. It appeared throughout the ancient world, more in the minds of men and peoples of action than in political philosophy. In one or another metamorphosis, it had major structuring influence in world history throughout antiquity and the Middle Ages. Then, with the appearance of the modern idea of the sovereign nation-state, it was buried for a while. It reappeared when the prospect became vivid that the military technology of advanced warring nation-states could bring world history to an end.

Though in doing so one passes over the visions of the pharaohs, the hopes of Cyrus the Persian, and the achievements of Philip of Macedon, it seems right to suggest that the idea of world community began with Alexander, Philip's son. Tutored for three years by Aristotle until he was sixteen, Alexander was a victorious general at eighteen, succeeded his father at twenty, and died not quite thirteen years later after founding an empire that stretched from Greece to India. Yet the sheer brilliance of his military and political career, coming down to us in the accounts of Plutarch and Arrian, and later floridly decorated in a branch of *world* literature called "the Alexander Romances," for a long time obscured his real achievement in world history. Thanks to intensely dedicated scholarship, preeminently that of W. W. Tarn, the true place of Alexander the Great in world history is now rightly seen.[3] It does not rest on the sheer fact of the extent of the empire he so quickly established. Indeed his premature death took from him the chance to see what would be at stake in maintaining that empire, and it quickly fell apart. What was really important about Alexander were the ideas he arrived at as he pondered the meaning of what he was doing. In brief, he was trying to rethink the idea of conquest, which no one before his time had regarded as being in any sense mysterious, and was feeling his way toward the idea of world community. That seems now to be the right interpretation of his extraordinary behavior toward those he conquered, though his unprecedented political, ceremonial, and even military moves did not effectively convey either to the Macedonians or to anybody else what he was about.

It is as the first Western ecumenical hero that Alexander has first place in this review. He did range in triumphs over a very large part of the ecumene—the inhabited world. As he did so, he thought about what ideas would yield a basis for peace and order in a world inhabited by entities that seemed somehow sufficiently alike to be regarded as men. To move toward a vision of the unity of mankind was not easy for Alexander, whatever we may think of our own capacities in that respect. It involved a repudiation of what he had been taught, not only by the general ethos in Greece, but by his tutor, the best mind Greece had to offer. Aristotle's *Politics* contains the doctrine of two kinds of men, freemen and natural slaves, and explicitly applies it to all non-Greeks: "But among barbarians no distinction is made between women and slaves, because there is no natural ruler among them: they are a community of slaves, male and female. Wherefore the poets say, 'It is meet that Hellenes should rule over barbarians,' as if they thought that the barbarian and the slave were by nature one."[4] It is known that Aristotle, as tutor, counseled the son of Philip that if he was to emulate his father in conquest, he should treat the Greeks as freemen and everyone else as slaves. Alexander tested this counsel against his actual experience of Persians, Egyptians, and Indians— peoples he had "conquered." His repudiation of that counsel in the light of his own experience and judgment was nothing less than a revolution in Greek thought. Alexander tried, even with the fierce demands of his continuing expeditions, to communicate his changed vision by all kinds of political, economic, social, ceremonial, and religious actions.

His brooding and dreaming about the meaning for human history of his conquests and his subsequent associations with the conquered gained focus from a constellation of three ideas. The best summary, and indeed the most fitting, is that of W. W. Tarn:

We have really been dealing with three things, though I cannot call them three ideas; all are interconnected, and they are rather three facets of a single idea. The first is the statement that all men are brothers; Alexander was the first man known to us, at any rate in the West, to say so plainly and to apply it to the whole human race, without distinction of Greek or barbarian. The second thing is his belief that he had a divine mission to be the harmoniser and reconciler of the world, to bring it to pass that all men, being brothers, should live together in Homonoia, in unity of heart and mind. This was a dream, or an inspiration; it was something which had come to him and was struggling for expression; he gave it expression for the first time at Opis, tentatively, in the form of Homonoia between all men, and one who was there crystallized it in the metaphor of a loving cup in which all men were mixed. . . . There is no question of his having had any cut and dried plan; indeed it is unlikely that he had any plan at all, though the recall of the exiles may conceivably have been meant as a first attempt to do something about it. It was, and was to remain, a dream, but a dream greater than all his conquests. Many have dreamt his dream since; but the honour of being the first remains his. But no one has ever seen how it could be made a reality; least of all perhaps do we see it today. It is not at all likely that he saw it either; but, being Alexander, he would, had he lived, have tried to do something to outlaw war, and would have failed as the world has failed since. The third thing of the three I mentioned was the desire, expressed in the libation and prayer at Opis, that all the peoples in his realm should be partners and not merely subjects; had he lived, this was a thing which he probably would have attempted. His policy of racial fusion (by intermarriage) may have been meant as a step towards this idea of partnership, as partnership itself was to be a step toward the fulfillment of his dream.

Hardly anyone at the time could understand what he meant.[5]

Yet the Alexandrian example was not wholly lost. Twenty-two years after Alexander's death, a hellenized Phoenician from Cyprus named Zeno began to lecture in the Stoa, the painted corridor on the north side of the marketplace at Athens—whence he became known as the founder of Stoicism. What Zeno said showed him to be directly influenced, as Plutarch tells us, by the implications of Alexander's deeds, and also, Tarn argues, by his ideas. In his treatise "On the Fortune of Alexander," Plutarch reports Zeno as "teaching that men are not to live divided into different states and peoples, each under its own particular law, but in a world state, of which all men are to be citizens, and all are to be one

people, with a common life, a common order, and a common law, like a
herd of cattle grazing together." Plutarch adds that "Zeno had a dream
or vision of a good law and politics based on philosophy, though it was
Alexander who gave reality to that idea." [6]

So began a new age—one in which, for example, the early Stoics, like
Zeno, could come from the East, lecture in Athens, and establish a philo-
sophic tradition that was deeply influential and long-lived in Rome. For
Alexander had made the *polis,* the very small city-state, an anachronism.
Because of him, and through the economic, social, and cultural effects of
his deeds, the civilized world was vastly enlarged.

In that Stoic tradition, at least in its early, most philosophical period,
the notions of a world-state and of a common law for men were presented
as implications of the general assertion of a cosmos made one, harmonious, and intelligible by an indwelling logos or Reason. Each man was
knit to that ruling Reason, and so to every other man. The law for human association was a law of nature, to be discovered by human reason as
the law for a universal society.

There is an ambiguity about the Stoic meanings for the term *city* (or
state) and the term *citizenship.* In the Stoic view, a man was by nature
a cosmopolite, a citizen of the cosmos. His duty was to realize his nature
by meditation and by right will in conformity with the indwelling harmony of the cosmos. Similarly, the world-state that the Stoics spoke of did
not have to be brought into existence by unifying conquerors or deified
emperors. The harmony of the world-state, which was coterminous with
the universe, already existed. The ethical and religious duty of men was to
discover and revere that harmony. Racial and political discords would
disappear in consequence of this spiritual effort.

In a way, then, Stoicism had no politics in the usual sense of the term.
It was more of a naturalistic religious philosophy, inviting the spirit of a
man to enlarge and order itself by contemplation and willed conformity
to the order of the world, and in consequence, to experience kinship with
all men beyond the provincialities of cities of birth and cities of rivalry.
Yet two things must be said in qualification of this point about the essentially nonpolitical character of Stoicism. First, most historians agree
that the Stoic doctrine of cosmopolitanism had irradiating or overflow
effects on political thought about the political unification of the world.
Second, such effect, it is generally agreed, is shown explicitly in Cicero's
fragments *De republica* and his treatise *De legibus.* Though he called
himself an Academic, Cicero had studied with Stoic teachers, and there
is Stoic influence in his conception of justice as derived from a principle
or law of nature, eternal and universal, the measure of the justice of all
civil positive laws.

Volume 12 of the *Great Books of the Western World* contains the
works of a Stoic teacher and a Stoic emperor. Epictetus, born in the reign
of Nero, while still a slave attended the lectures of the Stoic philosopher

Musonius Rufus. Later, when he was freed, he taught philosophy briefly in Rome until expelled on suspicion of republicanism. Throughout the reign of Hadrian, he taught at Nicopolis in northern Greece, receiving pupils from all parts of the empire. Flavius Arrian, later consul under Hadrian, and the author, incidentally, of a large life of Alexander, took careful notes on the lectures of Epictetus and published from them *The Discourses of Epictetus.*

The opening paragraph of chapter 9 in Book 1 shows Epictetus asserting both the idea of world citizenship and its inner psychological consequence:

> *If the things are true which are said by the philosophers about the kinship between God and man, what else remains for men to do than what Socrates did? Never in reply to the question, to what country you belong, say that you are an Athenian or a Corinthian, but that you are a citizen of the world. For why do you say that you are an Athenian, and why do you not say that you belong to the small nook only into which your poor body was cast at birth? Is it not plain that you call yourself an Athenian or Corinthian from the place which has a greater authority and comprises not only that small nook itself and all your family, but even the whole country from which the stock of your progenitors is derived down to you? He then who has observed with intelligence the administration of the world, and has learned that the greatest and supreme and the most comprehensive community is that which is composed of men and God, and that from God have descended the seeds not only to my father and grandfather, but to all beings which are generated on the earth and are produced, and particularly to rational beings—for these only are by their nature formed to have communion with God, being by means of reason conjoined with Him—why should not such a man call himself a citizen of the world, why not a son of God, and why should he be afraid of anything which happens among men? Is kinship with Caesar or with any other of the powerful in Rome sufficient to enable us to live in safety, and above contempt and without any fear at all? and to have God for your maker and father and guardian, shall not this release us from sorrows and fears?*[7]

A similar formulation appears in Marcus Aurelius, Emperor from A.D. 161 to 180, who on the opening page of his *Meditations* expresses his gratitude to the man who acquainted him with the discourses of Epictetus. He for a time assumed the dress and lived the abstemious life of the Stoic sect. His reign was filled with every kind of calamity; he wrote his *Meditations,* while campaigning against German tribes, as "Thoughts addressed to himself." The most widely echoed sentence from the *Medi-*

tations is this: "My nature is rational and social; and my city and country, so far as I am Antoninus, is Rome, but so far as I am a man, it is the world."[8] An earlier passage shows his manner of argument on the point:

> *If our intellectual part is common, the reason also, in respect of which we are rational beings, is common: if this is so, common also is the reason which commands us what to do, and what not to do; if this is so, there is a common law also; if this is so, we are fellow-citizens; if this is so, we are members of some political community; if this is so, the world is in a manner a state. For of what other common political community will any one say that the whole human race are members? And from thence, from this common political community comes also our very intellectual faculty and reasoning faculty and our capacity for law; or whence do they come?*[9]

Not only the Stoic current of thought but the whole history of Rome has some bearing, of course, upon the development of the idea of world community. What is of interest here need not involve any reference to the intricacies and harsh realities of Roman history. As in the case of Alexander's Macedonian Empire, what is relevant is merely the outline of that history and what the best minds thought, or tried to think, about the meaning of the Roman imperial unification of a large part of the Western world.

The central practical achievement of Rome, aside from feats of engineering and of arms, was of course in jurisprudence. The Roman conception of empire brought major changes in both constitutional and civil law. Pivotal was the extension of the franchise, first from Rome to Italy, and with the Antonine Constitution of A.D. 212, to all freeborn members of all the communities of the empire. Closely tied to the common citizenship was the development of a common civil law, which leveled historical privileges of Rome and of Italy, and of certain social classes. The work in jurisprudence culminated in the conception of a *ius gentium,* a law of nations, thought to be valid for all freemen in all countries, and considered by philosophical jurisprudents as the specification, for the association of diverse peoples in the world, of the Stoic and Ciceronian law of nature.

What did the best Romans themselves think and feel about the imperial fact? They regarded it as an achievement to which they owed the blessing of peace. Ernest Barker writes of this:

> *If we would understand the feelings towards the Empire which were general among its subjects in the days of its foundation, we must turn to the literature and inscriptions in which they are re-*

*corded. What Rome and the Empire owed to Augustus is testified
in Virgil and Horace; and their poetry is no adulation, but the expression of a feeling as genuine as that of Tennyson for Victoria
and the Victorian Age. The language of inscriptions is even more
instructive testimony, because it is more direct and more naive.
We may deduct a liberal discount on the ground of conventional
flattery from some of the Greek inscriptions: they still remain significant. Augustus is "the Saviour sent to make wars cease and to
order all things"; "through him have come good tidings"; "in him
Providence has not only fulfilled, but even exceeded, the prayers
of all: sea and land are at peace: cities flourish in order, harmony,
and prosperity: there is a height and abundance of all good
things: men are filled with hopes for the future and gladness in
the present." It is impossible to doubt, as one reads these words,
that the feeling of a new and better order lies behind them. A
century of war, of extortion, of insecurity, of misery has come to
an end. A new era is dawning. The Empire begins in hope, and
continues in comfort.*[10]

But it is Virgil himself who famously articulates and celebrates the imperial vision. In his fourth *Eclogue* occur the well-known lines:

> *Now the last age by Cumae's Sibyl sung
> Has come and gone, and the majestic roll
> Of circling centuries begins anew:
> Justice returns, returns old Saturn's reign,
> With a new breed of men sent down from heaven.*[11]

That prophecy becomes one of the world's great stories in the *Aeneid,* the
epic of the founding of Rome. In undertaking to write this, Virgil was encouraged by Augustus, to whom he read from it as a work in progress. He
never completed it to his satisfaction and on his deathbed expressed a
wish to have the manuscript destroyed, but the order was countermanded
by Augustus, who liked too much his place in the poem.

Early in the first book, "to ease the gnawing care" of Venus, mother of
Aeneas, about his destiny, Jupiter "wrings from fate's dark roll her in-
most secrets." The secrets are about Rome:

> *Here now shall reign full thrice a hundred years
> Great Hector's line, till Ilia, royal maid
> And priestess, shall twin offspring bear to Mars,
> Their sire; then glorying in the tawny hide
> Of the she-wolf, his nurse, shall Romulus
> Take up the nation, build the war-god's town,
> And call them Romans after his own name.
> For these nor goals of power, nor times I fix—*

> *Grant them a boundless sway. Fierce Juno too,*
> *Who now with terror scares earth, sea, and heaven,*
> *Shall turn to kinder counsels, and with me*
> *Cherish the Romans, masters of the world,*
> *The toga'd nation. So hath heaven decreed.*[12]

Then, in the underworld of sixth Aeneid, Aeneas receives from his father, Anchises, a prevision of what the end of his long labors will be, of what the mission of these Romans that Jupiter spoke of will be:

> *Others the breathing brass shall softlier mould,*
> *I doubt not, draw the lineaments of life*
> *From marble, at the bar plead better, trace*
> *With rod the courses of the sky, or tell*
> *The rise of stars: remember, Roman, thou,*
> *To rule the nations as their master: these*
> *Thine arts shall be, to engraft the law of peace,*
> *Forbear the conquered, and war down the proud.*[13]

These lines prefigure the famous eulogy of Rome written very much later by Claudian. Born in Alexandria (the connection with Alexander keeps returning), Claudian abandoned his native Greek and became the last important poet of the Roman classical tradition. In about A.D. 400, with the Goth at the gates of the city, he writes:

> *It is this Rome who has cared for the human race and given it a common name; who has taken the conquered to her bosom like a mother, and called them not subjects but citizens; who has united distant races in the bonds of affection. To the peace which she has brought us we owe it, every one of us, that every part of the Empire is to us as a fatherland; that it matters nothing if we drink of the Rhone or of the Orontes; that we are all one people.*[14]

Whatever one may think of the historical truth of the matter, the striking thing to note is the clear echo in what Claudian says, here in the last years of the empire, of what Virgil had said so long before at its beginning. And this constancy is not the less impressive for the fact that it was hardly a dozen years after Claudian made these remarks, when Rome had actually been sacked by Alaric, that another famous Roman, Augustine, wrote *The City of God* to answer the charge (anticipating Gibbon) that Christianity had made such a disaster possible—providing us with a far more complicated appraisal of the Roman achievement.

What has so far been passed over here is the degree to which religious claims were invoked in both the Alexandrian and Roman empires to impart some sort of authority for the "impositions" and some principle of cohesion for the subjected peoples. There is no need to go into the complexities of the various deifications of Alexander in various parts of his empire, of Augustus's deliberate efforts at the restoration of a civil religion, of the many altars of Augustus around the empire, or of the many posthumous deifications of Roman emperors. The point of interest is simply that at every stage of expansion in the ancient pagan world, from the family to tribes, to the polis and to empires, the ancient city had a religious character, which was deemed to be expressive, and somehow causative, of its unity and order.

But it is necessary at this point to turn in a different direction and to examine the contribution of Israel and the whole Judeo-Christian strain of the Western tradition in relation to the idea of the world community.

For centuries of its history, Israel would appear, from the outside, as just another nation with a national god who promised success in imperial adventures of expansion and conquest. However, as Étienne Gilson puts it, what distinguished the imperialism of Israel from all other ancient imperialisms was the character of its religious motives. "The fecund germ of jewish universalism," Gilson writes, "is jewish monotheism. . . . there must be but one society because there is only one God."[15] The issue of Israel's special mission was stated more spiritually and mysteriously in the time of the prophets. The vision of all the peoples of the earth united in worship of the same God appears in Isaiah: "And he said, It is a light thing that thou shouldest be my servant to raise up the tribes of Jacob, and to restore the preserved of Israel: I will also give thee for a light to the Gentiles, that thou mayest be my salvation unto the end of the earth."[16] Of course, while drawing out with grandeur, in the prophetic literature, the universalism implicit in its monotheism, Israel retained its sense of itself as called to play a special role in the historical evolution of the one religious society.

By the time of the apostolate of Paul, the privilege of Israel is interpreted by Christians as having been that of a witness, a people to whom the word of God was first entrusted. Hereafter, the conditions of membership and of salvation in the one universal religious society were to be the same for all. This society, founded explicitly as a church, was to be in this world, but not of it. Terrestrial distinctions had no import for such a mystical society; indeed their annulment is proclaimed by a famous verse of St. Paul's: "There is neither Jew nor Greek, there is neither bond nor free, there is neither male nor female: for ye are all one in Christ Jesus."[17] This new society was to be neither a national society nor an international society, but a kingdom not of this world, open in the same way to all.

Questions of every kind arose for the members of this society that was not of the world: questions about actions to be taken regarding the idolatry of the pagan state religion, questions about places in the world needed to practise the faith, to preach, and to evangelize, questions about the relations between the church and the empire, between the church and any other of the cities and peoples of the world.

The latter are the major questions here. Gilson speaks of two major responses by Christians to the situation of their being physically resident in earthly cities.[18] The first response, the earliest, was that of a withdrawal, a renunciation. The unknown second-century author of an Epistle to Diognetus writes of Christians as not being nationals like other peoples, "because they inhabit countries which are their own, but are domiciled there as strangers, because every foreign country is their country and every country is strange to them."[19] Later, Tertullian was to say flatly: "Nothing is more alien to us than the *res publica* (public thing). We acknowledge only one (*res publica*) for all, the world."[20]

This alienating effect was the basis for constant anti-Christian polemic by pagan Romans, who claimed to see in it the seeds of the empire's ruin. Celsus, writing toward the end of the second century, charged Christians with injustice in that they used the benefits of a temporal city which they did not love and were reluctant to serve. Gilson remarks that one can agree that "a pagan like Celsus was excusable in holding Christianity to involve, if not sedition, at least a secession from the body politic."

A second response, Gilson says, could not fail to suggest itself when Christianity became widely diffused. Instead of renouncing the temporal city, "why not Christianize it, and in doing so, take hold of it." The turning point for this response came, of course, with the conversion of Constantine, his founding of Constantinople as the beginning of a new Christian empire, his belief that he was God's chosen servant responsible for good government in the Christian church. Ecclesiastics, recognized by the new Christian emperors as having moral authority, increasingly gained power and influence.

Then an idea developed that brought Rome into the Christian theology of history—an idea that the Roman imperial achievement was something providential. Rome had offered the church a unified and pacified world, and it "needed only to be baptized," as Gilson puts it, "to become at least the center of a universal Christian society, of which one would be a member from the sole fact of being a Christian." With this way of integrating Rome, because of its providential role, into the only true history, "the universal history of which the Incarnation of Christ was the center," nothing in the order of thought could oppose the Christian appropriation of the empire. A Latin poet, Prudentius, writing at the end of the fourth century, gave the most famous expression to the providential view of Rome. Prudentius exclaims: "Great God, your hour is come. Penetrate these lands now reunited! It is ready to receive you, O Christ, this world which these two bonds unite, thy peace and Rome."[21]

This hope of a theocratic and ecclesiastical appropriation of the secular universal city is an important moment for the subject of this essay on the history of the idea of world community. It was not, however, to have an easy run. "The hope was beautiful," Gilson writes, "but the Roman empire was going to perish at the precise moment when the Christians were thinking of using it." In 410, Alaric, chief of the Visigoths and an Arian Christian, occupied, plundered, and burned Rome—a city that had not been captured by a foreign enemy for nearly eight hundred years. "The empire was crumbling at the very moment when the Church formed the hope of resting on it."

Rome had been conquered in the reign of a Christian emperor by a Christian barbarian chieftain. With the shock of the sacking of Rome, pagan anti-Christian polemic became intense, virulent, and widespread. A Christian, Marcellinus, received from a pagan, Volusien, charges that Christianity was responsible for the calamity. Marcellinus passed them on to the Bishop of Hippo, begging him to answer them publicly. Augustine's reply was in the twenty-two books of *The City of God,* which was begun in 413 and appeared serially for thirteen years.[22]

The preface to Augustine's huge, profoundly and perdurably influential book reads as follows:

> *The glorious city of God is my theme in this work, which you, my dearest son Marcellinus, suggested, and which is due to you by my promise. I have undertaken its defence against those who prefer their own gods to the Founder of this city,—a city surpassingly glorious, whether we view it as it still lives by faith in this fleeting course of time, and sojourns as a stranger in the midst of the ungodly, or as it shall dwell in the fixed stability of its eternal seat, which it now with patience waits for, expecting until "righteousness shall return unto judgment," and it obtain, by virtue of its excellence, final victory and perfect peace. A great work this, and an arduous; but God is my helper. For I am aware what ability is requisite to persuade the proud how great is the virtue of humility, which raises us, not by a quite human arrogance, but by a divine grace, above all earthly dignities that totter on this shifting scene. For the King and Founder of this city of which we speak has in Scripture uttered to His people a dictum of the divine law in these words: "God resisteth the proud, but giveth grace unto the humble." But this, which is God's prerogative, the inflated ambition of a proud spirit also affects, and dearly loves that this be numbered among its attritubes, to*
>
> > Show pity to the humbled soul,
> > And crush the sons of pride.
>
> *And therefore, as the plan of this work we have undertaken requires, and as occasion offers, we must speak also of the earthly city, which, though it be mistress of the nations, is itself ruled by its lust of rule.*[23]

Augustine spoke of his book as having two parts. The first ten books constitute his fierce reply to pagan charges that Christianity ruined Rome. It encompasses a wide-ranging review and judgment of Roman history, Roman manners, morals, politics, religion, and philosophy. At the beginning of Book 11, he speaks in this way of the second part, comprising the last twelve books:

> *The city of God we speak of is the same to which testimony is borne by that Scripture, which excels all the writings of all nations by its divine authority, and has brought under its influence all kinds of minds, and this not by a casual intellectual movement, but obviously by an express providential arrangement. For there it is written, "Glorious things are spoken of thee, O city of God." And in another psalm we read, "Great is the Lord, and greatly to be praised in the city of our God, in the mountain of His holiness, increasing the joy of the whole earth." And, a little after, in the same psalm, "As we have heard, so have we seen in the city of the Lord of hosts, in the city of our God. God has established it for ever." And in another, "There is a river the streams whereof shall make glad the city of our God, the holy place of the tabernacles of the Most High. God is in the midst of her, she shall not be moved." From these and similar testimonies, all of which it were tedious to cite, we have learned that there is a city of God, and its Founder has inspired us with a love which makes us covet its citizenship. To this Founder of the holy city the citizens of the earthly city prefer their own gods, not knowing that He is the God of gods, not of false, i.e., of impious and proud gods, who, being deprived of His unchangeable and freely communicated light, and so reduced to a kind of poverty-stricken power, eagerly grasp at their own private privileges, and seek divine honours from their deluded subjects; but of the pious and holy gods, who are better pleased to submit themselves to one than to subject many to themselves, and who would rather worship God than be worshipped as God. But to the enemies of this city we have replied in the ten preceding books, according to our ability and the help afforded by our Lord and King. Now, recognizing what is expected of me, and not unmindful of my promise, and relying, too, on the same succour, I will endeavour to treat of the origin, and progress, and deserved destinies of the two cities (the earthly and the heavenly, to wit), which, as we said, are in this present world commingled, and as it were entangled together.*[24]

The assignment Augustine thus sets himself for the second part of his book leads him to an exposition of a theology of history—a theology, not a philosophy, since the two cities he speaks of as "in this present world commingled, and as it were entangled together" are both spiritual or mystical cities, the heavenly city not to be confused with the church, and the earthly city not to be confused with existing political societies. It is of some importance to emphasize this point by setting down two passages, from the beginning and from the end of Book 14, which show how Augustine talks of the two cities:

> *We have already stated in the preceding books that God, desiring not only that the human race might be able by their similarity of nature to associate with one another, but also that they might be bound together in harmony and peace by the ties of relationship, was pleased to derive all men from one individual, and created man with such a nature that the members of the race should not have died, had not the two first (of whom the one was created out of nothing, and the other out of him) merited this by their disobedience; for by them so great a sin was committed that by it the human nature was altered for the worse, and was transmitted also to their posterity, liable to sin and subject to death. And the kingdom of death so reigned over men that the deserved penalty of sin would have hurled all headlong even into the second death, of which there is no end, had not the undeserved grace of God saved some therefrom. And thus it has come to pass that though there are very many and great nations all over the earth, whose rites and customs, speech, arms, and dress, are distinguished by marked differences, yet there are no more than two kinds of human society, which we may justly call two cities, according to the language of our Scriptures. The one consists of those who wish to live after the flesh, the other of those who wish to live after the spirit; and when they severally achieve what they wish, they live in peace, each after their kind.*[25]

And:

> *Accordingly, two cities have been formed by two loves: the earthly by the love of self, even to the contempt of God: the heavenly by the love of God, even to the contempt of self. The former, in a word, glories in itself, the latter in the Lord. For the one seeks glory from men; but the greatest glory of the other is God, the witness of conscience. The one lifts up its head in its own glory; the other says to its God, "Thou art my glory, and the lifter up of mine head." In the one, the princes and the nations it subdues are ruled by the love of ruling; in the other, the princes and the subjects serve one another in love, the latter obeying, while the former take thought for all. The one delights in its own strength, represented in the persons of its rulers; the other says to its God, "I will love*

Thee, O Lord, my strength." And therefore the wise men of the one city, living according to man, have sought for profit to their own bodies or souls, or both, and those who have known God "glorified Him not as God, neither were thankful, but became vain in their imaginations, and their foolish heart was darkened; professing themselves to be wise"—that is, glorying in their own wisdom, and being possessed by pride—"they became fools, and changed the glory of the incorruptible God into an image made like to corruptible man, and to birds, and four-footed beasts, and creeping things." For they were either leaders or followers of the people in adoring images, "and worshipped and served the creature more than the Creator, who is blessed for ever." But in the other city there is no human wisdom, but only godliness, which offers due worship to the true God, and looks for its reward in the society of the saints, of holy angels as well as holy men, "that God may be all in all." [26]

It is mainly in Book 19 that Augustine comes to some comment on human temporal affairs beyond their significance as events in the history of the two conflicting spiritual cities. Chapter 7 is a famous comment on war and the limitations of an imperially imposed peace:

After the state or city comes the world, the third circle of human society—the first being the house, and the second the city. And the world, as it is larger, so it is fuller of dangers, as the greater sea is the more dangerous. And here, in the first place, man is separated from man by the difference of languages. For if two men, each ignorant of the other's language, meet, and are not compelled to pass, but, on the contrary, to remain in company, dumb animals, though of different species, would more easily hold intercourse than they, human beings though they be. For their common nature is no help to friendliness when they are prevented by diversity of language from conveying their sentiments to one another; so that a man would more readily hold intercourse with his dog than with a foreigner. But the imperial city has endeavoured to impose on subject nations not only her yoke, but her language, as a bond of peace, so that interpreters, far from being scarce, are numberless. This is true; but how many great wars, how much slaughter and bloodshed, have provided this unity! And though these are past, the end of these miseries has not yet come. For though there have never been wanting, nor are yet wanting, hostile nations beyond the empire, against whom wars have been and are waged, yet, supposing there were no such nations, the very extent of the empire itself has produced wars of a more obnoxious description—social and civil wars—and with these the whole race has been agitated either by the actual conflict or the fear of a renewed outbreak. If I attempted to give an adequate description of these manifold disasters, these stern and lasting necessities, though I am quite unequal to the task, what limit could I set? But, say they, the wise man will wage just wars. As if he would not all the rather lament the necessity of just wars, if he remembers that he is a man; for if they were not just he would not wage them, and would therefore be delivered from all wars. For it is the wrongdoing of the opposing party which compels the wise man to wage just wars; and this wrong-doing, even though it gave rise to no war, would still be matter of grief to man because it is man's wrong-doing. Let every one, then, who thinks with pain on all these great evils, so horrible, so ruthless, acknowledge that this is misery. And if any one either endures or thinks of them without mental pain, this is a more miserable plight still, for he thinks himself happy because he has lost human feeling.[27]

The complementary chapter on peace, however, requires Augustine to distinguish the different meanings of the term in the two cities. As well as any single passage in the book, chapter 17 in Book 19 indicates the sense of his contention that the Christian, except on the point of idolatrous state polytheism, can "obey the laws of the earthly city" and secure for himself "the peace of earth":

But the families which do not live by faith seek their peace in the earthly advantages of this life; while the families which live by faith look for those eternal blessings which are promised, and use as pilgrims such advantages of time and of earth as do not fascinate and divert them from God, but rather aid them to endure with greater ease, and to keep down the number of those burdens of the corruptible body which weigh upon the soul. Thus the things necessary for this mortal life are used by both kinds of men and families alike, but each has its own peculiar and widely different aim in using them. The earthly city, which does not live by faith, seeks an earthly peace, and the end it proposes, in the well-ordered concord of civic obedience and rule, is the combination of men's wills to attain the things which are helpful to this life. The heavenly city, or rather the part of it which sojourns on earth and lives by faith, makes use of this peace only because it must, until this mortal condition which necessitates it shall pass away. Consequently, so long as it lives like a captive and a stranger in the earthly city, though it has already received the promise of redemption, and the gift of the Spirit as the earnest of it, it makes no scruple to obey the laws of the earthly city, whereby the things necessary for the maintenance of this mortal life are administered;

*and thus, as this life is common to both cities, so there is a har-
mony between them in regard to what belongs to it. But, as the
earthly city has had some philosophers whose doctrine is condemned by the divine teaching, and who, being deceived either
by their own conjectures or by demons, supposed that many gods
must be invited to take an interest in human affairs, and assigned
to each a separate function and a separate department—to one the
body, to another the soul; and in the body itself, to one the head,
to another the neck, and each of the other members to one of the
gods; and in like manner, in the soul, to one god the natural capacity was assigned, to another education, to another anger, to another lust; and so the various affairs of life were assigned—cattle
to one, corn to another, wine to another, oil to another, the woods
to another, money to another, navigation to another, wars and
victories to another, marriages to another, births and fecundity to
another, and other things to other gods: and as the celestial city,
on the other hand, knew that one God only was to be worshipped,
and that to Him alone was due that service which the Greeks call
λατρεία, and which can be given only to a god, it has come to
pass that the two cities could not have common laws of religion,
and that the heavenly city has been compelled in this matter to
dissent, and to become obnoxious to those who think differently,
and to stand the brunt of their anger and hatred and persecutions,
except in so far as the minds of their enemies have been alarmed
by the multitude of the Christians and quelled by the manifest
protection of God accorded to them. This heavenly city, then,
while it sojourns on earth, calls citizens out of all nations and
gathers together a society of pilgrims of all languages, not scru-
pling about diversities in the manners, laws, and institutions
whereby earthly peace is secured and maintained, but recognizing
that, however various these are, they all tend to one and the same
end of earthly peace. It therefore is so far from rescinding and
abolishing these diversities, that it even preserves and adopts
them, so long only as no hindrance to the worship of the one supreme and true God is thus introduced. Even the heavenly city,
therefore, while in its state of pilgrimage, avails itself of the peace
of earth, and, so far as it can without injuring faith and godliness,
desires and maintains a common agreement among men regarding
the acquisition of the necessaries of life, and makes this earthly
peace bear upon the peace of heaven; for this alone can be truly
called and esteemed the peace of the reasonable creatures, consisting as it does in the perfectly ordered and harmonious enjoyment of God and of one another in God. When we shall have
reached that peace, this mortal life shall give place to one that is
eternal, and our body shall be no more this animal body which by*

its corruption weighs down the soul, but a spiritual body feeling no want, and in all its members subjected to the will. In its pilgrim state the heavenly city possesses this peace by faith; and by this faith it lives righteously when it refers to the attainment of that peace every good action towards God and man; for the life of the city is a social life.[28]

Progressively, of course, through the Middle Ages, the one world of Europe became Christendom, a community of peoples with a cultural unity because of the common spiritual tradition. But there was no settlement of problems involved in the temporal direction and organization of that community. Augustine's lofty doctrine of two mystical cities, not to be confused with church and state, proved something too subtle for history. Indeed, it was cited to legitimize quite different positions about the struggles among church and states and princes for jurisdictional supremacy. These conflicts continued, passing through many transitory configurations, throughout the whole of the Middle Ages.

While acknowledging the intricate contingencies in that complex and inconclusive history, Gilson finds an intelligibility in the variety of positions that were taken. He formulates, as "a sort of law," a six-term proportion: "for a thinker of the middle ages, the state is to the church, as philosophy is to theology, and as nature is to grace." He means by this proportion that "a medieval doctrine tends to absorb the state into the Church, or to distinguish it from the state, to separate it or oppose it, in the same manner and with the same nuances with which it tends to absorb philosophy in theology and nature in the supernatural, to distinguish them, to separate or oppose them."[29]

Gilson's "law" is certainly verified in Dante's *De Monarchia*,[30] a treatise coming near the end of the long medieval disputation about the relations of the church in the world with the temporal city. In the following summative passage from the last chapter, it is perfectly explicit that Dante's novel assertion of a complete separation of church and state arises from extreme separating positions about philosophy and theology, reason and faith, nature and grace:

Man alone of all beings occupies a place mid-way between the corruptible and the incorruptible. Hence he has been rightly likened by philosophers to the horizon, which is between two hemispheres. Man has two essential parts, soul and body; considered from the point of view of one part, the body, he is corruptible; from the other, the soul, incorruptible. Of the soul the Philosopher has well stated the incorruptibility when he says, "By this alone, since it is eternal, man has achieved separation from the perishable." Accordingly, if man is a kind of mean between the corruptible and the incorruptible, like every mean, he partakes of the nature of the extremes. And since every nature is arranged to seek its proper and final goal, it follows that man exists for a double purpose. And since he alone among beings partakes of both corruptibility and incorruptibility, he alone among beings belongs in two final orders—one of which is his goal as a corruptible being, the other as incorruptible.

Twofold, therefore, are the ends which unerring Providence has ordained for man: the bliss of this life, which consists in the functioning of his own powers, and which is typified by the earthly Paradise; and the bliss of eternal life, which consists in the enjoyment of that divine vision to which he cannot attain by his own powers, except they be aided by the divine light, and this state is made intelligible by the celestial Paradise. These two states of bliss, like two different goals, man must reach by different ways. For we come to the first as we follow the philosophical teachings, applying them according to our moral and intellectual capacities; and we come to the second as we follow the spiritual teachings which transcend human reason according to our theological capacities, faith, hope and charity. Though these two goals and their ways are made plain to us, the one by human reason, which as it is used by the philosophers makes all these things known to us, the other by the Holy Spirit, which through the prophets, through the holy writers, through Jesus Christ the Son of God coeternal with the Spirit, and through his disciples, has revealed to us whatever supernatural truths we need, yet man's greed would keep them from us were not men like horses in their animal vagaries kept on the road by bit and rein. Thus the reins of man are held by a double driver according to man's twofold end; one is the supreme pontiff, who guides mankind with revelations to life eternal, and the other is the emperor, who guides mankind with philosophical instructions to temporal happiness. And since none or very few (and these with difficulty) can reach this goal, unless a free mankind enjoys the tranquility of peace and the waves of distracting greed are stilled, this must be the constant aim of him who guides the globe and whom we call Roman Prince, in order that on this threshing floor of life mortals may exist free and in peace. . . .

It is now clear that the authority for temporal world-government must come directly, without intermediary, from the universal Fount of authority, which, though it flows pure from a single spring, spills over into many channels out of the abundance of its goodness. And so I see that I have reached the mark set before us. For the truth is now unfolded concerning the basic questions in our inquiry, whether for the world's well-being a single govern-

ment must be established over it, and whether the Roman people has a right to its imperial power, and whether, lastly, the authority for world-government comes directly from God or through some other.[31]

For the purposes of this review, there are things about Dante's remarkable treatise more important than Rome's providential right to be the seat of a monarchical world government, or the civil monarch's independence of the papacy for rule in the temporal order, however novel and startling these positions were. The important thing here is Book 1 of Dante's treatise.[32] For there we have, and for the first time, a work in the order of reason, a work of political philosophy, tied to no historical imperial achievements, which argues for the existence, held to be implicit in the nature and unity of man, of a universal temporal community (*civilitas humani generis*) and argues for the necessity of world government to direct the whole of mankind toward the achievement of its collective end.

Dante proliferates arguments for his basic premises. (It is one of the finer ironies of intellectual history that his intellectual armory is taken entirely from the teleological metaphysics and the moral and political philosophy of Aristotle, the philosopher of the tiny polis.) However, the structure of his discourse is simple and clear. First, a definition: "By the temporal government of the world or universal empire we mean a single government over all men in time, that is, over and in all things which can be measured by time." To be sought: a proof that "such a government is necessary for the good of the world." The first principle for that proof will come from the discovery of "the universal goal of human civilization, if there be such a goal," since "in matters of action the final goal is the principle and cause of all, for by it the agent is first moved, it follows that any reasons for actions directed to this goal must be themselves derived from it. . . . It would be foolish to admit that one civilization may have one goal, and another, another, and not to admit one goal for all."

"We must now see what the whole of human civilization aims at," Dante continues. "And as evidence for what we seek we ought to note that just as nature makes the thumb for one purpose, the whole hand for another, the arm for still another, and the whole man for a purpose different from all these, so an individual man has one purpose, a family another, a neighborhood another, a city another, a state another, and finally there is another for all of mankind, established by the Eternal God's art, which is nature." Since "a proper functioning does not exist for the sake of the being which functions, but rather the being exists for the sake of its function . . . ," we must seek for "some proper function for the whole of mankind as an organized multitude which cannot be achieved by any single man, or family, or neighborhood, or city, or state. What that may be would be plain if we could see what the basic capacity of the whole of humanity is. . . . it is clear that man's basic capacity is to have a potentiality or power for being intellectual. And since this power cannot be completely actualized in a single man or in any of the particular communities of men above mentioned, there must be a multitude in mankind through whom this whole power can be actualized. . . . I have now made clear enough that the proper work of mankind taken as a whole is to exercise continually its entire capacity for intellectual growth, first, in theoretical matters, and, secondarily, as an extension of theory, in practice."

However, for this full flowering of the sciences and arts of mankind, the proper functioning and temporal happiness of humanity, there is a basic indispensable condition—"universal peace." For the attainment of that necessary condition, government is necessary, a government proportionate to the universal community of mankind, a "world government," over all the governments of particular peoples, "a supreme tribunal," before which "all contentions are judiciable."

Thus, in the beginning of the fourteenth century, we have an argument in the order of reason for the human necessity of a temporal, universal, and *governed* city of man. The argument does not rest on any vision of a particular people's mission to use power for "the imposition of the custom of peace." Again, though Dante in his first book has premises from a rational or natural theology, his argument for a temporal secular universal city is, taken by itself, not tied to any revealed religion. The spiritual universal Christian city, in which he remains beyond any doubt a true believer, is a city of another order, with a different end and therefore with a different ruler.

However important *De Monarchia* may be in the history of ideas, nothing in the history of Dante's times favored any practical attention to it. Indeed, within ten years there appeared a very different book that was really to become influential, the *Defensor pacis,* by Marsilius of Padua, which furnished the jurisprudence for the age of nation-states with its doctrine of absolute, voluntaristic, external sovereignty for every nation-state.

The proliferation of such sovereign absolutist states in the Renaissance and the Reformation divisions of Christianity would appear to have effectively put an end to the medieval unity of Western Christendom. Yet, as Borgese notes, "an undercurrent of unitary thinking and scheming, a mixture of nostalgia for antiquity or the Middle Ages with awareness of the approaching perils and projections of prophesied remedies, ran through the whole age of the divisive nations."[33] Some account of what Borgese is referring to is relevant to our purpose here.

What should be said first is that this "undercurrent" is a series of early projects for European unity, their authors being something like the prophets of what came to be called the Pan-European movement. Always cited as the beginning of this is the "Great Design" attributed to Henry IV, king of France from 1589 to 1610, in the *Memoires* of his trusted minister, the Duc de Sully. It was the design of constituting, after the defeat of Austria, a vast European confederation of fifteen states—a "Christian Republic"—directed by a general council of sixty deputies reappointed every three years.

An engraving of Henry IV subsequently appeared on the title page of a book, published in 1713, by the Abbé de Saint-Pierre and entitled *Project for Perpetual Peace*. This Abbé was a publicist and roving reformer, and a prolific publisher of "projects." He believed that what Henry IV or Sully had thought possible *was* possible if the sovereigns would will it. He thought he could give them reasons why they should will it, and a prefiguration of an institutional structure that would show the new Europe could work to its purpose of perpetual peace. He had not initially wished to narrow his vision to the confines of Europe. He had earlier also thought of Africa and America, but in the interest of immediate feasibility, as he saw it, he settled for the vision of a "Society of Europe."

There was much mockery of the Abbé's treatise as something absurdly visionary. But it drew attention and retained influence—indeed, it did so all the way to the Congress of Europe, convened at The Hague in 1948 by the International Committee for the Co-ordination of European Unity Movements.

Leibniz praised Saint-Pierre's work but called attention to what he considered a major flaw, its proposal to rest European unity on Christianity while ignoring the divisions within Christianity, which Leibniz himself was earnestly trying to heal. More important, the Abbé's book aroused the interest of Jean Jacques Rousseau. In 1761, Rousseau published a vigorous treatise, entitled *A Lasting Peace through the Federation of Europe*.[34] It consisted of a kind of tribute to the Abbé de Saint-Pierre, a condensed reprint of his work, and a section of critical comments on it.

Toward the beginning of this work, Rousseau has a three-part exclamatory question:

> *If the social order were really, as is pretended, the work not of passion but of reason, should we have been so slow to see that, in the shaping of it, either too much, or too little, has been done for our happiness? that, each one of us being in the civil state as regards our fellow citizens, but in the state of nature as regards the rest of the world, we have taken all kinds of precautions against private wars only to kindle national wars a thousand times more terrible? and that, in joining a particular group of men, we have really declared ourselves the enemies of the whole race?*

Rousseau's reply to such an intricate question is that "if there is any way of reconciling these dangerous contradictions, it is to be found only in such a form of federal government as shall unite nations by bonds similar to those which already unite their individual members, and place the one no less than the other under the authority of the law."

He next argues that Europe is ready for such a federation because it has in fact an underlying unity to support it:

> *The powers of Europe constitute a kind of whole, united by identity of religion, of moral standard, of international law; by letters, by commerce, and finally by a species of balance which is the inevitable result of all these ties.*

He has no doubts about the causes of this underlying European community. They lie in the decree of Claudius granting citizenship throughout the Roman Empire, the diffusion of a common Roman law, and "a third and yet stronger bond," Christianity:

> *Thus the priesthood and the empire wove a bond between various nations which, without any real community of interests, of rights, or of mutual dependence, found a tie in common principles and beliefs, the influence of which still survives even after its foundation is withdrawn. The venerable phantom of the Roman Empire has never ceased to unite the nations which once formed part of it. . . . All these causes combine to make of Europe not, like Asia and Africa, a purely imaginary assemblage of peoples with nothing in common save the name, but a real community with a religion and a moral code, with customs and even laws of its own, which none of the component nations can renounce without causing a shock to the whole frame.*

Rousseau goes on to "look at the other side of the picture," setting forth a passionate picture of disorders, quarrels, and ugly wars and saying:

> *Let us admit then that the powers of Europe stand to each other strictly in a state of war, and that all the separate treaties between them are in the nature rather of a temporary truce than a real peace.*

Rousseau's summary of his account of the situation has him practising, without benefit of Hegel or Marx, a thesis-antithesis-synthesis dialectic all his own:

> *From the above survey three certain conclusions may be drawn: the first that, Turkey excepted, there already exists among the nations of Europe a bond, imperfect indeed but still closer than*

*the loose and general ties which exist between man and man in
the state of nature; the second, that the imperfections of this association make the state of those who belong to it worse than it
would be if they formed no community at all; the third, that these
rudimentary ties, which make such an association injurious, make
it at the same time readily capable of improvement, that all its members might easily find their happiness in what actually makes their
misery, that from the state of war which now reigns among them
they might perfectly well draw an abiding peace.*

The question, then, is how this great work can come about—the means
by which "the free and voluntary association which now unites the states
of Europe may be converted, by taking to itself the strength and firmness
of a genuine body politic, into an authentic federation." Rousseau,
following but modifying Saint-Pierre, sets forth the first procedural steps
that the bodies and the powers of the federation would entail, five major
articles for the constitution of the Federation of Europe, the nations
that would enter, arguments to assure that it could work for its purpose,
thirteen evils the federation would abolish, and eight advantages it
would bring.

"To prove that the project of the Christian Commonwealth is not
utopian," Rousseau recalls "its original author, for no one will say that
Henry IV was a madman, or Sully a dreamer." Then, at the very end of
his work Rousseau confesses to considerable disillusionment about practical prospects and a shudder about the effects of revolution:

*Beyond doubt, a lasting peace is, under present circumstances, a
project ridiculous enough. But give us back Henry IV and Sully,
and it will become once more a reasonable proposal. Or rather,
while we admire so fair a project, let us console ourselves for its
failure by the thought that it could only have been carried out by
violent means from which humanity must needs shrink.*

*No federation could ever be established except by a revolution.
That being so, which of us would dare to say whether the League
of Europe is a thing more to be desired or feared? It would perhaps do more harm in a moment than it would guard against
for ages.*

Rousseau's intellectual influence on the French Revolution, so often
argued for, is not in evidence here in 1756.

The line of Pan-European pleading, from Henry IV through the Abbé
de Saint-Pierre, is not finished with Rousseau. In 1795, when he was
seventy-one years old, Immanuel Kant published as a pamphlet his
Perpetual Peace.[35] Louis XVI had been executed, and French revolutionary armies were threatening to topple monarchs all over Europe. Kant's

pamphlet is clearly influenced by Rousseau and, indeed, by Saint-Pierre. However, his effort is not so directly practical, nor so rhetorical. He tries to indicate the way in which the concern for perpetual peace could be grounded in a true philosophical jurisprudence. His section titles indicate something about his perspective: "Preliminary" and "Definitive Articles for a Perpetual Peace among States"; "On the Opposition Which Exists Between Morality and Politics with Respect to the Subject of a Perpetual Peace"; "Of the Harmony Which the Transcendent Idea of Right Establishes between Politics and Morality."

In the conclusion of his *Science of Right*, Kant states what attitudes regarding the prospect of perpetual peace he thinks must be taken, not in idle or pious hope, but as a matter of moral duty:

> *Now, as a matter of fact, the morally practical reason utters within us its irrevocable veto:* There shall be no war. *So there ought to be no war, neither between me and you in the condition of nature, nor between us as members of states which, although internally in a condition of law, are still externally in their relation to each other in a condition of lawlessness; for this is not the way by which any one should prosecute his right. Hence the question no longer is as to whether perpetual peace is a real thing or not a real thing, or as to whether we may not be deceiving ourselves when we adopt the former alternative, but we must* act *on the supposition of its being real. We must work for what may perhaps not be realized, and establish that constitution which yet seems best adapted to bring it about (mayhap republicanism in all states, together and separately). And thus we may put an end to the evil of wars, which have been the chief interest of the internal arrangements of all the states without exception. And although the realization of this purpose may always remain but a pious wish, yet we do certainly not deceive ourselves in adopting the maxim of action that will guide us in working incessantly for it; for it is a duty to do this. To suppose that the moral law within us is itself deceptive, would be sufficient to excite the horrible wish rather to be deprived of all reason than to live under such deception, and even to see oneself, according to such principles, degraded like the lower animals to the level of the mechanical play of nature.*
>
> *It may be said that the universal and lasting establishment of peace constitutes not merely a part, but the whole final purpose and end of the science of right as viewed within the limits of reason. The state of peace is the only condition of the mine and thine that is secured and guaranteed by* laws *in the relationship of men living in numbers contiguous to each other, and who are thus combined in a constitution whose rule is derived not from the*

mere experience of those who have found it the best as a normal guide for others, but which must be taken by the reason a priori from the ideal of a juridical union of men under public laws generally. For all particular examples or instances, being able only to furnish illustration but not proof, are deceptive, and at all events require a metaphysic to establish them by its necessary principles. And this is conceded indirectly even by those who turn metaphysics into ridicule, when they say, as they often do: "The best constitution is that in which not men but laws exercise the power." For what can be more metaphysically sublime in its own way than this very idea of theirs, which according to their own assertion has, notwithstanding, the most objective reality? This may be easily shown by reference to actual instances. And it is this very idea which alone can be carried out practically, if it is not forced on in a revolutionary and sudden way by violent overthrow of the existing defective constitution; for this would produce for the time the momentary annihilation of the whole juridical state of society. But if the idea is carried forward by gradual reform and in accordance with fixed principles, it may lead by a continuous approximation to the highest political good, and to perpetual peace.[36]

Two points need to be made about this almost two-hundred-year-long line of pamphlets and projects about perpetual peace. Gilson makes both of them. All of the pamphlets and short treatises are Pan-European works. But the good they hope and argue for is a universal good. As Gilson puts it: "Peace is not a European good, but a human good."[37] The spiritual thing sought is something more universalistic than the body politic for which it is sought. It has been clear, of course, that this contradiction has lain in the whole history. Neither Alexander's empire nor the Roman Empire, pagan or holy, encompassed the existing *civilitas humani generis,* to use Dante's term. They are part of the story because of their unitary thrust, not because they were firmly universalist. Indeed, only in the philosophical first book of Dante's treatise, and implicitly in the thought of Kant, did there appear a genuine universalism—an argument for a city that would really be the community of *all* mankind.

A second observation about the perpetual peace projects concerns the presence of Christianity as a factor taken for granted both in the arguments and in the plans for action. In the writings of the Duc de Sully, the Abbé de Saint-Pierre, and Rousseau, quite apart from any question of their being or not being true Christian believers, the denomination "Christian Republic" is used interchangeably with "the Society of Europe" or "the Republic of Europe." The possibility for perpetual peace, they seemed to take for granted, was grounded historically and practically on the unity of "Christendom," on the spiritual and cultural unity

Christianity had imparted to Europe, on the binding power that Christianity, it could be assumed, would go on exerting. Gilson comments that, apart from whatever is to be made of the saying "l'Europe, c'est la foi," it is "certainly not true to say that the faith is Europe. Europe can be included in the faith, but not the faith in Europe." And Gilson goes on, "One hopes not to scandalize anyone in emitting the bold propositions: Jesus Christ is not a European; Bethlehem is not in Europe. . . . What Christian could conceive the faith without horror as the salvation of one of the five parts of the world to the exclusion of four others?"[38] Yet the Pan-Europeans did not extend their vision to the universalism implicit in the idea of peace, and they tended to contract the universalism of Christianity into provincial or parochial civil service.

In the nineteenth century, the continuing tie to Christianity and Christendom of unitary and universalist social visions took some very strange forms. Saint-Simon, one of the founders of socialism and a prophet of the scientific, managerial, and technological society, was a relentless critic of theology and all established religion. His basic idea, in appealing to Louis XVIII to inaugurate a new social order, was that industrial chiefs should be given control of society in order to ameliorate the moral and physical existence of the poor. However, he did not think such a whole new order could come about unless some sort of religious thrust could be introduced. So he gave himself Charlemagne as an ancestor, claimed that "God had spoken to him," because "how could a man by himself invent a religion superior to all those which have existed," and entitled his major work *The New Christianity* (1825), one feature of which is that it is Newton who sits at the right hand of God.

Some have said that Saint-Simon was mad. But at least Auguste Comte, who was much influenced by Saint-Simon, was a somber, sober man—and he agreed as to the necessity of religion for any major social reform. He did not hesitate, however, to invent a new religion without word from God, because God, indeed, was not to be in it.

Comte announced that a third new epoch was beginning, in which positive science would take over the unifying roles previously played by theology and metaphysics. He did prodigious intellectual work to make good on that announcement and, as it were, to take intellectual charge of the new and last great epoch of human history. He founded the discipline of sociology, and his general positivist philosophy, in various ways, has had strong and lasting influence in the world of thought.

However, when he was twenty-four years old he had written *A Plan for the Scientific Works Necessary to Reorganize Society,* and when he was twenty-eight, *Considerations on the Spiritual Power.* Those youthful works gave intimations of his place in the history reviewed in this report. He believed that the new positive science would yield truths which could command universal acceptance and be the spiritual foundation for a new universal society, beginning in Europe but extended thereafter to all mankind. The establishment and maintenance of that new society would, however, require a new religion, a new faith, a new church. Comte proceeded diligently to meet that requirement and went so far in doing so that he lost several of his best disciples, among them John Stuart Mill.

Comte's new religion was not to be "a new Christianity," as Saint-Simon's had been. God had disappeared with the passing of the ages of theology and metaphysics. His place was to be taken by what Comte called "The Great Being," which was the spiritual community of all dead, living, and future men. The new religion was "the Religion of Humanity." For the lowly among the new faithful, Comte wrote *The Positivist Catechism, or Summary exposition of the Universal Religion.* He wrote a full ecclesiology, which posited a Great High Priest of Humanity and three orders of priests below him. This priesthood would hold, teach, and preach the new dogmas. It would draw from those dogmas, demonstrable to human reason, plans for the organization of society, which would be administered by the temporal power. The priesthood would administer the new nine sacraments and conduct worship in morning, midday, and evening prayers. Comte also indicated in considerable detail how the Church of Humanity was to be supported—by an equivalent of "Peter's pence," to be called "the Positivist Subsidy." Furthermore, the new pope was to have penal powers in the spiritual order, and Comte indicated a series of graded sanctions, extending to "social excommunication," for dissidents, schismatics, and heretics. The priesthood, however, was to have no power, except that which lay in the rational authority of its positivist, scientific sociology, over the temporal power, an elite of managers, industrialists, businessmen, and bankers.

Comte, of course, was completely conscious of the transposition he was making of medieval problems about the spiritual and temporal orders, and about ecclesiastical and political powers. He was aware that it would seem, almost grotesquely, that the ghost of the Roman Catholic church was dictating the very structure, processes, and powers of the new Church of Humanity. He defended his detailed analogical borrowing. It was sensible and justified from his point of view because in his philosophy of history the role of the Catholic church was to prepare the way, in the age of theology, for tasks that would be at last soundly performed in the age of positive science. Of course, that point is itself a kind of transposition of the point made by Prudentius and agreed to by Dante about the providential preparatory role of the pagan Roman Empire with respect to the Christian church.

Once again, after noting these extraordinary Comtian transpositions, it seems pertinent to comment that the echoes and reverberations one finds in the history of Western thought about a world community of mankind seem to suggest that there must be, in all the fervent speculations about the idea, some sort of inner binding logical structure to it.

Before closing this review, two moments, later in the nineteenth century, are worth recalling—moments in the imaginative worlds created by two great Russian novels, Tolstoy's *War and Peace* (1869)[39] and Dostoevsky's *The Brothers Karamazov* (1880).[40]

In the thought and actions of his later years, Tolstoy was in his own person a part of the history of nineteenth-century universalism. He evolved his own "new Christianity," for which he was excommunicated by the Orthodox church. His doctrine, urging a life of poverty and non-resistance to evil, was intensely individualistic, but nevertheless judged to be the way to universal peace. Converts, when "Tolstoyism" became an organized sect, made pilgrimages to the sage from all parts of the world.

However, it is a text from *War and Peace* that is to be recalled here. Pierre Bezúkhov, disillusioned with the low quality of his St. Petersburg Freemasonic lodge, has gone abroad "to be initiated into the higher secrets of the order." At his return, a solemn meeting of the lodge of the second degree is convened, at which Pierre promises to communicate to the St. Petersburg brothers what he has to deliver to them from the highest leaders of their order. After the usual ceremonies, Pierre rises to speak:

> "Dear Brothers," he began, blushing and stammering, with a written speech in his hand, "it is not sufficient to observe our mysteries in the seclusion of our lodge—we must act—act! We are drowsing, but we must act." Pierre raised his notebook and began to read.
>
> "For the dissemination of pure truth and to secure the triumph of virtue," he read, "we must cleanse men from prejudice, diffuse principles in harmony with the spirit of the times, undertake the education of the young, unite ourselves in indissoluble bonds with the wisest men, boldly yet prudently overcome superstitions, infidelity, and folly, and form of those devoted to us a body linked together by unity of purpose and possessed of authority and power.
>
> "To attain this end we must secure a preponderance of virtue over vice and must endeavor to secure that the honest man may, even in this world, receive a lasting reward for his virtue. But in these great endeavors we are gravely hampered by the political institutions of today. What is to be done in these circumstances? To favor revolutions, overthrow everything, repel force by force? . . . No! We are very far from that. Every violent reform deserves censure, for it quite fails to remedy evil while men remain what they are, and also because wisdom needs no violence.
>
> "The whole plan of our order should be based on the idea of preparing men of firmness and virtue bound together by unity of conviction—aiming at the punishment of vice and folly, and

patronizing talent and virtue: raising worthy men from the dust and attaching them to our Brotherhood. Only then will our order have the power unobtrusively to bind the hands of the protectors of disorder and to control them without their being aware of it. In a word, we must found a form of government holding universal sway, which should be diffused over the whole world without destroying the bonds of citizenship, and beside which all other governments can continue in their customary course and do every-thing except what impedes the great aim of our order, which is to obtain for virtue the victory over vice. This aim was that of Christianity itself. It taught men to be wise and good and for their own benefit to follow the example and instruction of the best and wisest men.

"At that time, when everything was plunged in darkness, preach-ing alone was of course sufficient. The novelty of Truth endowed her with special strength, but now we need much more powerful methods. It is now necessary that man, governed by his senses, should find in virtue a charm palpable to those senses. It is impos-sible to eradicate the passions; but we must strive to direct them to a noble aim, and it is therefore necessary that everyone should be able to satisfy his passions within the limits of virtue. Our order should provide means to that end.

"As soon as we have a certain number of worthy men in every state, each of them again training two others and all being closely united, everything will be possible for our order, which has already in secret accomplished much for the welfare of mankind."

This speech not only made a strong impression, but created excitement in the lodge. The majority of the Brothers, seeing in it dangerous designs of Illuminism, met it with a coldness that surprised Pierre. The Grand Master began answering him, and Pierre began developing his views with more and more warmth. It was long since there had been so stormy a meeting. Parties were formed, some accusing Pierre of Illuminism, others supporting him. At that meeting he was struck for the first time by the endless variety of men's minds, which prevents a truth from ever present-ing itself identically to two persons. Even those members who seemed to be on his side understood him in their own way with limitations and alterations he could not agree to, as what he always wanted most was to convey his thought to others just as he himself understood it.

At the end of the meeting the Grand Master with irony and ill-will reproved Bezúkhov for his vehemence and said it was not love of virtue alone, but also a love of strife that had moved him in the dispute. Pierre did not answer him and asked briefly whether his proposal would be accepted. He was told that it would not, and without waiting for the usual formalities he left the lodge and went home.[41]

So much for the dim reception of Pierre's trembling vision of an ennobled Freemasonry, taken by him, despite Christian condemnations, as having the same aim as "that of Christianity itself," that of founding "a form of government holding universal sway, which should be diffused over the whole world without destroying the bonds of citizenship."

Dostoevsky, too, has a place in his own right in the history of the nineteenth-century universalists. In the last years of his life, countering the increasing revolutionary agitation of that period, he developed a mystique about a universal mission for "Holy Russia." In a famous speech in 1880, at the unveiling of a memorial to Pushkin in Moscow, he proclaimed his belief that Russia and the Orthodox church were destined to lead the nations of Europe, and thereafter the whole world, into ways of righteousness.

But it is rather a text from *The Brothers Karamazov* that should be recalled here, from chapter 5 in Book 5, entitled "The Grand Inquisitor"—an immense, dense, mysterious fable composed by Ivan Karamazov and read by him to his brother, Alyosha. Christ, appearing "softly" in Seville, has almost immediately been imprisoned by the Cardinal of Seville, the Grand Inquisitor. In their meeting in prison, Christ speaks no words. To the silent Christ, the Inquisitor delivers an elaborate disquisition defending his denial to Christ of his right to return. Among many other things, he rebukes Christ for the folly of his answers to the three great wise questions Satan had asked him. The text in question here involves the third temptation:

> *Why hast Thou come now to hinder us? And why dost Thou look silently and searchingly at me with Thy mild eyes? Be angry. I don't want Thy love, for I love Thee not. And what use is it for me to hide anything from Thee? Don't I know to Whom I am speaking? All that I can say is known to Thee already. And is it for me to conceal from Thee our mystery? Perhaps it is Thy will to hear it from my lips. Listen, then. We are not working with Thee, but with him—that is our mystery. It's long—eight centuries—since we have been on his side and not on Thine. Just eight centuries ago, we took from him what Thou didst reject with scorn, that last gift he offered Thee, showing Thee all the kingdoms of the earth. We took from him Rome and the sword of Caesar, and proclaimed ourselves sole rulers of the earth, though hitherto we have not been able to complete our work. But whose fault is that? Oh, the work is only beginning, but it has begun. It has long to await completion and the earth has yet much to suffer, but we shall triumph and shall be Caesars, and then we shall plan*

the universal happiness of man. But Thou mightest have taken even then the sword of Caesar. Why didst Thou reject that last gift? Hadst Thou accepted that last counsel of the mighty spirit, Thou wouldst have accomplished all that man seeks on earth—that is, someone to worship, someone to keep his conscience, and some means of uniting all in one unanimous and harmonious ant-heap, for the craving for universal unity is the third and last anguish of men. Mankind as a whole has always striven to organize a universal state. There have been many great nations with great histories, but the more highly they were developed the more unhappy they were, for they felt more acutely than other people the craving for world-wide union. The great conquerors, Timours and Ghenghis-Khans, whirled like hurricanes over the face of the earth striving to sub-due its people, and they too were but the unconscious expression of the same craving for universal unity. Hadst Thou taken the world and Caesar's purple, Thou wouldst have founded the uni-versal state and have given universal peace. For who can rule men if not he who holds their conscience and their bread in his hands? We have taken the sword of Caesar, and in taking it, of course, have rejected Thee and followed him.[42]

Whatever else is to be said of them, these chilling remarks in Ivan's complex, bitterly ironic fable provocatively recapitulate themes in the history of what the Inquisitor calls "the craving for universal unity, the . . . last anguish of man." He calls "the great conquerors" (and he might well have mentioned Alexander) "but the unconscious expression of the same craving for universal unity." He rebukes Christ for his separation of the things that are Caesar's and the things that are God's. He tells him that the Catholic church, which for Augustine was the City of God in a pilgrim temporal existence, has become the City of the Devil, which, hold-ing "consciences and bread," will "found a universal state" and give "uni-versal peace."

Presumably, contemporary thought about the city of mankind and the government of that great city cannot, and probably should not, divorce itself from the tradition, so curious and so contorted, which has been here reviewed.

---

1 G. A. Borgese, *Foundations of the World Republic* (Chicago: University of Chicago Press, 1953), p. 22.

2 *See* chap. 4 of *The Common Sense of Politics,* by Mortimer J. Adler (New York: Holt, Rinehart & Winston, 1971), for a discussion of the ways in which, and the reasons for which, political philosophy is conditioned in its development, even on the level of principles, by the gradual "historical enlargement of our vision of the possible."

3 W. W. Tarn, *Alexander the Great* (London: Cambridge University Press, 1948).

4 Aristotle *Politics; GBWW,* Vol. 9, p. 445d.

5 Tarn, *Alexander the Great,* vol. 2, pp. 447–48.

6 Plutarch *Moralia* 1. 5–6, cited in Tarn, *Alexander the Great,* p. 419.

7 *The Discourses of Epictetus; GBWW,* Vol. 12, pp. 114c–115a.

8 Marcus Aurelius, *Meditations; GBWW,* Vol. 12, p. 278c.

9 Ibid., p. 264a.

10 Ernest Barker, "The Conception of Empire," in *The Legacy of Rome,* ed. Cyril Bailey (Oxford: Oxford University Press, 1923), pp. 58–59.

11 Virgil *The Eclogues; GBWW,* Vol. 13, p. 14a.

12 *The Aeneid; GBWW,* Vol. 13, p. 110.

13 Ibid., pp. 233b–234a. The most interesting phrase in this Virgilian statement is something sterner in the Latin than it is in James Rhoades's translation. Virgil does not use a horticultural metaphor, "to engraft." He writes, "imponere morem pacis"—to *impose* the *custom* (or habit) of peace. That one precise word, *imponere,* quite wonderfully acknowledges the role of force in the Alexandrian and Roman unifications of the world. (The "others" to whom Virgil refers in these same lines are the Greeks, whose accomplishments are here foreseen.)

14 Claudian *De Consulta Stilichonis* 3. 150–59, cited in Tarn, *Alexander the Great,* p. 417.

15 Étienne Gilson, *La philosophie au moyen âge,* 2d rev. ed. (Paris: Éditions Payot, 1944), p. 162.

16 *Isaiah,* 49:6.

17 *Galatians,* 3:28.

18 Étienne Gilson, *Les métamorphoses de la Cité de Dieu* (Louvain: University of Louvain, 1952), pp. 20–29.

19 Cited in Gilson, *Les métamorphoses,* p. 20.

20 Tertullian *Apologeticus* 38.

21 Prudentius *Contra Symmachum* 2. 609–35, cited in Gilson, *Les métamorphoses,* pp. 28–29.

22 Augustine, *The City of God; GBWW,* Vol. 18, pp. 127–618.

23 Ibid., p. 129. There are curious echoes that impart some continuity to the history of the idea of world community. Augustus, when he became emperor, put an effigy of Alexander on his shield. Here, Augustine, preparing his countercharge against pagan Rome, reaches back some 431 years to a line of Virgil, which he brilliantly counterposes to the line from the New Testament. Virgil's line is from the passage cited earlier in this paper, on page 96, reading at the end: "remember, Roman, to rule the nations as their master. These thine arts shall be, to impose the custom of peace, spare the conquered, and war down the proud." The translation above for the Latin phrase *parcere subjectis* ("spare the conquered") is not fortunate.

24 Ibid., pp. 322–23.

25 Ibid., pp. 376–77.

26 Ibid., p. 397.

27 Ibid., p. 515.

28 Ibid., pp. 522–23.

29 Étienne Gilson, *La philosophie au moyen âge,* pp. 254–55.

30 Dante, *On World Government,* trans. Herbert W. Schneider (New York: Liberal Arts Press, 1949).

31 Ibid., pp. 59–60.

32 Book 1 of Dante's *De Monarchia* is in *Gateway to the Great Books,* Vol. 7, pp. 379–99.

33 Borgese, *Foundations of the World Republic,* p. 14.

34 *GGB,* Vol. 7, pp. 400–36.

35 Ibid., pp. 437–75.

36 Kant, *The Science of Right; GBWW,* Vol. 42, pp. 457–58.

37 Gilson, *Les métamorphoses,* p. 217.

38 Ibid., p. 218.

39 *GBWW,* Vol. 51.

40 *GBWW,* Vol. 52.

41 *GBWW,* Vol. 51, pp. 244d–245d.

42 *GBWW,* Vol. 52, p. 133b–d.

PART TWO

The Year's Developments in the Arts and Sciences

M. I. Finley

A widely read and highly respected
classical scholar who has done much to
revise our understanding of the ancient
world, M. I. Finley was born in New York
City in 1912. He had a distinguished
professional career in the United States
before moving to England, where since
1957 he has been a Fellow of Jesus College

and, since 1970, Professor of Ancient
History at the University of Cambridge. He
is the author of *Studies in Land and Credit
in Ancient Athens* (1952), *The World of
Odysseus* (1954), and *Early Greece: The
Bronze and Archaic Ages* (1970), and has
edited *The Greek Historians* (1959) and
Slavery in Classical Antiquity (1960),
among other works. His published articles
have appeared in literary reviews as well
as in professional journals. He lives in
Cambridge and since 1962 has been a
British subject.

New Developments in
Classical Studies [*]

Writing at the end of the pre-Christian era, the Sicilian Greek historian Diodorus told how in 384 B.C. Dionysius I of Syracuse raided the Etruscan port known in Greek as Pyrgi, took much booty and many captives, whom he sold as slaves, and so raised enough money to hire and equip a large army.[1] What Pyrgi was called in Etruscan is unknown; today it is an unimportant little bathing resort, Santa Severa, about forty miles west by north of Rome, but in Dionysius' time it was filled with wealth because it was the harbor of the powerful Etruscan town of Cisra (Caere in Latin, Cerveteri today).

In 1957 Massimo Pallottino, the outstanding Etruscologist, and his pupil, Giovanni Colonna, began to excavate Santa Severa systematically. They discovered the foundations of two temples, lying parallel to each other facing the sea, typically Etruscan in ground plan, the earlier dating about 500 B.C., the later two or three decades after that. Then, on July 8, 1964, came a spectacular discovery. In a niche between the two temples, carefully folded away, were found three tablets of pure gold, one-third to one-half millimeter in thickness. Tucked in the folds were bronze, gold-headed nails with which the tablets had originally been affixed to something, perhaps the doors of the older temple. Each of the tablets was beautifully inscribed, two in Etruscan and the third in Punic, the Phoenician dialect of Carthage (in modern Tunisia). The texts, no more than ninety words altogether, overlap, and there are doubts about some of the reading. The Punic text seems to say something like the following:

> *To the lady Astarte. This is the sacred place made and given by Thefarie Velianas, king of Cisra, in the month of the Sacrifice of the Sun in gift within the temple and sanctuary[?], because Astarte has raised [him] with her hand[?], in the third year of his reign, in the month of Krr, on the day of the Burial of the Divinity. And the years of the statue of the goddess in her temple [are as many] as these stars.*[2]

---

* A more precise title would be "Some new developments. . . ." I have touched only lightly on the Bronze Age in Greece and on the so-called Hellenistic period following the conquests of Alexander the Great. Science, philosophy, and the fine arts hardly appear; even under the subheadings I have introduced, I have permitted my own interests to carry undue weight. Nor are the references to books and articles meant to be exhaustive. In particular I want to disclaim any implication, in the deliberate concentration on publications in English, that there is little, or less, of importance in other languages.

This discovery is surprising in so many ways, and raises so many questions, that it makes an admirable introduction to the complexity of the idea of "new developments" in our knowledge of the ancient Greeks and Romans. First and most obvious is the question of language. Etruscan remains one of the few major linguistic obscurities in Europe—not, as is still widely and wrongly believed, because the alphabet of twenty-six letters is undeciphered, but because the language has no known affinity with other European (or Asiatic) tongues, and because all but a few of the more than ten thousand Etruscan texts now known are brief formulas, such as "I am the jug of Enotenus." What the experts have been waiting for is a larger bilingual text, which would open the way to completion of the now partial decipherment. Naturally it was an Etruscan-Latin bilingual that was hoped for; instead Pyrgi produced an Etruscan-Punic pair that do not translate each other literally. Since this is just about the oldest Punic text found anywhere, there are difficulties with it too.

The second big question is religious and political combined. Why did an Etruscan ruler near Rome go to such lengths to honor Carthaginian Astarte, the Ishtar of the Bible? Why, furthermore, does the longer of the two Etruscan tablets call her Astarte-Uni? That combination is of particular interest because Uni was identified with the Roman Juno and sometimes also assimilated to the Greek Hera, consort of Zeus. It was characteristic of ancient polytheism that gods and goddesses traveled to new shrines in new regions, that they were sometimes "identified" with each other, that they acquired new attributes, that, in sum, the pantheon was not something fixed for all time but rather a changing accumulation of divinities and functions responding to new needs and situations. But the changes were neither whimsical nor meaningless; there was always a reason, though it may be lost to us today.

Nothing in the Pyrgi tablets hints at an explanation directly, but we may draw some plausible inferences from the well-known Roman legends and traditions about early Rome. In particular, two events in that tradition are relevant. The first is that in 509 or 508 B.C. the Romans overthrew their Etruscan king and established a republic. The second is that the new, independent Roman regime immediately signed a rather complicated political-commercial treaty with Carthage. Many historians have in the past expressed doubt about the early date assigned to that treaty, because Rome was then too insignificant to warrant such recognition from powerful Carthage. But the Pyrgi tablets point the way to an explanation, namely, that Roman emancipation was part of a larger story of breakdown in the Etruscan league that had dominated central Italy and that the Carthaginians, who had had a *modus vivendi* with the Etruscans, thought it desirable, even necessary, to come to terms with petty Italian states now claiming independence. Hence the treaty with

Etruscan jug with painted figure of Lasa, a female Eros; fourth–third century B.C.

Rome; hence, too, a relationship with Thefarie Velianas of Cisra, symbolized by the (temporary) worship of Astarte in Pyrgi.

This is not the place for a full discussion of the implications of the Pyrgi tablets.[3] Enough has been said to reveal the frustrating condition that is chronic in classical studies: paucity of evidence (often in difficult and sometimes unintelligible language) forces heavy stress on every new scrap that comes to light, not only for its own sake but, as the Pyrgi tablets show, also for a reconsideration of older, generally accepted views of broad issues and major developments. It is therefore not surprising that university students, for example, frequently express the idea that ancient history is somehow qualitatively different from modern history. Certainly the ancient historian envies his colleagues who specialize in the American Civil War or Victorian England; for each of those short periods there is probably more documentation available than for the whole of the Greco-Roman world, from Homer to Constantine. In reality, however, the difference is one of degree rather than of kind. A treaty is still a treaty, even though we need the accident of the Pyrgi discovery to help assess the otherwise suspect tradition of a Roman-Carthaginian treaty as early as 508 B.C. It can also be argued that modern historians, with their wealth of written documents, do not make sufficient use of archaeology, of objects. It is only in recent decades that aerial photography has radically influenced our knowledge of late medieval and early modern agricultural field systems. It was in 1956 that the late Erwin Panofsky, in a brilliant series of lectures at the Institute of Fine Arts, New York University, expounded a new concept of the changing function of funeral monuments, from "prospective" to "retrospective," based on an examination of tomb sculpture from the ancient Egyptians to the Renaissance, materials which had been very familiar long before he put new questions to them.[4]

A mere catalog of recent finds would therefore constitute only one aspect of "new developments" and, if left at that, would give a false image of what is happening in classical studies. "New," like "original," is a complex concept. In 1964 a committee on postgraduate instruction in Cambridge University reported that the old requirement that a Ph.D. dissertation must represent "original work" put "a premium on novelty for its own sake, with the result that many Ph.D. dissertations, though technically 'original,' are concerned with peripheral and even trivial subjects of study." The committee recommended, and the university adopted, a new definition: a satisfactory dissertation is one that "represents a substantial contribution to scholarship, for example, through the discovery of new knowledge, the connection of previously unrelated facts, the development of new theory, or the revision of older views."

This statement will serve to define the scope of the present survey. It is a commonplace, but nonetheless true, that every age rewrites history, Greco-Roman history included.[5] I shall be primarily concerned with some of the major issues and topics, rather than with individual finds, no matter how spectacular—with the counterpoint between discovery and interpretation (or "understanding"). However, in view of the important place of archaeology in classical studies, already noticed, it is first necessary to have a clear idea of the nature and number of new finds, of just what new raw materials are at the disposal of the student today for the process of interpretation.

The evidence of archaeology[6]

A crude but fundamental distinction must be drawn at the start: excavations, whether licensed or illicit, planned or accidental, produce two different kinds of material—written and unwritten, documents and objects.

Documents have to be divided in turn. On the one hand there are literary texts, a term I use broadly to include not only *belles lettres* but also historical, philosophical, and scientific writings, technical manuals, legal treatises, political pamphlets. The normal "paper" was made of dried thin strips of an Egyptian reed called *papyrus,* worked into sheets, which could be pasted together side by side to form a roll. Each new copy of such a book was handwritten on papyrus, like the original, and we must assume that few copies of any book were in existence at any one time. (The more durable *parchment* was a late invention and never in antiquity a serious competitor with papyrus.) The permanent danger was not merely that a book would go out of print, but that it would go out of existence altogether. What survives today is what was deemed worthy of being copied and recopied for hundreds of years of pagan history, and then for more hundreds of years of Christian history, Byzantine in the east, Latin in the west, centuries during which tastes and values changed more than once, often radically. Thus, although the names of some 150 authors of Greek tragedies are known, plays by only 3 of them are extant in full: 7 of Aeschylus' 82 compositions, 7 of perhaps 123 by Sophocles, 19 of Euripides' 92. Of the rest, we are left with mere names or with occasional quotations (often misquotations) by later authors and anthologists. Nor are the surviving texts completely accurate. That would be too much to expect of centuries of copyists.

The search for medieval and Byzantine manuscripts has been so thorough ever since the Renaissance that the chance of finding new works from that source has become very remote. Everything must therefore be pinned on the peculiar climatic and historical condition of Egypt. There the absence of moisture permits papyrus to survive indefinitely if it is protected by sand or sealed tombs from the floodwaters of the Nile. After Alexander the Great conquered Egypt in 332 B.C., the country was controlled by a new, originally Greco-Macedonian ruling class, whose language and culture remained Greek until the Arab conquest in A.D. 642. In the excavated debris of that thousand-year period, complete or nearly complete books in the form of papyrus rolls can be counted on one's fingers, but fragments turn up year after year. A catalog published in 1965 runs to nearly twenty-eight hundred items (fragments of individual volumes, not separate titles), including commentaries or grammatical treatises but excluding school exercises and shorthand manuals.[7] Of these, Homer alone accounts for a third or more, followed by Euripides, Demosthenes, and Plato, with works by writers later than Alexander very much in the minority.

In assessing these statistics, one should bear in mind that they reflect the possessions of provincials. Alexandria, the capital of Egypt and also, in the centuries following Alexander the Great, the rival of Athens to the title of intellectual capital of the Greek-speaking world, has produced virtually no papyri, for physiographic and historical reasons. Given that qualification, the literary finds provide an interesting index of taste, a subject that needs more investigation than it has so far received. Otherwise, the importance of papyrus fragments of already known works stems from their age. Usually much older than the medieval manuscripts, they are helpful in the continuing struggle to get back to the exact original text of a poem, play, or book. Scholarly notes and commentaries, sometimes accompanying a literary text, sometimes written independently, also have their value. Though few can claim intrinsic interest as works of criticism, they add to our meager stock of information, occasionally in a sensational way. One such papyrus, published not quite twenty years ago, revealed that Aeschylus' *Suppliant Women*,[8] previously thought to be one of his earliest tragedies, was in fact quite late, probably written and performed in 463 B.C. That one new fact has undermined quantities of modern scholarship about the development of Aeschylus' technique, such as his use of the chorus (and one hopes, probably in vain, will serve as a warning against the sandy foundations of certain kinds of literary history).

All this will be of greater interest to the scholar than to the layman. Not so those papyri that have rescued major lost works in whole or in part. Included are poems by Sappho and Alcaeus, who lived on the Aegean island of Lesbos in the years immediately before and after 600 B.C., among the most famous of all Greek lyric poets, in Rome as in Greece. Horace boasted that he was the first to fit the Aeolic lyric to Italian measures[9] (Aeolic was the dialect of Lesbos). Though the Alcaic meter was his favorite, the Sapphic next, his claim was not strictly true: Catullus had already used them; one of his poems, the fifty-first, is an adaptation of one of Sappho's; he called his ladylove Lesbia, though her real name was the good Latin Clodia. The scholars of Alexandria had published editions of Alcaeus in ten books, of Sappho in nine. As late as the fourth century A.D. Sappho was being quoted by orators, and we are told that her poems were still being taught in schools then. Afterward they disappeared, so completely that Sappho survived in some half-dozen long quotations (up to twenty-eight lines), a few short quotations, and a hundred-odd phrases and lines, Alcaeus in hardly enough lines to be worth adding up. Today, thanks to the papyri, we have a genuine appreciation of the poetry of Alcaeus (and of his political career), while the number of long selections from Sappho has more than doubled.

Another example, that of Menander, takes us from the realm of fragments to a complete work. An Athenian born in 342 or 341 B.C., Menander was the creator of so-called New Comedy, and its greatest artist. The availability of his plays in the original can be traced into the sixth or seventh century before the trail dies. Latin adaptations by Plautus and Terence of at least eight of his plays still exist, but the question remains controversial as to how close to the original they are. We also have the usual ragbag of quotations, particularly misleading in this case because they reflect the narrow interests of the two main anthologists—food and drink for the one, moral uplift for the other. Then, at the beginning of this century, longer sections of three of Menander's mature works were discovered on papyrus, and in the 1950s a complete play, the *Dyskolos* or *Misanthrope,* copied with considerable inaccuracy in a hand of about A.D. 300. This is an early play, produced in 316 B.C., and an inferior one. Yet one cannot carp: until the publication of the *Dyskolos* in 1959, Greek comedy had been really known to us only through the works of Aristophanes.[10] His genius does not lessen the importance of the new finds, introducing us directly as they do to the master of the later, extremely influential genre of New Comedy.[11]

My final example is of a different kind of book. Aristotle and his disciples, working as a research organization, produced short treatises on the "constitutions" of 158 states, Greek for the most part but a few of them "barbarian," such as Carthage. They became a quarry for later writers, for example, Plutarch, whose life of Lycurgus[12] drew heavily on the *Constitution of Sparta.* Eventually all 158 disappeared, save for the usual quotations, until the discovery of a papyrus, published early in 1891, of the complete *Constitution of Athens,* with only the first few chapters missing.[13] In seventy smallish pages (of modern print) the history was summarized first, and then the working of the Athenian government in Aristotle's own day was described in detail. No other work of its kind has come down from antiquity about the Greek world, and every modern account of Athens starts from there.

It need hardly be said that private records and letters as well as public documents were normally written on perishable materials, too, nor would they attract copyists in later ages unless they chanced to be quoted in a book, by a historian or an antiquarian. Happily, both the Greeks and the Romans inscribed certain types of document on durable material, usually stone, occasionally metal (the gold of the Pyrgi tablets being most exceptional), baked clay, or leather.[14] Boundary stones, tombstones, statue bases, helmets and other articles dedicated to gods, all commonly carried inscriptions—that is familiar enough to us—but the ancients went further and, to a degree unparalleled in other civilizations, employed inscriptions as a means of public notice for laws and decrees, treaties, public honors to individuals, financial statements, public leases and contracts, sacrificial calendars, and a variety of other activities. Practice was far from uniform: it was no accident, for example, that democratic Athens made extensive use of stone in this way, whereas oligarchic Corinth never did. Nor was there any uniformity in the length of time such inscriptions were allowed to stand. Inscriptions carved into the wall of a public building or temple would normally remain as long as the edifice itself, but most lost purpose in a matter of years. Besides, good stone was too valuable: it could be reinscribed, or it could be used in a pavement, a wall, or a cistern. With luck, the writing remains legible when and if an archaeologist recovers the stone two thousand or so years later.

By convention all such texts are known as "inscriptions," and they constitute the second subdivision of documents. By now, it would not surprise one if the number in Greek and Latin, plus a few bilinguals, runs to more than a hundred thousand, adding in the broken scraps and the names on tombstones along with the long major texts and everything in between. One example will give an idea of the tempo of new finds in this category. In 1933 the Clarendon Press published the first volume of *A Selection of Greek Historical Inscriptions,* edited with detailed commentary by Marcus N. Tod. That volume was limited to the earliest period, down to 400 B.C., during which the total number of known inscriptions is anyhow small. In 1969 a completely new selection was issued, on the same principles, edited by Russell Meiggs and David Lewis, with ninety-five documents (against Tod's ninety-six). Apart from different standards of selection, the many revised and corrected readings, and the vastly different commentaries, reflecting a generation of further study by scholars in many countries, the essential point for us is that the Meiggs-Lewis volume replaces seventeen inscriptions by sixteen texts that were unknown or unavailable when Tod prepared the first edition.

By their nature, even the longest inscriptions, considered individually, will be more limited in their appeal and in the significance of their contribution than the best of the literary papyri. However, there is one exception remarkable enough to merit special notice, though it is strictly speaking not a new find. When the first Roman emperor, Augustus, died in A.D. 14, he left among his papers an account of his stewardship during his forty-five-year reign. This document, occupying ten pages in modern print, was, on his instruction, inscribed on bronze tablets set up before his mausoleum in the city of Rome. The tomb and tablets have long since disappeared. What is surprising is that, though the original remained available in the imperial archives, and though its importance is obviously of a high order, there are only two references in the surviving literature of the Roman Empire, and not a single quotation. Outside Rome, the province of Galatia in Turkey received permission to repeat the text on a local monument, a temple to Augustus and Rome in the city of Ankara. The inscription is still standing, somewhat mutilated, written both in the original Latin and in a rough Greek translation (since Greek was the language of the eastern provinces). It was described by a number of European travelers from as far back as the year 1555, but the first publication was not until 1872. A generation ago, Greek fragments were also found in Antioch and in Apollonia, both in the district of Pisidia in southern Turkey. By a fortunate coincidence, all the gaps created by time in the Ankara text can now be filled in, so that with the publication of the latest finds in 1933 the complete *Res gestae* of Augustus is once more available to anyone who cares to read it.[15]

To consider even a sampling of the more important inscriptions and what has been learned from them, would involve us in a long, disjointed, and not very illuminating catalog. Essentially, there is nothing new about this aspect of classical studies, nothing fundamentally different from any other study of documents ever since historians, in every field, began to make use of them. What is really new and extraordinarily promising is the way "meaningless" inscriptions are now being forced to yield interesting information by a sort of statistical approach. In the purely linguistic field, that has been going on for a long time, simply because inscriptions provide detailed information about regional dialects, in Greek or in the Italic languages close to Latin, in a way that the polished literary language does not permit. In the study of institutions, however, scholars have been relatively slow to employ quantitative analysis, partly because the number of available inscriptions of any single type has first to be significant, but also because a new concept of archaeological research was needed (a point to which I shall return at the end of this section).

I begin with ostracism, that curious device employed in Athens on a number of occasions during the fifth century B.C. to remove a "dangerous" political leader by a ten-year exile, without loss of property or citizen rights (the consequences of penal exile, for example). Once a year there was a preliminary vote to decide whether or not there should be an ostracism that year. If the decision was in the affirmative, every citizen was invited to participate by handing in a broken bit of pottery (in Greek *ostrakon*) bearing the name of his candidate for exile. Provided the total number of "votes" cast reached six thousand, the man receiving the largest number was ostracized. Among the victims were such outstanding leaders as Aristides, Themistocles, and Cimon. This much was known, despite some uncertainties, from such writers as Herodotus, Thucydides, Aristotle (in the *Constitution of Athens*), and Plutarch. But somehow we had the picture askew from the literary sources, with their concentration on the great names and on picturesque stories. Excavations in Athens have so far turned up nearly two thousand ostraca, not at all interesting individually, just potsherds with names scratched on them, the kind of object that would have been discarded a century ago; 1,658 out of that number have been properly tabulated. Of these, 568 bear the name of Themistocles, which is accidental but not too surprising; next, with 263, comes Callixenus the son of Aristonymus, a man whose very existence had been unknown to us. He and the other unknowns who appear show that the "scatter vote" was far greater than the literary sources led historians to expect. One group of 191 ostraca found together, all with the name of Themistocles, clearly come from a single potter's stock and were inscribed by only 14 different hands. This lays to rest the traditional belief, expressed by Arnold W. Gomme in the *Oxford Classical Dictionary* (published in 1949 but largely written before the war), that "the name of the individual to be ostracized *was cut by the voters* on the ostraca" (my italics). On the contrary, with so much at stake, organized political factions carefully prepared for an ostracism, having the ostraca ready beforehand to pass round to prospective voters.[16]

Much more far-reaching in their implications were two studies published in 1952, one by J. V. A. Fine of Princeton, the other by myself, each of us working independently.[17] Our starting point was a group of inscribed stones from Athens known as *horoi*, many of them ordinary fieldstones roughly carved, which were posted on boundaries of farms or were set into the walls of houses, recording the fact that a piece of property was subject to a mortgage. A *horos* was originally just a boundary stone; thousands have been found throughout the Greek world, but this particular group represented a new, peculiarly Athenian practice of giving public notice about a legal encumbrance. At the time we were writing, 222 of them had been published, 182 in a sufficiently complete state

Red-figured Grecian vase; *c.* 475–465 B.C.

to be analyzed. They all seem to fall within the period 400–250 B.C., and they were all found within the territory of ancient Athens save for a few from four Aegean islands under Athenian influence. A longer-than-average text, translated literally with the addition in square brackets of words that do not appear on the stone, reads as follows:

> [*In the archonship*] *of Praxibulus* [*i.e. 315—314* B.C.]. *Horos of the land and house put up as security to Nikogenes of* [*the deme*] *Aix-one, 420* [*drachmas*], *according to the agreement deposited with Chairedemos of* [*the deme*] *Rhamnus.*

Few of the stones have longer texts; most are shorter, for a date is given in only 27 or 28, a written agreement is mentioned in but 15, even the name of the creditor and the amount of the debt are sometimes omitted.

Thus, one marble block found in the city of Athens proper says merely: *"Horos* of a workshop put up as security, 750 [drachmas]"—three words and a numeral in the Greek.

No one will pretend that such texts are very informative. Nor do I claim that collectively they could lead to much understanding, not even by the most elaborate tabulation. However, when combined with the fragmentary information that had always been available, primarily in several court speeches by Demosthenes and others that have survived because of their literary interest, they enabled Fine and myself, in different ways, to throw new light on the Greek law of property and creditors' rights; on the emergence of a real estate market; on the shortage of liquid capital in the hands of richer landowners and the considerable indebtedness into which they could therefore be forced by social (rather than business) demands, such as expensive dowries for their daughters; on the financial activity of the many small private cult-associations that were a feature of Athenian life in this period. These may seem extravagant claims, given the unpromising nature of the stones, but the fact is that on the whole they have stood up to nearly twenty years of further study. And, with our imperfect knowledge of Greek law and economics, they are important claims.

My third and final example of this type of analysis pertains to a central development in the government of the Roman Empire—the creation of a civil service. Bureaucracy was a familiar institution in the older empires of the Near East, but it was long unknown to either Greeks or Romans (except where Alexander's successors took over Oriental monarchies, as in Egypt). They managed well enough with amateur administration, aided by a few clerks. But after Augustus put an end to the civil war that had riven Rome for decades, he needed a professional establishment to administer the stabilized empire. The top posts—provincial governors, legates, military commanders and the like—were reserved for the two highest "orders" or "estates," the senators and *equites.* For the rest Augustus turned to his own slaves and freedmen, and this group, the *familia Caesaris,* constituted the imperial civil service for the next two centuries. This much is well known and will be found in every history of Rome. The bald outline lacks vital, concrete detail, and it has been traditionally colored by the disdain with which the *familia Caesaris* is occasionally mentioned by Roman writers, a disdain that turned into savage hatred when, under Claudius and Nero, several freedmen attained personal positions of power and wealth at the very top of the ladder—this being attributed, naturally, to their ability to corrupt weak and debauched emperors.

The literary evidence is so meager that nothing new can be made of it, though one might have been a bit more suspicious of the picture of an empire not far short of two million square miles, with a population that reached perhaps sixty million, being run as if it were the Pasha-land of

Mozart's *Abduction from the Seraglio.* The only other source of information is again a group of brief inscriptions—tombstones recording in summary fashion the last post held, the marriages and children, and the age at death of members of the *familia Caesaris.* They have been found in various regions of the empire, though not equally distributed, and, as always with such documents, not all give the same information. Not even the age at death is always recorded; others are more detailed. Yet, thanks to the current work of one historian, P. R. C. Weaver, who has assembled the names of about four thousand individual slaves and freedmen of the emperors and analyzed every scrap of information possible about them, we now have a picture of this important Roman institution that adds a new dimension to our understanding of the hierarchical and status-ridden society of imperial Rome. Weaver has been able to show that the slave-freedman civil service had a regular bureaucratic hierarchy of its own, that promotion and status differed between the capital and the provinces, that the age at which the slaves were freed was closely linked with the posts they held, and that recruitment into the service was achieved by the surprising method of permitting, and probably encouraging, the men to take freeborn women as wives. Their children would nevertheless be slaves, automatically enter the *familia Caesaris,* and follow their father's careers if they were able enough. In this way much of the paper work of the empire was carried on successfully, though as a result there was created a dissonant segment within Roman society that added to the tensions when conflict arose between the emperor and the nobility.[18]

When we then turn from documents to objects, we find a parallel range of possibilities. At the one extreme there are such ruins as Mycenae, Pompeii, or the fourth-century Roman villa near Piazza Armerina in southern Sicily (with mosaic pavements that originally covered nearly an acre of floor space); and such individual works as the 4-foot bronze boy fished up from the Marathon Bay in 1925, or the unique bronze urn, 5 feet 4½ inches tall, of Greek manufacture of the sixth century B.C., discovered in 1953 in a Celtic grave at Vix near Châtillon-sur-Seine. They speak for themselves, in a sense; one can respond to them without lengthy commentaries. At the other extreme is the rubble that fills every archaeological site: pottery fragments, marble chips, twisted and corroded metal, food refuse. The practical question is where to draw the line beyond which the rubble is not worth studying. That line is not fixed. Specialists in the Stone Age have, of necessity, had to draw it near the lower end ever since the study of prehistory began, for the simple reason that they have little else to work with. Classical archaeologists, in contrast, have long permitted themselves the luxury of a different line, given the existence of books and documents, and the promise of new works of art to be found.[19]

Pyrgi symbolizes a new stage in the story. It required courage and dedication for Pallottino to set out on a lengthy excavation of Santa Severa.

Etruscan archaeology has been tomb archaeology: that is where the treasure lies, and no one knows how many thousands more remain to be explored. Most Etruscan cities are beyond reach because they have been continuously inhabited to this day. An exception such as San Giovenale, southwest of Viterbo, virtually deserted for some fifteen hundred years, produced miserable stuff and no treasure when a Swedish team excavated it. The gold tablets Pallottino found in Santa Severa were a bonus he could not have dreamed of—and was not looking for. He, like the archaeologists at San Giovenale, was posing questions about the life and history of the Etruscans that could not be answered from the tombs. All archaeology has been moving in this new direction in the past generation or so, the prehistorians perhaps more rapidly than the classicists, toward a greater interest in culture complexes as a whole, in the growth of communities and their institutions (including their economies), in their interrelations through trade, cultural interchange, migration, and war. New scientific techniques have helped, but so has the recognition that, when studied collectively, the most insignificant objects and documents acquire significance often greater than beautiful individual treasures. That seems to me to be the most important "new development" in this section of my subject, and that is why I have devoted so much space to it. One final, very simple example will serve to sum up the point.

For two hundred years, beginning about 550 B.C., Athens had a near monopoly in the production of fine painted pottery with human and mythological scenes, exported throughout the Greek world and to the Etruscans. This black- and red-figured ware is familiar in museums every-

Fragment of a Greek calendar (parapegma) found at Miletus

where. A number carry the signatures of the potters and painters, and starting from this basis, specialists led by Sir John Beazley have succeeded, through close stylistic analysis, in identifying the workshops in which virtually all known Athenian vases, jugs, cups, and plates originated (including the larger fragments). That was a remarkable accomplishment, enough to rest on for decades, until Robert M. Cook asked the question in the late 1950s (which appears so obvious in retrospect), What was the size of the Athenian fine pottery industry? His calculations, restricted to the red-figured ware, suggest that some 500 painters were active in the course of the fifth century B.C., or 125 in any one generation, and that the total work force in the trade was four times that number. Allow a fair margin for error, and these estimates are still a capital contribution to Greek economic history that could not have been squeezed out of any other source of information.[20] Contemporary Athenians would themselves not have known the precise totals.

Languages and scripts

A century ago Hittites were only a name, mentioned some dozen times in the Old Testament, distinguished from the Hivites or the Jebusites only because they supplied Esau and Solomon with wives, bought imported Egyptian horses from Solomon, and once helped the Israelites in a war against the Syrians. They began to emerge as a great nation in the last quarter of the nineteenth century with the identification of some of their monuments and their appearance in recently discovered Egyptian documents. In 1906 the German Orient Society started to excavate their capital at Bogazkoy in central Turkey and promptly found the royal archives. Decipherment went on during and immediately after the First World War, and by 1933 a serious account could be published of their history and civilization.[21]

The recovery of lost worlds has been one of the great intellectual achievements of the nineteenth and twentieth centuries, in which the archaeologist was joined by the decipherer in providing the basic raw materials—starting with Georg Grotefend's (neglected) paper of 1802 on the cuneiform script and Jean François Champollion's letter to the Academy of Paris in 1822 announcing his decipherment of Egyptian hieroglyphics.[22] There is now little that is wholly undeciphered in Europe and western Asia, and that little is represented by a tiny number of texts, most of them very short. However, room for progress is greater than we like to admit, and it is necessary to consider why that should be the case.

To begin with, the word *decipherment* covers a variety of rather distinct operations, or at least situations. There is first the case of Egyptian and Sumerian, in which both the language and the script were unknown at the start. Then there is Etruscan, an unknown language written in a well-known script (borrowed from the Greek). And the Linear B or Cypriot type explained below, a known language (Greek) in an unknown script. Cutting across all three there is the further distinction between a language belonging to a known "family" and one with no apparent connections. Indo-European Hittite and Semitic Babylonian or Assyrian are examples of the former, Etruscan and Sumerian of the latter. Hence Sumerian is much less perfectly understood than Babylonian, though both were written in the same cuneiform (wedge-shaped) script; so, too, Etruscan remains a major problem, as indicated at the beginning. There is finally the distinction based on the volume and nature of documentation: the chance of a complete decipherment increases with the number of individual texts and the amount of continuous writing they contain. An endless succession of short formulas, as in Etruscan or Linear A and B, leads to early frustration.

If that were all, one could draw up a simple correlation table and express the state of a decipherment and the prognosis in simple mathematical terms, barring future discovery of material of a new kind in any given language or script. What upsets the pattern is the fact that languages have a social history, too. The syntax, morphology, and phonetics of ancient Egyptian are better known than one might imagine from the number of question marks that still disfigure every translation of a hieroglyphic document (and still more so of a late Egyptian development, the rapid script known as *demotic*). Nor is it a weakness in grammar that leads to so much divergence among translators of the Hittite law code found in Bogazkoy. These were distant and alien societies, and we need to decipher their social structures and their values as much as their scripts. Had they produced a Thucydides, an Aristotle, or a Cicero, we should have clues and controls we now lack.

Much of the achievement, it will be noticed, touches the Greeks and Romans rather lightly; the recovery of lost worlds affects our knowledge of the classical world chiefly at or even before its dawn, and soon the Greeks and Romans were themselves the agents who drove the competing languages out of existence—in Europe below the Rhine-Danube line, in western Asia (except for Hebrew and Aramaic), in much of northern Africa. The major writing systems were invented outside, too, and the last of them, the Phoenician alphabet, passed to the Greeks about 750 B.C., from them to the Etruscans and Romans, and in time to most of the world. None of this is surprising: the need for writing was felt very much earlier in Mesopotamia and Egypt than elsewhere, for bureaucratic record-keeping (not literary) reasons, and then the superiority of the alphabet over pictographic and syllabic systems assured a monopoly. What is a puzzle is the exception of Crete, where at least three different, though relatively short-lived, scripts were created. First, perhaps before

2000 B.C., came a modified picture writing which Sir Arthur Evans labeled "hieroglyphic" on the analogy of the Egyptian script. There then emerged a more sophisticated script, called *Linear A* by Evans, in which most of the signs represented syllables. That gave way, in turn, to an outgrowth called *Linear B* (before 1500 B.C.), and it was diffused for a time to the mainland of Greece.[23]

These particular scripts offer a classic instance of the difficulties of decipherment when the documents are short and formulaic. Apart from signs engraved or scratched on seal stones, pottery, and miscellaneous objects, Linear A and B are known to us in bulk only from small, leaf-shaped clay tablets, a few hundred written in Linear A, several thousand in Linear B. No doubt perishable materials were also used, but we have no trace of them, and even the clay tablets have survived by accident. They were palace records (or lists) of property relationships, stocks of goods on hand, ration allocations, and the like, not meant to be kept for long periods and therefore inscribed on unbaked clay. Only the conflagrations that accompanied the destruction of the great palaces at Cnossus in Crete, Mycenae and Pylos in Greece, preserved whatever inscribed tablets happened to be on hand at the moment. Neither the hieroglyphic script nor Linear A has been deciphered, despite several claims to the contrary, and it seems likely that the language of those tablets, certainly not Greek, is not any known tongue. The suggestion that it is a Semitic language, among others, has found little support. The Linear B tablets, however, turn out to have been written in an early form of Greek, and the announcement in 1953 of their decipherment by Michael Ventris is the last great chapter in the story that began in 1802.[24] Further progress has been disappointingly slight (and a few scholars still refuse to accept the decipherment): there are, for example, too many words on the tablets that still cannot be reasonably shown to be Greek.[25] Nevertheless, the importance of Ventris's discovery for our knowledge of Bronze Age Greece cannot be overstated, though to go into that subject would take us outside the scope of this survey.[26]

The employment of the Cretan scripts was so closely and narrowly geared to the administrative needs of the palace-dominated society that, when that society was destroyed about 1200 B.C., the art of writing disappeared from both Crete and Greece. Only on the island of Cyprus was there a curious survival. There Greek was written as late as the fourth century B.C. in a syllabic script that included seven signs from Linear B and others that were modifications of that otherwise long-extinct script. Not only is the phenomenon itself an imperfectly understood puzzle, but the texts cannot be read with certainty.

In Greece proper when the art of writing returned, some four hundred or more years after the end of the palace society, it was in the new alphabetic form, and it found new uses—the writing of poetry, for one.

Literature: the spoken and written word

Plutarch relates that when an Athenian expeditionary force in Sicily was captured at Syracuse in 413 B.C., some prisoners were set free because they could recite by heart choruses from the plays of Euripides, "whose poetry, it appears, was in request among the Sicilians more than among any of the settlers out of Greece."[27] The story may or may not be true, but it is absolutely right. The Greeks were the first really literate people in history. That is to say, in all the more advanced, more urbanized regions of the Greek world (and of the Roman world), a majority, probably a large majority, of the males knew how to read and write.[28] This was not the case with the ancient Near Eastern peoples, as is shown by the high standing of the class of scribes among them, a class that simply did not exist in the Greco-Roman world. Paradoxically, it is correct at the same time to insist that Greek and Roman culture was as much one of the spoken word as of the written (and in some contexts more). That is the lesson of Plutarch's anecdote. Syracuse was a civilized, cosmopolitan city; no doubt copies of the plays of Euripides were available there, but the average Syracusan depended on their transmission by word of mouth. In Athens itself, where these plays originated, for every man who read a tragedy there were tens of thousands who knew the tragedies from performing in them or from hearing them. Lyric poetry acquired its very name from the fact that the poems were written to be sung to a stringed accompaniment, normally on ceremonial occasions—a wedding, a religious festival, a military celebration—and often by choruses rather than by individuals. Even the earliest political writings, those of Solon, and philosophical writings as late as the fifth century B.C. were in poetic form, partly at least because that facilitated memorization. Books, Plato said, are not to be trusted: they cannot be questioned, and therefore their ideas are closed to correction and further refinement; besides, they weaken the memory.[29]

Plato himself wrote books, to be sure, but he usually cast them in the form of "dialogues"—more precisely, of conversations, and very dramatic ones, in which real people argued, joked, cheated a bit, became angry. Oratory rapidly developed into a major art form in its own right, and rhetoric dominated higher education from the time Isocrates founded his school in Athens in the fourth century B.C. to the end of antiquity.[30] Orations were a feature of the Olympic Games and other such festivals; cities hired famous orators to honor them with an example of their art; Roman emperors patronized them: Marcus Aurelius endowed a chair of rhetoric in Athens. Oratorical skill was essential for a political career. Demosthenes and Cicero made their way into the political elite that way; their speeches were published, assessed, and criticized not merely as *political* speeches but as high literature. In their turn, historians, reflecting the realities and values of their time, interlarded their narrative with carefully composed speeches.

Closely linked was the public character of literature, thematically and institutionally. Thus, throughout the fifth and fourth centuries B.C., the classical period in Greece, it was almost the case that no one wrote a poem about love or any other private theme. That had been common among lyric poets from about 650 to 500 B.C., and then it ceased as if by fiat. In Rome we have to come down to Catullus for the first personal poetry; even the Roman writers of comedy on the model of Greek New Comedy, though they dealt with caricatured personal situations, were filled with ethical and social observations and lessons. What dominated choral odes or tragedy or prose (history and oratory) were religion, mythology, ethics, public affairs, war, politics, and humanity. Appropriately enough, the state itself was the chief patron of the arts, either through the numerous religious festivals or through imperial patronage in the periods when there were emperors.

Nothing I have said so far in this section is in the least new—except for the stress.[31] Formal classical study since the mid-nineteenth century was until recently dominated by the concept of *paideia,* intellectual and moral formation for life, for the life of an intellectual and social elite. (Scottish universities still have Departments of Humanity, elsewhere known as Departments of Latin.) That concept not only determined the selection of authors to be studied—Thomas Arnold at Rugby could not bring himself to read Aristophanes until he had reached the age of forty, found the tragedians overrated, Petronius unmentionable—but also led to basic misjudgments about the Greeks and Romans themselves. One misjudgment arose from a sort of evolutionary scheme, in which the introduction of literacy was regarded as symbolizing the movement from barbarism toward the life of reason, with the corollary that what really mattered appeared in books, in some books, especially the more high-minded among them.

No one wishes to deny the significance of literacy, nor the legitimacy of selection, whether for reasons of *paideia* or for some other purpose. But it has become clear, at least to some of us, that such narrow focusing on one facet of Greco-Roman civilization is the wrong way to understand that civilization *in its own terms.* A world that relies as much on the spoken word as did the ancients will, for example, have a different view of its own past or of its religion from one that transmits such ideas primarily through books (let alone the Book). It cannot have the same canons of truth and falsity, orthodoxy and heresy, when the controls are one man's "memory" against another's. It cannot recover lost information about the past, except by inventing it. It can neither compose nor respond to poetry in the "individual" way familiar in the age of printed books—in the age, that is, in which the scholars who study the Greeks and Romans themselves live.

By far the outstanding example of a modern revaluation in this respect is the unique, and therefore unfair, one of Homer. "By the general consent of critics," wrote Dr. Johnson in his life of Milton, "the first praise of genius is due to the writer of an epic poem, as it requires an assemblage of all the powers which are singly sufficient for other compositions." Milton's *Paradise Lost,* he concluded, "is not the greatest of heroic poems, only because it is not the first," a place preempted by Homer, whom the Greeks themselves referred to simply as "the poet." Since Johnson's day an occasional voice has remarked on the puzzling fact that the earliest works in European literature, and particularly the *Iliad,* are of such towering genius. By and large however, that question was dismissed—how can one ever explain genius?—and critics, assuming that Homer was the first in the line of poets that includes Virgil, Dante, and Milton, examined, dissected, and criticized him in the same way.[32]

One of the central problems in Homeric criticism is the amount of repetition in the poems. The coming of day is nearly always "And when rosy-fingered dawn appeared, the child of morn." Athena is "owl-eyed," the island of Ithaca "sea-girt," Achilles "city-sacking." When a verbal message is sent (and messages in Homer are never in writing), the poet has the messenger hear the exact text and then repeat it to the recipient word for word. How do we explain this practice? The answer was given by Milman Parry in the late 1920s and early 1930s, first by an elaborate analysis of the two poems and then by extensive fieldwork among living bards in Yugoslavia. This is the technique, he demonstrated conclusively, of oral poetry, composed by illiterate bards during actual performance before an audience. The formulaic language serves like building blocks: about one-third of the *Iliad* consists of lines or blocks of lines that occur more than once in the work. The first twenty-five lines alone have some twenty-five formulaic expressions (or fragments of formulas). Yet this is no simple monotonous repetition: there are thirty-six different epithets for Achilles, and the choice is rigorously determined by the position in the line and the required syntactical form. These formulas were developed and modified, and a stock of heroic incidents and tales built up, during the centuries when not only the bards were illiterate but the whole society (which was not the case with the Yugoslavs). Homer came at the end of a long tradition. After him, the more creative talents turned to other kinds of poetry, behind which there was also an oral tradition, though a different one.[33]

None of this explains the genius of Homer. One question, in particular, is currently the subject of considerable controversy. How could the *Iliad* and *Odyssey,* some sixteen thousand and twelve thousand lines long, respectively, each with an intricate and coherent structure, have been composed and transmitted orally? For me the reasonable answer is that each is the work of a poet who not only had a long tradition behind him but who also had the newly acquired (or reacquired) art of writing available to him.[34] Even so, the *Iliad* and *Odyssey* must be located, and therefore studied, with oral "heroic" poetry—a genre independently developed in many parts of the world—and not, as Dr. Johnson did, with Virgil or Milton. When Virgil sat down to compose the *Aeneid,* he had on his desk books of poetry, the *Iliad* and Greek tragedy among them; he was a man of learning surrounded by literate and learned friends and patrons; he could check and recheck, borrow and modify patiently, avoid "structural anomalies," inconsistencies in details, misplaced epithets, and all the "faults" that have distressed generations of Homeric scholars working from a fundamental misconception of the nature of the two poems. Nor is it only the literary quality of the *Iliad* and *Odyssey* that requires total reexamination after Milman Parry. The society in which they were created, the long "Dark Age" between the destruction of the Mycenaean world and the emergence of a new kind of Greek society in the eighth century B.C., has to be reassessed as well, in its institutions, its values and beliefs, its poetry.[35]

The very fact that Virgil wrote the *Aeneid* as late as the end of the pre-Christian era, I should add, is the consequence of the fact that the Romans produced no heroic poetry of their own in their preliterate period. They of course had their traditions, transmitted orally from generation to generation, and they had their singers of songs and tales. But it was a different tradition, as we can see in the largely fictionalized version in Virgil's contemporary, the historian Livy, culminating in the struggle for independence from the Etruscans. By then both Etruscans and Romans were at least partially literate, and much influenced by the Greeks intellectually and culturally, as they continued to be for centuries thereafter. To fix the relative time scales, it should be enough to note that when Rome achieved her independence, Sappho had been dead for nearly a century, Aeschylus was in his teens.

For all practical purposes, Aeschylus was the inventor of the drama. Even if Aristotle should prove not to be right in asserting that Aeschylus introduced the second actor into tragedy,[36] his *Persians* (472 B.C.) is the earliest play ever written that still survives. And we are at once plunged into a very complex problem, on which Frank R. Leavis has laid so much stress in English literature. Put succinctly, it is this: we cannot read Aeschylus as we can read Shakespeare, and we cannot read Aeschylus as if Shakespeare did not exist. Obvious as that may appear, it is remarkable how difficult the struggle still is to avoid sliding into "modernization" of the ancients, into reading and interpreting them as if they were near contemporaries, almost as familiar with our accepted conventions (of drama, for example) as we are. In an article on "Inconsistency of Plot and Character in Aeschylus," published in 1963, R. D. Dawe opened with a brutal protest:

> *The plays of Aeschylus contain many contradictions, and much recent criticism of the dramatic technique of this author has been*

directed at attempts to extract from these contradictions a unified picture of what the poet really intended us to understand in the case of each particular play. . . . All this may seem entirely praiseworthy; and yet, as we come to read more and more of these books and articles, the sensation may grow upon some of us that we are not so much learning about Aeschylus as witnessing the transactions of a private club. . . . Although the members of this club are willing to challenge each others' viewpoints, they are all agreed that no gentleman would venture to call in question the one great assumption that underlies all their discussions: namely that Aeschylus could not possibly have constructed plays in which such contradictions were deliberately intended; and only seldom can he be allowed to have contradicted himself by oversight.[37]

In a long and persuasive analysis, Dawe proceeded to demonstrate that the "inconsistencies" normally disappear when one considers only individual scenes, written for performance before a live audience under the "abnormal" conditions of an Athenian religious festival. The intent is deliberately to create a certain effect, for example, to lead the audience to anticipate something which then does not happen, or to plunge the audience into confusion, or to achieve some other dramatic objective. In the leisure of his study, a scholar (or any attentive reader) soon enough discovers the "inconsistencies," and he objects. He will not allow the poet, in Dawe's words, to "sacrifice consistency in order to purchase greater effectiveness in the individual scene."

Up to a point this is no more than the danger, familiar to all literary scholarship (witness that of Shakespeare), of living with a work or an author until one forgets that plays were written to be performed, to be heard and not read; and one forgets that great poets (or historians) are not necessarily, even not probably, systematic thinkers. But there is more to it. For us it is almost axiomatic that consistency and development of character are a necessary and major ingredient in plays and novels, so axiomatic that there is insufficient appreciation of the fact that our idea of character, our psychology, is radically different from the ancient Greek. Aeschylus could portray an inconsistent Agamemnon in the play of the same name without giving it a second thought. It is not even possible to answer definitively the question, Was Aeschylus' Agamemnon a good man or not? Impossible in a play which by universal consent is one of the greatest masterpieces in world literature! And Agamemnon, at least, was recognizably a tragic hero, which Oedipus was not. Indeed, we now know that the tragic hero, who has mesmerized critics of Greek tragedy for centuries, ever since he was wrongly attributed to Aristotle in the *Poetics,* is nothing but a hindrance to the understanding of tragedy. Oedipus was the central figure in more than one Greek play, but he was no hero except in the most strained sense of that word. He committed no moral fault and had no "moral flaw." He was doomed before he was born, and nothing he could do, flawed or unflawed, could forestall the workings of fate.[38]

In my view, probably a minority view, stripping away the anachronisms imposed over the centuries is one of the more urgent tasks not only in classical literary study but in all classical study.[39] That requires great effort of the imagination, and the results are bound to be limited: not only are there the limits set up by the interposition of Shakespeare, to return to that example, but also those imposed by the alienness of much in the system of values. Consider Oedipus again. The audience that first saw and heard Sophocles' *Oedipus the King* had not just "taken in a show"; they were participants in a great public religious festival, at which the god himself was present and received the preliminary sacrifices. The starting point is an oracle warning King Laius of Thebes that his unborn son, Oedipus, would one day kill him and marry his widow (Oedipus' own mother). Do we believe in the oracle, in the strict sense of that verb? The audience did, and so did Sophocles. No evasion such as "dramatic device" will do. Midway through the play, the chorus of Theban elders says:

> *The old prophecies concerning Laius are fading; already men are setting them at nought, and nowhere is Apollo glorified with honors; the worship of the gods is perishing.*[40]

"Worship is perishing" not because of revulsion against a god who decreed such a terrible fate for a child still unborn but, on the contrary, because what a god had prophesied seemed not to be fulfilled; worse, seemed to have been successfully thwarted by human artifice. No wonder John Jones, who rightly insists that "we should allow them to mean what they say," finds it all "desperately foreign." We "know nothing," he continues, "in the least" like the "bottomless, relativistic insecurity" of the Sophoclean faith. "There can be no contact between Christianity or individualistic humanism and a cosmic Mutability which averages out rather as the weather does. And because no contact, no experience of Mutability's compensating application to this or that man's singular fate."[41]

Not all Greeks shared Sophocles' cool acceptance of such a value system. Greek intellectual history is one of conflict and struggle, not rarely within a single artist or thinker. But the struggle cannot be understood until we fully acknowledge both sides. "Euripides the rationalist," as he was once unhappily labeled, also wrote the *Bacchae* at the end of his life, a powerful and terrible demonstration of the perils of resistance to maenadic ecstasy and other "irrational" drives. One must accept the coexistence of "mythical" and "tragic" and "rational" modes of thought, sometimes in separate compartments, sometimes overlapping, sometimes in brutal conflict. Yet experience has shown that this is far from easy: there is a strong pull, at least among scholars, toward what they conceive to be "rational." When Eric R. Dodds published his fundamental *The Greeks and the Irrational* in 1951,[42] he turned for support and guidance to modern anthropology on shamanism and other taboo topics. In his Preface he wrote:

> *To my fellow-professionals I perhaps owe some defence. . . . In a world of specialists, such borrowings from unfamiliar disciplines are, I know, generally received by the learned with apprehension, and often with active distaste. I expect to be reminded, in the first place, that "the Greeks were not savages," and secondly, that in these relatively new studies the accepted truths of today are apt to become the discarded errors of tomorrow. Both statements are correct. But . . . why should we attribute to the ancient Greeks an immunity from "primitive" modes of thought which we do not find in any society open to our direct observation?*

There, I suggest, is the justification for the view I have expressed of what is one of our most urgent tasks in classical studies.

If, it is then legitimate to ask, Greek tragedy (by way of example) is "desperately foreign," how is it able to arouse in a modern audience "pity and fear, wherewith to accomplish its catharsis of such emotions," to quote from Aristotle's definition of tragedy?[43] No simple answer is available—this is in fact one of the most difficult questions in the history of art—and I shall not attempt one here beyond repeating the commonplace that there are several levels of response to a work of art. What I want to look at for a moment is one particular aspect of the broad question, and that is the special and inescapable problem of translation, which has its own history. In antiquity there was no "problem." That is to say, translations were made as a matter of course. We have already seen how Roman comedy was founded on avowed, if free, translations. Cicero translated several Greek works including Plato's *Timaeus*. The Renaissance translated like mad in all countries,[44] not always with the insouciance of one of the most influential Tudor translators, Sir Thomas North, whose *Plutarch* (without which we should not have had Shakespeare's *Julius Caesar, Antony and Cleopatra,* or *Coriolanus*), was based not on the Greek original but on Jacques Amyot's French translation. Dr. Johnson, no respecter of dilettantism, never read the whole of the *Odyssey* in the original; he also defended Pope's *Iliad* despite its free rendering. Another Homer translation, Chapman's, evoked a beautiful sonnet by Keats. Then, somehow, pedantry seized control, summed up in that wicked Italian pun, *traduttore traditore* ("to translate is to betray"); translations were labeled cribs (and too many began to read like cribs). More precisely, translations from Greek and Latin (and perhaps French) were

The Dead Sea Scrolls

"Dead Sea Scrolls" is a rather broad term referring to the groups of leather manuscripts and papyri discovered in caves and ancient ruins near the Dead Sea and the Wilderness of Judaea. Numerous documents, found in eleven caves in the vicinity of Khirbet Qumran, turned up evidence about an ancient Jewish sect that flourished there. These scrolls date from as far back as the third and early second centuries B.C., up to the first century of the Christian era. (Above) Fragments of papyrus discovered in a cave some one thousand feet above the Dead Sea; (above, center) manuscript roll, found near the Dead Sea in 1947, from which a page shedding new light on the Old Testament was separated; (above, far right) fragments of a blessing that was appended to the rules of the community; (below) the documents, from left, are three relatively well-preserved scrolls: "manual of discipline," Book of Isaiah fragment, and commentary on the prophet Habakkuk.

denigrated, while the same pedants, if they were also cultured, read their Ibsen and their Dostoevsky but not in Norwegian or Russian.

Cribs, let it be said, have a legitimate function, but it is not the function of a genuine translation. "Coming after the original," wrote Walter Benjamin, "translation makes for significant works, which never find their proper translator in the era of their creation, the stage of their continuing life." The word *continuing* needs underscoring. "Translation," Benjamin added, "is far removed from being the deaf, inert equation of two dead tongues. Translation is among all communicative modes, the one most concerned to mark the ripening process in a foreign language and the pulse of changing life in its own."[45] Just as every age must rewrite history, so it must make its own translations.

Myth and religion

In the second half of the sixth century B.C., the Greek philosopher Xenophanes protested that "Homer and Hesiod have attributed to the gods everything that is a shame and reproach among men, stealing and committing adultery and deceiving each other." In a loose way, that remark may be considered the beginning of the discussion, which still goes on and is indeed now more lively than ever, of the problem of myth. It is almost impossible to read an ancient author without coming across mythical elements. Not only did myths provide most of the themes for the tragedians, or for such poets as the Greek Pindar and the Roman Ovid, but they were frequently quoted by public orators and by the most austere philosophers in order to illuminate one point or another. Beyond that, Greek and Roman myths are so worked into the fabric of Western literature that Oedipus, Orestes, Jason, Aeneas are known to every literate person.

Myths, legends, and folktales are hard to define and distinguish (leaving aside fables of the type associated with the name of Aesop). They share certain elements: they are all narratives, they are supposed to have occurred in the past (usually no more clearly dated than "once upon a time"), and they have a strong touch of fantasy, of the impossible. However, we can separate myth from the others by a rough rule of thumb: it usually involves gods or other supernatural beings (though it need not be a story *about* gods), it frequently deals with origins (Prometheus and the use of fire, the Tower of Babel and the diversity of languages among the descendants of a common ancestor, the rape of Persephone and the foundation of the cult of Demeter at Eleusis near Athens), it tends to involve reversal of fortune (Oedipus) or physical transformation.

Almost to the end of the nineteenth century, the study of myth was concentrated on the Greeks, and secondarily on the Romans (whose stock of genuine original myths, as distinct from historical legends, is poor). That is easily explicable from the predominance of these myths in Western culture, but the result of this narrow concern was disastrous for at least two reasons. The first was the barrier set up by the insistence that "the Greeks were not savages." Myths were explained away as allegories (a game everyone can play, since there are no rules and no controls, and which was already played by sophisticated intellectuals in antiquity); or they were explained by fantastic theories, each short-lived and none worth repeating now. The second weakness was a failure to appreciate how distorted Greek myths are as we know them, through the trick lenses of great literature.[46] One obvious fact, at least, should have put students on their guard: the freedom with which myths were changed about. The ending of Aeschylus' *Eumenides,* the closing play in the Orestes trilogy, is a blatant invention by the playwright, reflecting on political developments in Athens at the time of writing. Or one may compare the fundamentally different ways in which Aeschylus, Sophocles, and Euripides deal with the story of Orestes and his sister Electra in three surviving plays.* Or, to turn to Rome, there is the untidy way the Aeneas myth (which is legend as well as myth) is woven into the Romulus myth about the foundation of Rome.

There was no hope for serious advance until anthropologists began direct observation of myth in action, as it was repeated and as it functioned among the preliterate "primitive" peoples still inhabiting parts of the Americas, Asia, Africa, and Australia. Archaeology also made its contribution with the rediscovery of the rich mythology of the Sumerians, Babylonians, and other ancient Near Eastern people, who were literate like the Greeks but who still retained a less distorted, less "sophisticated" store of myths. With this new body of raw material available, the problem of myth was raised to a new level of analysis, though it can hardly be said that anything like agreement has been reached. A recent survey has classified modern theories of myth into seven main types, and, since their proponents tend each to think of his theory as the only correct one, the seven become mutually exclusive.[47] Three are familiar outside specialist circles. One of these, most closely associated with Sir James George Frazer and his *Golden Bough,* is that all myths are attached to rituals. The weakness is that although some myths are thus attached, many are demonstrably not, despite desperate efforts to establish a connection. This theory is no longer seriously held as a general explanation, except, for some curious reason, among specialists in ancient Near Eastern myths.[48] The second is the psychoanalytic theory, or rather theories, as they diverge into two main streams, the Freudian and the Jungian, and from there into smaller branches. The popular model of the myth as an

---

* *GBWW,* Vol. 5, pp. 70–80, 156–69, 327–39.

expression of the unconscious is, of course, the Oedipus complex. Finally, and most recently, there is the subtle, complex, and difficult "structuralist" theory of Claude Lévi-Strauss: myth is a symbolic language which "mediates" the contradictions or opposites in human experience. One of the most important opposites for Lévi-Strauss is that between nature and culture, the point to the title of one of his major books, *Le cru et le cuit* [The raw and the cooked] (1964).[49] In place of Freud's Oedipus complex, we have the contradiction between nature's tolerance of incest and the cultural taboo against it, a point already noticed in antiquity, though in a very different context—for example, by Diogenes.[50]

The way out of these conflicting theories that seems to be emerging is a recognition that myths have different functions, that even a single myth often has more than a single function. Some myths do explain rituals: the example of the Demeter cult at Eleusis has already been mentioned. Others are "charters" (a term coined by the anthropologist Bronislaw Malinowski) giving sanction to authority, social order, rules and laws, ceremonies, and beliefs. Many of the symbols repeat themselves in dreams and are so universal that the psychoanalysts have a strong case. And the intricate myth-structures of Lévi-Strauss do sometimes appear without undue forcing of evidence. We are finally coming to realize that there is an intellectual, even speculative, side to many myths, that the narrative is in some ways an explanation; in other words, that there is a "mythical mode of thought" among Greeks as among "savages" for all the profound differences between them.

However *we* explain the phenomenon of myth, the point that must never be lost sight of is that myths were believed to be true. Otherwise a myth has little value or function (the example of the oracle about Oedipus has already been mentioned). This concrete quality of ancient religion, the tendency to answer questions about origins, rituals, even natural phenomena and beliefs—by a narrative involving gods and goddesses, either directly or indirectly, is very striking. The changes in the pantheon mentioned at the beginning of this essay normally took the form of yet another story, how Apollo came to Delphi or Heracles swam the Strait of Messina and wandered across Sicily. Neither the skepticism of Xenophanes and later philosophers nor the (to us) irreverent jokes of Aristophanes or Lucian about the gods invalidate the general formulation.

The skepticism of the few had its limits. There were no atheists in antiquity; the word *atheist,* which comes from the Greek, meant someone who does not accept the conventional, official religion of his society. Even Epicurus, whose name became the Hebrew word for *atheist,* did not deny the existence of the gods; he denied only that they concerned themselves with, and intervened in, man's daily affairs. That was shocking enough, for it was very rare, in all circles including the most advanced intellectual ones, to disbelieve in the techniques by which the will of the gods could be divined or in the efficacy of sacrifice. Socrates' last words were, "Crito, I owe a cock to Asclepius; will you remember to pay the debt?"[51] Asclepius was the healer god, into whose temples men went to be cured while asleep, in gratitude for which they then dedicated models of the diseased parts of their bodies. His worship was introduced in Athens at the time of the great plague of 430–426 B.C. One of the god's sacred snakes was brought from Epidaurus in the Peloponnese in solemn procession. Until a proper temple could be erected, the snake was housed and an altar was provided for it by the playwright Sophocles. Greco-Roman religion, in sum, did not divide neatly and simply, as modern "rational" accounts often tend to suggest, into "rational theology" and "popular superstition."[52]

One consequence of the concreteness of religion, with its stress on life on earth rather than on salvation and the hereafter, with its extreme localization, its profusion of myths and rituals, and with the absence of an organized, authoritative "church," was a wide measure of tolerance. Since there was not (and could not be) anything one could call orthodoxy, there was also no heresy. Tolerance ended only at the point where there was suspicion of blasphemy, of an act which openly flouted the gods. There were two closely related reasons for drawing that line: angry gods might, and sometimes did, take revenge on the whole community, not just on the individual; besides, the community felt itself flouted. Cases of persecution for ideas about the gods, as distinct from actions, were rare; the notoriety of the trial of Socrates, charged with "not believing in the gods in which the city believes," should not lead to a false generalization on this score.[53] Ironically, his admiring pupil Plato, in his last work, the *Laws,* in effect took up the position of the state against Socrates, when he proposed severe punishment for impiety "in word or deed," culminating in the death penalty for recidivists.[54] This was not the only one of Plato's ideas that did not become common practice.

The greatest test came in the Roman Empire, with its vast agglomeration of peoples and therefore of religious ideas and practices. As a matter of policy, the imperial state went to considerable lengths not to interfere, unless there was deemed to be a political (subversive) threat, most notably in the revolt of Judaea in A.D. 66–70. But then, Jews and Christians stood outside the whole Greco-Roman tradition. For them, there was true belief and false belief, so that conversion involved not the normal polytheistic accumulation of divinities but rejection of all others.[55] For complicated reasons the Roman state was able to accept, though it did not particularly like, Jewish exclusiveness; it would not accept Christian exclusiveness.

If myths with their sacral element could be believed, there was of course no difficulty in accepting the secular, often "historical" legends. The Trojan War provides the elementary example. Xenophanes started a line of doubt about the morality of the Homeric poems, but no one extended that skepticism to the narrative. Even the hardheaded historian

Thucydides, who thought that only contemporary history was really knowable and who warned his readers to turn elsewhere if they wished "romance,"[56] accepted without question the basic historicity of the *Iliad.*[57] And so throughout antiquity, with Jason and the Argonauts in their search for the golden fleece, the Seven against Thebes, the coming of Aeneas to Rome from Troy, Horatius at the bridge, and the rest of the long list.

What are *we* to make of these tales? That has been a bitterly disputed question since the beginning of the nineteenth century, and it remains so today. Psychologically, it is difficult to assign to the realm of fantasy some of the best-known characters and tales in the Western cultural tradition, all the more so for those periods of antiquity for which there is otherwise so little evidence or none at all. Nor is it easy to produce decisive arguments on either side of the debate. Again the Trojan War will serve as the first example. No one disputes the presence of much impossible and contradictory material in the Homeric poems, even on the strictly human side without reference to the continuous divine interventions. On the other hand, enough remains that is plausible, and the question is then simply, How can we know whether the plausible is in fact true? It need not be; after all, every good novel is plausible. Archaeology has contributed less than is commonly believed. Heinrich Schliemann found a place that roughly corresponds to what could be Troy, and the city he found was repeatedly destroyed, once at a date, about 1200 B.C., which coincides with the end of the Mycenaean period. However, nothing in the archaeological record informs us who the destroyers were, and that is of course crucial for a control over the Homeric tale of a great mainland coalition led by Agamemnon. For early Rome, as a second example, archaeology has done a bit better: it has supported the tradition that Rome was once under Etruscan domination and that it broke free about 500 B.C. But no more, nor can we expect archaeology to throw light one way or another on the massive detail that appears in Livy, neither the names of the kings nor the story of the rape of Lucretia nor anything else in that category. As with Troy, much of the tradition is impossible, some is plausible, and beyond that we cannot go except on subjective arguments.[58] In particular, it is poor logic to maintain that because a kernel of demonstrable fact has been discovered in one legend, there must be a similar kernel in every other legend.

Nor should we deny the Greeks and Romans as much imaginative power as we have. The novel as an art form was unknown to them until near the end, and then only in a very rudimentary sense. That implies not a lack of creative imagination but its divergence into other channels. To hold, as some do, that the Jason story is a mythical cover for hard reality —the metal trade with the Near East—is unnecessary, unprovable, and a denigration of Greek powers of invention. So is the supposed historical background to the story of Daedalus, the master craftsman who made wings with which he and his son Icarus fled from Minos, king of Crete. Icarus flew too close to the sun and died, but Daedalus landed in Sicily and entered the service of King Kokalos there. Minos came after him with an army and was routed by Kokalos. This tale, some historians believe, has behind it the colonization of Sicily in the Bronze Age (not later than 1500 B.C.) by "Minoan" Crete, and they continue to believe it despite the complete absence of any Minoan objects in Sicily, where archaeologists have been systematically exploring for many decades. Heracles' "grand tour" of Sicily provides no analogy. That myth was simply part of the continuing process of transporting gods and demigods to new places as the Greeks migrated to them, in Sicily beginning in the middle of the eighth century B.C. The details of Heracles' tour, it is of some interest to note, are nearly all wrong when matched against the known history of the actual colonization movement.

An extreme example is currently receiving much publicity—the myth of Atlantis as told by Plato,* a myth that everyone in antiquity agreed was a Platonic invention. It is now suggested that behind it lay a genuine occurrence, a staggering underwater volcanic explosion that destroyed much of the island of Thera (modern Santorin) in the Aegean Sea about 1500 B.C. Linking the two requires major surgery: Atlantis has to be removed from the Atlantic to the Aegean, Crete has to become Thera, Athens has to be removed from the myth, all the numbers in Plato have to be reduced by lopping off the final zeros, and much else. I find this wholly incredible and, what is worse, pointless.[59] Why should Plato, of all people, not be allowed poetic license? The creation of historical legends was not in his day a lost art. There is the famous case of Lycurgus, the legendary founder of the Spartan system. His name does not even rate a mention in the extensive surviving fragments of the Spartan poet Tyrtaeus, writing late in the seventh century B.C. By the middle of the fifth century B.C., Herodotus had heard of him, in a confused way, but no more than that he was a king's uncle and tutor and the great lawgiver. Herodotus had no idea when Lycurgus lived, nor did he know his patronymic, by which every good Greek was identified.[60] More than five hundred years later Plutarch wrote a full-scale biography of the same Lycurgus, all the details of which had been invented in the intervening centuries.[61] The growth of the Aeneas story in Rome is a comparable instance, again starting out with nothing (and indeed with the very different Romulus tradition which had to be knitted with it in the end).

A somewhat comic note seems appropriate as an ending to this section. In the closing centuries of antiquity, one question vigorously debated between Christian and pagan apologists was, Who came first, Homer or

---

* *Critias; GBWW,* Vol. 7, pp. 479b–485d. *Timaeus* 20D–25D; Ibid., pp. 444a–446b.

Stamped hieroglyphs on the Phaestus disc; Middle Minoan III, after 1600 B.C.

Moses? And often it was turned into the blunter question, Who plagiarized from whom? As an anonymous writer of about A.D. 200 phrased it,

> *I think you are not ignorant of the fact. . . that Orpheus, Homer,*
> *and Solon were in Egypt, that they took advantage of the histor-*
> *ical work of Moses, and that in consequence they were able to take*
> *a position against those who had previously held false ideas about*
> *the gods.*

Among his many "proofs" were the "borrowing" of the opening of Genesis for one bit of the description of the shield of Achilles in the *Iliad;* the portrayal of the Garden of Eden in the guise of the garden of King Alcinous in Book VII of the *Odyssey;* and Homer's referring to the corpse of Hector as "senseless clay," copied from "Dust thou art and to dust thou shalt return."[62]

Politics and political theory

The Greeks created politics. That claim is to be taken literally (with one possible qualification). Before 600 B.C. it was accepted in many Greek communities that there were different, conflicting interests within a state, that public policy therefore required public discussion, which led either to the triumph of one interest or viewpoint over the others, or to a compromise, or, if it came to the worst, to civil war. Much of Greek history then became the history of political debates and maneuvers, in the course of which in many communities, though not all, the people as a whole finally won recognition as the holders of sovereignty. (The objection that the "people" excluded a majority—women and slaves—does not invalidate the significance of the Greek innovation, though it is correct as a statement of fact.)

The proposition can be stated in a different way. Politics is about authority and obedience. Every society must have a mechanism for decision-making; the decisions must be initiated from some source, they must be enforceable in some way, and they must have a sanction, a justification. One pattern is the ancient Near Eastern, that of a hierarchic and hieratic organization in which the orders travel down the line and obedience travels back up.[63] A text of the Hittite king, Hattusilis III, who reigned from about 1275 to 1250 B.C., begins with these words:

> Thus speaks Tabarna Hattusilis, the great king, king of Hatti, son of Mursilis, the great king of Hatti, grandson of Suppiluliumas, the great king, king of Hatti, descendant of Hattusilis, king of Kussara. I tell the divine power of Ishtar; let all men hear it, and in the future may the reverence of me, the Sun, of my son, and of my son's son, and of my Majesty's seed be given to Ishtar among the gods.[64]

In Mesopotamia, too, "the 'good life' was the 'obedient life'. . . . an orderly world is unthinkable without a superior authority to impose his will. The Mesopotamian feels convinced that authorities are always right."[65] Even among the ancient Hebrews, the prophets were the exception that proved the rule: they failed in the long run to unseat theocratic absolutism. The Greeks, in contrast, expected obedience only to the law and the community; the law could be changed, and more and more members of the community claimed freedom (*eleutheria*). Freedom is never a simple concept, and the tension between freedom and authority was a constant factor in Greek history, as in later history, but it is fundamental that the word *freedom* cannot be translated into any ancient Near Eastern language (or into any Far Eastern language). Greeks could lose their "freedom," for example to tyrants, but that implies they had something to lose (and to regain).

The importance of politics permeated Greek life and thought. Not only did Greeks accept political activity as a necessary kind of activity; they also attributed positive value to it, in the sense that they ranked it high among the activities to which a citizen should devote himself, even full-time when personal circumstances permitted. And the activity led to thinking about politics, at first in terms of vague concepts and ideological notions, by the end of the fifth century B.C. in more systematic and theoretical ways. Political behavior was a common subject of discussion and of moral judgment. That is apparent in the innumerable jokes, some of them earnest ones, in the comedies of Aristophanes; in Thucydides' *History,* which made politics and its extension, war, the central themes of historical writing, as they have continued to be almost to our day; above all, in the writings and teachings of Plato and Aristotle in the fourth century B.C. No other society before the modern era, Eastern or Western, produced a work like Aristotle's *Politics*—with its mixture of political and ethical analysis, the crowning touch to Greek originality in this respect.[66]

The one possible qualification I mentioned at the beginning of this section stems from our complete ignorance about life in the Phoenician city-states, Tyre and Sidon, and among the Etruscans. It is not impossible that Roman political activity, visible as soon as Rome broke away from the Etruscans about 500 B.C., had an Etruscan background. What is certain, anyway, is that the Romans then failed to develop on their own any systematic thinking about politics. The first Roman historian, the aristocratic Fabius Pictor, wrote during the crisis of the war with Hannibal, nearly two hundred years after Thucydides—and he wrote in Greek.[67] Another century was to go by before one can see a serious interest in political theory in Rome, and again the Greek influence was direct and undisguised. Men like Cicero naturally adapted Greek ideas to their own society, but it is difficult to find any original Roman political theory.

Cicero's influence on later ages was not diminished by his lack of originality. And it went in the direction laid down by his Greek models, in favor of an ethical approach to politics. The result has been paradoxical in modern classical studies. On the one hand, everyone approves of freedom, and everyone in the twentieth century, if not in the nineteenth, is for democracy, best represented in antiquity by Athens. On the other hand, ancient writers, drawn from the leisured classes, are almost unanimous in their condemnation of the actual behavior of Athens or of quasi-democratic Rome in Cicero's day. These writers are among the greatest moralists the West has produced, so we must accept their judgments. That leads to the odd situation in which many modern histories approve the principles of the best ancient states and condemn their practices. The contradiction is then customarily explained by greed, unbridled license, or some similar, and ill-defined, moral concept.

Closer examination reveals that Plato, Aristotle, Cicero were not being so paradoxical: they disliked democracy in practice and argued that it was also defective in principle. One cannot be prodemocratic and pro-Plato at the same time. A different approach is required and is slowly being introduced into the study of Greco-Roman society. This approach does not (and need not) withdraw politics from morality, but it does not see everything in blacks and whites, and, with the help of modern political science and political sociology, it raises a series of fundamentally new questions about the operational side. It goes beyond the traditional narrow constitutional study—the powers of the assembly and Senate, the duties and prerogatives of magistrates, and so on—to consider leadership and elites and the techniques of decision-making, to define more closely the different classes and "estates" and their psychology, to examine propaganda techniques and the creation of ideology, or the costs and benefits of empire in concrete terms.

A few illustrations are all that space permits. Ostracism provides a good starting point. It was a curious institution, depriving Athens of some of its most experienced political leaders at important moments, and it has regularly been criticized as nothing but a tool for the fickle populace and their demagogues. One has now learned, however, to distrust such loaded terminology: demagogues seem somehow to be restricted to the other side. If one translates suspicion into precise operational questions, interesting conclusions emerge. Athens was a direct (not a representative) democracy, in which the citizens voted directly on issues as well as at elections. The citizen body as a whole could not have the necessary expertise and had to rely on professional politicians, who were not paid and who were therefore drawn from men of independent means. No one else could afford the time required to become, and act as, a professional. This leadership was responsible directly to the people meeting in assembly, without the mediation (or buffer) of a political party. Those who had the ear of the people at any period were challenged by other potential leaders, with alternative policies (or just with a desire for places of authority). The same thing goes on today, but the techniques in a small, face-to-face community were necessarily different from ours, above all because of the direct, almost weekly intervention of the popular assembly. Hence there was more of an all-or-nothing quality about political battles: getting an opponent out of the city physically was clearly the best possible insurance for the opposition short of assassination, and that is how ostracism became a factional political instrument. Before one rushes to condemn, it is worth remembering that political assassination was almost unknown in Athens during its nearly two centuries of democracy, that the Athenians had no precedents to guide them and had to invent as they went along, that all political societies require leadership as well as ways of removing unsatisfactory leaders, and that the Athenians managed to make their system work, achieving the difficult combination of direct rule by the people as a whole on the one hand, and, on the other, political leadership that was completely in the hands of the wealthy.[68]

Given the bias of our sources, the fact is not surprising that *demagogues* in its negative sense is regularly reserved for those leaders who spoke most directly for the lower classes. The word *democracy* is itself ambiguous: it means rule by the *demos,* and *demos,* like *the people* in English, means both the people as a whole and the lower classes. Antidemocratic writers were quick to seize on the possibilities of word-play. Eventually the Greek historian Polybius, who lived and wrote in Rome in the second century B.C., abandoned the game and coined the substitute word, *ochlocracy* ("mob rule"). Within a century after Polybius, the Roman "mob" took the center of the stage, paralyzed legitimate governmental functions, demanded bread and circuses, rioted frequently, and, together with corrupt politicians, destroyed the Roman Republic. At least that is the familiar picture, and it is not wholly devoid of truth. The vast Roman expansion after the defeat of Hannibal led, by various means, to the creation of the largest fortunes hitherto known in private hands, to the disappearance of a substantial portion of the Italian peasantry, and to a sharp increase in the population of the city of Rome, where the majority lived in frightful slums with little prospect of earning a regular livelihood by legitimate means. Many were therefore available for corrupt and riotous activities.

However, availability is only half an answer. Someone must make use of available instruments, and anyway "mobs" that have been observed in other countries and other times have never rioted continuously decade after decade. A close study of the Roman evidence, chiefly from Cicero who can scarcely be accused of bias in favor of the mob, has now proved what we ought to have been able to guess anyway, that there was continual manipulation, that the mob was being openly and flagrantly used by ambitious men from the highest social and intellectual circles.[69] That Roman society in the last pre-Christian century was wildly corrupt is clear beyond question, but this was true of all classes. To single out the mob and the demagogues is a distortion. Besides, to moralize about corruption, even when the target is correctly selected, is an evasion of historical explanation. Corruption never takes over a society for no reason at all.

One factor in Rome was imperial expansion and exploitation. Empire was a central institution in much of Greco-Roman history, as it had been in the Near East earlier. *Empire* is an umbrella word: there is more than one way of ruling over subject people, there are different reasons for doing so, and there are differences in the distribution of the benefits among the ruling population. Surprisingly, this remains one of the most neglected fields in ancient history. Endless study has been devoted to the details of the expansion with its innumerable wars, to the rules of provincial administration, to the tax collectors, to the colonial personnel who succeeded in rising into the ruling elite, and to "good" and "bad" emperors. But there has been insufficient comparative analysis and too little differentiation within each empire, among both the rulers and the ruled. Again the moralists have tended to take over, condemning the Athenian empire out of hand, singling out the publicans and corrupt individuals in Rome.[70]

The Athenian case is particularly interesting because the empire has been tied in with the demagogues and the people, to be condemned as the outstanding manifestation of wicked democratic practice. Thucydides put into the mouth of Pericles the improbable remark that our empire "is, to speak somewhat plainly, a tyranny,"[71] and he has not often been challenged by historians. In 1954, however, G. E. M. de Ste. Croix took a close look at Thucydides' own narrative, and the other available evidence, and discovered that among the 150-odd small subject communities in Asia Minor, Thrace, and the Aegean islands, there was a remarkable amount of loyalty to the Athenians even when the Peloponnesian War was turning badly against Athens. Why should that have been? His answer is that the subject communities were not homogeneous but factionally divided and that the democratic factions, often weak and threatened by oligarchy, frequently welcomed Athenian suzerainty because it supported them against their internal enemies. Liberty from imperial rule was a fine thing, but not when the price was subjection at home.[72] This was the inverse of the position taken by some French generals (and others) in 1939: Better the Boches than our own Reds.

The word *libertas* (the Latin for *eleutheria*) came easily to the lips of Roman orators and historians. We can hardly avoid translating it as *liberty,* thus introducing a false note. Shakespeare's *Julius Caesar** provides the model, but in fact what sort of liberty did Brutus stand for? Not the liberty of the provincial population: as a young man, Brutus had lent money to the city of Salamis in Cyprus at 48 percent interest and had then gotten the Roman army to squeeze the payments out of the Salaminians for him. Nor really the liberty of anyone else, save that of the Roman ruling class to live according to their lights and to retain a monopoly of government. This was Cicero's idea of *libertas,* as it was of the lost *libertas* that provided the historian Tacitus with his main theme under the emperors.[73] Not even the great edifice of the Roman law offered a fundamentally different conception, though it required a conscious break from the abstract juristic approach, dominant since the late Middle Ages, in order to establish an appreciation of the social bias of Roman law in practice.[74]

Reexamination of institutions and concepts has led to a reassessment of the main ideological spokesmen, such as Cicero and Tacitus.[75] The sharpest contemporary controversy, however, has not developed around any Roman thinker but around Plato. With the rise of the Nazis to power,

---

* *GBWW*, Vol. 26, pp. 568–96.

a number of philosophers, especially in England and the United States, saw a frightening kinship with Plato's political ideas, and they felt fortified in their view by the Nazis' own claim to Plato as a forerunner. The climax of the attack was reached in the first volume of Karl Popper's *The Open Society and Its Enemies,* published in 1945.[76] Defenders were quick to reply with equal heat; they were able to catch errors, and in particular they were right to object to the anachronistic labeling of Plato as a fascist. Where does the argument now stand? I find it difficult not to agree with Renford Bambrough, editor of a recent anthology of important contributions to the debate, a close and in many respects admiring student of Plato. He writes, "Plato's enemies mislead us when they say that he is a Fascist, but his friends cannot be allowed to rebut the charge with such force and in such terms as to obscure the fact that his doctrine is totalitarian in the sense in which Fascism is totalitarian." The issues, we also conclude with Bambrough, "are still alive in everyday and political life."[77]

The masters and the slaves

When slavery was introduced into the Americas, both North and South, one interesting aspect of the story was the ease with which Europeans, who had had no contact with large-scale slavery for centuries, were able to establish the institution, provide the necessary laws, and find the moral justification. The explanation lies in the biblical and classical worlds, and in the accommodation made with slavery by the early Church Fathers. Roman law, the Bible, and classical literature were familiar to every educated Englishman, Frenchman, and Spaniard of the period, and no institution was mentioned so frequently, if not often systematically, in these writings as slavery.[78] Everything was there ready to hand. So were such pleas for benevolent treatment of slaves as Seneca's, borrowed by the Jesuits who sought to protect Amerindians in South America from enslavement, and by other humanitarian men, who, however, were at that time not challenging slavery as an institution.

On neither side was there a systematic inquiry into ancient slavery—merely a picking and choosing of suitable texts. The Enlightenment and the French Revolution saw the first analytical interest, but it was the nineteenth-century abolitionists who produced the first serious studies, in particular the three-volume history of slavery in antiquity by the Frenchman Henri Wallon. The first edition appeared in 1847, the second in 1879, when Wallon was Dean of the Faculty of Letters of the University of Paris. The three volumes, a work of genuine erudition and still

Section of Aristotle's *Constitution of Athens*, a papyrus manuscript found at Asyut, in Egypt; second century A.D.

the only history of ancient slavery on that scale, were at the same time an open tract for abolition, charged with emotion. By 1879 Marx had already published the first volume of his *Capital,* and numerous other works. Ancient slavery thus became an important historical element in another, widely unpopular, movement—Communism. A reaction soon set in. The counterattack was not a defense of slavery as such, but a two-pronged argument: first, that ancient and modern American slavery were so different that all comparisons are misleading (especially any projection of the horrors of modern Negro slavery back onto antiquity); second, that the extent and the impact of slavery in antiquity were grossly exaggerated anyway. The most influential voice in the counterattack was Eduard Meyer, the outstanding ancient historian of his day in Germany; but the fullest statement of that position will be found in a relatively recent book by an American pupil of Meyer's, William L. Westermann.[79]

Most ancient historians implicitly agreed with Meyer, at least to the extent of ignoring slavery. The exceptions were the Marxists and the Roman lawyers. The latter had no choice, because, as William W. Buckland pointed out in the preface to his 735-page *Roman Law of Slavery,* "There is scarcely a problem which can present itself, in any branch of the law, the solution of which may not be affected by the fact that one of the parties to the transaction is a slave, and, outside the region of procedure, there are few branches of the law in which the slave does not prominently appear."[80] If that is so, one might have thought, then students of ancient religion or social institutions also have no choice. And indeed, one German scholar has now published a four-volume monograph, totaling nearly 800 pages, on the religion of the slaves in Greece and Rome.[81] Nevertheless, the fact remains that this kind of thorough inquiry began only after the Second World War (barring the occasional exception), and the old neglect of the topic still persists. An extreme example is Martin P. Nilsson's standard, massive reference work on Greek religion, also in German, first published in two fat volumes in 1941 and 1950. It contains a single paragraph on the religious aspects of the slave revolts of the second century B.C., and other than that the word *slave* does not appear in the index.[82]

On balance, the Nilssons are losing ground, and slavery is today a major concern among classical students. In part, the change may be attributed simply to the diminishing pull of the old sentimental adulation of the Greeks and Romans. However, there is more to it, and that is the increasing recognition that classical studies have something to learn from other disciplines. From social anthropology we have learned that some form of bondage has been the most general form of labor (apart from self-employment and family labor) in early and more primitive societies; that wage labor is a relatively late, sophisticated institution; and that outright slavery, in which human beings are mere chattels, is only one of a range of servile forms.[83] Even within the Greco-Roman world, a more complex analysis is necessary, distinguishing between slaves and so-called debt slaves (familiar from the Bible as from early Greece and Rome), for example, or between the helots of Sparta and the chattel slaves of Athens, between the slaves in industry and commerce and the slaves on the large landed estates of Italy and Sicily. We have also learned from the anthropologists that slavery has a profound impact not only on the economy but also on popular psychology and behavior in such areas as sexual ethics, attitudes to work, technology, even attitudes to human life (as symbolized by the cruel gladiatorial shows, for example). This side of the problem is extremely elusive when we can no longer observe the society in action and are dependent entirely on ancient writers, who, it should be stressed, were unable to test or judge their own experience against societies that did not possess slaves. Conjectural as our analyses are therefore bound to be, I nevertheless rate this group of problems high on any list of urgent research subjects in the classical field.

The old debate about the validity of comparisons with American slavery has also been taken to a new level, both because of the more intensive investigation of ancient slavery and because there has been an upsurge, within the last two decades, of very sophisticated new work on American slavery. It is now clear that there are at least three fundamental distinctions between the American institution and the ancient one. The first is the element of color, affecting not only the slaves but also the ex-slaves. By and large, slaves had a far higher chance of being freed in antiquity, and when that happened, their descendants melted into the total population, lacking as they did the permanent mark of color. The second distinction stems from the importance of slaves in the urban sector of antiquity, in particular in manufacture; plantation slavery was paralleled for only one period in Italy, and even then there was nothing like the monoculture of the cotton states. Finally, there is the fundamental distinction in the underlying economies and the corollary that modern slavery existed within a world that also included important non-slave economies. These are all limitations on comparative study, grounds for caution, but they do not warrant Eduard Meyer's total rejection of all comparisons.

The glory that was Greece and the grandeur that was Rome

These two lines from Edgar Allan Poe's "To Helen" were chosen as the titles for two of the most successful books ever written about the classical world, both by John C. Stobart. The Greek volume, published in 1911, went through fourteen printings before a posthumous fourth edition was issued in 1964, and the Roman book had nine printings from 1912 until its fourth edition in 1961. As the titles already warn us, the picture is idealized in the extreme, and explanation is reduced to little more than reference to innate character and eternal verities. The break from an attitude summed up by Stobart has been one of my main themes. It would be a pity, however, if it were thought that I have been making a plea for "debunking," for chopping the Greeks and Romans down to size. The Parthenon still stands, Greek tragedy is still read and loved, Plato remains one of the towering figures in the whole history of philosophy, Tacitus a remarkable historian. Interpretation in place of sentimental adulation should make these men, and the whole achievement, more meaningful, not less so, precisely because it humanizes an otherwise wholly unreal civilization and because it seeks to explain what was accomplished, and why, and how, and where the limits were. If the study of dead civilizations is to be justified as an enrichment of contemporary experience, that is the way to achieve the objective.

When the rediscovery of the ancient Near East began in the latter part of the nineteenth century, the most powerful voices in the classical field were nearly unanimous in their contempt. Very interesting, they said, but let no one imagine that any new light would be thrown on classical history and civilization. East and West were each a closed compartment; when they met, it was only in mortal combat. And there could be no doubt where the victory would lie, since the "West" had total moral and intellectual superiority. In time other voices were raised, and in the past two or three decades there has been scrupulous examination of the flow of ideas and skills from the Near East to Greece during the Bronze Age, later in science, religion, and mythology, and in the fine arts. A considerable list of outright borrowings can be drawn up: metallurgy (not to go back earlier to agriculture), elementary mathematics, astronomy, individual myths, the Phoenician alphabet, possibly sculpture, decorative motifs on pottery and ivory. And why not? Why should the Greeks have refused such skills and knowledge when they became available? Any more than in a later age the early Christians borrowed the Greek philosophical concepts with which they were able to construct a systematic theology?

Except as miscellaneous facts, however, such lists of borrowings are not very interesting. What matters is what the borrowers made of their borrowings. Christian theology was Christian, not pagan Greek. And in every instance I have just given, the Greeks transformed what they took into something new and original. The Phoenicians invented the alphabet, but there were no Phoenician Homers. No Babylonian wrote the *Theogony* of Hesiod or the *Elements* of Euclid. That is "glory" enough.

1 *Universal History* 15. 14. 3–4.
2 Alternative translations should be noted: "because Astarte commanded [it] through him" instead of "because Astarte has raised [him] with her hand"; and "may the years . . . be as many" in the final sentence.
3 I have gone into further detail in *Aspects of Antiquity* (New York: Viking Press, 1968), chap. 9.
4 The lectures were later published in a handsome illustrated volume, *Tomb Sculpture*, ed. Horst W. Janson (London: Thames & Hudson, 1964) .

5 Some of the chapter headings in the recent book by Antony Andrewes, *The Greeks* (New York: Alfred A. Knopf, 1967), make the point succinctly. It would not be easy to find an earlier book on Greece with chapters entitled "Tribes and Kinship Groups," "Landowners, Peasants and Colonists," "Social Values and Social Divisions," or "Open Speculation," with "Outline of Political History" also a single chapter.

6 Recent advances in the application to archaeology of new scientific equipment and techniques will not be discussed.

7 Roger A. Pack, *The Greek and Latin Literary Texts from Greco-Roman Egypt*, 2nd ed., rev. and enl. (Ann Arbor: University of Michigan Press, 1965). The Latin items, not included in my figures, are a mere 110, of which 41 are treatises on Roman law. The explanation is that even after Egypt became a Roman possession in 30 B.C., the language of the educated classes remained Greek until replaced by Arabic.

8 *GBWW*, Vol. 5, pp. 1–14.

9 *Odes* 3. 30. 13–14.

10 *GBWW*, Vol. 5 pp. 449–649.

11 I say "finds" in the plural because since 1959 there have been published papyri containing three acts of the *Samian Woman*, two acts of the *Shield*, a group of long selections from the *Man from Sicyon*, and other important fragments.

12 *GBWW*, Vol. 14, pp. 32–48.

13 *GBWW*, Vol. 9, pp. 549–84.

14 They did not, however, use clay tablets, virtually indestructible, for day-to-day writing purposes, as was the practice in Mesopotamia for more than two thousand years, from the Sumerians to the Neo-Babylonians. The most important leather documents are the Dead Sea Scrolls, which fall outside this survey.

15 A convenient cheap edition, with English translation and notes, is that edited by Peter A. Brunt and John M. Moore (London: Oxford University Press, 1967).

16 This conclusion ties in with the larger topic of current reexamination of the workings of Athenian politics, discussed below. Photographs of the Themistocles ostraca are reproduced in *Hesperia* 7 (1938): 231–42.

17 J. V. A. Fine, *Horoi* (*Hesperia*, supp. 9, 1951); M. I. Finley, *Studies in Land and Credit in Ancient Athens, 500–200* B.C. (New Brunswick: Rutgers University Press, 1952); "Land, Debt, and the Man of Property in Classical Athens," *Political Science Quarterly* 68 (1953): 249–68.

18 Weaver's most general statement of his results will be found in his article "Social Mobility in the Early Roman Empire," *Past & Present*, no. 37 (1967), pp. 3–20.

19 In writing *Early Greece: The Bronze and Archaic Ages* (New York: W. W. Norton & Co., 1970), I wanted to consider the gradual disappearance of swords, spearheads, and other military equipment from graves after the breakup of the Mycenaean palace society, but I was largely frustrated by the casual attitude, in much archaeological reporting, about such material once it ceased to consist of quality goods.

20 Robert M. Cook, *Greek Painted Pottery*, reprint with corrections (New York: Barnes & Noble, 1966), pp. 274–75.

21 The standard survey in English is Oliver R. Gurney, *The Hittites*, 2nd ed. rev. (Baltimore: Penguin Books, 1961), which begins with a good short introduction on "The Discovery of the Hittites."

22 The most reliable account, well illustrated but not interestingly presented, is Johannes Friedrich, *Extinct Languages*, trans. Frank Gaynor (New York: Philosophical Library, 1957). The 2nd German edition (1966) brings the story up to date.

23 I am ignoring the further complications created by several isolated objects, such as the Phaestus disk, with still different characters inscribed on them.

24 *See* John Chadwick, *The Decipherment of Linear B*, 2nd ed. (London: Cambridge University Press, 1967).

25 For a balanced statement of the position, *see* Geoffrey S. Kirk, *The Songs of Homer* (New York: Cambridge University Press, 1962), pp. 24–29.

26 It is equally impossible to enter into a discussion of the effects of more than 150 years of decipherment on linguistic study itself.

27 *Life of Nicias* 29; *GBWW*, Vol. 14, p. 438b.

28 The best presentation of the evidence is by F. D. Harvey, "Literacy in the Athenian Democracy," *Revue des études grecques* 79 (1966): 585–635.

29 *Phaedrus* 274–8; *GBWW*, Vol. 7, pp. 138c–140d.

30 *See* Henri I. Marrou, *A History of Education in Antiquity,* unreliably translated by George Lamb (New York: Sheed & Ward, 1956).

31 In the remainder of this essay I repeatedly contrast "new" with "old" or "traditional" approaches. If I rarely stop to discuss, or even to mention, scholars whose work represents alternative or exceptional views, that does not imply that they do not exist.

32 The poems of Homer are published in *GBWW,* Vol. 4, of Virgil in Vol. 13, of Dante in Vol. 21, of Milton in Vol. 32.

33 The best introduction is Kirk, *Songs of Homer.* There is a shorter, paperback version, *Homer and the Epic* (New York: Cambridge University Press, 1965). I am ignoring many difficult Homeric questions such as whether or not the *Iliad* and the *Odyssey* are the work of two different composers.

34 This view is most cogently argued by A. Parry, "Have We Homer's *Iliad?*" *Yale Classical Studies* 20 (1966): 177–216.

35 *See* my *World of Odysseus,* rev. ed. (New York: Viking Press, 1965).

36 *Poetics* 1449a16; *GBWW,* Vol. 9, p. 683b.

37 *Proceedings of the Cambridge Philological Society,* n.s., no. 9 (1963), p. 21.

38 *See* John Jones, *On Aristotle and Greek Tragedy* (London: Chatto & Windus, 1962).

39 It is worth noting the date of Jones's highly polemical book, cited in the previous note. Dawe was applying to Aeschylus a type of analysis that had already been made of Sophocles as far back as 1917 by a young German scholar, Tycho Wilamowitz, and that had been promptly and rudely rejected by most specialists.

40 *GBWW,* Vol. 5, p. 107c.

41 Jones, *On Aristotle,* p. 233.

42 *The Greeks and the Irrational* (Berkeley and Los Angeles: University of California Press, 1951).

43 *Poetics* 1449b27; *GBWW,* Vol. 9, p. 684a.

44 A long list is published in Appendix II of Robert R. Bolgar, *The Classical Heritage and Its Beneficiaries* (New York: Cambridge University Press, 1954; Harper & Row, Publishers, Harper Torchbooks, 1964).

45 "The Task of the Translator," *Delos,* no. 2 (1968), pp. 78 and 82, respectively. The existence of *Delos,* subtitled *A Journal on and of Translation,* is itself deserving of note.

46 This point is fully developed in Geoffrey S. Kirk, *Myth: Its Meaning and Functions in Ancient and Other Cultures* (Berkeley and Los Angeles: University of California Press, 1970).

47 P. S. Cohen, "Theories of Myth," *Man* 4 (1969): 337–53.

48 In view of the wide circulation of Robert Graves, *The Greek Myths* (London: Penguin Books, 1955), it should perhaps be said that he still clings to this theory, that he does not apply it consistently, and that his account of the myths is not always reliable.

49 A lively introduction is now available in Edmund Leach, *Claude Lévi-Strauss* (New York: Viking Press, 1970).

50 *See* my *Aspects,* chap. 7, on Diogenes.

51 Plato *Phaedo* 118; *GBWW,* Vol. 7, p. 251d.

52 As a model of the approach I am challenging, *see* Martin P. Nilsson, *Greek Popular Religion* (New York: Columbia University Press, 1940).

53 *See* my *Aspects,* chap. 5, on the trial of Socrates.

54 *Laws* 10. 907D–909C; *GBWW,* Vol. 7, pp. 769d–770c.

55 The fundamental book remains Arthur D. Nock, *Conversion* (London: Oxford University Press, 1933).

56 *The Peloponnesian War* 1. 22; *GBWW,* Vol. 6, p. 354c.

57 *Ibid.* 1. 8–11; *GBWW,* Vol. 6, pp. 350d–352b.

58 The reader should be warned that my own position is an extreme one on the side of disbelief. *See* my *Aspects,* chap. 2, and my article "The Trojan War," with comments by J. L. Caskey, G. S. Kirk, and D. L. Page, *Journal of Hellenic Studies* 84 (1964): 1–20. On early Rome, *see* Arnaldo Momigliano, "An Interim Report on the Origins of Rome," *Journal of Roman Studies* 53 (1963): 95–121, reprinted in his *Terzo contributo alla storia degli studi classici e del mondo antico,* 2 vols. (Rome: Edizioni di Storia e Letteratura, 1966), pp. 545–98.

59 The most sober statement of the Atlantis argument is that of John V. Luce, *Lost Atlantis* (New York: McGraw-Hill Book Co., 1969). My objections were published in *New York Review of Books,* May 22 and December 4, 1969.

60 *The History* 1. 65–66; *GBWW,* Vol. 6, p. 14b–c.

61 *GBWW,* Vol. 14, pp. 32–48.

62 A full account of the Moses-Homer debate will be found in Jean Pépin, *Mythe et allégorie: Les origines grecques et les contestations judéo-chrétiennes* (Paris: Éditions Aubier-Montaigne, 1958).

63 I am not concerned with "pre-state" systems, in which tribal or other kinship groupings organize the affairs of the community. Some historians believe that such communities continued to exist within Near Eastern kingdoms—a much debated question today.

64 Quoted from Gurney, op. cit., p. 175.

65 Thorkild Jacobsen in Henri and Henriette A. Frankfort et al., *Before Philosophy* (Harmondsworth, Middlesex: Penguin Books, 1951), pp. 217–18.

66 *GBWW,* Vol. 9, pp. 437–548.

67 *See* Arnaldo Momigliano, "Linee per una valutazione di Fabio Pittore," in his *Terzo contributo,* pp. 55–68. This article will be published in English in a collection of Momigliano's papers, probably not before 1972.

68 I have developed this analysis at length in "Athenian Demagogues," *Past & Present,* no. 21 (1962), pp. 3–24.

69 P. A. Brunt, "The Roman Mob," *Past & Present,* no. 35 (1966), pp. 3–27; idem, *Social Conflicts in the Roman Republic* (London: Chatto & Windus, 1971), chap. 6.

70 The gap has been partly filled by an important book, Ernst Badian, *Roman Imperialism in the Late Republic* (Ithaca, N.Y.: Cornell University Press, 1968).

71 *The Peloponnesian War* 2. 63. 2; *GBWW,* Vol. 6, p. 403c.

72 G. E. M. de Ste. Croix, "The Character of the Athenian Empire," *Historia* 3 (1954): 1–41. Attempts to challenge his main thesis have been unsuccessful.

73 *GBWW,* Vol. 15. *See* above all Chaim Wirszubski, *Libertas as a Political Idea at Rome during the Late Republic and Early Principate* (New York: Cambridge University Press, 1950).

74 *See* John A. Crook, *Law and Life of Rome* (London: Thames & Hudson, 1967).

75 Richard E. Smith's encomiastic *Cicero the Statesman* (London: Cambridge University Press, 1966) is a reminder that new trends are not universally accepted. One cannot leave this subject without mentioning the seminal work of Ronald Syme, *The Roman Revolution* (Oxford: Clarendon Press, 1939).

76 *The Open Society and Its Enemies,* 2 vols.; the fourth edition, including a reply to his critics, was published in 1962 (London: Routledge & Kegan Paul).

77 *Plato, Popper and Politics* (New York: Barnes & Noble, 1967), pp. 16–17.

78 The continuity in the history of slavery has been brilliantly analyzed by David B. Davis, *The Problem of Slavery in Western Culture* (Ithaca: Cornell University Press, 1966), pt. 1. On the early discussion in Latin America, *see* Lewis Hanke, *Aristotle and the American Indians* (London: Hollis & Carter, 1959).

79 Eduard Meyer, "Die Sklaverei im Altertum" (Lecture originally published in 1898), in his *Kleine Schriften,* 2nd ed. (Halle: Max Niemeyer, 1924), 1: 169–212; William L. Westermann, *The Slave Systems of Greek and Roman Antiquity* (Philadelphia: American Philosophical Society, 1955).

80 *The Roman Law of Slavery* (Cambridge: At the University Press, 1908).

81 F. Bömer, *Untersuchungen über die Religion der Sklaven in Griechenland und Rom,* published in the *Abhandlungen der geistes- und sozialwissenschaftlichen Klasse* of the Akademie der Wissenschaften und der Literatur, Mainz, 1957 no. 7, 1960 no. 1, 1961 no. 4, 1963 no. 10.

82 Martin P. Nilsson, *Geschichte der griechischen Religion,* 2 vols. (Munich: C. H. Beck'sche Verlagsbuchhandlung, 1941–50).

83 Space does not permit me to go into detail on any of the points that follow in this section, nor to cite the now voluminous bibliography, for which I refer to *International Encyclopedia of the Social Sciences* (New York: Macmillan Co. and Free Press, 1968), for my article "Slavery."

Peter J. Wyllie

Peter J. Wyllie, born in London in 1930, began early to show distinction in his chosen field, geology. By the time he was twenty, and before he had completed his undergraduate studies at the University of St. Andrews, Scotland, he had been selected to go as Glaciologist with a British expedition to west Greenland. Two years later he accompanied a similar expedition

to north Greenland as Geologist and received the Polar Medal from Queen Elizabeth for his work. Since 1955 he has taught at various British and American universities and is currently Professor of Petrology and Geochemistry at the University of Chicago. The author of a recently published book called *The Dynamic Earth: A Textbook in Geosciences,* he has also published more than ninety papers in scientific journals. He was awarded the medal of the Mineralogical Society of America in 1965.

Revolution in the Earth Sciences

A decade of new ideas

We read much in the popular press these days about social revolutions. Less well publicized but probably of greater long-range influence on our life-patterns and life-styles are revolutions that are reshaping the conceptual frameworks of science. These have been discussed in previous issues of *The Great Ideas Today*. For example, in his 1967 review of "The Physical Sciences" Stephen Toulmin observed that "in the world of science, as in the worlds of society and technology, the second half of the twentieth century is proving to be a period of 'perpetual revolution,' and scientists are learning to live with that fact." And in the same year, writing about "The Biological Sciences," Theodore Puck said:

> *It has become increasingly clear during the past decade that biology is undergoing a new and revolutionary development. . . . Molecular biology has provided for the first time a master plan [or] at least a generalized picture into which everything we know of the more complex systems seems to fit.*

A similar revolution has been proclaimed for the earth sciences. The concept known as *sea-floor spreading* (figure 1) serves as a master plan that appears to accommodate and link together many subjects in the earth sciences previously regarded as subjects for independent research. Whereas the revolution in biological sciences is based on microscale studies, that in earth sciences is based on a scheme of macro-scale. Molecular biology seems to be capable of explaining large, more complex biological systems. Sea-floor spreading is a scheme for the whole earth that provides a framework for the explanation of localized geological phenomena. Many writers have compared the potential effects of these revolutions in biological and earth sciences with those produced in physics when classical views were replaced by modern physics.

Figure 1 illustrates schematically the process of sea-floor spreading based on a model proposed in 1960 by the late H. H. Hess of Princeton.

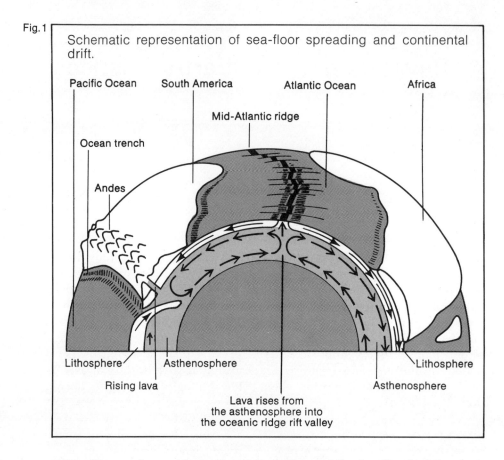

Fig. 1

Schematic representation of sea-floor spreading and continental drift.

Pacific Ocean   South America   Atlantic Ocean   Africa

Mid-Atlantic ridge

Ocean trench

Andes

Lithosphere   Asthenosphere   Lithosphere

Rising lava   Asthenosphere

Lava rises from
the asthenosphere into
the oceanic ridge rift valley

We will examine evidence for this model and its implications in more detail below; at this stage we need note only its main features. What is called *convective motion* occurs in the hot, solid material of the earth's interior. Convecting material rises beneath the mid-oceanic ridges and moves away laterally, carrying as if on a conveyor belt a surface layer of cool, rigid rock called the *lithosphere*. The sea-floor is thus spread apart at the mid-oceanic ridges, and the tensional gap is filled with new ocean crust generated by the injection and eruption of lava rising from the depths. Where two convection cells converge, the pressure causes one slab of lithosphere to be carried down into the earth's interior where it is heated and eventually assimilated. These locations are sites of mountain ranges of oceanic trenches and associated volcanic island arcs. The continental land masses form part of the lithosphere.

At the time when Hess proposed this model, the concept of sea-floor spreading seemed such a fanciful one that he himself characterized it as "geopoetry." But critical evidence sufficient to convince many geologists and geophysicists that the idea is essentially correct became available during the winter of 1966/67. What had been a working hypothesis was

170

then elevated by these scientists to the status of a theory—some even claimed that the theory was now proven fact—and the fervor of revolution gripped the whole geological community. A counterrevolution followed. But before we examine the theory and consider its present implications for the earth sciences, we should view the developments leading up to the proclamation of revolution. For no revolution is born during the brief period of a single winter, and the seeds of this one were nourished through half a century by the debate about continental drift.

The earth sciences have been shaped by a series of great controversies and a host of minor disputes. It has sometimes seemed that geologists enjoy the excitement of debate more than getting together to define their terms in an effort to resolve a dispute. The great controversies include the battle between the Neptunists and the Plutonists during the period 1775–1825, the conflict of Catastrophism and Uniformitarianism between about 1775 and 1835, and the vigorous debate about continental drift during this century, with Drifters or Mobilists challenging the Fixists or Stabilists. The lesson to be learned from these controversies is that a theory that appears in one generation to be unassailable may appear incredibly wrong and naïve to the next generation. In these days of revolution and excitement over the new global theory (figure 1), recollection of the fate of some earlier theories is in order.

In 1775, at the age of twenty-five, Abraham Werner was appointed lecturer at the Freiberg Mining Academy. In his lectures, he promulgated the Neptunian theory. He maintained that all geological formations, and rocks of all types except those actually observed to emerge from volcanoes as lavas, had originated as successive deposits or precipitates from a primeval ocean. His stimulating lectures attracted many students, who then went forth and applied the Neptunist creed to the solution of geological problems in their various countries. But Werner's thesis was soon challenged by the school of Plutonists, who denied that a single primeval ocean was the source of rocks. The leader of the Plutonists, James Hutton of Edinburgh, presented evidence eventually satisfying most geologists that many rocks had formed by the cooling and crystallization of hot material that had risen in fused condition from subterranean regions. Rocks formed in this way were accompanied by earthquakes and eruptions, in sharp contrast with the peaceful creative processes involved in the Neptunian conception of their origin, and of the origin of the world.

Hutton's contributions are contained in his 1788 paper entitled "Theory of the Earth" and in a book called *Theory of the Earth with Proofs and Illustrations* published in 1795, two years before his death. The rival schools argued their cases until finally the Plutonists won out. Neptunism simply disappeared about fifty years after its sudden rise. By then the conflict between its tenets, considered by many persons to conform to the Book of Genesis, and those of Plutonism, considered by other people to be atheistic, had passed beyond the confines of scientific discussion and entered contemporary literature. It appears, for example, in Goethe's *Faust,* in the dialogue between the Sphinxes and Seismos in Act II, and in that between Faust and Mephistopheles in Act IV.*

Another controversy of long duration concerned the interpretation of fossils. Many imaginative explanations for these "figured stones" were proposed, and it was argued that they were not of organic origin because this was contrary to the Book of Genesis. When fossils were eventually recognized as the remains of living things, champions of the theological cause maintained that such remains had been carried to their present positions above sea level by the Noachian deluge. Indeed, the existence of fossils in mountains was cited as scientific evidence that the biblical deluge had occurred.

The science of paleontology developed from the study of fossils, and one of its early masters was a Frenchman, Baron Cuvier. He discovered that certain fossils were confined to specific rock formations, and to explain this he invoked a series of widespread catastrophes. Sudden floods and successive retreats of the water caused the disappearance of faunas characterizing certain formations. The doctrine of Catastrophism swept everything before it for a time, Cuvier's major contributions being published in 1811 and 1812. But Hutton's "Theory of the Earth" paper not only led the Plutonists to victory over the Neptunists; it also introduced the ideas that toppled Catastrophism. Hutton noted the continuity of geological processes and emphasized that in the geological record there is "no sign of a beginning—no prospect of an end." This idea that geological history should be explainable in terms of continuous events led to a controversy between Catastrophism and Uniformitarianism, as the competing principle was called by Sir Charles Lyell. The publication in 1833 of Lyell's *Principles of Geology* marked the end of Catastrophism, and Uniformitarianism became the new creed. However, it is now recognized that the uniform flow of geological history is punctuated by local, intermittent catastrophes, as we shall see in a later section.

Continental drift is an old idea, formulated originally to explain the striking parallelism of the Atlantic coasts. The idea of a mobile earth, with the crust floating on a molten interior, was familiar to geologists by 1900, but the concept of continental drift did not gain a large following until 1915, when Alfred Wegener published an expanded version of his 1912 paper in the first edition of his book *The Origin of Continents and Oceans.* Wegener and his followers compiled an impressive list of evidence supporting continental drift, drawn from paleoclimatology, paleontology, the geometrical fit of the continents, and the matching of rock successions and truncated geological structures across oceans. Wegener proposed the name *Pangaea* for a single supercontinent presumed to exist before continental drift began, about 180 million years ago. At that time, Pangaea split up, with the southern continents moving westward, or toward the equator, or both. According to Wegener, South America and Africa began to drift apart about 70 million years ago, with opening of the North Atlantic being accomplished mainly during the past few million years.

An alternative scheme was proposed by A. L. du Toit, who maintained that there were two primordial continents, *Laurasia* (North America, Greenland, Europe and Asia) in the Northern Hemisphere, and *Gondwanaland* (India, Africa, South America, Australia, and Antarctica) in the Southern Hemisphere, separated by a single huge ocean, *Tethys*. These supercontinents began to split up about 65 million years ago. As the fragments drifted to their present positions, the Tethys ocean became smaller, and the Alps and Himalayan mountain chains emerged from this ocean basin.

The theory of continental drift suffered from a lack of definitive evidence, and every argument developed in favor of the theory was opposed by a counterargument. Opponents of drift argued that the known physical properties of the earth would not permit the assumed movements. Proponents of drift, on the other hand, argued that geological facts should not be ignored simply because there was no physical explanation available for them. Then, other experts disputed what were claimed to be geological facts, referring to them instead as inferences. The arguments continued in this indeterminate vein, like some medieval philosophical controversy, until a stalemate was reached in the 1940s. Just about everything that could be argued for and against continental drift had been written many times, and the debate faded for lack of additional evidence.

The controversy was revived in the 1950s with research into paleomagnetism by two physicists, P. M. S. Blackett in London and S. K. Runcorn in Cambridge. It had long been known that some rocks become weakly magnetized as they are formed and that the direction of magnetization preserves a fossil record of the direction of the earth's magnetic field at the time and place of formation. Paleomagnetic evidence offered by Blackett and Runcorn indicated that the positions of the earth's magnetic poles have changed relative to the continents. This new evidence led many geophysicists to consider the theory of continental drift seriously, though many geologists remained unimpressed by the paleomagnetic approach, and suspicious of it—a reversal of the situation during previous years, when geophysicists denied the physical feasibility of the drifting proposed by geologists.

During the same decade, exploration of the ocean floor by marine geologists and geophysicists showed that submarine mountain ranges

---

* See *GBWW,* Vol. 47, pp. 184–85, 246.

were more nearly continuous than previously suspected, and that the mid-Atlantic ridge was remarkably parallel to the continental borders of the Atlantic Ocean. The presence of a rift valley along the crest of the ridges indicates that they are in a state of tension. It was discovered that the ocean basins contain far less sediment than previously assumed and far less than would have accumulated during the long span of geological time if the ocean basins had remained unchanged through this time. There is a continuous outflow of heat from the earth's interior, and the rate of heat flow from the mid-oceanic ridges was found to be unusually high. These observations led geologists to conclude that the ocean basins were relatively young, and that some recent upwelling within the earth had occurred beneath the oceanic ridges.

By 1960 the time was ripe for syntheses of the new data gathered during the 1950s, and it is notable that the attention of most investigators was directed toward the ocean basins, rather than toward possibly drifting continents. Many geologists and geophysicists related the tensional character of the oceanic ridges and the high heat flow from these regions to rising convection cells within the earth's interior. The convective motions occurred not in molten material, as indicated in early arguments for continental drift, but in solid material, as had been suggested first by A. Holmes of Edinburgh University in 1928. The scene was set for formulation of the hypothesis of sea-floor spreading by Hess. His paper on "History of the Ocean Basins" was presented orally in 1960 and published in 1962.

Hess proposed that the major structures of the sea floor are direct expressions of a convection process within the earth's solid interior, as depicted in figure 1. Mid-oceanic ridges mark the sites of rising convection cells, and the deep oceanic trenches bordering island arcs and some continental margins are associated with convergences or descending limbs of convection cells. New sea floor is generated by uprise and solidification of volcanic lava at the mid-ocean ridges, and the older, displaced sea floor is carried downward into the earth's interior at the sites of converging convection cells. The ocean floor is essentially the outcropping of the earth's interior covered by a thin veneer of sediments and volcanic lavas. The continents are carried by the convection movement of the interior, as if on a conveyor belt; they do not plow through the oceanic crust, as proposed by most earlier hypotheses of continental drift.

What transformed Hess's speculative geopoetry into a revolutionary movement were two major developments related to the earth's magnetic field. First, it was confirmed that this field had reversed polarity in epochs with duration of less than one million years (figure 4). Second, it was discovered that a series of anomalies in the present earth's magnetic field occurring parallel to the mid-oceanic ridges is remarkably symmetrical about the ridges, and that specific anomalies can be cor-related through great distances, and from one ocean to another. The significance of these developments was that, together with certain other phenomena observed at about the same time, they seemed convincing evidence that sea-floor spreading provided a valid global framework for the explanation and prediction of geological and geophysical phenom-ena. Moreover, as the scheme was refined, and as precise estimates of the direction and rates of movement of large sectors of the earth's outer layer were arrived at, the further theory of plate tectonics was formu-lated, incorporating both the notions of sea-floor spreading and of conti-nental drift. We shall have more to say about these matters later on.

Since 1967, hundreds of papers dealing with various aspects of sea-floor spreading and plate tectonics have been presented at annual meet-ings of the American Geophysical Union, the Geological Society of America, and the American Association of Petroleum Geologists. The effect has been to elevate Hess's poetical working hypothesis of sea-floor spreading to the status of a theory. Results of the recent deep-sea drilling program undertaken by the special drilling ship *Glomar Challenger* have even been hailed as proof. In an editorial for *Science* on December 5, 1969, P. H. Abelson noted:

> *To date, examinations of the cores have been conducted on ship-board, but major conclusions have already been announced. . . . Results from the drilling strongly support hypotheses of sea-floor spreading and continental drift. . . . The deep-sea drilling has changed speculation into something that must be regarded as established.*

Of course, there have been both advantages and disadvantages to this result, as there always are when any ruling theory is established. "The history of geology," C. E. Wegmann wrote in 1963, "shows that a con-ceptual development in one sector is generally followed by a harvest of observations, since many geologists can only see what they are asked to record by their conceptual outfit." The conceptual development of sea-floor spreading is indeed gathering a harvest of data and interpretations. Earth scientists are being forced to reevaluate almost everything they thought they knew about geological processes. Geological observations that appeared to be isolated now seem to fall into place in the global scheme. But the second half of Wegmann's statement is also being borne out. Protagonists of plate tectonics tend to neglect the data and argu-ments not explained by the theory, arguing that these can probably be ascribed to our lack of understanding rather than to inadequacies of the model and that time and improved understanding will bring forth explanations.

Not all geologists consider that the theories of sea-floor spreading and plate tectonics solve everything. There has been continuing opposition to the notion of continental drift over the past decade, but since the formulation of the plate tectonics model, the anti-drift arguments are rarely cited. A. A. Meyerhoff published two papers in 1970 marshaling the rather scattered anti-drift arguments in an attempt at counter-revolution. He presented geological and paleoclimatological evidence that appears to indicate that the Atlantic Ocean has remained in approximately its present position for the past 800 million years. According to plate tectonic theory, the Atlantic Ocean has closed and opened again during this period. Meyerhoff maintains that until an alternative explanation is found for his evidence, the hypothesis of sea-floor spreading should be treated as speculation only.

Continental drift is an older idea, having in fact been debated for about thirty years. But recent developments have aroused new passions, as shown by a letter from A. O. Kelly to *Science News* on January 3, 1970:

> *Now, when some authority proposes a hypothesis like ocean floor spreading, every junior scientist in the country jumps on the bandwagon. Criticism, it seems, is rude, egotistical and out of style. . . . These me-too scientists are piling hypothesis upon hypothesis. . . . Reasons, it seems, are no longer necessary; one simply backs up one speculation with another.*

V. V. Beloussov, who has a large following among Soviet geologists, has written several papers arguing against sea-floor spreading and plate tectonics. Beloussov emphasizes that although our knowledge of the structure of the ocean basins is still much more sketchy than our knowledge of continental geology, the new oceanic results "have cast a hypnotic spell and thrown a shadow over much that is old and familiar." He states that the results of two centuries of data gathering from the continents should not be oversimplified in order to bring them down to the level of the schematic data available for the oceans.

Some Western geologists believe that Soviet scientists are following a scientific party line that denies the validity of plate tectonics. Beloussov is very influential in Russia. However, an interview with V. A. Magnitsky reported in *Science News* on July 11, 1970, following an international symposium in Flagstaff, Arizona, suggests that the Russians are not rigidly dogmatic about the subject. At least Magnitsky seems to regard it as an interesting idea. He is quoted thus:

> *. . . I think the final solution to this problem will depend on the new material from the ocean floor which we expect to have in two or three years. Let's wait and see. . . . The history of the geotectonics of the whole century has been the introduction of new ideas and then their collapse. This is why so many of my colleagues are in this position.*

Like other Soviet geologists, he is less impressed with the new evidence from the ocean floors than with geological data from the Eurasian continent. He advocates a little more patience.

Whether or not the new global schemes prove to be correct, there is no doubt that a revolution is in progress. Earth scientists are examining old evidence through new eyes. Proposals are being presented for the reorganization of geological curricula and the rewriting of textbooks. If it is true that a new principle in the behavior of the earth has been discovered, then we are on the verge of understanding more clearly the origin and distribution of metallic ore bodies and the geological structures that trap oil. The practical implications for the mining and petroleum industries are obvious. As we shall see in the next few pages, the distribution of earthquakes and volcanoes is directly related to the new global models, and earth scientists are exploring the implications for the prediction of earthquakes and eruptions, and for the control of earthquakes.

Stable plates and active belts: the theory of plate tectonics

Plate tectonics is the name given to the theory concerned with the relative movements and interactions of the plates of lithosphere, shown in figure 1, and with their consequences. It is concerned largely with the surface and crust of the earth, although the causes of plate movements are correlated with movements within the earth.

The surface features of the earth are shown in figure 2. There is a primary division into stable continental platform at an average elevation of 2,760 feet above sea level, and stable oceanic platform at an average depth of 12,450 feet below sea level. About 10 percent of the continental land mass is covered by ocean; this region is termed the continental shelf. The boundary between the two platforms is not the present shoreline between continents and oceans, but the continental slope extending steeply down below the edge of the continental shelf.

Each of the stable regions of the earth's surface is traversed by elongated belts that are geologically active; these belts are characterized by earthquakes and volcanoes. Figure 2 shows the distribution of the suboceanic mountain ranges, the mid-oceanic ridges, which rise an average of about 3,000 feet above the abyssal ocean floor. The existence of rift valleys along the crest of the ridges, as well as other evidence, indicates that the ridges are in a state of tension.

Also shown in figure 2 is the distribution of the geologically recent mountain ranges, formed during the past 65 million years, which rise above the continental platforms. The contorted rock structures in these mountain ranges indicate that they are regions of compression. There are other mountainous belts, but these are geologically older, and they are not active in the sense that earthquakes are associated with them. The volcanic island arcs that are particularly well developed in festoons around the Pacific Ocean are considered to be extensions of the active, recent mountain chains. The active mountain chains and island arcs form two main belts that follow great circles, roughly speaking, around the earth. One extends through the Alps, Turkey, Persia, the Himalayas, Indonesia, New Guinea, and New Zealand; the other forms the circum-Pacific belt, from the Philippine Islands, Japan, Alaska, the Rocky Mountain system, and the Andes Mountains, into Antarctica. The island arcs and some active continental margins such as western South America are bordered by the oceanic trenches, incisive elongated hollows in the ocean floor, extending to depths as much as 24,000 feet below the average abyssal ocean basin. These trenches, the lowest portions of the earth's solid surface, are located almost adjacent to some of the highest mountains on earth.

Figure 2 shows a third feature of the earth's surface that indicates activity, in addition to the tensional oceanic ridges and the compressive recent mountain belts. This is the series of great faults that transects and displaces the crest of the oceanic ridge system. These lines are interpreted as regions where one section of the earth's surface has moved laterally relative to the adjacent section, with neither significant compression nor tension resulting. Some of these transform faults, or fracture zones, are believed to extend into continental regions.

The study of earthquakes has made important contributions to development of the theory of plate tectonics during the past five years. Earthquakes are caused by the abrupt release of strain energy stored up in rocks as a result of slow deformation. Earthquake energy release occurs from foci at all depths from near surface to a maximum of 700 km. The distribution of earthquakes coincides remarkably closely with the oceanic ridges, the young mountain belts, and the volcanic island arcs. Deep-focus earthquakes occur only in parts of the compressive belts; only shallow-focus earthquakes are associated with the tensional oceanic ridges.

The theory of plate tectonics builds upon the concept of sea-floor spreading and depends heavily on the distribution of earthquakes. According to the theory, the surface of the earth consists of a few rigid plates in motion relative to each other. The cooler, rigid, outer layer of the earth, about 100 km thick, is called the *lithosphere*. The temperature within the earth increases with depth, and the warmer layer beneath the lithosphere, called the *asthenosphere,* is relatively mobile although still solid. The eruption of lava, which is molten rock, in the active belts shows that temperatures at depths where the lavas form may exceed 1,200° C. Apparently the asthenosphere is capable of movement by slow deformation, or creep, in contrast to the brittle lithosphere, which fractures if it is deformed. The lithosphere plates are aseismic, that is, almost free of earthquakes, and the boundaries between plates where the relative motion is manifest are the sites of earthquake belts. The plates have been compared with large floating sheets of sea ice grinding against each other in the ice packs of the polar regions.

The significant features of the surface of the earth according to plate tectonics are not the oceans and continents illustrated in figure 2, but the lithosphere plates defined by the active earthquake belts. In 1968 X. Le Pichon suggested that the major features of the earth's surface could be represented in terms of the six separate plates outlined in figure 3. Others suggested slightly different plate distributions, and recent work has shown that there are in addition a number of smaller plates such as the Caribbean plate and portions of the Mediterranean Sea.

Further deductions can be made from the study of earthquake waves. An earthquake is caused by some kind of fracture or displacement of rocks within the earth, although the precise details remain uncertain. The relative directions of movement of the adjacent rocks can be determined from the earthquake waves, and analysis of these on a global scale is consistent with the concept of plate tectonics. Research published since 1967 shows that in a given earthquake belt the cumulative effect of all the minor displacements through a period of several years indicates significant movement of one lithosphere plate relative to another. The average direction of the minor displacements in an earthquake belt gives the direction of movement of one plate relative to the adjacent plate.

Analysis of earthquakes in this way confirms the picture required by the hypothesis of sea-floor spreading, with two types of plate boundary, tensional and compressional (figure 1). The lithosphere plates shown in figure 3 are moving away from each other at the oceanic ridges and moving toward each other along the lines of volcanic island arcs and active mountain chains. It appears, therefore, that new lithosphere is generated at the oceanic ridges. Unless the earth is expanding, an old idea not viewed with favor at the present time, this requires that lithosphere is removed in some way. According to the sea-floor spreading hypothesis, the lithosphere is pushed or dragged down into the earth's interior along the belts of compression. The occurrence of deep-focus earthquakes along these belts and in no other locations is considered to be good evidence that cool slabs of lithosphere do extend down into the interior to depths as great as 700 km. In other regions, temperatures become too high at depths greater than about 100 km for rocks to fracture and produce earthquakes.

A third type of plate boundary is represented by the great fracture zones shown in figure 2 that transect the oceanic ridges. The evidence from earthquakes indicates that lithosphere plates are sliding past each other along these boundaries, without significant tension or compression. The general picture of the directions of relative movement of rigid litho-

Fig. 2

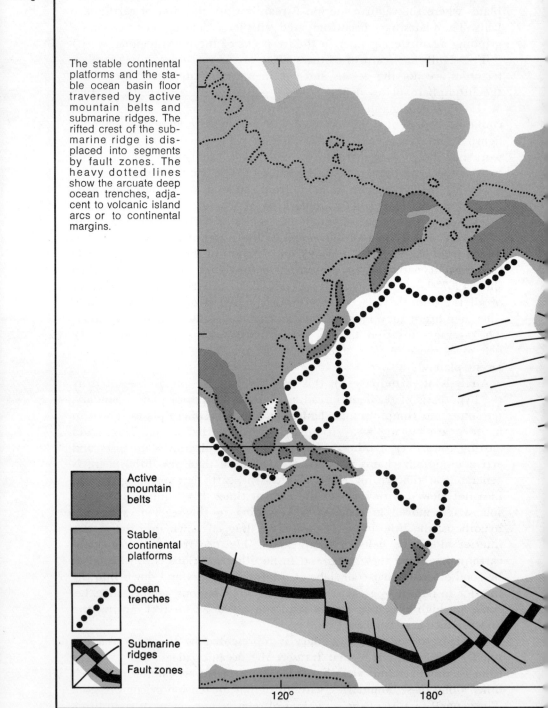

The stable continental platforms and the stable ocean basin floor traversed by active mountain belts and submarine ridges. The rifted crest of the submarine ridge is displaced into segments by fault zones. The heavy dotted lines show the arcuate deep ocean trenches, adjacent to volcanic island arcs or to continental margins.

Active mountain belts

Stable continental platforms

Ocean trenches

Submarine ridges
Fault zones

120°   180°

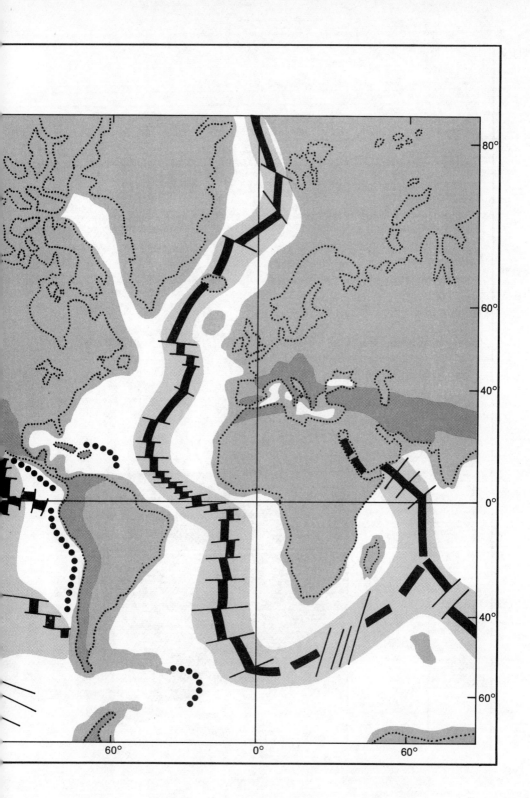

Fig. 3

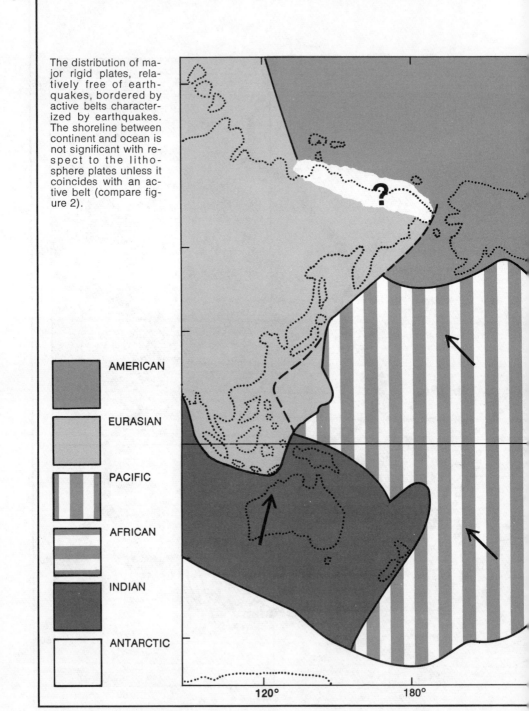

The distribution of major rigid plates, relatively free of earthquakes, bordered by active belts characterized by earthquakes. The shoreline between continent and ocean is not significant with respect to the lithosphere plates unless it coincides with an active belt (compare figure 2).

AMERICAN

EURASIAN

PACIFIC

AFRICAN

INDIAN

ANTARCTIC

?

120°   180°

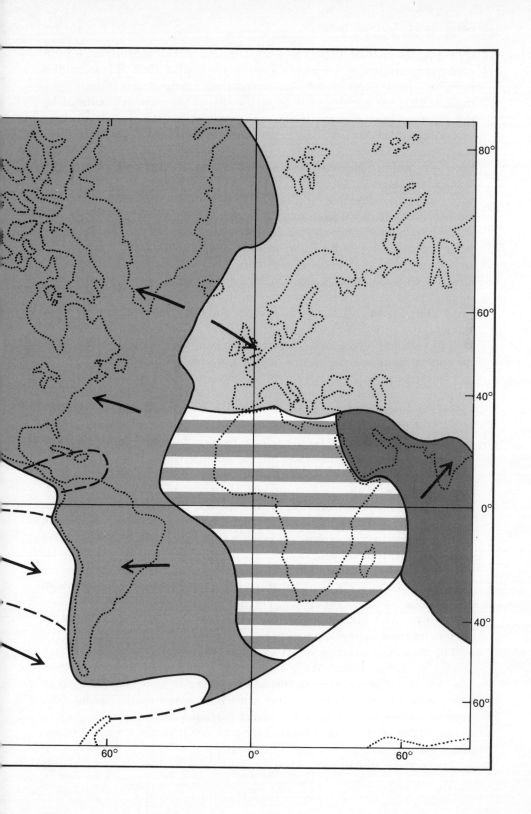

sphere plates at these three types of plate boundaries became clear from earthquake studies in research papers published in 1968. These studies provide strong support for the concept of sea-floor spreading. They indicate that the recent behavior of the lithosphere was as predicted by the concept. Furthermore, if the interpretation of slabs of lithosphere extending to 700 km into the earth's interior beneath compressive plate boundaries is correct, then the evidence indicates that the process has been continuing for a long time—at least long enough to transport the lithosphere laterally through 700 km. Rates of movement are required to estimate the time involved, and we shall return to this topic in the next section where we examine the evidence for sea-floor spreading.

We have noted that volcanic eruptions are associated with the active belts shown in figure 2. These are the plate boundaries characterized by extension or compression. However, volcanoes are not confined exclusively to these belts. A series of mighty volcanoes rises from the floor of the Pacific Ocean, for example, within the stable Pacific plate of figure 3. The Hawaiian Islands are simply the upper parts of one of these lines of volcanoes. It is still uncertain how volcanoes within plates fit into the scheme of plate tectonics and sea-floor spreading, although they do appear to be associated with major fractures within plates.

The type of volcanic activity and the compositional ranges of the lava erupted are related to the general environment. From the mid-oceanic ridges the dominant lava is a *basalt* with distinctive chemical characteristics. Volcanic activity in island arcs and the recent mountain ranges is quite different. The lavas include basalts, but their compositional range is much wider than those of the oceanic ridges. Characteristic of these belts is the more explosive eruption of a different kind of lava, called *andesite*. Andesite is unknown along the oceanic ridges, as it is among lavas erupted from the oceanic plates, such as those composing the Hawaiian Islands. The ocean plate lavas are basaltic, similar in many respects to those from the oceanic ridges, but with representatives corresponding more closely to those erupted from the island arcs. It seems clear that different processes or different materials are involved in the formation of the lavas in these three different environments. Although the reasons for these differences are not fully understood, the sea-floor spreading model indicates that differences are to be expected (figure 1), as we shall see in the next section.

The theory of plate tectonics explains why the earthquakes and volcanoes are concentrated along specific belts. Comprehension of the reasons for the location of these disruptive phenomena is the first step in the prediction of their occurrence, and it is now hoped that methods may be developed not only to predict earthquakes but also to prevent them. If this goal can be achieved, it could result in the saving of countless lives.

The present distribution of active belts tells us the present distribu-

Fig. 4

The lines of force associated with the earth's magnetic field, *A*, with normal polarity; *B*, with reversed polarity; *C*, the geomagnetic time scale determined by the directions of magnetization of radiometrically dated lavas.

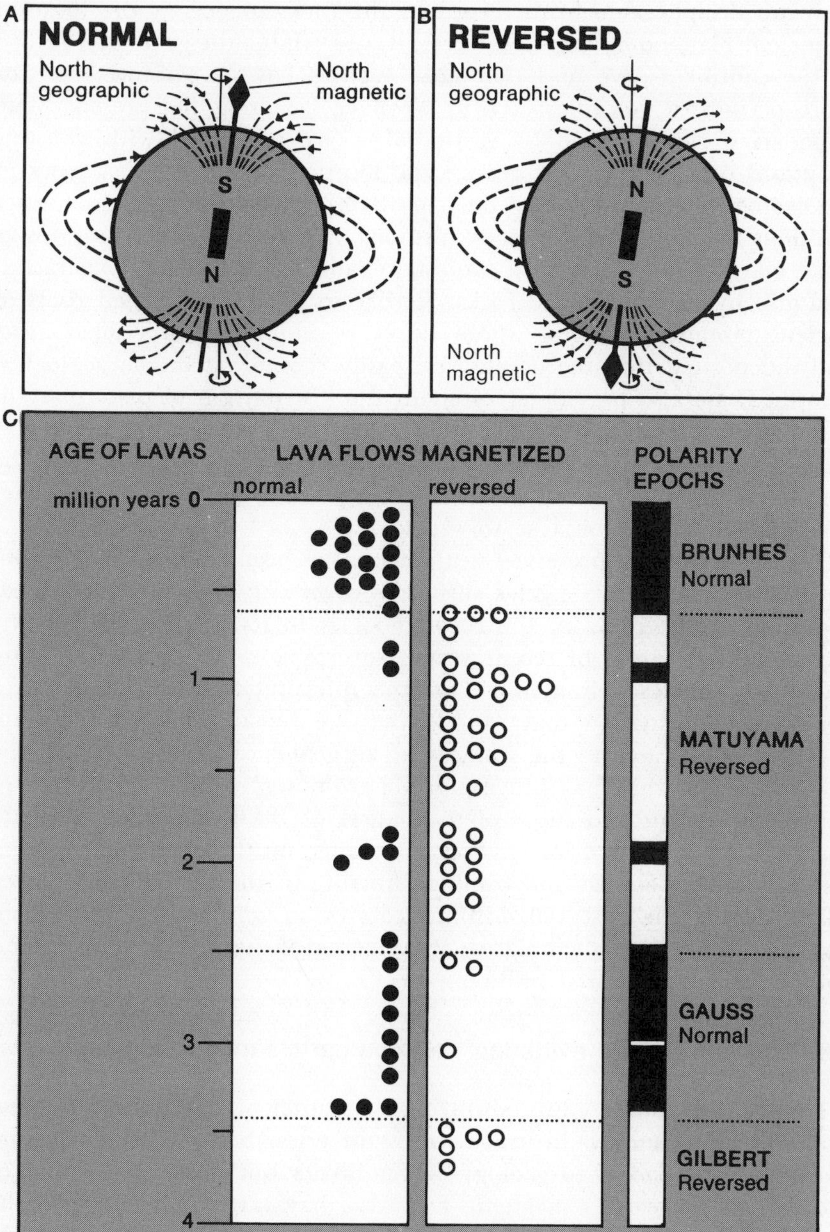

tion of lithosphere plates, and study of the relative motions indicated by earthquakes tells us the relative movement of the plates at the present time or for a few years back. It does not tell us how long the movements have continued, or whether the movements have remained continuous in direction and speed or have changed with time. Earthquakes leave no decipherable fossil record in the rocks to permit the location of ancient plate boundaries. However, if we examine the geological record of the continents, we find that most regions have experienced one or more periods of volcanic activity. We have seen that the present plate boundaries, characterized by earthquakes, are associated with volcanic eruptions of rather specific types. The location of similar lava types in the geological record is being used in attempts to reconstruct the former positions of plate margins, many millions of years ago. The compressive plate margins are the sites of mountain ranges, and these are characterized also by strongly folded rocks. Similar rocks in the exposed roots of ancient mountain ranges, whose peaks were long since eroded away and redeposited into the oceans, are easily recognized in the geological record. These also provide clues about the distribution of plate margins through geological time.

Attempting to unravel the complexities of geological history on the continents for reinterpretation in terms of plate tectonics has just begun. The task is difficult because the geological record is incomplete. Much of the evidence once preserved in the rocks has been removed by erosion. Seventy percent of the earth's surface is covered by the oceans, and exploration of the rocks of the ocean floor is in its infancy, despite the tremendous advances of recent years. Nevertheless, the concept of plate tectonics provides a framework for the interpretation of fragments of geological information that would otherwise remain isolated. This approach is applicable to the whole span of geological time, although the reconstructions that may prove possible are never likely to give us more than intermittent and incomplete pictures of the distribution of plate margins. The evidence for sea-floor spreading, on the other hand, promises to yield a detailed and complete picture of the relative motions of plates during the past 100 million years or so, and the evidence from paleomagnetism for the relative movements of continents may extend this for several hundred million years.

Sea-floor spreading: evidence from the earth's magnetic field

The critical evidence adduced during the winter of 1966/67 for the sea-floor spreading model illustrated in figure 1 was based not on any conventional approaches to geology or geophysics but upon the history of changes in the earth's magnetic field. We have already mentioned the polarity reversals of the magnetic field, their fossil records in weakly magnetized rocks, and the linear magnetic anomalies of oceanic regions that appear to be related to the polarity reversals. We may now examine the evidence arising from the fact that many rocks preserve a fossil record of the magnetic field existing at the time of their formation.

Figure 4A shows schematically the distribution of lines of magnetic force for the earth's magnetic field. The background for understanding this diagram is delightfully presented in Britannica *Great Books* Volume 28 by the work of William Gilbert, who earned the title "the first investigator of the powers of the magnet." In 1600, after eighteen years of study, he published a book called *On the Loadstone and Magnetic Bodies and on the Great Magnet the Earth.* Loadstone, now spelled *lodestone,* is a rock known to the ancients as a material that attracts iron. The mariner's compass was designed with the discovery of another curious property of lodestone: when suitably suspended, it rotates into a north-south direction. Lodestone contains varying proportions of the mineral magnetite, an iron oxide (Fe_3O_4). The mineral is magnetized and imparts magnetic properties to its host rock.

Gilbert went on to "formulate our new and till now unheard-of view of the earth . . . that the terrestrial globe is magnetic and is a loadstone," [*] and he illustrated the directions of the lines of magnetic force by sketches of the earth with small magnets at the surface lining up along the directions shown in figure 4A. The magnetic field at each point on the earth's surface is uniquely defined by two properties—a direction, and an intensity or strength. Figure 4 shows that the direction is not tangential to the horizontal surface except at the equator; elsewhere it dips toward the interior. The angle of dip, which at the equator is zero, is $90°$ at the magnetic poles. At points between, the angle is directly correlated with the latitude, unless the local rocks have properties that disturb the normal distribution of the magnetic lines of force. Disturbances of this kind are called anomalies in the earth's magnetic field.

The earth behaves as if it enclosed a large magnet with magnetic axis almost parallel to the earth's rotational axis. This hypothetical magnet is referred to as the magnetic dipole. The poles of magnets at the earth's surface that point toward the north are defined as north-seeking poles, or north poles for brevity. Because north magnetic poles are attracted to south magnetic poles, the hypothetical magnet within the earth must have its south magnetic pole directed to the north geographic pole, as shown in figure 4A. This confusing juxtaposition of "north" and "south" directions need not concern us, because we are interested in the magnetic field and not in the internal properties of the earth that produce it. What is important is that the present field produced by the earth's magnetic properties (figure 4A) has been reversed periodically, as shown

---

[*] *GBWW*, Vol. 28, p. 23b.

in figure 4B. Reversal of the magnetic field requires reversal of the earth's hypothetical internal magnet.

Nearly all rocks exhibit weak magnetic properties, caused by a small proportion of minerals that become magnetized during formation of the rock. The minerals become magnetized or aligned parallel to the direction of the existing magnetic field. If this magnetization is not subsequently modified by one of several processes, it provides the means for determining the directions of the earth's magnetic field at various times. It has been known since 1906 that some rocks are magnetized in a direction opposite to the earth's present magnetic field, but this received very little attention until the 1950s, when a controversy developed. Proposals that the earth's magnetic field had reversed direction at intervals were challenged by interpretations involving self-reversal of certain rocks after normal magnetization, caused by some chemical or mineralogical peculiarity. It is known that self-reversal can occur, and there was no independent proof that the earth's magnetic field was capable of reversal.

The conclusive test for reversals of the earth's magnetic field came with the demonstration that the magnetic polarities, or directions of magnetization, were the same in rock units of the same age on different continents. It is hardly conceivable that the regular pattern of normal and reversed polarities depicted in figure 4C could be caused by magnetic self-reversal in magnetized rocks, occurring on a global scale and only within specific time intervals.

The geomagnetic time scale for polarity reversals shown in figure 4C was determined by measuring both the age and the direction of magnetization in carefully selected rocks from series of lava flows in various parts of the world. The first study with ages of sufficient accuracy was published in 1963 by A. Cox, R. R. Doell, and G. B. Dalrymple. They used the potassium-argon radiometric method of dating. All lavas contain potassium, and one of the potassium isotopes, K^{40}, is radioactive. This decays to yield the gas argon of mass 40, Ar^{40}. It was discovered in 1948 that at least some of the argon generated in potassium-bearing minerals was retained within the mineral structure, and by the end of the 1950s potassium-argon dating had become an effective technique for the solution of geological problems. From measurement of the amount of K^{40} and Ar^{40} in a rock or mineral, and the known radioactive decay properties of K^{40}, the time of formation of the rock can be dated with an accuracy of about 3 percent.

The first studies of magnetic polarity in radiometrically dated lavas indicated a pattern of alternating polarities with periodicity of the order of 1 million years. These intervals were termed polarity epochs. But extension of the studies of lava sequences revealed the existence within such epochs of polarity intervals having shorter durations of about 100,000 years, and these were termed polarity events. Two such events are shown in figure 4C by the two black or normal segments that interrupt the otherwise white portion of the vertical scale indicating the reversed Matuyama epoch. Figure 4C shows the correlation between the radiometrically dated lavas, indicated by black and white dots, and the directions of magnetization as it appeared in 1967.

The sequence of polarity epochs during which the earth's magnetic field was alternately normal (as in figure 4A) and reversed (as in figure 4B) is punctuated by these shorter polarity events. Figure 4C shows the problem of resolving the limits of such events, caused by the uncertainties in the potassium-argon dating method. A dating error of 3 percent in a rock 4 million years old amounts to more than 100,000 years, which is the total duration of many polarity events. The polarities shown in figure 4C by the black and white dots may be intermixed for about 100,000 years on either side of the boundaries given between normal and reversed magnetization. The epochs are clearly demarcated, but the events are less clearly defined. The errors in the potassium-argon dating method become too large for extension of the geomagnetic time scale further back than 4.5 million years.

Additional events within this period have been discovered since the compilation of data represented in figure 4C, from the study of lavas and the magnetic properties of rocks in deep-sea cores. The magnetic properties of deep-sea cores have also provided information about behavior of the earth's magnetic field during the transition from normal to reversed polarity. We shall return to this in a later section, because removal of the magnetic field could admit greater fluxes of cosmic rays, which could possibly influence the course of evolution of life on earth.

Figure 4C illustrates changes in the earth's magnetic field as a function of time. The polarity epochs and events are synchronous in widely spaced parts of the earth, and there can be no reasonable doubt that these events are caused by a rather rapid switching of the earth's magnetic dipole, represented by the reversal of the hypothetical magnet in figures 4A and 4B.

According to the simple model in figure 4A, the magnetic field at any point on the earth's surface is caused solely by the magnetic dipole. In fact, most rocks in the earth's crust are weakly magnetized, and the normal field due to the dipole is modified by the influence of these rocks. If the rocks in a particular region are magnetized in the same direction as the earth's existing magnetic field, the magnetic intensity in this region is greater than the average due to the dipole alone. The magnetic field is strengthened, and this is called a positive anomaly. On the other hand, if the rocks are magnetized in direction opposite to the existing field, they will oppose the earth's magnetism, and the intensity of the magnetic field will be reduced compared with the average due to the dipole alone. This is called a negative anomaly. Thus, at any given point of time, the intensity of the earth's magnetic field at the surface will vary according to the magnetic characteristics of the under-lying rocks. These variations are usually small compared with the total magnetic field strength, but they may be very significant. The hypothesis of sea-floor spreading became theory when sequences of weak linear magnetic anomalies observed at the present point in time were correlated with the time scale for the earth's polarity reversals.

The normal intensity of the earth's magnetic field varies as a function of magnetic latitude, being lowest at the equator and highest near the poles. There are short-term and secular periodic variations in both the direction and the intensity of this field, as well as irregular fluctuations known as magnetic storms. These are neglected in the following account, which is concerned only with the anomalies caused by rocks in the crust.

The intensive collection of magnetic data in oceanic regions was ini-tiated in 1948 during oceanographic cruises from the Lamont Geological Observatory and the Scripps Institution of Oceanography. By 1957 it was established that a large positive anomaly had occurred over the rift valley of the mid-Atlantic ridge, with negative anomalies being de-tected over the adjacent submarine mountains. Results of a detailed magnetic survey of the northeast Pacific Ocean were published in 1958. The survey revealed a pattern of narrow, remarkably straight anomalies, alternately positive and negative and about 30 km in width, trending north-south for as much as 1,000 km. The largest anomaly in this alter-nating sequence is less than 2 percent of the average field for the region. The remarkable regularity of this striped magnetic pattern pointed to some simple cause, but no satisfactory explanation was forthcoming at this stage.

The explanation that has come to be generally accepted, and that eventually led geologists and geophysicists to embrace the concept of sea-floor spreading, was one proposed in 1963 by F. J. Vine and D. H. Matthews, when Vine was a graduate student at Cambridge, England. L. W. Morley independently presented essentially the same hypothesis in 1963 at a meeting of the Royal Society of Canada.

Vine and Matthews suggested that the pattern of linear magnetic anomalies was due to strips of the ocean floor being magnetized in op-posite directions. The strips magnetized in the same direction as the earth's magnetic field enhance the field intensity and produce a positive anomaly, and the strips magnetized in the opposite direction produce a negative anomaly. Vine and Matthews explained the existence of such strips by correlating the anomalies with sea-floor spreading and reversals of the earth's magnetic field, as illustrated schematically in figure 5.

According to the theory of sea-floor spreading (figure 1), a convective upcurrent in the earth beneath an oceanic ridge is accompanied by the formation of new oceanic crust resulting from the intrusion and ex-trusion of lava. Let us assume, quite arbitrarily, that sea-floor spreading began at the mid-Atlantic ridge 3 million years ago. Figure 5A shows the effect produced during a portion of the Gauss normal polarity epoch (figure 4C) between 3 and 2.5 million years ago. As the lava cooled and solidified, it became magnetized in the direction of the existing (normal) magnetic field, producing a positive magnetic anomaly. As sea-floor spreading occurred, this magnetized crustal strip was transported laterally away from the ridge as if on a conveyor belt, retaining parallelism with the ridge. The Matuyama reversed polarity epoch began 2.5 million years ago. Continued spreading for 0.25 million years produced the situation in figure 5B, with the block of new crust *cd* magnetized in the opposite direction to the original block *ab* in figure 5A. The latter has now become separated into the two blocks *ac* and *db,* which produce negative anomalies in the earth's reversed magnetic field. The block of crust *cd* which was magnetized during the Matuyama epoch produces a positive anomaly above it until the earth's polarity changes again. In this way, the sequence of polarity reversals for the whole earth (figure 4C) has been imprinted on a strip of oceanic crust as if on a tape recorder. Figure 5C is a cross section of the sequence of magnetized strips resulting from the polarity reversals of the past 3 million years. The alternating directions of magnetization of the strips produce the sequence of positive and negative anomalies, as depicted.

If the observed sequences of linear anomalies associated with mid-oceanic ridges can be correlated with the polarity reversal scale, then we have a means for calculating rates of lateral movement during sea-floor spreading. The average velocity of movement is given by the distance of a specific anomaly from the ridge crest, divided by the age of the correlated polarity epoch. This age is the time taken for that strip of crust to be conveyed to its present position from the ridge where it was generated.

The Vine and Matthews hypothesis was at first received with some skepticism, because not one of the three basic assumptions invoked was generally accepted in 1963. These were (1) sea-floor spreading, (2) the contribution of magnetized crustal rocks to the production of the oceanic magnetic anomalies, and (3) polarity reversals of the earth's magnetic field. There were other difficulties. The best known examples of linear anomalies, in the northeast Pacific Ocean, did not appear to be parallel to any existing or preexisting oceanic ridges, and in surveys of known mid-oceanic ridges the existence of linear anomalies paralleling the central anomaly was not established.

By 1965 the two basic assumptions about magnetic anomalies and polarity reversals had become accepted, and H. W. Menard of Scripps had identified a belt of ridges and troughs in the northeast Pacific, parallel to the linear anomalies. J. T. Wilson of Toronto showed that the apparent absence of oceanic ridges elsewhere in the northeast Pacific is due to complications caused by the large horizontal fault zones shown in figure 2. Wilson also introduced the concept of transform faulting, show-

Fig. 5

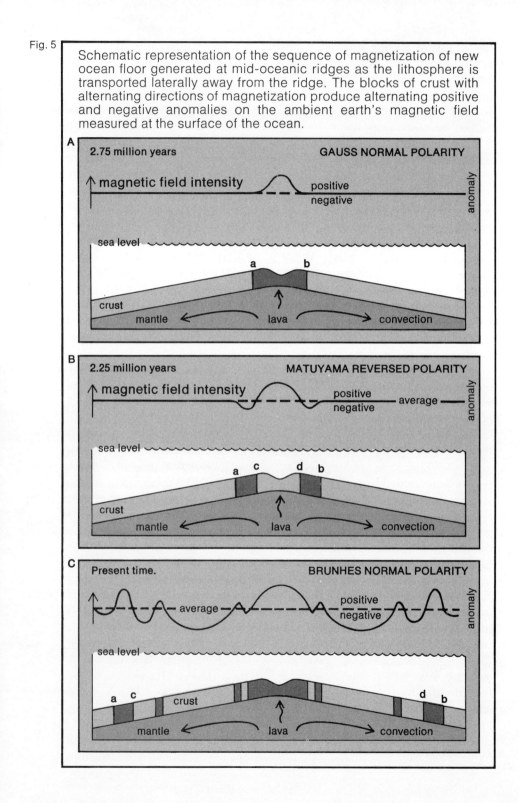

Schematic representation of the sequence of magnetization of new ocean floor generated at mid-oceanic ridges as the lithosphere is transported laterally away from the ridge. The blocks of crust with alternating directions of magnetization produce alternating positive and negative anomalies on the ambient earth's magnetic field measured at the surface of the ocean.

A

2.75 million years   GAUSS NORMAL POLARITY

↑ magnetic field intensity   positive

negative

anomaly

sea level

a   b

crust

mantle ← lava → convection

B

2.25 million years   MATUYAMA REVERSED POLARITY

↑ magnetic field intensity   positive — average —

negative

anomaly

sea level

a   c   d   b

crust

mantle ← lava → convection

C

Present time.   BRUNHES NORMAL POLARITY

↑ — average — positive

negative

anomaly

sea level

a   c   crust   d   b

mantle ← lava → convection

ing that these fault zones are a special kind of lateral fracture related to opening up of the crust along the ridge crests. We need not consider this further, except to note that it illuminated the mechanics of sea-floor spreading.

Despite this evidence, J. R. Heirtzler and his associates at Lamont Geological Observatory remained uncertain. At a symposium on "The World Rift System" in 1965 (published 1966), they wrote:

> *We are not sure of the ultimate origin of the ridge magnetic anomalies. . . . However, we feel that the variation in amplitude of the axial anomalies as well as the completely different character of the flank anomalies argues against the Vine and Matthews hypothesis.*

Then, in a *Science* article of December 16, 1966, Vine reviewed new evidence from several magnetic surveys that linear magnetic anomalies can be correlated from one oceanic ridge profile to another, that these do parallel the ridge crests, and that the anomalies are remarkably symmetrical about the axis of the ridge in many regions. Vine considered this evidence to be virtual proof of sea-floor spreading.

Also in *Science,* December 2, 1966, Heirtzler and W. C. Pitman compared the magnetic anomaly patterns from the Pacific-Antarctic ridge with those from the Reykjanes ridge south of Iceland. They concluded that the results "strongly support the essential features of the Vine and Matthews hypothesis and of ocean-floor spreading as postulated by Dietz and Hess." With acceptance by the Lamont group, the bandwagon that had been rolling slowly since Hess proposed sea-floor spreading in 1960 gathered such momentum that it carried most earth scientists along with it. The revolution had come.

Average rates of movement away from various ridges for the past 4 million years have been determined by plotting the distances of anomalies from ridge crests against the geomagnetic time scale for the corresponding polarity reversals. The gradients of the lines so obtained gave rates varying from 1 cm/year to more than 6 cm/year. The distances of the oldest dated linear anomalies from ridge crests thus range from 40 km to more than 240 km. The pattern of magnetic anomalies extends much farther than this, and probably completely from the ridge axis to the continental shelf in many regions. If the assumption is made that spreading rates have remained reasonably constant, which might be anticipated for inertial reasons, then the spacing of the linear anomalies from a ridge axis can be used to extrapolate the time scale beyond the 4-million-year limit imposed by the error in potassium-argon dating methods.

Vine constructed a magnetic anomaly profile for a 3,500-km section of the northeast Pacific Ocean crust extending from the Gorda ridge, and calibrated part of it against the geomagnetic time scale to obtain an average spreading rate of 4.5 cm/year for the past 4 million years. Assuming the same spreading rate for the total section, he was able to extend the time scale of polarity reversals to more than 80 million years. Each anomaly identified in the profile was correlated with a polarity epoch or event and assigned a provisional age, and the ages became dates for the deduced polarity reversal sequence. Vine emphasized the speculative nature of this extended geomagnetic time scale but noted its utility as a means for prediction and correlation of anomalies in other oceanic areas.

Heirtzler and his associates published four contiguous papers in the March 1968 issue of the *Journal of Geophysical Research* comparing and correlating the linear magnetic anomaly pattern that had been mapped over extensive regions of the North Pacific, South Pacific, South Atlantic, and Indian oceans. They found that the pattern was bilaterally symmetrical about the crest of the ridge in each ocean, and that the pattern was the same in all oceans. Easily identifiable anomalies were numbered for reference purposes and for correlation from one profile to another. By assuming that the pattern is caused by a sequence of normally and reversely magnetized blocks produced by sea-floor spreading at the axes of the ridges, they showed that the sequences of blocks correspond to the same geomagnetic time scale.

Using paleomagnetic and paleontological data, the authors assigned a provisional age scale to the sequence of anomalies up to 79 million years. Each anomaly is thus assigned an age, and the distribution of anomalies in the ocean basins corresponds to the distribution of isochrons (age-lines) for the ocean basin floor. The locus of a specific magnetic anomaly is a line of constant age, where the age corresponds to the time of magnetization, which is interpreted as the time that this part of the ocean floor was brought to the surface as lava at an active oceanic ridge. Despite the provisional character of the ages, the ability to contour the ocean basins with isochrons provides us with the prospect of unraveling the history of the ocean basins and the resultant movement of the continents, with a precision of detail inconceivable during the debate about continental drift that occupied the first half of the century.

There is some evidence that spreading rates have not remained constant, and that the rates of spreading of one ridge relative to another may change with time. More detailed geological and geophysical studies of the oceanic ridges and the flanking oceanic crust are required for comparison with the patterns of magnetic anomalies. As more data are acquired during the next few years, we can anticipate that interpretations of linear anomalies in terms of crustal structure and relative displacements of crustal blocks will be modified. Already there are differences of opinion about whether the magnetic anomalies should be interpreted in terms of steady spreading, of variable worldwide increases in spreading rates, or of episodic spreading where all movement stops completely for a period. The uncertainties were expressed by Sir Edward Bullard in his Bakerian Lecture to the Royal Society of London:

> *The lecture on which this paper is based was given in June 1967; it was a well chosen time, the threefold story of the reversals of the field had just become clear and could be easily and elegantly set out. In the few months needed to write the paper there has been an avalanche of new results which has revealed many discrepancies. . . . The usual chaos of the Earth sciences is clearly about to be re-established at a higher level of understanding.*

The cruise of the *Glomar Challenger* will be reviewed in a later section. Here, we refer only to the results published in 1970 from deep-sea drilling in the South Atlantic. The sea-floor spreading model proposed by Hess (figure 1) predicts that the greater the distance from a ridge, the older should be the deepest sediments overlying the oceanic crust. At each drilling site the paleontological age of the deepest sediment overlying the lava of the crust was determined from the calcareous microfossils abundant in the sediment, and the ages do increase with distance from the ridge, as predicted by theory. Moreover, the paleontological ages show good agreement with the age of the crustal lava predicted from the magnetic anomaly pattern, assuming a constant spreading rate. The paleontological ages indicated a constant spreading rate of 2 cm/year.

Figure 1 shows the South Atlantic Ocean increasing in width by sea-floor spreading. The continents of Africa and South America are drifting apart because they are carried in the lithosphere conveyor belt. If the spreading process were reversed at the same half-rate of 2 cm/year, then 4 cm of ocean would disappear each year, and in less than 150 million years the ocean would be closed and the two continents would be in contact.

Continental drift and polar wandering

Given the process of sea-floor spreading as depicted in figures 1 and 5, then continental drift follows. We have noted that before sea-floor spreading was proposed, the quiescent controversy about continental drift was revived in the 1950s by paleomagnetic research. Paleomagnetism provides evidence for the relative movement of continents quite independently of the evidence for sea-floor spreading, although both depend upon the magnetization of rocks at their time of formation. The lines of magnetic force in figures 4A and 4B show that the direction of magnetization of a rock will be toward the magnetic north, making an angle above or below the horizontal. This angle varies with the magnetic latitude and provides a measure of the distance between the magnetized rock and the magnetic pole. Therefore, measurement of the fossil magnetization preserved in a rock specimen from its time of formation gives the distance between the specimen location and the pole, as well as the direction of the pole at this time. By convention, the paleomagnetic pole positions are recorded in the Northern Hemisphere, and the polarity is neglected. Interpretation of paleomagnetic results is completely dependent upon a knowledge of the geology of the rock samples, and their application depends upon a number of assumptions that we need not consider.

Figure 4 shows that at the present time the magnetic North Pole is not coincident with the geographic pole. It is well known that the magnetic pole has moved relative to the geographic pole within historical times, but the difference between magnetic and geographic axes has not amounted to more than a few degrees. Paleomagnetic results for rock samples from many parts of the world with ages up to 20 million years or so indicate that the position of the magnetic pole has remained near to the geographic pole throughout this period. Results for older rocks offer a different picture, with the paleomagnetic poles departing significantly from the position of the present geographic pole.

The paleomagnetic method is to locate the average position of the paleomagnetic pole for rocks from one continent that were formed during a specific time interval. For a given continent, it is found that the positions of the paleomagnetic poles vary with the ages of the rocks sampled. The loci of paleomagnetic poles are called the path of polar wandering for a particular continent. It turns out that each continent has a different path of polar wandering as determined for rocks older than about 60 million years, and these paths have been traced back for more than 500 million years.

Interpretation of the paths of polar wandering is difficult. The magnetic pole may have remained close to the present geographic pole, and the paths of apparent polar wandering may in fact represent paths of continental wandering relative to the pole. Alternatively the geomagnetic pole may have been displaced from the present rotational axis, which probably requires that the rotational axis has been displaced as well. The results indicate that all continents except one have moved relative to each other, and they may all have moved.

The rates of relative movement determined from paleomagnetic studies are a few centimeters per year, which is the same as results obtained from sea-floor spreading and analysis of the magnetic anomalies. The paleomagnetic results suggest rapid drifting of the continents at times, interspersed with periods of little or no movement. Much more information is needed to complete the picture, but it seems possible that the evidence from paleomagnetism for the relative movements of the continents during the past 500 million years or more, combined with the evidence from sea-floor spreading, may permit the detailed reconstruction of plate movements and continental drift through this whole period.

The idea of continental drift was at first conceived by Wegener in 1910, "when considering the map of the world, under the direct impression produced by the congruence of the coastlines on either side of the Atlantic." After initially dismissing the idea as improbable, Wegener found other evidence that convinced him of its validity, and the great debate began when he published his first paper on the subject in 1912. Since then, many geologists have used the congruence of coastlines in attempts to reconstruct the supercontinents of Pangaea, or of Gondwanaland and Laurasia, as they existed before the onset of drifting. Most of the results have been rather generalized sketches, and some of them have taken considerable liberties with both geometry and geology.

In 1965, Sir Edward Bullard and his Cambridge colleagues introduced the computer to the business of fitting together continental masses on an objective basis. They examined the fit of the continents around the Atlantic Ocean by numerical methods and found remarkably good fits at the 500-fathom depth contour, which lies on the steep part of the continental slope between continental shelf and ocean basin floor (*see* figure 2). In 1969 and 1970 other scientists published computerized fits for Australia against Antarctica, Africa against Antarctica, and for the complete reassembly of Gondwanaland (South America, Africa, Arabia, Australia, Antarctica, India, Madagascar, and New Zealand). The computer was constrained in its selection of geometric fits to those configurations that were geologically plausible. Most of the geological support for the reconstruction of Gondwanaland by A. G. Smith and A. Hallam of Cambridge and Oxford, respectively, came from studies published only during the last four years.

In 1970, R. S. Dietz and J. C. Holden of the Environmental Science Services Administration in Florida were able to repeat Wegener's reconstruction of Pangaea with cartographic precision. In the October issue of *Scientific American* they used the new geometrical and geological fits to position Pangaea for the first time in absolute coordinates on the globe. Their guiding rationale for the reconstruction was the drift mechanism associated with plate tectonics and sea-floor spreading (figures 1, 3, and 5). Using these same guidelines, they prepared four maps illustrating the breakup and dispersion of the continents during the past 180 million years. Absolute geographic coordinates were assigned for the continents as well as for the active oceanic rift zones and the oceanic trenches as they migrated to their present positions (figure 2).

Dietz and Holden also extrapolated present-day plate movements to predict the appearance of the world 50 million years from now. Among the predicted changes are continued opening of the Atlantic Ocean, movement of Australia to the Asian plate, virtual closure of the Mediterranean Sea by the northward drift of the African plate (figure 3), creation of new land in the Caribbean by compression and resulting uplift, and some significant changes in the geography of California.

The San Andreas Fault is part of a large fracture system responsible for most of the earthquakes that periodically shake California. The disastrous San Francisco earthquake of 1906 was caused by horizontal displacement of up to 20 feet along the fault line, extending for 435 km. Intermittent displacements of this type amount to average movement rates on the order of centimeters per year, which is that required by seafloor spreading. The boundary between the Pacific plate and the North American plate (figure 3) appears to follow the trace of the San Andreas Fault zone. Baja California and a sliver of California west of the San Andreas Fault are apparently drifting to the northwest with the Pacific plate, while the North American plate drifts westward. Dietz and Holden estimated that in about 10 million years Los Angeles will be abreast of San Francisco, still fixed to the mainland, and that in about 60 million years Los Angeles will start sliding into the Aleutian trench south of Alaska, as the Pacific plate sinks down into the earth's interior.

We have considered the occurrence of continental drift during the past 180 million years, and for the next 60 million years. This represents a very small fraction of the immense span of geological history. Figure 6 compares the geological time scale with the extent of the dated and

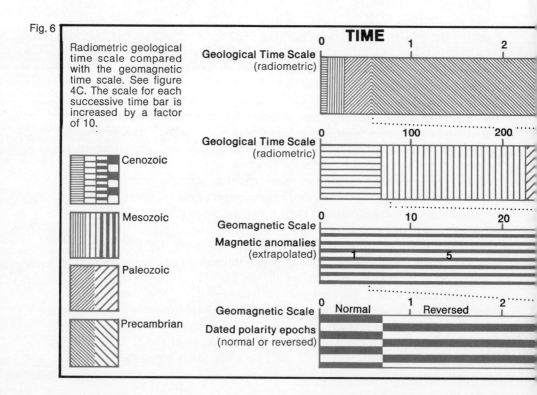

Fig. 6

Radiometric geological time scale compared with the geomagnetic time scale. See figure 4C. The scale for each successive time bar is increased by a factor of 10.

Cenozoic

Mesozoic

Paleozoic

Precambrian

extrapolated geomagnetic time scales. The scale for each successive column is increased by a factor of 10.

The earth was formed about 4.5 billion years ago, and 85 percent of this time is classified as Precambrian. Traces of primitive life forms have been detected in rocks as old as 3 billion years, but abundant fossils of more advanced forms appear rather abruptly in rocks only 570 million years old, from the beginning of the Paleozoic period. At this time, creatures began to build shells, which are more readily preserved as fossils than the earlier soft-bodied animals. Erect, two-legged primates developed only about 2 million years ago, which may help readers to appreciate the magnitude of the scales in figure 6.

The episode of continental drift that began 180 million years ago occupies only 4 percent of geological time. The drift of lithosphere plates is believed to be responsible for the elevation of the active mountain ranges of the Cenozoic age, whose distribution is shown in figure 2. Geological history includes many periods of mountain building, and present investigations are seeking links between these periods and earlier episodes of continental drifting. Geological research papers published in 1970 have traced the relative movements of North America and Europe for the past 600 million years and suggested that the Eurasian land mass was formerly separated into two plates.

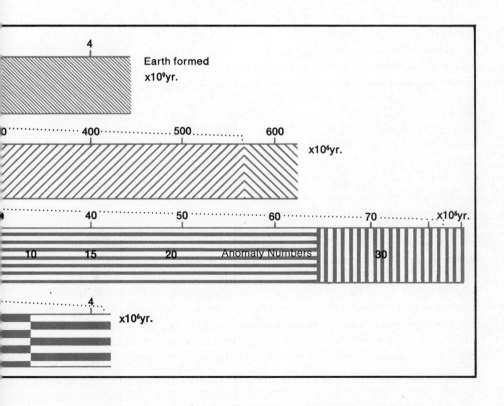

According to A. M. Ziegler of the University of Chicago, there is evidence that an Atlantic Ocean existing during the Lower Paleozoic (figure 6) was closed about 350 million years ago when the bordering continents collided and produced an active mountain range in the zone of compression. The continents opened again about 150 million years ago along a slightly different line during the present period of spreading from the mid-Atlantic ridge (figures 1 and 3).

Paleomagnetic data for rocks in Asia suggest that the Siberian and Russian platforms were widely separated in the Lower Paleozoic, that they began to converge about 400 million years ago, and that they collided about 230 million years ago. It was suggested as long ago as 1924 that the prominent north-south zone of the Ural Mountain system represents the scar of a collision boundary between two drifting continental masses, but, as noted above, most Soviet geologists have not accepted the concept of long-distance horizontal transport of the continents. They regard the paleomagnetic data as too unreliable to be used as evidence either for or against continental drift. W. Hamilton, a member of the U.S. Geological Survey and an advocate of plate tectonics, reviewed the Soviet literature and concluded that the geology of the Ural Mountain system is quite in accord with the collision concept. From the geology of the region, he deduced the histories of the margins of the two continental masses before and during the inferred collision.

At the annual meeting of the Geological Society of America in November 1970, E. M. Moores of the University of California presented a paper in which he reconstructed a history of fragmentation and assembly of all the continents through a period extending back into the Precambrian (figure 6). The history begins with the assembly of dispersed continents to form a single supercontinent, *Pangaea I*. This was fragmented by continental drift until by about 500 million years ago there existed four continents. These collided and became sutured successively at times of about 400, 280, and 230 million years ago, forming once again a supercontinent, *Pangaea II*. This then separated in the sequence deduced by Dietz and Holden beginning about 180 million years ago.

These examples suggest a succession of continental collisions and separations, with mountain ranges resulting from the collisions. Other evidence led P. M. Hurley of the Massachusetts Institute of Technology to conclude in 1970 that there had been no large-scale breakup of the supercontinent of Laurasia prior to the current drift episode that began about 200 million years ago. He compiled all available data on the ages of rocks and plotted zones of equal age ranges on the reconstructed continent of Laurasia. The concentric arrangement of age zones supports the concept that Laurasia formed by continental accretion. The ancient nucleus became enlarged as successive zones of volcanic material from the earth's interior were welded onto the continental margins. This pattern of concentric age zones presents difficulties for models involving repeated separation and collision of portions of Laurasia.

New theories of mountain building

The concept of geosyncline and orogenic cycle has been important in geology ever since 1859, when James Hall realized that the rocks of the Appalachian Mountains in New York State had been formed originally beneath water, in an elongated subsiding trough. The products of weathering of the neighboring lands were transported to the trough mainly by streams and rivers, both in solution and as discrete particles. There, the particles were deposited, and some of the material in solution was precipitated around them. In this way, a great pile of sedimentary rocks accumulated as the trough subsided to accommodate the incoming material. Eventually, the sediments were folded and elevated to produce the mountain range. In 1873, J. D. Dana gave to such troughs the name geosynclinal, which was later changed to geosyncline. This concept of a great inversion of relief from a depressed zone of the earth's crust to an elevated, folded mountain chain was revolutionary at the time, and it has been followed by innumerable geological syntheses. Until recently, it served as the master geological scheme, the comprehensive framework into which all of the standard geological subjects could be accommodated.

With the revolution of the 1960s—revival of the idea of continental drift, and formulation of the theory of plate tectonics—many geologists have come to feel that this conventional cycle is obsolete. According to the classical concepts, the onset of orogenesis (mountain building) is preceded by geosynclinal deposition of sediments. New models for mountain building involve the movement and collision of lithosphere plates. The new models also require thick sequences of sedimentary rocks for conversion into mountain ranges, but their deposition does not presage the onset of orogenesis. Sites for contemporary sedimentation occur mainly along continental margins. These include the continental shelves, the abyssal ocean floor at the foot of the continental slopes, the oceanic trenches, and sites associated with island arcs and small ocean basins.

Figures 1 and 3 show different types of continental margins. The eastern borders of the American continents are stable, and moving simultaneously with the Atlantic Ocean lithosphere. The piles of sediment off the Atlantic coasts are accumulating still. The western borders of the American continents, in contrast, are plate boundaries, and the continents are uncoupled from the converging Pacific Ocean plate. Mountain building begins when a stable continental margin, such as the eastern side of the Americas, becomes uncoupled from the oceanic portion of a lithosphere plate and changes to a convergent juncture such as the western margins of the South American plate.

Geologists are exploring possible sequences of events and their consequences for orogenesis. Detailed syntheses were presented by A. H. Mitchell and H. G. Reading of Oxford University in the *Journal of Geology* for November 1969, and J. F. Dewey (Cambridge University) and J. M. Bird (State University of New York) in the *Journal of Geophysical Research* in May 1970. Dewey and Bird believe that the major mountain belts that have formed during at least the last 1,000 million years of the earth's history (*see* figure 6) can be explained by plate tectonics, "notwithstanding strong arguments to the contrary" presented by Hurley on the marginal accretion of Laurasia.

These ideas were explored at a Penrose Conference of the Geological Society of America held in December 1969, at Asilomar, California, in a discussion of the topic: "the meaning of the new global tectonics for magmatism, sedimentation, and metamorphism in orogenic belts." There is no printed record of the informal Penrose Conferences, but reports were published by the convener, W. R. Dickinson of Stanford University. In the issue of *Science* for June 5, 1970, he wrote:

> *The plate tectonic model explains orogenic belts, where most mountain-building and rock deformation occur, as the narrow, elongate regions of juncture between moving plates or segments of the lithosphere. . . . The complexity of the telescoping and overlapping of crustal rocks observed along ancient convergent plate junctures became evident from discussions at the conference.*

Dickinson went on to review and systematize the ideas discussed at the conference and then considered the classical geosynclinal theory:

> *In a sense, then, the geosynclinal theory of orogeny remains valid if the causative function of a thick sediment prism is replaced by a notion of coincidence or consequence . . . for a thick sedimentary pile simply to exist at a continental margin thus predestines eventual deformation when, inevitably, the margin becomes active. . . . Each step ought to be one of a finite array of types, but the order of the steps should vary from place to place. . . . A single, sequential orogenic progression . . . cannot be expected to remain part of the plate tectonic model of orogeny.*

The classical mountain-building cycle that has been dominant in geology for about a century is thus greatly modified by the current revolution in earth sciences. The formation of mountain ranges is relegated to a second-order product of the first-order process of plate migrations.

Peter J. Wyllie

Voyages of the *Glomar Challenger:* deep-sea drilling

When Charles Darwin was a young man of twenty-two, he sailed in H.M.S. *Beagle* as a naturalist on a round-the-world expedition that lasted five years, from 1831 to 1836. This voyage provided Darwin with data for a lifetime of study, resulting in, among other things, the publication in 1859 of *The Origin of Species by Means of Natural Selection,** probably the most widely known scientific book ever written.

The data obtained from the voyages of the *Glomar Challenger,* a strange-looking ship constructed specifically for the purpose of drilling and recovering long cores of sediments from the ocean floor (figure 7), will exceed in quantity the data collected during the voyage of the *Beagle,* and it seems possible that this will ultimately have scientific results to match even the theory of evolution in significance.

The first of nine cruise segments of the *Glomar Challenger* began on August 11, 1968, and the ninth leg was completed on January 27, 1970, when the ship docked in Panama after drilling 149 holes in the Atlantic and Pacific ocean floors. In March 1970, *Glomar Challenger* left on the first of fifteen additional cruise segments, or legs, that will include deep drilling operations in the Mediterranean Sea and the Indian Ocean; this series is due to end in June 1973. According to a pamphlet from the National Science Foundation dated August 1970, the first two years of operation of the Deep Sea Drilling Project "produced information of such significance as to mark it as one of the most successful scientific expeditions of all time."

In this period approximately 195 holes were drilled at 125 sites in the Atlantic and Pacific Oceans. Sediment and rock cores were obtained from the earth's crust under water more than 20,000 feet deep. Several holes were drilled deeper than 3,200 feet into the ocean bottom. The drilling ship has used the longest drill string ever suspended from a floating platform—20,760 feet, almost four miles.

By the end of the thirteenth cruise leg, through the Mediterranean, on October 6, 1970, the score had increased to 219 holes at 154 drilling sites, and the total length of sediment and hard rock core recovered exceeded 30,000 feet, or 9 km. Rates of deep-sea sedimentation vary considerably from place to place, but values typically range 1 to 10 cm per 1,000 years. The cores recovered thus represent much geological time, and their significance lies in the events recorded in the sediments during the time intervals covered by each core.

---

* *GBWW*, Vol. 49, pp. 1–251.

203

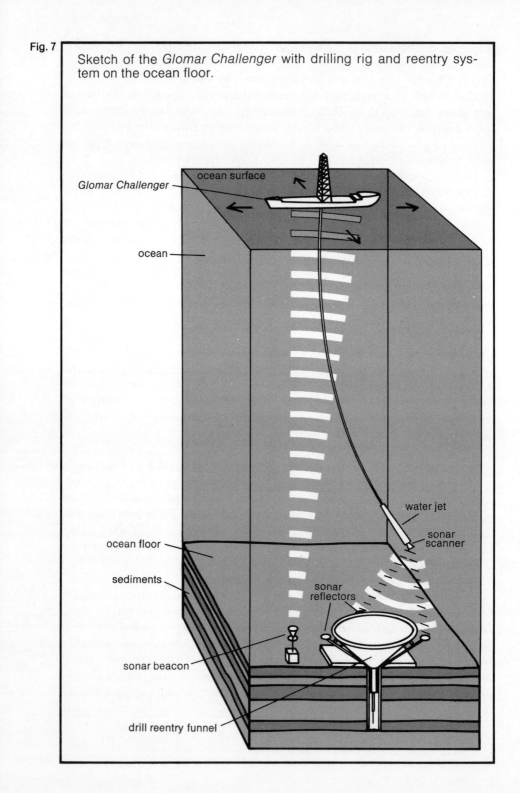

Fig. 7

Sketch of the *Glomar Challenger* with drilling rig and reentry system on the ocean floor.

ocean surface

Glomar Challenger

ocean

water jet

sonar scanner

ocean floor

sediments

sonar reflectors

sonar beacon

drill reentry funnel

Glomar Challenger

Oceanic sediments are derived from two sources. From the land come the products of weathering and erosion, such as sand, silt, and volcanic ash, which are transported by the wind, rivers, or drifting icebergs. Rivers also carry dissolved material which contributes to the salinity of the oceans as water is evaporated to the atmosphere. Part of this material is precipitated among the sedimentary particles when conditions are appropriate, and part of it is secreted by growing organisms. A host of microscopic animals and plants live near the surface of the ocean. These creatures, drifting at the mercy of the currents, are called *plankton*. As they die, they produce a steady "rain" of shells and skeletons, which falls to the ocean floor.

The sequence of microfossils and mineral particles together become part of the record of the earth's history, containing evidence about sedimentation, the geological history of the sediment sources, biological history, climatic changes, geochemical events in the oceans and sediments, and paleomagnetism. The sedimentary cores, which are available for detailed investigation by interested scientists, will provide reference material for a multitude of future studies. The completeness of the oceanic sediment record contrasts with evidence from the continents, where the continuity of history has usually to be pieced together from many sources and locations. The results obtained from the cores provide base lines permitting confident interpretation of data obtained from geophysical surveys over large areas.

The main aim of the Deep Sea Drilling Project is to gather information about the age and processes of formation of the ocean basins. The new theories associated with the revolution in earth sciences led to specific predictions about the history of the earth's magnetic field and the origin of magnetic anomalies, the spreading of the sea floors and drifting of continents, and the history of temperature changes in the oceans and atmosphere. These and other predictions could best be checked by direct sampling of the sediments from the deep ocean basins and continental margins, and from the underlying rocks.

Geophysical investigations of the past twenty years have revealed the structure of the oceanic crust overlying the earth's interior, or *mantle,* as this is called. The boundary between the crust and the mantle, defined on the basis of a change in properties that can be measured by the speed of earthquake waves, is called the Mohorovicic discontinuity or, more familiarly, the Moho. The lithosphere, which is distinguished from the underlying asthenosphere because it is cool and relatively rigid, includes both the crust and part of the upper mantle (figure 1). Whereas the lithosphere is about 100 km thick, the oceanic crust beneath several kilometers of water is only 6.4 km thick. Three layers can be distinguished in an average cross section through the crust. The upper layer of unconsolidated sediments averages 0.3 km in thickness. The main layer, with a thickness of 4.7 km, is assumed to consist of lava or related rocks; this is the material generated at the mid-oceanic ridges (figures 1 and 5). Between the main layer and the sediments is a 1.4 km layer with slightly different properties, generally assumed to be composed of lavas but possibly with some consolidated sedimentary rocks included. Consistent regional variations occur in these values near the mid-oceanic ridges, and abrupt changes occur approaching the continental margins.

According to the new theories, the old oceanic crust is replaced completely by new crust spreading from the oceanic ridges within a time interval of the order of 200 million years. The old crust is consumed in the mantle at convergent plate junctures, and the overlying sediments are either carried down into the mantle as well, or plastered onto the sides of the continent or island arc. Several legs of the *Glomar Challenger's* cruises were designed specifically to test this hypothesis. Major conclusions were announced after preliminary examination of cores on shipboard, and detailed papers were published in 1970 issues of *Science* on results from the South Atlantic Ocean (May 29), and the western North Pacific Ocean (June 5).

The basement rocks beneath the sedimentary layer were reached by drilling in the Atlantic Ocean, but in the Pacific Ocean tough layers of sediment prevented penetration right through to the underlying basement. The drilling results confirm the youth of the ocean basins. No sediments older than 150 million years were encountered. This contrasts with the continents, where rocks as old as 3,500 million years are known. Evidence for the lateral movement of the ocean floor, based on the thickness and age of the deepest sediments at various distances from the mid-Atlantic ridge, was outlined in the section on sea-floor spreading. Because of this result, it is claimed, sea-floor spreading and continental drift must now be considered as established theories. However, not all geologists are completely satisfied that no more sediments lie beneath what was interpreted as basement in the South Atlantic drill holes.

Many other conclusions have been announced as study of the sediment cores proceeds, and they are of such significance that probably even the most optimistic hopes of the program planners have been exceeded. It has been established that:

(1) Oil and gas exist in deep-sea conditions in the Gulf of Mexico. This will have a profound impact on geological thinking and on the exploitation of marine energy sources.

(2) Iron and manganese are enriched in a zone 5 to 10 meters thick at the base of the sedimentary layer.

(3) In many parts of the Atlantic Ocean evidence for strong bottom currents transporting sediments dispels the once prevalent textbook view that the ocean depths display little erosion or current motion.

(4) Solid evidence shows that the glaciation of the northern continents began about 3 million years ago, more than 1 million years earlier than the date usually assumed.

(5) Salt layers in the deep Mediterranean ocean indicate that the ocean was alternately dried up and flooded in the period between 10 and 5 million years ago, presumably as its connection with the Atlantic Ocean was closed and opened by mountain-building movements.

(6) There is evidence that Africa and Europe are approaching each other, with the compression causing parts of the eastern Mediterranean ocean floor to rise in the initial stages of formation of a mountain chain.

(7) The sediment cores show that dozens of major volcanic explosions have occurred from the Italian volcanic arc in the last 2 million years.

(8) Several sites in the eastern Atlantic have a gap in the sedimentary sequence between 60 and 30 million years ago, which coincides with continental mountain building. Possibly both phenomena may relate to a change in the pattern of continental drift.

(9) There is evidence that a narrow proto-Atlantic Ocean existed before the last episode of drift; North America and northwest Africa were never completely joined.

Two further items are especially relevant to the theory of plate tectonics. First, there is evidence from the cores that the Pacific Ocean plate has moved at varying speed and direction during the past 35 million years, supporting the idea that the plate is being pulled away from the

East Pacific Rise by gravity, rather than by convection as indicated in figure 1, with the pull being exerted by the edge of the plate sinking down into the earth at the oceanic trenches near the Asian continent (*see* figures 2, 3, and 8B). Second, while theoretical treatments of plate tectonics do not incorporate complexities introduced by vertical movements, there is now evidence for general subsidence and elevation in several parts of the ocean basins. In some oceanic regions there have been substantial vertical movements in short periods of geological time: one area sank 1.5 km in 5 million years, and another sank 1.8 km at a rate of 10 cm/year.

The history of the Deep Sea Drilling Project really begins with Project Mohole, which was an ambitious program designed to drill through the oceanic crust and the Mohorovicic discontinuity to obtain a sample of the earth's upper mantle. It is not true that the project was terminated because of fears that the ocean waters would empty out through any hole drilled in the ocean floor, although many citizens did write letters of protest to the government, insisting that this would happen. Geological mythology about a hollow earth apparently persists even today. The project was terminated amid engineering, scientific, and political wrangling about procedures and about estimated and actual costs. However, in 1961, before the project became defunct, the Mohole group accomplished the first successful drilling of the sea floor in deep water, when the ship *CUSS I* drilled more than 600 feet of sediments and lava in 12,000 feet of water east of Guadalupe Island, Mexico.

In May 1964, a deep-sea drilling program was formally established by four of the major American oceanographic institutions having strong interests and programs in the fields of marine geology and geophysics: the Institute of Marine Science, University of Miami; Lamont Geological Observatory of Columbia University; Scripps Institution of Oceanography, University of California; and Woods Hole (Massachusetts) Oceanographic Institution. These constituted the JOIDES (Joint Oceanographic Institutions Deep Earth Sampling) group, which was later joined by the University of Washington.

In the summer of 1965 an experimental program off the coast of Florida by the drilling ship *Caldrill* confirmed the feasibility of drilling holes 1,000 feet deep and recovering cores below water as deep as 3,000 feet, and this stimulated plans for work in deeper water. Scripps was awarded $12.6 million by the National Science Foundation to operate the program, and they relied on advice from a number of advisory panels sponsored by JOIDES. Global Marine, Inc., made excellent progress constructing and outfitting the *Glomar Challenger* in only forty weeks; this is probably a record for a vessel as intricate as the *Challenger*. The project was right on schedule and operating within its budget, two remarkable accomplishments compared with many other government-sponsored projects. The operational and scientific success of the first eighteen-month series of cruises generated an additional $34.8 million in support from the National Science Foundation, which will cover operations between 1970 and 1973.

The profile of the *Glomar Challenger* is striking. This is clear even from the sketch in figure 7. The ship is 400 feet long with 10,500 tons displacement, and amidships there towers a 142-foot drilling derrick, its top almost 200 feet above the waterline. Most of the topside space forward of the derrick is occupied by an automatic pipe-racking device with more than 4 miles of drill pipe stacked in 90-foot lengths. During drilling, the drill pipe is suspended from the derrick through an opening about 20 by 22 feet in the bottom of the ship. At the tip of the drill string is a drilling bit, and above this is the core barrel which captures and stores the cores of sediment as they are drilled. Once the drill bit touches the ocean floor, the entire drill string is rotated from the drilling deck. Drilling continues until the bit is worn out, and then the string is retracted and the core recovered.

What makes the drilling operation possible, in water too deep for anchors, is a dynamic positioning system that maintains the ship's position within a radius of a few hundred feet. A beacon that emits acoustic signals is dropped to the ocean bottom, and the sonar beams are received by four hydrophones beneath the ship's hull. A computer translates the pulses into directions and distances from the ship to a point directly above the hole, and actuates some combination of the ship's main propellers and four side thrusters to move the vessel back to its station.

The layers of hard sediment encountered in the Pacific Ocean dulled the bits and frequently forced drilling to stop. At other sites the hard rock interpreted as basement beneath the sedimentary layer could not be drilled deeply enough to make certain that this was not just a layer of lava with more sediments below it. A new mechanism, illustrated in figure 7, permits a drill core to be removed, the bit replaced, and the drill string to reenter the borehole on the ocean floor. The target is tiny: an invisible 5-inch-diameter hole thousands of feet away, with both the drill stem and the vessel being constantly affected by ocean currents.

In June 1970, a new bit was for the first time successfully placed into a previously started hole. Before drilling of the first hole, the drill stem was inserted at the surface through the stem of a metal funnel 16 feet in diameter, and the entire assemblage was lowered to the ocean bottom. Drilling began when the funnel's heavy base was secure on the ocean floor. This remained in position when the drill string was raised and the bit replaced. The drill string was relowered with a sonar scanner on the bit assembly. This emitted sound signals that were echoed back from three reflectors spaced around the funnel brim. The information was relayed to the ship, and the stem was steered into the funnel by jets of water forced out of a hole on the side of the drill stem 60 feet above the bit. This system will be used selectively at sites where extensive drill wear is anticipated.

Within the miles of sediment core stacked in storage, awaiting detailed examination, are many undiscovered and unanticipated facts about the history of the continents around the ocean basins, about biological changes in the oceans, about the ocean waters, and about climatic changes. The cylinders of mud and oozes represent the greatest treasure trove yet yielded by Davy Jones's Locker.

The influence of continental drift and magnetic reversals on the diversity and extinction of species

When Darwin discussed *The Origin of Species* in 1859, and *The Descent of Man* in 1871, he convinced most naturalists that living creatures were not created in fixed and immutable forms, but that they had changed through the generations by natural processes operating over great periods of time. This concept of evolution revolutionized biology.

Darwin's evidence and arguments, which are reproduced in Britannica *Great Books* Volume 49, did not include the possible effects of continental drift and of polarity reversals of the earth's magnetic field, because these phenomena were not known at the time. Their effects were reviewed in two papers presented at the November 1970 annual meeting of the Geological Society of America. J. W. Valentine of the University of California examined the theme that the theory of plate tectonics provides a whole new framework for the study of past life forms, and he concluded that drifting continents may have regulated the ebb and flow of life. J. D. Hays of Columbia University concluded that reversals of the earth's magnetic field may have exerted a selective force on the extinction of species.

Valentine plotted the number of fossil marine animals in continental shelf environments as a function of time and found a period, 500 to 400 million years ago, with many species, or high diversity. The curve dropped to low levels between about 350 and 250 million years ago and began to rise to new high values for the diversity of species about 200 million years ago. Valentine noted that the two periods of high diversity of species correspond to periods when supercontinents were breaking up and dispersing, and the period of low diversity corresponds to the reassembly of the second supercontinent, Pangaea II.

Model studies of community structure indicate that the diversity of marine shelf communities depends on the stability of food resources. Valentine pointed out that where the food resources fluctuate in abundance and type, only a few species are found; the animals must be flexible in order to eat a wide variety of foods and to cope with the changes that cause the fluctuation in food abundance. When food resources are stable, then animal populations can become very specialized and many species develop.

The food supply is controlled largely by solar energy and nutrient supply. Solar radiation promotes a diversity of species at low latitudes, with fewer species at higher latitudes where seasonal variations in solar radiation are large. The primary regulator of longitudinal trends in community structure is fluctuation in nutrient supply; the greatest fluctuation in nutrients and the least diversity in marine shelf species occur along large continents facing small oceans, and the least fluctuation and greatest diversity occur along small continents in large oceans. Valentine related these two factors to continental plate tectonic processes and concluded that increasing diversity of species would be expected as continents break apart, which agrees with his empirical data curve for the variation in number of marine shelf species with geological time.

In the years preceding the Deep Sea Drilling Project, relatively short columns of sediment had been recovered from the deep ocean floor by a free-falling coring tube that was dropped to the ocean bottom. This penetrated soft sediments to depths of 50 to 100 feet, but in packed sands, penetration was limited to a few feet. Reversely magnetized sediments were first discovered in the cores in 1964, and since 1966 the magnetization has been intensively studied and correlated with the appearance and disappearance of species of the organisms represented by microfossils in the sediments.

The intensity of magnetization is very weak compared with that of the crustal rocks beneath the sedimentary layer, and the sediments make effectively no contribution to the magnetic anomalies depicted in figure 5. The sequence of normally and reversely magnetized sediments extending down from the ocean floor can be correlated with the polarity reversal scale of figures 4C and 6. This provides a method for dating the sediment cores on the basis of depths of magnetization-direction reversals and the times of the corresponding polarity reversals for the whole earth, and it provides a method for the correlation of synchronous stratigraphic horizons from one core to another. Average rates of accumulation of sediments can be calculated from the time scale and the depths, or thickness intervals.

Detailed studies of closely spaced sediment samples across the boundaries between reversals have revealed the nature of the earth's magnetic field during a transition interval from normal to reversed polarity. The intensity of the field decreases by 60 to 80 percent through about 10,000 years before there is any change in direction, the field reverses during an interval of only 1,000 or 2,000 years, and the magnetic field intensity then builds up again for another 10,000 years in the opposite direction. It is known that the earth's magnetic field is decreasing at the present time, and if the rate remains constant the field will be reduced to zero at about 2,000 years from now and then reverse its polarity. However, this change is probably part of a cyclic fluctuation of shorter duration than the reversal, and the probability that a geomagnetic reversal will result from the present decrease is only 5 percent.

There has been much speculation about what happens during the interval when the earth's magnetic field is zero or of very low intensity. It has been suggested that the particles normally trapped in the Van Allen radiation belts would fall to the surface, and that the solar wind and a larger proportion of cosmic rays would reach the surface. In the upper atmosphere, cosmic rays might increase the production of radioactive isotopes, and the solar wind might produce more ozone, absorbing radiation and causing large changes in climate.

Claims that these effects could cause extinctions and transformations of species have been disputed on the grounds that the earth is adequately protected from ionizing particles by the atmosphere, even in the absence of a magnetic field. Evidence was presented between 1964 and 1967 that several species of marine microorganisms represented by fossils in deep-sea cores either became extinct or made their first appearance in the geological record at a level very close to the most recent reversal of the earth's polarity, 0.7 million years ago (figures 4C and 6), but it was not certain that extinction of a single species was simultaneous all over the world.

Hays presented results from the study of twenty-eight deep-sea piston cores from locations throughout the world strongly suggesting that magnetic reversals either directly or indirectly do exert a selective force on the extinction of the microorganisms that populate the upper ocean levels. He found that eight species had become extinct during the last 2.5 million years, and each extinction was synchronous throughout the geographical range of the species. Six of the species disappeared immediately following magnetic reversals recorded in the magnetized sediments. This degree of correlation is too high to be the result of chance, and Hays concluded that the evidence is mounting that the earth's magnetic field may have played an important role in the development of life.

Mass extinctions of marine and land animals occurred within intervals of a few million years at the close of the Paleozoic and Mesozoic periods, near 230 and 65 million years ago, respectively (figure 6). The latter interval is famous for the extinction of the dinosaurs. Man did not appear on earth until about 2 million years ago, despite the stories and movies that portray early cavemen watching or partaking in battles between giant dinosaurs. Many animal species have disappeared during the past 20,000 years or so, and there has been some speculation that we may be entering another period of mass extinction, but this is far from established.

According to figure 6, the earth's magnetic field has experienced polarity reversals at frequent intervals during the past 80 million years. This conclusion and the time scale to which it applies are based upon interpretation of the oceanic magnetic anomalies (figure 5), and the extrapolation of recent spreading rates back in time through about 75 million years. There is evidence from the paleomagnetism of rocks on the continents that there were several long intervals when the earth had constant polarity, followed by renewed reversal activity. According to Hays, the mass extinctions of marine and land animals at the close of the Paleozoic and Mesozoic periods coincide in large part with this renewed reversal activity. He suggested that during the intervals of constant polarity of the earth's field many of the species that evolved were potentially susceptible to the effects of polarity reversals, and that these became extinct when reversal activity resumed. Possibly the earth's magnetic field has a direct effect on animal life.

We noted above the view that the earth is adequately protected from cosmic rays and ionizing particles by the atmosphere, even when the magnetic field is reversing. An alternative suggestion is that although the increase in radiation during a polarity reversal would be very slight, it would be enough to produce permanent changes in the genes of animals; the mutations, inevitably harmful, would build up in generations through thousands and millions of years, making the animals less and less fit for survival until they eventually became extinct.

The deep-sea cores recovered in the *Glomar Challenger* cruises include many sequences of sediments with ages extending back to 100 million years or more. The study of magnetic reversals in these cores and their correlation with fossils should be very informative.

The theory of plate tectonics and the changes in the earth's magnetic field that provided crucial evidence for the theory are thus exerting a strong influence on the development of paleontology and of evolutionary biology. The revolution in earth sciences has produced insights into possible causes for both the diversity and the extinction of species; here we have revolution elucidating evolution.

The causes of plate tectonics and sea-floor spreading

The evidence that plates of lithosphere are moving is convincing, but the energy source and the mechanism that maintains the motion remain uncertain. Figure 8 illustrates diagrammatically four models that have been proposed. Sea-floor spreading as depicted in figures 1 and 8A is driven by convection cells in the asthenosphere. The flow exerts a viscous drag on the strongly coupled lithosphere, forcing it into the mantle where the cell turns downward. This kind of process looks reasonable in cross section, but no one has yet proposed a global pattern of convection cells that explains the distribution of the oceanic rift system shown in figure 2; transverse faults displace the crests of the ridges into relatively short segments.

According to the scheme illustrated in figure 8B, the cold slab of lithosphere sinks into the warmer, less dense asthenosphere, pulling the surface lithosphere behind it. This is the model that appears to fit the evidence obtained from the Deep Sea Drilling Project of an accelerating Pacific plate. Hays suggested a bathtub analogy, like laying a towel on water. The towel sinks first at the edge, and the more towel that goes under water, the faster it sinks, and the faster the part remaining on the surface is pulled along. The lithosphere cannot move in this way without movements being generated in the asthenosphere as well.

A third process, depicted in figure 8C, is gravitational sliding of the lithosphere on a partly melted asthenosphere. Calculations have shown that a very small angle of slope at the base of the lithosphere is capable of producing stresses and energies of the right order of magnitude for movement to occur. Figure 8D illustrates a fourth process, where the lithosphere plates are pushed apart by molten lava making its way to the surface at the mid-oceanic ridge.

Probably all of the mechanisms illustrated schematically in figure 8 are in operation, but the relative contribution of each mechanism at different environments is not known. None of these schemes takes into account the recent discoveries from the Deep Sea Drilling Project that large areas of the ocean floor have moved through significant vertical distances in relatively short times.

The emergence and growing strength of the theories of sea-floor spreading and plate tectonics, and their support of and explanation for continental drifting, are based upon a large number of observations from a variety of sources and from apparently unrelated subjects. Many geophysicists feel that we may be on the brink of an even more comprehensive theory involving a major synthesis relating the internal dynamics of the earth, its magnetic field, and the dynamics of its orbital motions.

The only plausible explanation for the existence of the earth's magnetic field is the presence of electric currents resulting from convective motion in the molten portion of the earth's metallic core. The hydrodynamics of fluid in the core is dominated by the motion of the earth in space. Energy is probably transferred outward from the core into the nonmetallic portion of the earth, and this energy may be translated into some kind of motion. The migration of the lithosphere plates must be coupled with some kind of motion in the rocks of the earth's interior (figures 1 and 8).

The paleomagnetic results suggest that displacements of the earth's rotational axis may have occurred, and such displacements could influence the dynamics of the earth's interior sufficiently to produce significant geological effects at the surface. For example, the earth's rotational axis experiences a slight wobble, known as the Chandler wobble. There is growing evidence, published in 1970, that very large earthquakes are

Fig. 8

Diagrammatic representation of mechanisms proposed for moving plates of lithosphere. States of compression and tension in the plates are indicated.

TENSION ←─○─→   COMPRESSION ──→○←──

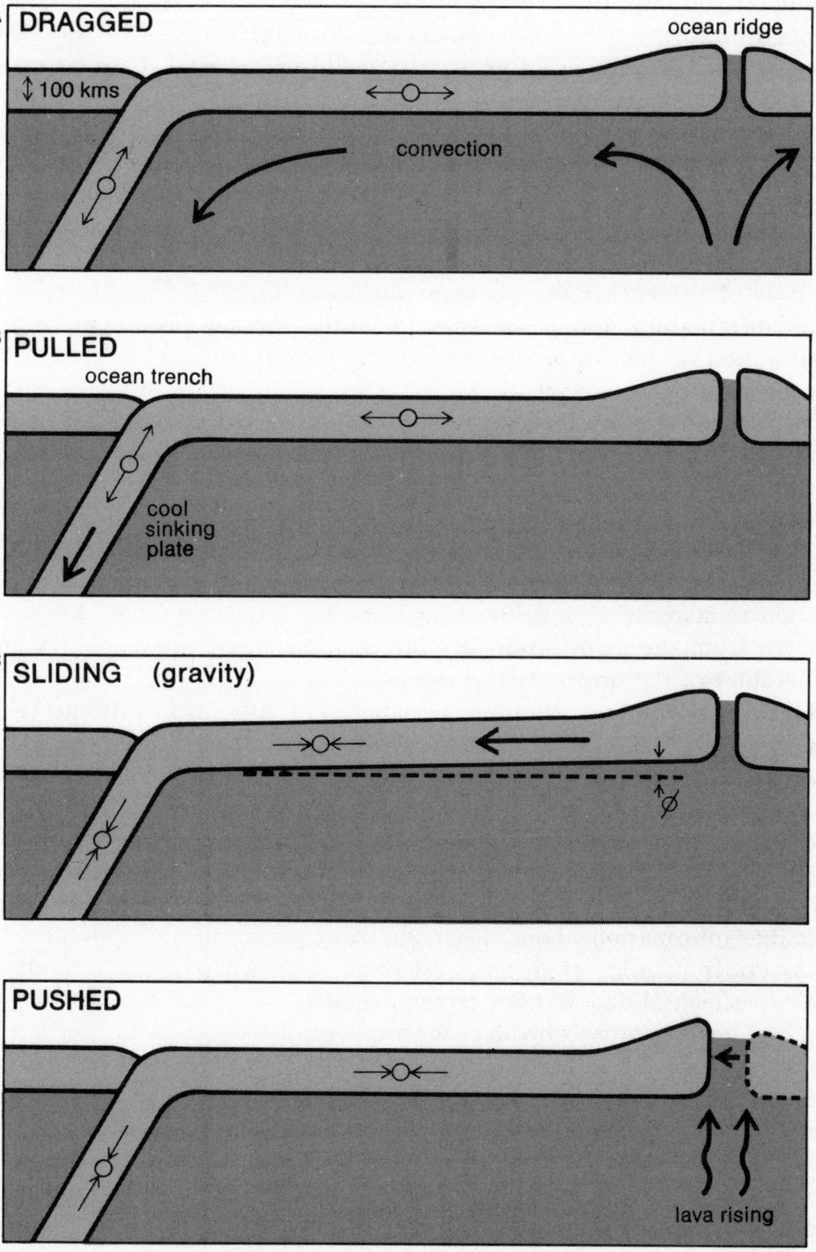

A DRAGGED

ocean ridge

↕ 100 kms

convection

B PULLED

ocean trench

cool
sinking
plate

C SLIDING (gravity)

D PUSHED

lava rising

associated in some way with changes that occur in the amplitude and phase of the Chandler wobble. Possibly, these events may be able to trigger magnetic reversals as well.

There is also speculation that there exists some correlation between magnetic reversals and mantle movement, supported by the presence of abundant volcanic ash in Antarctic deep-sea sediment cores at depths corresponding to the major magnetic reversals of 0.7 and 2.4 million years ago (figures 4 and 6). Volcanic activity could be stimulated by increased convection in the mantle, associated with the magnetic reversal.

A prerequisite for understanding the underlying causes of plate tectonics (figure 8) is an understanding of the structure, composition, mineralogy, and physical properties of the earth's interior. Mainly, there are four approaches to this problem, and significant advances have been made in all of them during the past few years.

Study of the energy waves emanating from an earthquake focus provides information about the structure and physical properties of the earth's interior. The approach is similar to examination of the interior of the human body by means of X-ray pictures. The waves from the earthquake are affected by the material through which they pass, just as the X-rays are affected by the properties of bone and tissue. Sensitive instruments record the emergent waves, and analysis yields the required information.

Lavas erupted at the surface were formed by partial melting of the rocks of the interior. Some lavas carry to the surface solid fragments of the source material. The study of the lavas, the fragments, and other rocks derived from the mantle provides information about the chemistry and mineralogy of the upper part of the mantle.

High-pressure experiments in the laboratory, using minerals and rocks of appropriate composition, are now capable of reproducing the conditions of temperature at various depths within the earth. These experiments provide direct information about the conditions for melting and the formation of lava, and the depths at which various phase transitions occur in mantle materials. Measurement of the physical properties of minerals and rocks at selected pressures and temperatures has provided valuable information about the mode of deformation and flow of solid rocks under mantle conditions, and recent research papers have related the experimental data to plate tectonic models.

The fourth approach involves the study of meteorites. A meteorite is a solid body arrived on the earth from an orbit in outer space. Meteorites are generally considered to represent fragments of disrupted planets, and study of their chemistry and mineralogy tells us something about the size and thermal history of the former planet. Many meteorites are derived from the asteroid belt that passes between Mars and Jupiter. Others may have been blasted from the moon's surface. There are many different types of meteorites, and the relationships among them all are used to infer the history of planetary origin and evolution. These inferences are then applied to models for the formation and differentiation of the earth. There are more than fifteen hundred well-authenticated meteorites, many of which comprise numerous individual pieces of the original fragment that entered the earth's atmosphere. Despite this large number of rocks, the evidence is far from complete. Models for planetary evolution still rank as speculation, and inferences about the earth's interior based on extraterrestrial rocks must be treated with caution.

Much more extraterrestrial material is needed to fill in the many gaps in the story of the origin and evolution of the planets, and the Apollo missions to the moon have provided the first samples other than meteorites. Since 1969, earth scientists have found themselves looking downward into the earth's interior in order to explain the origin of continents on which our civilization developed, and upward to the moon in the hope that this would improve our knowledge of the earth's interior.

Geological exploration of the moon

Before the first moon landing, accomplished by Apollo 11 in July 1969, there were four hypotheses as to the origin of the moon. The Apollo 11 flight brought back 22 kg of rock, which was given the most intensive study of a small quantity of material in the history of science. Every detail of mineralogy was determined in experiments by numerous and independent groups of scientists. But after the examination was over, and despite general agreement as to the resulting data, there were still four hypotheses about the moon's origin. There are serious objections to all four, and this has made it simpler for protagonists of each one to find in the new data presented some information to support their view.

The four hypotheses are (1) *Capture hypothesis:* the moon was formed elsewhere in the solar system and captured when it passed too close to the earth; (2) *Double planet hypothesis:* the earth and moon were formed simultaneously from condensation of the solar nebula; (3) *Fission hypothesis:* the moon is a portion of the earth that was broken off and ejected into orbit; and (4) *Precipitation hypothesis:* a massive primitive atmosphere of hot silicates present in the early stages of formation of the earth formed a ring of planetesimals circling the earth, which then coalesced to form the moon. This is considered to be a variant, or a close relative, of the classic fission hypothesis.

The lack of consensus among scientists was demonstrated by publication of three papers in the September 1970 issue of the *Transactions* of the American Geophysical Union, each arguing the case for a different hypothesis. S. F. Singer of Washington, D.C., favored the capture hypothesis; J. A. O'Keefe of the Goddard Space Flight Center, NASA, preferred the fission hypothesis; A. G. W. Cameron of Yeshiva University,

New York, supported the precipitation hypothesis as it has been developed by A. E. Ringwood of Australian National University, Canberra.

Differences in scientific approach underlie these disagreements. Several groups have used the available, admittedly scanty, moon landing data to erect comprehensive working hypotheses for the origin and evolution of the moon. Others regard such an undertaking as decidedly premature. There are also differences in philosophy, suggested by those who use the term *lunar geology* and those who prefer the term *selenology* on the ground that the moon is not a terrestrial body. Some scientists treat the lunar rocks as products of the same physicochemical processes as those

Fig. 9

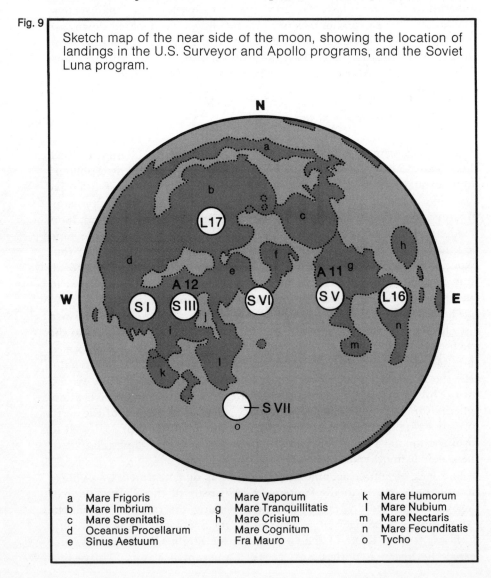

Sketch map of the near side of the moon, showing the location of landings in the U.S. Surveyor and Apollo programs, and the Soviet Luna program.

a	Mare Frigoris	f	Mare Vaporum	k	Mare Humorum
b	Mare Imbrium	g	Mare Tranquillitatis	l	Mare Nubium
c	Mare Serenitatis	h	Mare Crisium	m	Mare Nectaris
d	Oceanus Procellarum	i	Mare Cognitum	n	Mare Fecunditatis
e	Sinus Aestuum	j	Fra Mauro	o	Tycho

operating on earth, modified to the extent that the chemistry and physical environment on the moon differ from those on the earth, now and for the past 4.5 billion years or so. Others maintain that selenologists must not cling to the familiar earthly geology but must be imaginative and intellectually adaptable to new ways of thinking.

The high hopes of many optimistic scientists and a news-hungry public were not fully realized when the international scientific assembly known as the Lunar Science Conference met at Houston, Texas, in January 1970, to present results of the study of the first moon rocks. Nevertheless, several problems that had been controversial for many years were settled unequivocally, and some very significant facts have been discovered that provide boundary conditions for the development of hypotheses and point the way for further investigations. We shall examine the major facts established from the study of the Apollo 11 rocks, together with some additional information from the Apollo 12 rocks, against the background of what was known before the Apollo 11 flight. Apollo 11 was possible only because of the very careful preparation in earlier space programs during the 1960s.

Figure 9 is a sketch map of the near side of the moon, showing the major features that were well known from studies using earth-based telescopes before the space program commenced. It was Galileo who first used a telescope to examine the moon, and in 1610 he described the level, dark maria (sealike areas) among the lighter-colored mountainous regions, as well as the ring-shaped features, or craters.

U.S. Air Force photographs of the moon have been used to construct a detailed topographic map with contour interval of 300 m. Members of the U.S. Geological Survey used this as a base for a geological map of the moon, using standard photogeological techniques. The most important geological work was that of E. M. Shoemaker and R. J. Hackman in 1962. They determined the relative ages of the major and minor physiographic features objectively and unambiguously. The mare basins are younger than the heavily cratered highlands which they cut, and the maria material filling the mare basins and flooding some of the neighboring regions is still younger. Younger features include many craters, ridges, scarps, and peculiar valleys called *rilles*. The youngest craters are those with rays extending from them; the rays are interpreted as material ejected from a crater during its formation.

Photography of the moon from space began with the launching of spacecraft Luna 3 by the U.S.S.R. on October 4, 1959. Luna 3 transmitted enough photographs of the far side of the moon to permit construction of a map. The most notable feature discovered was the dearth of large maria compared with the near side. The U.S. Ranger program was designed to obtain photographs of the lunar surface, and in 1964 and 1965 Rangers 7, 8, and 9 obtained more than seventeen thousand closeup pictures, with features as small as a foot becoming visible for the first time. Resolution was a thousand times better than that obtainable with earth-based telescopes. This was followed by the Lunar Orbiter program, with the first launching on August 10, 1966. The five Orbiter spacecraft obtained complete photographic coverage of the moon and considerable geophysical data. Gravity measurements revealed surprising and unexpected concentrations of mass beneath about thirteen mare basins. These were called *mascons*. A Soviet spacecraft, Luna 10, orbited the moon on April 3, 1966, with a gamma-ray spectrometer. This is an instrument capable of providing chemical data about the rocks below. The results were reported as consistent with the composition of basaltic rock, which is a common lava on earth.

To results from orbiting spacecraft were added data from automated spacecraft making soft landings on the moon. The positions of these and subsequent landing sites are shown in figure 9. The first soft landing was made by the Russian spacecraft Luna 9 on February 3, 1966. Despite prophecies and fears that the lunar surface might be covered by a thick layer of dust capable of swallowing up a spacecraft, the surface proved to be quite solid and stable. Luna 9 transmitted photographs of the lunar surface. A series of soft landings, the Surveyor program, was designed by NASA to transmit engineering and scientific data from the lunar surface as a basis for planning landing sites for the Apollo manned flight program. Surveyor 1 landed on the moon on June 2, 1966, Surveyor 7 on January 10, 1968.*

One of the high points in the space program for earth scientists was the success of the alpha-scattering experiment on Surveyor 5, which landed on Mare Tranquillitatis, September 11, 1967, and transmitted back to earth the first direct chemical analysis of the lunar rocks. A small cube with edges about six inches long was lowered to the surface, and this emitted alpha particles. The box enclosed detectors for alpha particles back-scattered by the surface, and for protons generated in the surface material by the alpha particles. The spectra transmitted back to earth provided quantitative data on all elements present in a thin surface layer about four inches in diameter, except for hydrogen, helium, and lithium. It was reported by A. L. Turkevich, of the University of Chicago, who directed the experiment, that the surface analysis corresponded more closely to basalt than to any other of the half dozen different rock types that had been proposed as candidates for maria material. As similar results were obtained from Surveyor 6, which landed in Sinus Medii, most earth scientists were convinced that the first results could be extrapolated with confidence to the maria as a whole. These were composed of lava, similar to the basalt common on earth, which confirms the conclusion from the experiment on Luna 10. This suggested that the moon had been hot at some stage in its history and that it had been chemically differentiated.

Surveyor 7 landed near the ray crater Tycho and sampled the rugged highlands. The chemical analysis differs in significant respects from the maria analyses, and from terrestrial basalts. It corresponds more closely to a rock called *anorthosite,* which contains a high proportion of the mineral feldspar. Fragments of this kind of rock were subsequently found among the Apollo 11 samples. The chemical differences between maria and highlands material provided the first direct evidence for chemical differentiation of the moon as a whole.

A striking feature of the Surveyor 5 analysis was the high content of titanium. It was much higher than in terrestrial basalts, and some of Turkevich's geological colleagues suggested that he recheck his numbers very carefully, because geologists would not believe such high titanium values. Turkevich maintained that his results were reliable. The rocks returned from Mare Tranquillitatis by Apollo 11, and analyzed in many laboratories, yielded the same high titanium values recorded by Turkevich's instrument from a distance of almost 400,000 km.

While the U.S. space effort has concentrated on getting men to the moon, the Soviet Luna series of space flights has achieved an impressive list of "firsts": the first to hit the moon, the first to orbit the moon, and the first to make a soft landing on the moon. In 1970 there were two more remarkable achievements. Luna 16 was the first spacecraft to land on another body and return to earth automatically. It landed on Mare Fecunditatis on September 20, picked up samples of lunar soil (possibly including some rocks) to a depth of fourteen inches, sealed them in a container, and blasted off on a journey back to earth, leaving the landing stage behind to send back additional measurements from the surface.

In November, Luna 17 made a soft landing in Mare Imbrium, and a remote-control robot machine rolled down a ramp and moved forward under the guidance of operators on earth. Lunokhod 1 (the "moon-walker") is powered by solar cells and driven by eight independent spoked wheels. The ground around the moonwalker is monitored by TV cameras at front, back, and sides. The device carries an X-ray spectrometer to analyze soil scooped up by the machine, and special mirrors to reflect laser beams sent from earth, similar to the reflector left by Apollo 11. The vehicle has survived through the extreme cold of the two-week lunar night. It has resumed its explorations and could possibly travel hundreds of miles from the landing site. The Russians have described similar automated stations, Planetokhods and Marsokhods, for future exploration of Venus, Mercury, and Mars.

The relative ages of the lunar land forms and associated rock types were known by 1962. Age dating by radiometric methods of the rock

---

* An excellent guide to the geology of the moon, using an assemblage of photographs from the various missions completed since 1964, is given in *Lunar Panorama* (1969), a volume by P. D. Lowman of the Goddard Space Flight Center. The photographs are organized with enough background explanation to provide the reader with a guided tour of the moon, with interpretations added.

samples returned by the Apollo 11 and 12 missions gave absolute ages to the relative lunar time scale, and the detailed study of the rocks provided information about the conditions and processes of formation. Together, these three pieces of evidence have provided a consistent history of the evolution of the moon's surface. What remains uncertain is the origin of the moon and the causes of some of the lunar processes.

The comprehensive reconstruction of the moon's evolution by R. B. Baldwin in his 1963 book *The Measure of the Moon* has been verified in many respects. Four main stages of evolution are distinguished by P. D. Lowman of the Goddard Space Flight Center in an article to be published by the *Journal of Geology* in 1971 or 1972. In Stage I, 4.7 billion years (b.y.) ago, the moon was formed by unknown means and was rapidly heated to at least 1,200°C. During Stage II, 4.6 to 3.7 b.y. ago, a major chemical differentiation of the moon occurred, leading to the formation of the lunar highlands. Large bodies orbiting the earth with the moon impacted on the surface, forming the mare basins. Impact craters and volcanic activity modified the highlands. In Stage III, 3.8 to 3.4 b.y. ago, during a second chemical differentiation of the moon, molten material from the moon's interior erupted as lava flows to form the maria. Stage IV, stretching from 3.4 b.y. ago to the present, has seen the development of post-mare physiography by landscape degradation resulting from sporadic impact of asteroid belt meteoroids and comet nuclei, and by minor volcanic activity. The moon is now cold and rigid to a depth of at least 300 km, but hot enough below for the occurrence of sporadic vulcanism. The main conclusions arising from the Apollo 11 and 12 rock samples can be examined against this four-stage history.

The lunar rocks are of volcanic origin, modified by effects of the impact by meteorites ranging in size from small fragments to enormous bodies possibly 100–200 km in diameter. The rocks are covered by a layer of "soil" which comprises local fragments from the rocks below, fragments from rock blasted by meteorite impact elsewhere on the moon, and meteorite fragments. The lunar surface lacks water and organic compounds. No longer tenable are the hypotheses that the sinuous valleys (rilles) were carved by flowing water, and that the maria material represents sedimentary deposits formed beneath former oceans, now evaporated.

The oldest known earth rocks are 3.0 to 3.5 b.y. old (*see* figure 6), and most of the earth's surface was formed more recently than 2.5 b.y. ago; we have seen that the ocean basin floors, almost 70 percent of the earth's surface, are no more than about 200 million years old. Thus the evolution of most of the present surface features of the moon was accomplished before the formation of the oldest rocks known on earth. The maria material in Mare Tranquillitatis is 3.7 b.y. old, and in Oceanus Procellarum it is 3.4 b.y. old, with some apparent ages of 2.7 b.y. reported. The lunar soil from Mare Tranquillitatis, which is obviously younger stratigraphically than the rocks beneath it, gives an apparent age of 4.6 or 4.7

b.y., which is the accepted time of formation of the solar system itself. Scientists have been seeking a "cryptic" or "magic" component mixed into the soil that could account for the remarkably old apparent age of the whole assemblage; small rock fragments as old as 4.4 b.y. have been discovered. Interpretation of the radiometric ages of the mixed soil remains a problem.

It has been proposed that some meteorites found on earth represent rocks blasted from the lunar surface by impacts. The chemistry and mineralogy of the lunar rocks available do not favor this hypothesis, although it cannot be ruled out entirely for some classes of meteorites. Many earth scientists had anticipated that the lunar surface would be covered by meteorites from outer space, accumulated over billions of years. Chemical analyses of the Apollo 11 soil indicate the presence of no more than 2 percent of admixed meteoritic material.

All evidence shows that the lunar rocks crystallized from a molten condition. They are lavas with several significant chemical differences from terrestrial basalts, their nearest known equivalents. They were formed under anhydrous and very reducing conditions. The rocks are greatly depleted in volatile elements such as alkalies, and enriched in titanium and a number of other refractory elements. Opposing explanations proposed are that either the moon as a whole lost its volatile elements during the closing stages of formation, or the elements were lost by surface volatilization from large lava lakes at the surface. There is evidence to suggest that the lunar highlands may be composed of the rock type *anorthosite*, small fragments of which are found in the soil, or of a rock richer in silica and alkalies, or possibly a variety of rocks including these and others as yet unknown.

Since about 1950, the views of H. C. Urey that planetary origin is a cold process have dominated cosmological thought. On the other hand, Baldwin and G. P. Kuiper have argued that the moon's interior must have been hot and at least partially molten. Whatever its temperature of formation, the major chemical differentiation of the moon during Stage II indicates that it heated up very rapidly after its formation, producing at least partial melting. Eruption of the maria material during Stage III indicates that the lunar interior remained hot, or heated up a second time, about 1 b.y. after its formation. From the density of the moon and the properties of the lunar lavas at pressures corresponding to the moon's interior, it is certain that the composition of the moon as a whole differs from that of the lavas. The lavas therefore represent a liquid fraction from the moon, and it is difficult to explain them by the proposal that tremendous meteoritic bombardment about 3.7 b.y. ago caused melting of an outer layer of the moon.

There has been considerable discussion about the cause and location of the melting process leading to the eruption of the maria lavas. The problems involved are fundamental for determination of the origin and evolution of the moon, but they are too technical and complex to be reviewed in this essay. It has been proposed that the lavas were residual liquids remaining after crystallization of a largely molten moon, or that they were produced by a small amount of partial melting of the lunar interior at depths of 200 km or more, and that the compositions of the lavas produced by either of these mechanisms may have been modified by prolonged surface crystallization in large lava lakes. It can be anticipated that these topics will continue to be argued for some time because, despite the fact that the available evidence has increased by several orders of magnitude compared with that available a few years ago, it remains very scanty.

We can close this section on the moon with a version of the future presented in a recent book, *Where the Winds Sleep* (1970), by N. P. Ruzic, editor and publisher of *Industrial Research*. The book is written as if the author were based on the moon in the year 2045, looking back over the history of man's lunar colonization. It is emphasized that this is not science fiction but extrapolated science based on current NASA programs. The author ranges widely but systematically through aspects of science, industry, and sociology. He discusses the use of lunar bases as meteorological stations surveying the earth's weather patterns, as astronomical observatories surveying the stars without the obscuring veil of the earth's atmosphere, and as stepping-stones to planetary exploration. He describes the growth of mining and industry on the moon. Lunar factories make use of the hard vacuum, sterile environment, extreme cold, and low gravity. They manufacture ultrapure metals, semiconductor materials, thin-film materials, certain pharmaceutical products, optical glass products, and many other items. The development of cryogenics has led to the use of superconductors, which form the basis of lunar transportation systems utilizing a superconductive levitating effect, and of large, economical cyclotrons. The moon has been farmed to feed the 50,000 lunarians living in its cities, and the tourists who come to see its wonders.

Environmental geology

Recently there has been a tremendous increase in public awareness of the environment, ecology, and the possible effects of pollution of the environment and of ecological systems. Many scientists have suggested that the present sensitivity of man to his own environment is due not merely to tearful eyes, gasping lungs, and views of muck-laden streams, but that it might also have been stimulated by astronaut Aldrin's description of the lunar landscape as "Beautiful, beautiful—magnificent desolation." The desolate lunar landscape may have awakened people to actual and potential disasters on earth—disasters of their own making. Many have questioned the desirability and the ethics of spending billions of dollars on the exploration of space, proposing instead that the money be applied to the construction of sewage plants, the reduction of effluents from fuels, and the alleviation of poverty.

The development of the subject of "Environmental Geology" is, according to W. R. Dickinson,

> *one of the great ideas, perhaps the key idea, of human civilization. ... the realization that mankind must learn to live in balance with his physical environment. ... and I believe its time has come.*

These remarks are from one of several papers published in the *Journal of Geological Education* of November 1970, from a symposium on "Education in Environmental Geology," held at San Jose, California, the preceding April. In his introductory remarks, G. B. Oakeshott of the California Division of Mines and Geology noted that *all* geology is environmental, and that there is no such thing as a geological hazard without people. Greatly intensified and unwise use of the environment in metropolitan areas has turned ordinary geological processes into "geological hazards."

It has become clear that our industrial civilization and our demand for fuels that energize the industrial processes, our transportation systems, and our homes have combined to disrupt the normal chemical cycles through rocks, water, and the atmosphere. Earth scientists seek and extract chemicals from the ground, and the users, industrial and personal, scatter the remains into water or air where they accumulate. Accumulation has been ignored until dangerously high concentrations are achieved, with serious effects for life forms, such as contamination of tuna fish with mercury or the aggravation of human bronchial tubes in city smog.

One of the worst air pollutants in the United States is sulfur dioxide. In 1970, electric power plants fueled by coal or oil contributed more than half of the total emissions of sulfur dioxide, and other sources include fuel combustion and smelting of metallic ores. Not only the obvious pollutants cause problems. Recent studies suggest that elements present in air and water in only trace amounts may reach toxic concentrations. Lead, nickel, and cadmium, although present only in parts per million in the atmosphere, are already concentrated sufficiently to cause serious concern. Lead and nickel come mainly from gasoline and fuel oil, respectively. Cadmium enters the air mainly from metal-refining industries, and it enters the water from galvanized pipes.

The generation of power from fossil fuels is a major source of environmental pollution, and the smelting and refining of metallic ores is another. This makes it a matter of professional as well as personal concern for earth scientists, who are concerned with finding, explaining, mining, and exploiting, coal, oil, and metallic ore deposits. The situation would be improved considerably if techniques were introduced for removal of sulfur from the fossil fuels before or during combustion, or from the effluent gases. Apparently it will be five to ten years before effective techniques can be in operation, and these will be costly. Coal, residual fuel oil, and natural gas are in short supply, and the costs of coal and fuel oil have escalated.

An impending energy crisis became evident during 1970. Shortages of fossil fuels and rising costs have contributed to the shortage of power, and so has growing public concern over the environment and a revulsion against the polluting power plants. Throughout the United States, new power-plant construction has been blocked by environmentalists for various reasons, involving both pollution and aesthetic factors. Yet, in order to keep pace with the increasing demands of our society, including demands for the home appliances of the environmentalists, it has been estimated that by 1979 the United States must build at least 250 large new power plants.

Utility engineers are considering the possibilities of new, low-polluting kinds of power generation to replace the fossil fuels. It was once anticipated that nuclear power plants would eventually accomplish this, but there is a backlog of orders, and costs are increasing rapidly. Environmentalists are not happy with nuclear power plants, either, because of potential long-term radiation hazards and thermal pollution. In 1970 the prospect of tapping heat from the earth's interior was considered seriously for the first time in the United States. In December the House and Senate reached an agreement on provisions of a bill for the leasing of federal land for geothermal development and sent the bill to the White House.

Geothermal energy becomes available when underground water is heated by molten rock at depth. The occurrence of molten rock is normally restricted to the active volcanic belts of the earth (figures 1 and 2). Japan, Italy, Iceland, and New Zealand—countries with volcanoes and a shortage of fossil fuels—already have developed geothermal resources. There is only one U.S. commercial producer of geothermal power, in northern California. Establishment of leasing policies for geothermal resources on federal land would probably lead to the development of this effectively pollution-free energy source as one of national significance.

Stimulus for geothermal prospecting has come from a 1970 report by scientists at the University of California at Riverside, led by R. W. Rex. The report contains a detailed study of California's Imperial Valley and concludes that as much as 20,000 to 30,000 megawatts of electrical generating capacity could be installed. This would be enough to meet most demands of Southern California. By-products of the hot water and steam from the geothermal wells could be large quantities of water for irrigation of the water-short lower Colorado River Basin. There are also possibilities for supplying heat and refrigeration to food-processing industries. The first geothermal well in the region is planned for the fall of 1971. The Geothermal Energy Commission, an agency of Mexico's Federal Electricity Commission, is already constructing a 75,000-kilowatt power plant in the Mexicali Valley to the south, after a decade of geothermal exploration.

The existence of this potential source of pollution-free electrical power can be explained by the theory of plate tectonics. Figures 2 and 3 show that the Pacific Ocean ridge meets the North American continent through the Gulf of California. Apparently, convective uprise of hot mantle material beneath the ridge (figure 1) is causing Baja California to be separated from the continent by sea-floor spreading. The Mexicali Valley and Imperial Valley appear to be the locus of sea-floor spreading penetrating beneath the continental crust, and this explains the rise of molten rock toward the surface and the high heat flow in the region. The hot springs distributed all over the American West may be related to the same process, which brings the earth's store of internal heat closer to the surface. Prospecting for other suitable geothermal sites would be facilitated if the locus of mantle uprising could be mapped further beneath the continent.

The U.S. Department of the Interior at present estimates that geothermal resources have a potential for supplying about 1 percent of the nation's power requirements, but Rex believes that the figure may be much higher. Industrialization of underdeveloped nations lacking fossil fuels would be aided if they could locate sources of geothermal power. The international importance of geothermal power is shown by the dispatch of United Nations technical assistance teams to nineteen countries. In September and October 1970, two hundred scientific papers were presented at an international conference on geothermal energy in Pisa, Italy. A Soviet report stated that the geothermal energy potential of the Soviet Union is greater than all other Soviet energy sources together, despite their vast reserves of coal, oil, and gas.

One of the key ideas of human civilization may be the realization that mankind must learn to live in balance with his physical environment. Much of environmental geology is concerned with the prediction of the future, which involves planning in three ways. First, natural resources must be discovered and acquired; second, the land and its resources must be used in the best way possible; and, third, natural hazards must be avoided.

Pollution of the environment results from inadequate planning under the second item. The acquisition of natural resources can be enhanced by application of the conceptual revolution in earth sciences, as with geothermal resources. A geological hazard occurs when man gets in the way of a perfectly natural geological process, and when the process causes an earthquake the hazard can become a disaster. If man chooses to colonize an earthquake belt, the hazard exists. But the revolution in the earth sciences may prove useful in environmental geology by making it possible to predict and possibly control the result.

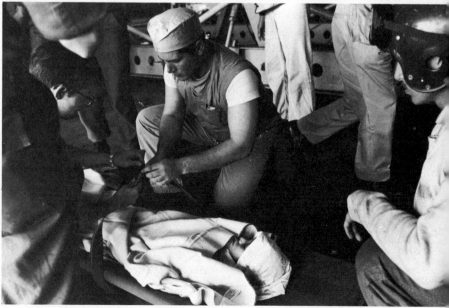

(Opposite page, top) Scene in Pira, a small village in Peru that was completely destroyed by the violent earthquake that struck the country in 1970. (Opposite page, bottom) The seriously injured were flown by helicopter for the intensive medical care available on the *Guam,* a U.S. Marine helicopter carrier located near Chimbote, Peru. (Right) Helicopters from the *Guam* flew in clothing, food, and medical supplies for the earthquake victims.

The prediction and control of earthquakes

It is the power of explanation and prediction that makes the new global tectonic theory so different from previous concepts in the earth sciences. With the new theory and greatly improved geophysical instruments, some scientists are optimistic that accurate prediction of earthquakes will be possible within three to five years, and that their control may follow very soon after this.

Plate tectonics explains the observation that earthquakes are concentrated in narrow belts, and the three types of plate boundaries can be distinguished on the basis of the type of earthquakes occurring. Alternatively, for a given type of plate boundary it is possible to predict the types of earthquakes to be expected. For example, in California the boundary between the Pacific and North American plates is a fracture zone where the two plates are slipping past each other. Shallow earthquakes occur in this environment following the buildup of strain caused by horizontal stresses. In contrast, the boundary between the Pacific and South American plates is of the compressive or collision type, where the Pacific plate slides underneath the other as shown in figure 1. In this environment the epicenters of the earthquakes occur close to a plane that starts at the floor of the oceanic trench and dips at an angle of about 45° beneath the continent. The cause of the deep earthquakes lies in the slippage of material in the direction of this plane to depths of 700 km.

Earthquakes are infrequent in the large, stable plates. However, the most violent earthquakes known to have occurred in the United States were located well within the North American plate. These were the New Madrid earthquakes, which shook the central part of the Mississippi Valley in 1811 and 1812 with such intensity that they were felt over two-thirds of the United States. Eight hundred miles away, in Washington, D.C., sleepers were awakened, dishes and windows were rattled, and walls were cracked. The earthquakes caused major changes in topography over an area of 50,000 square miles. Large areas sank from 3 to 9 feet, and depressions 20 to 30 miles long and 4 to 5 miles wide were produced. The region was sparsely populated at the time, and the loss of life, though not precisely known, was presumed to be small. If the same earthquake had occurred in 1970, the wreckage would have been catastrophic. At present, we have no way of predicting the likelihood of such an occurrence in the supposedly stable plates. In California and Japan, where earthquake activity is accepted as a fact of life, building codes include provisions for earthquake-resistant construction. No such provisions are deemed necessary in the central United States.

An earthquake is a minor consequence of the global process of sea-floor spreading and plate collision, but the magnitude of the devastation that it can wreak is almost beyond belief. Most of the losses of life are due to scondary causes such as building collapse, fires, landslides, and giant waves called *tsunamis*. On All Saints Day in 1755, a triple earthquake followed by a tsunami destroyed the city of Lisbon and killed 40,000 people. Perhaps 250,000 lives were lost in the 1923 Tokyo earthquake. In Kansu, China, catastrophic landslips of unconsolidated soil deposits caused by earthquakes killed 200,000 people in 1920 and another 100,000 in 1927. These examples may seem unreal, like ancient history, but many earthquakes of varying severity have occurred recently. More than 1,000 people died not long ago in an earthquake in Turkey, and the deadliest earthquake in the recorded history of Latin America occurred in Peru on May 31, 1970. At least 50,000 people died, another 100,000 were injured, and more than 800,000 were left homeless. Estimates of property damage exceeded 250 million dollars.

Peru is one of the countries situated in the belt of compression between the Pacific and South American plates. Figure 1 shows the thick slab of the Pacific plate extending down into the earth beneath the Andes. The Andes Cordillera are slowly rising in response to the tremendous compressive pressure below, producing magnificent mountain peaks but great instability. The instability is shown by the enormous range in vertical relief between the high peaks and the great depths in the ocean trench adjacent to the continental margin, and it is manifest in earthquakes and volcanic eruptions.

The epicenter of the shock for the earthquake of 1970 in Peru was located beneath the ocean trench, about 16 miles west of the Peruvian coast, and 27 miles below the surface. As the energy vibrations were transmitted to the continent, towns and villages collapsed. The area affected covered 25,000 square miles. Nearly all of the buildings in the affected region were of adobe construction, and many of the villages are situated on poorly consolidated alluvial soils. Eighty percent of the houses were destroyed or made uninhabitable. Additional damage was caused by secondary effects, including a massive avalanche of ice, water, mud, rocks, and other debris that swept down a valley in the Cordillera Blanca. This type of avalanche, a *huayco,* killed 41,000 in Ecuador and Peru in 1797, and another in 1939 killed 40,000 in Chile.

Vibration damage caused most of the destruction of buildings in 1970, and at least 60 percent of the fatalities. The second major cause of life loss was the *huayco* in the Cordillera Blanca that buried about 90 percent of the resort town of Yungay, with a population of 20,000, and the neighboring village of Ranrahirca. The *huayco* had its source about 9 miles east of Yungay and about 12,000 feet higher in the mountains. Apparently, the earthquake broke loose a mass of glacial ice and rock about 3,000 feet wide and a mile long. This moved downslope, picking up earth and rocks and melting during its descent. It was accompanied or preceded by a turbulent air blast. Survivors of the earthquake in Yungay were praying in the streets amid the wrecked buildings when they heard the thunderous roar of the *huayco* as it swept down the valley. Within a few minutes the wreckage was covered by earth, mud, and boulders to a depth of 45 feet in some places.

The avalanche covered the 9 miles from its source to Yungay in 2 to 4 minutes. Thousands of boulders weighing up to 3 tons were hurled more than 2,000 feet across a valley in the middle part of its course, and calculations from the trajectories indicated a velocity of 248 miles an hour. This high speed was due to the very steep slopes in the source region, and the great vertical drop along the valley floor. The mixture of melting ice and snow lubricated the mass of debris, reducing the frictional resistance, and there is evidence that locally the motion took place over a thin cushion of compressed air trapped between the debris and the valley floor.

It was estimated that the huge mass contained about 80 million cubic feet of water, mud, and rocks by the time it reached Yungay. Its momentum carried it across the Rio Santa near Yungay and 175 feet uphill on the opposite bank. This sent a wave of water, 45 feet high, rushing down through the narrow canyon occupied by Rio Santa. This wave of water was the third major cause of destruction arising from the earthquake.

Aerial photographs of the morass distributed later by the government showed little evidence of the former existence of Yungay. The tops of four palm trees in the main square emerged above the debris, and a statue of Jesus was preserved because it stood on a small hillock that divided the avalanche material. Many nations rushed aid to the stricken country, but it will probably take ten to fifteen years to repair the damage. Meanwhile, more strain builds up beneath the ocean trench and Andes Mountains as the Pacific plate is forced beneath the South American continent (figure 1).

The attention of scientists engaged in research related to earthquake prediction is largely concentrated in densely populated regions. Active research programs exist in California and Japan. The urgent need for such research is shown by a report released in 1970 by the California legislature. This describes the probable effects if an earthquake equivalent to the 1906 San Francisco earthquake were to recur at the present time. An earthquake of this magnitude can be anticipated at intervals of sixty to one hundred years. Many buildings would collapse. The alluvial soils around the Bay Area would turn into quicksand, and buildings would sink. Communications would be disrupted as the freeways buckled and railway tracks twisted. At least one of the many dams would fail, releasing floodwater from the reservoir to inundate large areas. Water mains would break. The 1906 earthquake caused the death of only about 390 people in San Francisco, with property damage estimated at $400 million. Much of this damage was caused by the great fire which raged out of control for three days because broken water mains left no water for firefighting. For the hypothetical 1970 earthquake, estimated property damage would amount to about $30 billion, and estimated deaths would number tens or even hundreds of thousands. During the past century, earthquakes in the United States have killed more than 1,500 people and caused property damage of about $1.3 billion. But all previous losses caused by earthquakes in the United States are insignificant compared with those anticipated for the next major one.

The population of California is often warned by the news media that sooner or later the state will be shaken by another major earthquake. This is virtually certain, given the passage of the plate boundary through the state (figure 3). Prediction of precisely when such an earthquake will occur is not yet possible, but this does not prevent some bold individuals from guessing. These individuals were supplied with useful information when the concept of plate tectonics was formulated in 1967 and 1968, because it was announced then that the earthquakes were caused by the slow movement of one part of California independently of the main American continent. Some rather distorted versions of the plate tectonic theory became current among the population. Clairvoyants and sooth-sayers began to predict that the state of California would soon split asunder, and that half of it would drift away and founder in the Pacific Ocean. This separation would, of course, be accompanied by earthquakes and tidal waves causing additional devastation. A number of religious sects announced that Doomsday was imminent and prepared themselves for the end of the world. For normal, educated citizens the topic provided entertaining material for cocktail party banter, but they knew perfectly well that California could not possibly sail off into the Pacific Ocean. Nevertheless, the occurrence of an earthquake certainly is an ever-present prospect, and the prophesied schism of the state did appear to have the respectable scientific backing of the highly touted new global theory of geology. Many articles in the popular press informed readers that most geologists now believed in the reality of continental drift.

By 1969, when the prophets of doom began to specify dates, the telephone switchboards into university departments of earth sciences hummed with inquiries from the anxious citizenry. The growing concern of the public made newspaper headlines across the country. For example, the *Chicago Tribune* on March 30, 1969, reported:

DISASTER TALK RUNS RAMPANT IN CALIFORNIA: QUAKE WILL DESTROY STATE, SEERS SAY

Monday, April 14, 1969, the day most frequently cited for the great event, was awaited with interest, concern, or disdain by various groups of people. The day came and went. Another Monday had started another working week, and the state remained in one piece. No earthquakes rumbled from the faults to test the stability of the fine high-rise buildings in the urban centers. The citizens laughed and told each other that they had known it was a hoax all along. A number of prominent politicians whose business had forced them to be out of state on April 14 returned to their offices in California. Some disappointed religious sects prayed that next time Armageddon was announced it would really come.

Yet the predictions of the seers and soothsayers had erred only in one respect: they used the wrong time scale. We have seen that, according to the scientifically based predictions of Dietz and Holden, one section of California is indeed destined to slide away from the rest of the state and to disappear 60 million years hence beneath Alaska. The seers, in their far-sighted visions, compressed the anticipated events of a few million years into a few hours.

The fact that data from the study of earthquakes give strong support for the sea-floor spreading hypothesis is closely related to increased understanding of the distribution and characteristics of earthquakes. Prospects for earthquake prediction and modification have been greatly improved by the new global theories and by recent quantitative approaches to the physics and geology of earthquake processes. Quantitative approaches have become possible because of advances in geophysical instrumentation and the geophysical application of high-speed digital computers. The question of earthquake control is now a subject for serious consideration, and considerable research effort is directed to the subject, especially by universities and federal and state agencies in California, where attention is concentrated on the San Andreas Fault system.

It was discovered only recently that, along parts of some faults in the San Andreas system, deformation is accomplished by fault slippage without accompanying earthquakes. This process of fault creep appears to be an important mode of deformation, at least locally. While parts of a fault may creep in distinct episodes at rates up to 10 cm/year, other parts of the same fault may not creep at all. In these locked portions the deformation causes accumulation of elastic strain energy with the prospect that later energy release will produce a large earthquake. Hopes for earthquake control lie in development of methods for releasing locked portions of faults so that accumulation of strain energy is inhibited, the crustal blocks being made or allowed to slide past each other with only small energy-dissipating tremors.

Before prediction becomes possible, it is necessary to learn the patterns of movement and of energy storage and release. There are now more than a hundred seismic stations deployed to locate the boundaries of moving blocks in California from the occurrence of small earth tremors. The locations and mechanisms of movements and micro-earthquakes in relation to fault structures have been precisely located with the help of new, ultrasensitive instruments. Attempts to monitor the movements along the Inglewood Fault that runs through Los Angeles were unsuccessful in the past because the very small earth tremors were swamped by the noises and vibrations of city traffic. Improved electronic equipment installed near downtown Los Angeles in 1970 was designed specifically to monitor these movements.

Fault creep is accompanied by warping of the rocks and tilting of the ground. The changes are very small, but careful measurement of ground tilt and rates of fault creep can be correlated with subsequent earthquake tremors. Another method is to study in the laboratory the conditions for rock failure, and recent work has been directed toward a better understanding of fault formation and earthquake processes.

Clear sky lightning has traditionally been regarded as a precursor of earthquakes in Japan. This has some scientific basis. There is evidence that the electrical and magnetic properties of rocks can be changed by strain, and it has been calculated that in rocks where the mineral quartz is arranged in suitable crystalline order and texture, the effects of strain could generate enough voltage to produce lightning. There is also evidence that certain fluctuations in the earth's magnetic field are associated with earthquakes.

The measurement of earthquake activity, fault creep, accumulation of strain in rocks, ground tilt, and continuous monitoring of the magnetic field provide clues that ought soon to permit short-range prediction of earthquakes with a warning interval of hours or days. Present knowledge of the processes involved in the generation of earthquakes is not sufficient to guide an engineering program for earthquake control, but there is evidence that the trigger can be of several kinds.

The occurrence of earthquakes appears to be linked with the construction of dams and the impounding of large masses of water in reservoirs. Earthquakes also appear to be associated with the injection of fluids into the ground, and seasonal fluctuations in earthquake activity show some correlation with rainfall. Underground explosions of nuclear devices also have been associated with increased earthquake activity, apparently by releasing natural strain energy in the region. Earthquake hazards can possibly be reduced if fluid injections and perhaps explosions can be employed to free locked portions of fault systems to release the accumulating strain before it builds up to dangerous levels.

The role of water or other interstitial fluid in earthquake activity is receiving considerable attention. The first serious suggestion that control might be possible arose from study of the series of earthquakes triggered near Denver by injection of waste fluids into a deep disposal well at the Army's Rocky Mountain Arsenal. Fluids were injected into the fractured rocks below the arsenal between 1962 and 1966. In 1965 a monthly average of 5.9 million gallons of fluid was injected for six months, and earthquake activity reached a peak rate of forty-five per month. For the next few months, until the pumping stopped, an average of 2.9 million gallons was injected each month, and earthquake frequency dropped to eighteen per month. After the well was closed, earthquakes averaged only ten per month for thirteen months, though seventy-one were recorded in April 1970.

The case is strong for a cause-and-effect relationship between the injection of fluids and triggering of earthquakes in the Denver region. At the time, questions were raised about the continuation of earthquakes after injection ceased, but it was pointed out that the injected water would have migrated only very slowly through the crustal rocks of this region. Until the high fluid pressure at the injection site became equalized throughout the underground reservoir, the possibility of rock movement and associated earthquakes would have continued, and apparently did. It is now believed by most geologists and geophysicists that water plays an essential role in fault creep and fault slip. Small amounts of water may produce the effect of a lubricated surface on which fault displacements can occur. The injection of water may free locked fault systems.

Earthquake control may thus become feasible within a few years, but only in regions where the locked fault zones can be reached by drilling. This approach will not work for the earthquakes originating beneath ocean trenches, like the 1970 Peru earthquake and the 1964 Alaska earthquake. Many engineers emphasize that it is not the earthquakes that kill people but the failure of buildings that people construct. They maintain that the best approach is not to predict and control earthquakes but to erect sound buildings, bridges, and dams on relatively safe sites. Then comes the problem of judging the safety of development sites and the effectiveness of building codes.

Catastrophic Uniformitarianism

The *huayco* initiated by the Peru earthquake of May 31, 1970, made a massive contribution to erosion of the Andes Mountains within a few minutes. The awesome power of this enormous debris avalanche indicates a geological process never before recorded, according to the two U.S. Geological Survey geologists sent at the request of the Peruvian government to help carry out a preliminary scientific study of the disaster. The process not only results in devastation in human terms; it is clearly catastrophic in geological terms. This harks back to the philosophy of Catastrophism that was overcome by Uniformitarianism, following the work of Hutton and Lyell. The subsequent age dating of rocks by radiometric methods, once the principles of radioactivity were discovered and applied to minerals, supported Uniformitarianism with the assurance that an immense amount of time was available for earth processes (figure 6).

There is no doubt that many geological processes are very slow and that many parts of the crustal record are due to their continuous operation through long periods of time. Most geology textbooks emphasize this. Increasingly, however, it has been realized that faster, intermittent processes should not now be ignored merely because they had formerly been overemphasized by Catastrophism.

Evidence for the modification of Uniformitarianism into some kind of "Castastrophic Uniformitarianism" comes from many geological studies. It has been discovered in the past decade, for example, that waves and tidal effects from hurricanes are sufficient to account for nearly all of the supratidal sedimentation off Florida. It appears likely that little or no sedimentation occurred between hurricanes during the past 2 million years.

John Wesley Powell led an expedition down the Colorado River in 1871, returning with an invaluable collection of geological photographs. In 1968 the U.S. Geological Survey sent another expedition along the same route that took photographs from 150 points used as camera stations during the Powell expedition. According to E. M. Shoemaker of the California Institute of Technology, the main preliminary result of a comparative study of these two sets of photographs is that most of the geological changes that have occurred in the Green and Colorado rivers during the past century resulted from a series of catastrophes. In most places, large and small boulders in the rivers remained unmoved. The main changes had apparently been caused by rock slides and similar movements. These changed the scene entirely within minutes, and the rearranged material then persisted without significant change for years.

The 1970 Peru earthquake demonstrates the major contribution of rapid, catastrophic processes. Landslides of this magnitude are rare, but landslides and avalanches are quite frequent events, even compared with a human lifetime. Several disastrous avalanches have occurred near popular ski resorts in the European Alps during the past year or two. Even if major avalanches or landslides occur with a frequency of only once in each thousand years, they would make a major contribution to the erosion pattern of a mountain chain through tens of millions of years. From the historical record in the Andes Mountains, it seems that in earthquake belts the frequency is much higher than this.

We have seen that the evolution of the moon for the past 4.7 billion years has been dominated by meteorite impact and vulcanism. The concept of uniformitarianism thus has little validity on the lunar surface.

Progress in the earth sciences, as well as other sciences, follows a pattern analogous to the pattern of geological processes—uniformitarian punctuated by catastrophes. For decades the ideas are developed slowly with no very dramatic results. Then, rather abruptly, there comes a new conceptual development which reorientates the old ideas and amounts to a catastrophe for them. After the revolution the new ideas generated continue to develop more slowly. This is a period of revolution in the earth sciences.

BIBLIOGRAPHY

Apollo 11 Lunar Science Conference. Washington, D.C.: American Association for the Advancement of Science, 1970 (this contains the articles published in *Science* of January 30, 1970).

BALDWIN, R. B. *The Measure of the Moon.* Chicago: University of Chicago Press, 1963.

LOWMAN, P. D., JR. *Lunar Panorama: A Photographic Guide to the Geology of the Moon.* Zurich: Weltflugbild, Reinhold A. Müller, 1969.

MASON, B. H., and MELSON, W. G. *The Lunar Rocks.* New York: John Wiley & Sons, Interscience Publishers, 1970.

PHINNEY, R. A., ed. *The History of the Earth's Crust.* Princeton: Princeton University Press, 1968.

RUZIC, N. P. *Where the Winds Sleep: Man's Future on the Moon, a Projected History.* New York: Doubleday & Co., 1970.

TAKEUCHI, H., UYEDA, S., and KANAMORI, H. *Debate About the Earth: Approach to Geophysics Through Analysis of Continental Drift.* 2nd ed. San Francisco: Freeman, Cooper & Co., 1970.

Recent articles in *Scientific American* treat many of the subjects discussed in this essay. A selection follows:

COX, ALLAN, DALRYMPLE, G. B., and DOELL, R. R. "Reversals of the Earth's Magnetic Field." February 1967, pp. 44–54.

HURLEY, P. M. "The Confirmation of Continental Drift." April 1968, pp. 52–64.

HEIRTZLER, J. R. "Sea-Floor Spreading." December 1968, pp. 60–70.

BULLARD, SIR EDWARD. "The Origin of the Oceans." September 1969, pp. 66–75.

MENARD, H. W. "The Deep-Ocean Floor." September 1969, pp. 126–42.

HESS, WILMOT, KOVACH, ROBERT, GAST, P. W., and SIMMONS, GENE. "The Exploration of the Moon." October 1969, pp. 54–72.

OROWAN, EGON. "The Origin of the Oceanic Ridges." November 1969, pp. 102–119.

WOOD, J. A. "The Lunar Soil." August 1970, pp. 14–23.

DIETZ, R. S., and HOLDEN, J. C. "The Breakup of Pangaea." October 1970, pp. 30–41.

MACINTYRE, FERREN. "Why the Sea Is Salt." November 1970, pp. 104–115.

Preliminary reports from the voyages of the *Glomar Challenger* have been published in the monthly issues of *Geotimes* during 1969 and 1970. *Geotimes* is published by the American Geological Institute, 2201 M Street NW, Washington, D.C. 20037.

Marshall Cohen

Marshall Cohen is Professor of Philosophy
at Richmond College and at the Graduate
Center, the City University of New York.
He has taught at Harvard, the University
of Chicago, and Rockefeller University
and was a Junior Fellow at Harvard and a
Senior Fellow at the Yale Law School.
Although his commitment seems chiefly

to political and legal philosophy, he is in
fact equally interested in aesthetics and
criticism. He has written drama criticism
for the *Partisan Review* and the *Atlantic,*
and has given the Christian Gauss Seminar
at Princeton on the subject of "Aesthetics
and Poetics." The author of many articles
on legal and political questions, he has
edited *The Philosophy of John Stuart Mill*
for the Modern Library. He is the editor also
of a new journal, recently announced,
called *Philosophy and Public Affairs,* published by the Princeton University Press.

Civil Disobedience

According to Locke, legitimate government rests on the consent of the governed, and this consent is widely taken to be a crucial feature of the liberal theory of government.[1] But the idea of consent is obscure, and the liberal theory is, in any case, unsatisfactory in a variety of ways. Thus, when we examine the details of Locke's theory we discover that consent is far easier to impute than we should have supposed, and far more difficult to withdraw than we might have imagined. For, according to Locke, tacit consent, the type of consent that the unenfranchised, propertyless majority accords to its government, is so weak and attenuated a thing that

> every man that hath any possession or enjoyment of any part of the dominions of any government doth hereby give his tacit consent, and is as far forth obliged to obedience to the laws of that government, during such enjoyment, as anyone under it, whether this his possession be of land to him and his heirs forever, or a lodging only for a week; or whether it be barely traveling freely on the highway; and, in effect, it reaches as far as the very being of anyone within the territories of that government.[2]

Whatever plausibility there may be to this view of the relation between obligation and consent is surely undermined if consent can be established by an act so apparently noncommittal as traveling on a highway or remaining, for a time, within the territory of a government. After all, by this standard, not only the man who silently endures the outrages of a regime he deplores, but even the man who openly disavows and denounces them, is taken to give his consent. That is to say, even what we should ordinarily take to constitute the express withdrawal or withholding of consent does not count against the view that the man nevertheless "tacitly" consents. Surely there is paradox here, as there is in the related view that the only way to establish the withdrawal or withholding of consent is to emigrate or to make a revolutionary attempt on the government. If consent is to carry its normal implications, semantic and moral, it surely requires more than Locke says to infer that a man has consented to a government and its laws. In addition, there must be ways of indicating that he qualifies that consent, or withdraws it, short of resorting to the extreme measures Locke suggests.

Some have felt that the Lockean conception could be strengthened by holding that the possibility of participation or, indeed, that actual participation in government must be present for consent to be inferred. Thus, it has been held that consent can be inferred only where the right of suffrage is enjoyed, or actually exercised. But this amendment is unpersuasive on two counts. We are sometimes willing to find consent where the right of suffrage is not in fact enjoyed or, if enjoyed, not actually exercised. On the other hand, and for the present purposes more importantly, it by no means follows, even from the fact that men exercise the franchise, that they consent to the government that extends it, or to the laws it enacts.

The phenomenon of voter apathy is pertinent here. It has been noted in modern empirical studies that the democratic electorate is often uninterested in, and to a remarkable degree fails to participate in, the issues before it in elections. Are these signs that the electorate consents to its government, or the reverse? In fact, they may betoken either attitude. We may distinguish between the "benign" apathy exhibited by the citizens of the stable, contemporary democracies, and the "malign" apathy of, say, the Weimar Republic's electorate.[3] In the one case, abstinence may simply indicate a relative lack of concern with the issues contested in typical elections, and it may be compatible with consent and even with active support for the regime—a support that would display itself in a willingness to fight and even to die for the regime if it were in any serious way threatened. On the other hand, as in the Weimar case, apathy may betoken a lack of consent that will exhibit itself in repudiation at an opportune or tempting moment. The failure to vote may, in this sort of case, indicate profound hostility, and even active participation may simply be a form of action *faute demieux,* a way of influencing events while biding one's time.

Even where a more vigorous kind of support for the government exists than exists in the Weimar case, it is faulty to infer consent or, more particularly, consent to individual decisions, from a willingness, or even from an eagerness, to participate in elections. Often enough, men participate in elections, as, indeed, they ought to participate in elections, in an attempt to prevent the enactment of laws or the adoption of policies that, should they come into existence, would provide grounds for a partial, or even for a complete, withdrawal of consent. Therefore, one cannot agree with a writer like Plamenatz, who attempts to bolster the Lockean theory by offering a stronger criterion of consent of just the type we have been considering. He writes that *where there is an established process of election to an office, then, provided the election is free, anyone who takes part in the process consents to the authority of whoever is elected to the office. This, I think, is not to ascribe a new meaning to the word consent but is only to define a very ordinary and important political use of it. The citizen who votes at an election is presumed to understand the significance of what he is doing, and if the election is free, he has voluntarily taken part in a process which confers authority on someone who otherwise would not have it.*

By consenting to someone's authority, you put yourself under an obligation to do what the possessor of it requires of you. . . .[4]

But, surely, as consent cannot be inferred from traveling on the highway, neither can it be inferred from entering into the polling booth. If one votes against a potential tyrant, one does not necessarily consent to his authority should he be elected. And, if a regime enacts oppressive and burdensome laws, depriving a man of his fundamental rights, his participation in the election of those who bring these things to pass does not impose on him an obligation to obey their commands. Participation in elections does not, in fact, establish consent, nor does it obligate in the way Locke thought consent obligates.

Some have felt, Hannah Arendt most recently, that if the right of suffrage and the active exercise of it does not establish consent in a sufficiently strong sense to obligate, some other criterion might.[5] They have felt, in particular, that if men were to enjoy a right to something like civil disobedience, then abstinence from disobedience would imply consent of a kind that a liberal theory of obligation requires. This view is attractive, and there is no doubt that the easier it is for the citizen to indicate his dissent, the more plausible it will be to infer consent when there is no expression of dissent. But Miss Arendt's doctrine, as it stands, is neither persuasive nor wholly intelligible. Certainly, it is possible to extend to citizens a right to do, or to abstain from doing, certain things that they might commit civil disobedience to do if these things were against the law. Perhaps this is the case with striking and with conscientious objecting. But what does it mean to extend a general legal or de facto right to civil disobedience? And if there were such a right, in what sense would those who exercised it thereby express dissent, or the withdrawal of consent? Do strikers or conscientious objectors express such dissent? Would it, in any case, be viable for a government to extend such a right? This is highly doubtful, for the government must sometimes, and I think rightly, impose its will on those who have moral objections to a course of action it has undertaken to pursue. It is possible, nevertheless, to imagine accommodations to Miss Arendt's conception. One could make dissent less burdensome by, say, an appropriate exercise of prosecutory discretion or by altered sentencing procedures. And other possibilities suggest themselves.

But even if Miss Arendt's proposal were made more precise, it is doubtful whether it would render the revised theory of obligation acceptable. For no matter how reasonable it may become to infer a man's consent, there are limits to what his consent can put him under obligation to do.

In fact, of course, there are many passages in Locke that make a similar point, and it is far from clear that Locke held, or held consistently, to the theory that we, following others, have so far attributed to him. For in certain crucial passages Locke suggests that one consents, not to the specific laws and orders issued by a government, or indeed to a particular political regime but, rather, to the terms of the original social contract. Thus, if you live, or use the roads, or hold property under a regime that violates its trust—taking property without due compensation or "altering the legislature"—you cannot be understood to have consented to this, no matter what you have said or done. Indeed, the very content of the original contract is determined, not by a historical act of consent, but by the standards of rational choice. Thus, in trying to reconstruct the original contract (and no one is committed to anything more than the terms of the original contract), it is necessary to consider what reason requires men to give away and what it requires them to retain. Thus we can see that they must surrender sufficient of their rights to make government possible and to surmount the "inconveniences" of the state of nature. As Locke says,

> *Whosoever, therefore, out of a state of Nature unite into a community, must be understood to give up all the power necessary to the ends for which they unite into society. . . .*[6]

But they cannot be understood to surrender anything more:

> *though men when they enter into society give up equality, liberty, and executive power they had in the state of Nature into the hands of the society, to be so far disposed of by the legislative as the good of the society shall require, yet it being only with an intention in everyone the better to preserve himself, his liberty and property (for no rational creature can be supposed to change his condition with an intention to be worse), the power of the society or legislative constituted by them can never be supposed to extend farther than the common good, but is obliged to secure everyone's property by providing against those . . . defects . . . that made the state of Nature so unsafe and uneasy.*[7]

What it would be irrational to do, one does not have the power to do. So, to quote Hanna Pitkin's account of Locke, " 'nobody has an absolute arbitrary power over himself' to give to another; he '*cannot* subject himself to the arbitrary power of another.' Arbitrary or absolute power can never be legitimate, consented to, because 'God or Nature' does not allow 'a man so to abandon himself as to neglect his own preservation.' Thus says Locke, 'the law of nature stands as an eternal rule to all men, legislators as well as others.' "[8] On this reading of Locke one must say that legitimacy provides the criteria of valid consent, not that consent provides the criteria of legitimate government. And, however it is with Locke, this is substantially true.

The phenomenon of civil disobedience had best be viewed, then, not as Hannah Arendt views it, as providing liberal theory and liberal government with the opportunity to confer genuine content on the notion of consent, and thereby on the claim to legitimacy. Rather it should be viewed as a political technique that permits minorities to make a special kind of appeal to liberal governments when, in their opinion, these governments have violated the conditions of legitimacy. Disobedience may protest illegitimacy, but its absence cannot, in itself, establish legitimacy.

Civil disobedience is, to be sure, an appeal outside the realm of normal politics, but its great value is that it is not a revolutionary "appeal to Heaven"—the only alternative to normal politics that Locke recognized, or even imagined. In Lockean terms, civil disobedience may be considered a partial reversion to the state of nature that is undertaken in the hope of preventing a state of war. Unfortunately, and in part due to Locke's influence, many writers refuse to see in civil disobedience anything less than a declaration of war. This is, I think, a mistake of theory, and one with fateful and unfortunate practical consequences. In fact, the technique of civil disobedience provides us with an important mode of action, short of revolution, that can sometimes restore the conditions of civil society when they are threatened by actions to which rational men ought not to consent. As such it must find a place in liberal political theory.

Unfortunately, the term *civil disobedience,* which has always suffered from a certain ambiguity, has now been utterly debased in the vulgar national debate on "law and order." It has been employed by respectable writers to describe everything from bringing a test case in the federal courts to taking aim at a federal official. Anyone who wishes to defend civil disobedience must therefore explain just what it is that he wishes to defend. And in doing so I shall not hesitate to free Gandhi's conception[9] from its religious bias and from those political emphases peculiarly appropriate to the fundamentally undemocratic circumstances in which he worked. Only then will it be possible to appreciate the contribution that his brilliantly original conception can make to moral philosophy and to political theory.

The civil disobedient is often described as a man who defies the law out of conscience or moral belief. But this description is imprecise, and it fails to distinguish him from the moral innovator on the one hand or the conscientious refuser on the other. Unlike the moral innovator, the civil disobedient does not invoke the standards of a higher morality or of a special religious dispensation. He is no Zarathustra proposing a transvaluation of all values, and he does not ask the public to act on principles that it plainly rejects. If he acts out of conscience it is important to remember that he appeals to it as well, and the principles he invokes are principles that he takes to be generally acknowledged. It is to protest the fact that the majority has violated these principles that the disobedient undertakes his disobedience, and it is this element of protest that distinguishes his actions from those of the conscientious refuser. For the doctor who performs a clandestine abortion, or the youth who surreptitiously evades the draft, may be acting out of moral motives—the doctor to fulfill his obligations to a patient, the youth to avoid complicity in an evil undertaking—but they are not defying the law in order to protest the course of public conduct. They can achieve their purposes in private, and their defiance of the law need never come to light. The civil disobedient's actions are political by their very nature, however, and it is essential that they be performed in public, or called to the public's attention.[10]

It is for this reason that the civil disobedient characteristically notifies government officials of the time and place of his actions and attempts to make clear the point of his protest. Obviously, one of the problems of a modern democracy is that many immoral actions taken in the people's name are only dimly known to them, if they are known at all. In such cases, the main difficulty in touching the public's conscience may well be the difficulty in making the public conscious. The civil disobedient may therefore find that in addition to making his actions public it is necessary to gain for them a wide publicity as well. Indeed, Bertrand Russell has suggested that making propaganda and bringing the facts of political life to the attention of an ignorant and often bemused electorate constitutes the main function of disobedience at the present time.[11] It is certainly true that nothing attracts the attention of the masses, and of the mass media, like flamboyant violations of the law, and it would be unrealistic of those who have political grievances not to exploit this fact. But it is important, especially in this connection, to recall Gandhi's warning that the technique of law violation ought to be used sparingly, like the surgeon's knife. For in the end the public will lose its will, and indeed its ability, to distinguish between those who employ these techniques whenever they wish to advertise their political opinions, and those, the true dissenters, who use them only to protest deep violations of political principle. The techniques will then be of little use to anybody.

After openly breaking the law, the traditional disobedient willingly pays the penalty. This is one of the characteristics that serve to distinguish him from the typical criminal (his appeal to conscience is another), and it helps to establish the seriousness of his views and the depth of his commitment as well. Unfortunately, paying the penalty will not always demonstrate that his actions are in fact disinterested. For the youth protesting the draft, or the welfare recipient protesting poverty, has an obvious and substantial interest in the success of his cause. If the majority suspects that these interests color the disobedient's perception of the issues involved, its suspicions may prove fatal to his ultimate success. This is one reason why the practice of civil disobedience should not be limited to those who are directly injured by the government's immoral or lawless course (as Judge Wyzanski and others have suggested).[12] A show of support by those who have no substantial interest in the matter may carry special weight with a confused, and even with an actively skeptical, majority. The majority simply cannot dismiss those over thirty-five as draft dodgers, or those who earn over thirty-five thousand dollars a year as boondogglers. It may therefore consider the issues at stake, and this is the first objective of the civil disobedient.

It is in misinterpreting the role of punishment in the theory of civil disobedience that many errors are made. For the theory of civil disobedience does not suggest (although exponents of civil disobedience have sometimes suggested) that the disobedient's actions are justified by his willingness to pay the penalty that the law prescribes. The idea that paying the penalty justifies breaking the law derives not from Gandhi and the tradition of civil disobedience but from Oliver Wendell Holmes and the tradition of legal realism.[13] According to Holmes and the legal realists, the law characteristically presents us with an option—either to obey, or to suffer the consequences that attach to disobedience. This doctrine is indefensible even in the area of contract law where it arose, and where it has a fragile plausibility, but it is plainly absurd to suppose that the citizen has such an option in the area of criminal law. Criminal punishments are not a simple tax on criminal misconduct, and the citizen is not given the option of engaging in such conduct on the condition that he pay the tax.[14] It is mindless to suppose that murder, rape, or arson would be justified if only one were willing to pay the penalty, and the civil disobedient is committed to no such mindlessness. Holmes was looking at the law from the point of view of a bad man for whom paying the penalty is always an option and often a source of advantage. Gandhi considered it from the point of view of a good man for whom paying the penalty is often a necessity and always a source of suffering. This suffering does not justify the act of civil disobedience, but it helps to establish the disobedient's seriousness and his fidelity to law in the eyes of the majority whose actions have, in his opinion, justified it.

The disobedient's willingness to face suffering and punishment may be seen, then, as a useful way of reinforcing the effects of his protest and appeal. His actions may force the public to consider, or to reconsider, the law or policy the disobedient rejects. But, if the majority remains unconvinced, it is free to act as it wishes. In the Vykom Temple Road satyagraha, Gandhi's followers, after dramatizing the issue, and even after negotiating a withdrawal of the police barricades, refrained from entering the Vykom Temple Road until the Brahmans were converted to the Gandhian view of the matter.[15] Often enough, however, those who are called disobedients do attempt to coerce the majority—by forcing the majority to secure obedience at a price it finds morally unacceptable. It is for this reason that Gandhi regarded fasting as a form of coercion (even as a form of violence) and regretted his own use of this technique in the Ahmedabad labor satyagraha.[16] And it is for this reason that one may question the tactics of the captain and crew of *The Golden Rule*. For when they sailed into the government's testing grounds in the Central Pacific, these men were not simply registering a protest against its testing program and hoping that their arrest would give the public painful second thoughts. Rather, they were telling the government that it would have to incinerate them if it wished to proceed as planned, and this, they hoped, the government would find impossible to do.[17] In cases like this, the dissenters cross the line that separates civil disobedience from those forms of action that attempt to paralyze the majority's will or the government's actions. No doubt, the fact that the disobedient acts at great cost to himself (he is the nonviolent equivalent of Camus's *meurtrier délicat*)[18] affects one's judgment of his actions, as does the fact that he employs moral jujitsu instead of physical violence. Nevertheless, the fact that his coercion is nonviolent is not finally decisive, and it must be understood that he has entered upon a course of action that invites comparison with the public strike, with attempts to make the administration of government impossible (filling the jails as distinguished from accepting punishment), and even with acts of sabotage. As such, he poses a more radical challenge to authority than the civil disobedient wishes to pose.

The disobedient's interest in establishing that his actions are neither rebellious nor revolutionary provides him with a final reason for accepting punishment. For, by accepting the punishment prescribed by law, the disobedient is able to emphasize his commitment to law, and it is especially important for him to do so in a democratic society. The values that the disobedient wishes to defend are, after all, precisely the values that are best served by a democracy under law, if only these laws remain within bounds. Should it come to a choice, the disobedient's ultimate commitment is certainly to justice, and not to the will of the majority. But his present purpose is to persuade the majority not to force this choice upon him, and his present intention is to make the established system viable. It must not be supposed, incidentally, that the civil disobedient's position implies that he will never submit to the requirements of an unjust law. In fact, the citizen in a democracy often has a moral obligation to do precisely that. But there are limits to the injustice he will endure, as there are limits to the injustice he will perpetuate. It is the civil disobedient's conviction that these limits have been reached.

Of course, it does not follow from the fact that the disobedient is willing to pay the penalty that the government ought to exact it. The disobedient has been placed in an acute moral dilemma, and he may have acted with good will toward the community. Certainly, his punishment may cause profound ruptures in the community. All these facts, and others, ought to be considered in deciding whether to prosecute and, if the government does prosecute, in deciding the terms of sentence. It will often be in the government's and, indeed, in the community's best interests to act with flexibility and discretion in these matters, and it is a particularly barbarous fallacy to suppose that the government owes the disobedient his just portion of punishment. That it may owe him a day in court when he wishes to raise constitutional issues, perhaps even a day free from the threat of punishment, is another, insufficiently canvassed question that cannot be pursued here.

Although we have accepted the view that the civil disobedient ought to accept the punishment provided by law, it will be useful to consider certain unpersuasive arguments—in particular certain unpersuasive arguments of Socrates—that are often urged in favor of that view.[19] It will also be useful to answer the objections of those like Professor Nielsen and Professor Zinn who argue against the view that the disobedient ought to accept punishment.[20]

Socrates is often put forward as the paradigm of a civil disobedient, or at least as a thinker whose arguments ought to be decisive with the civil disobedient. Neither view is acceptable. To be sure, in some ways Socrates resembles the civil disobedient. He defies the public in obedience to his daimon (that early precursor of the modern conscience), and he does so to rouse the public from its sloth. His actions are by normal standards disinterested, and he acts for the public good at considerable cost to himself. Indeed, when Socrates finds himself in court, his primary objective is not to win an acquittal but, rather, to act in the manner best calculated to maintain his moral dignity, and to further the principles that have brought him to this pass. Fidelity to these principles is more important to him than his own fate if, indeed, it is not simply to be understood as his fate.

Despite these facts, the Socrates of the *Apology* and the *Crito* is not standing trial as a civil disobedient. For, if Socrates is a gadfly who defies the public, he has not, as he sees it, violated the law under which he is charged. Certainly he has not violated the law with the intention of protesting it or any other law. On the contrary, the *Crito* is a sustained and deeply felt hymn of praise to the laws of Athens. It is an impressive argument designed not only to show that these laws are just in their fundamental conception but also to indicate that Socrates takes no excep-

247

tion to them in particular. It is not the laws that do him an injustice but Anytus and Meletus. Since, in Socrates' view, he has violated no law, his willingness to accept punishment cannot be understood, as it should be in the case of the disobedient, as a way of characterizing and interpreting that disobedience. Certainly it is not an attempt to establish that his actions, though violations of law, are not criminal violations or violations undertaken with revolutionary objectives. Nor is it a way of weakening the will of the majority or of softening hard hearts. On the contrary, Socrates argues that he is innocent and that he should not be punished at all. Indeed, his offer to pay a fee of one mina, and his contention that, far from deserving punishment, he ought to be rewarded with a seat on the Prytaneum, is calculated, if anything, to stiffen the jury's will and to harden its heart. In any case it does, and Socrates' death is voted by a majority larger than the one that decided his guilt.

It is true, even if Socrates is not on trial for having committed a civilly disobedient act, that some of his arguments, if successful, would bear on the predicament of the civil disobedient and are therefore relevant to our theme. First, however, we should put aside those arguments that are quite special and show only that in view of what Socrates has said and done, before and during his trial, he ought to drink the hemlock and shun the course that Crito urges on him. Thus, Socrates has attempted to show, and has argued in the course of his trial, that it is important not simply to live but to live well. He has attempted to show, in particular, that going into exile would be incompatible with living well. For if he were to go to well-governed places, he would be regarded as an enemy of law and order; if to ill-governed ones, he would find it, for that very reason, impossible to live well. If Socrates were to withdraw these arguments now (arguments that, in any case, he believes to be true), his earlier remarks would look in retrospect like empty bluffing. Worse yet, he was in effect presented with the option of going into exile earlier, and he rejected the offer in the hope of vindicating himself before the court. To escape now would be to violate a gentleman's agreement and to add dishonor to inconsistency. Therefore, he should not escape as Crito urges; he should submit to the punishment determined by the court. These may be persuasive arguments, but they will only be persuasive if one has acted and spoken as Socrates has, and, in general, this will not be true of the civil disobedient. These arguments, then, cannot establish that the civil disobedient ought to accept the punishment imposed by the law.

Socrates does, however, offer more general arguments concerning one's obligation to obey the law, and these arguments must now claim our attention. Socrates maintains, for instance, that like the parent, but to an even greater extent, the state confers benefits upon a man and that the enjoyment of these benefits—education, protection, the facilities of the law—imposes a duty of obedience on the citizen. Then too, Socrates argues, in a passage anticipating Locke and the theory of consent, that the Athenian citizen has an obligation to obey the laws because he has freely agreed to do so.

"We brought you into the world, we raised you, we educated you, we gave you and every other citizen a share of all the good things we could," Socrates imagines the Laws arguing to him. "Yet," they continue,

> *we proclaim that if any man of the Athenians is dissatisfied with us he may take his goods and go away wherever he pleases; we give that privilege to every man who chooses to avail himself of it as soon as he has reached manhood and sees us, the laws, and the administration of our state. No one of us stands in his way or forbids him to take his goods and go wherever he likes, whether it be to an Athenian colony or to any foreign country, if he is dissatisfied with us and with the state. But we say that every man of you who remains here, seeing how we administer justice, and how we govern the state and other matters, has agreed, by the very fact of remaining here, to do whatever we tell him. . . . we offered him an alternative; we gave him his choice either to obey us or to convince us that we were wrong; but he did neither![21]*

Thus, according to Socrates, one has a duty, deriving from benefits received, and an obligation, deriving from one's undertakings, to obey the law. These arguments are, however, open to question.[22] After all, there are limits to a man's duty to obey his parents, and there are limits, too, to the duty he owes the state. Even if it follows that the enjoyment of state-conferred benefits imposes an obligation on a man, it is not clear that it imposes an obligation to abide by any law the state promulgates or enforces. The citizen may have accepted these benefits on certain assumptions and with certain reasonable expectations. And his obligation may lapse, or be overridden, when these assumptions are undermined or these expectations defeated. The argument from the obligation to abide by one's agreements is open to objection as well. It is plain from Socrates' argument that he takes the agreement to obey Athenian law to rest on a knowledge of how justice is administered and how the state is run. Surely, then, it is plausible to argue that the agreement binds only if the state continues to act as it has acted in the past. And in any case no agreement can oblige one to do what it is morally intolerable to do. Besides, if we are to apply Socrates' arguments to contemporary circumstances, we may doubt whether the agreement the citizen is supposed to make with the state is, in fact, free of duress or undertaken in the presence of genuine alternatives. All this argues that even if considerations such as the ones Socrates adduces do create duties and obligations, these duties and obligations have limits, or they may be overridden by other and weightier duties, obligations, and commitments. Apparently Socrates disagrees. He seems to hold that since violating the duty or obligation to obey the law would have disastrous consequences for the state, the limitation or subordination of such obligations or duties cannot be justified. He imagines the Laws appearing to him and saying,

> *Tell us, Socrates, what have you in mind to do? What do you mean by trying to escape but to destroy us, the laws and the whole state, so far as you are able? Do you think that the state can exist, and not be overthrown, in which the decisions of law are of no force, and are disregarded and undermined by private individuals?* [23]

But, surely, this argument is ineffective. Even if the refusal to obey the law had the consequence that Socrates (and the Laws) imagine, it would not follow that one had an absolute obligation to obey. There are situations in which it is permissible to "destroy" the laws and the whole state. But, is it true, in any case, that the violation of law does have the disastrous consequences that are thought to impose so strong a duty of obedience? Far from it. Individual violations of the law may have no discernible effect at all. No doubt, Socrates is implicitly appealing to the argument that if everyone violated the law, the laws and the state would be destroyed. This may well be true, and it may therefore be unfair for anyone to exempt himself from obedience. But the force of this argument is greatly altered if disobedience is entered into on special grounds and in special ways. Yet Socrates may believe, and with some plausibility, that this more discriminating type of the argument will not help him. If it is implausible to hold that the state will be destroyed if Socrates himself escapes punishment, it may well be true that if everyone who believed as Socrates believes were to escape punishment the legal system would be undermined. Thus, if everyone who believed that the laws of the state were just and, indeed, that the very law under which he was tried is just, but that, since he is the victim of an administrative error or a mistaken judgment, he may seek to evade punishment, the system of law would doubtless suffer grave injury. But, as we have seen, Socrates' position differs significantly from that of the civil disobedient. For it is far from clear that the state would be destroyed if everyone were to engage in civil disobedience who believed that the laws he disobeyed were themselves in violation of the fundamental principles of civilized society. On the contrary, it is possible to believe that, often enough, such disobedience would, in fact, strengthen the state and the legal system. Nor is it true that such persons would be acting unfairly in acting as they did. They would not be acting on a principle that persons similarly situated could not act on, nor, I should argue, would they be acting in violation of duties and obligations they ought to honor on more general grounds. For these duties and obligations are either limited in themselves, or are overridden by the deeper principles upon which such persons act. Often enough, then, the civil disobedient need not be dissuaded from his course of action either by the fear of destroying the state or by considerations of fairness. There is no absolute obligation to obey the law, and the arguments of the *Crito* need not be decisive for him.

If the arguments of the *Crito* do not establish that the disobedient must always conform to the requirements of the law, they do not establish, as a corollary, that he must always accept the punishment required by law. Nevertheless, it will typically be desirable that he do so for reasons that have already been suggested. Despite the differences between them, the disobedient may hope to enlist the kind of sympathy and admiration that history has given to Socrates and to the image of innocence imprisoned. Engaging this sympathy may be crucial to his ultimate success.

We may turn, then, to the views of those who argue that the civil disobedient need not accept punishment at all. For instance, Professor Kai Nielsen, in commenting upon some observations of mine made elsewhere that anticipate the views defended here, writes as follows:

> Cohen remarks that "*After openly breaking the law, the traditional disobedient willingly pays the penalty." This might be taken in two ways. It might be taken simply as a description of what people who regard themselves as engaging in civil disobedience do. But then it is surely not the case that all people who engage in what they believe to be civil disobedience are willing to pay the penalty. Their public defiance of a law they regard as so immoral that it requires disobedience is sometimes followed by forms of legal evasion. I think Cohen would reply that in such a circumstance their acts are not properly characterizable as "civil disobedience."*[24]

It is not perfectly clear what Professor Nielsen has in mind when he speaks of "legal evasion." But if this means, say, that the persons in question act anonymously, fail to make the significance of their actions clear to the public, or go into exile after performing them, then he is correct in thinking that I find it useful to distinguish such actions, for purposes of analysis and justification, from what I here call acts of civil disobedience. It would be even more important to insist on such a distinction if the objectives of those who engage in such evasion are revolutionary, if they employ personal violence, or if they are willing to employ disobedience as a first attempt rather than as a last resort. There are significantly different kinds of actions—even of actions undertaken with moral or political objectives—that involve disobeying the law, and I am only discussing one of them here, though the one I am discussing is a very significant type of such action. Nielsen is essentially correct, then, in thinking that I am putting forward a definition and a definite conception of civil disobedience, and there is, therefore, no reason why he should think that another construction must be put upon the remarks he quotes. Nevertheless, he does propose another one. He writes that

> Cohen's *"After openly breaking the law, the traditional disobedi-*
> *ent willingly pays the penalty"* would take my second reading,
> namely, it would be a statement about the defining characteristics
> of what would count as *"legitimate civil disobedience."* That is to
> say, an act would not be a legitimate act of civil disobedience un-
> less the disobedient were willing to pay the penalty if the courts
> find against him.[25]

But this is surely not correct, nor what I wish to say. In defining civil disobedience in such a way that the civil disobedient necessarily accepts the punishment, I have in no way committed myself on the question of legitimacy. It certainly remains open to me to say that there are justi-fiable acts of legal disobedience that do not require the acceptance of punishment. The definition offered simply has the consequence that where the disobedient does not accept punishment (and conduct himself in a number of other specified ways), his actions will not count as civil disobedience in the sense sketched here, and he will not be subject to the observations made about that form of political action. This unwillingness to concede the value of concentrating on a particular type of violation of the law, one with a special history and a special justification, in fact underlies most of the criticism and misunderstanding of the position taken here concerning the relation between civil disobedience and the acceptance of punishment.

Nielsen argues, more particularly, that the views defended here miss an important insight contained in Ronald Dworkin's remarkable essay, "Civil Disobedience: The Case Against Prosecution."[26] Nielsen, following Dworkin, writes that

> when people challenge the draft laws, for example, and refuse to
> obey them in the public, principled and deliberate fashion of a
> civil disobedient, they are persuaded that the laws are often un-
> constitutional and in such a situation, Dworkin argues, their case
> about constitutionality is a strong one. But then they do not re-
> gard themselves as having broken a law, for they believe on
> reasonable grounds that the law they are disobeying is invalid, i.e.,
> unconstitutional, and believing this they have no obligation at all
> in terms of fair play or anything else to accept the punishment.[27]

These remarks do an injustice to Dworkin's essay, which does not, I think, have the consequences that Nielsen reads into it. What Professor Dworkin says, and what I believe to be true, is that "in the United States, at least, almost any law that a significant number of people would be tempted to disobey on moral grounds would be doubtful—if not clearly invalid—on constitutional grounds as well."[28] Dworkin's observations are not perfectly general, then. They rely on special features of the U.S. Constitution, and his requirement of "a significant number of people" is crucial, for, when it is met, it shows that the moral opinions in question are not personal or eccentric but rooted in the community's moral traditions. But given all this, all that Dworkin says is that when a significant number of people are so inclined, the constitutionality of the law they are tempted to violate will be "doubtful." It certainly does not follow from this, nor does Dworkin think that it follows from this, that such persons therefore "have no obligation at all" to obey the law. On the contrary, although these dissenters may have a "strong" argument, those who uphold the law may have a stronger one. And, in that case, the dissenter's view of the law, however plausible, is wrong. In such a case Dworkin would certainly claim that they have an obligation to obey the law, especially so if, as in the case of the segregationists, their disobedience requires them to invade the rights of others. (Dworkin's special and sympathetic attitude toward the draft cases depends on his view that the draft refusers do not, in fact, violate the rights of others, and even here he does not maintain that, in general, such persons have no obligation to obey the law—it may, however, be only a *prima facie* obligation—or to accept punishment.) Indeed, Dworkin maintains that in a case like that of the segregationists the courts ought to enforce the law and that fairness requires that the segregationists submit to the government's view of the law. The plausibility of their constitutional views, and the fact that these views are widely, sincerely, and even reasonably maintained, does not alter this fact.

It does not follow, then, that those who conscientiously believe the law to be doubtful "have no obligation at all in terms of fair play or anything else to accept the punishment." All that Professor Dworkin argues is that, in certain special circumstances, such persons should not be prosecuted and, in still more special ones, not convicted if prosecuted. Even if Dworkin had argued that those who conscientiously object to the law, or doubt its validity, never have an *obligation* to obey the law or accept punishment, it would not follow that they *ought* not to accept such punishment. For our argument is that, given certain social circumstances, they ought to accept punishment even when they have no obligation to do so, and this for a variety of reasons that have already been suggested.

A related misunderstanding underlies some of Howard Zinn's objections to the view that the civil disobedient ought to accept punishment. For Zinn's discussion shows little appreciation of the fact that, or the reasons why, apologists as well as critics of civil disobedience have urged the disobedient to accept punishment. He argues as though the purpose of this suggestion is simply to limit protest, and he does not acknowledge that it might, in appropriate circumstances, serve to make it more effective. So, Professor Zinn claims that if disobedience is morally justified, it is justified to the very end. Now this argument is either platitudinous or false. If "it is justified to the very end" means that if protest is justified at all it is justified until the offending situation is rectified, that goes without saying, and it is this indisputable point that Zinn relies upon. But he soon takes "justified to the end" to mean not that the protest should be tireless and unyielding but that the protesters are justified in employing uncivil means if these are required to achieve their purposes. In this connection he even speaks of "toppling" the government. Now it certainly does not follow from the fact that an evil is worth protesting, however vigorously, that uncivil and even revolutionary means may be used to eradicate that evil. To be sure, a time may come when such measures are appropriate, but until that time, it may be necessary to act within the limits of civil disobedience.

Unfortunately, Zinn offers an extremely tendentious and unacceptable account of what it means to keep within such limits. His full statement is:

> *If the protest is morally justified (whether it breaks the law or not) it is morally justified to the very end, even past the point where the court has imposed the penalty. If it stops at that point with everyone saying cheerfully, as at a football match, "Well, we played a good game, we lost, and we will accept the verdict like sports"— then we are treating social protest like a game. It becomes a token, a "gesture."* [29]

And again:

> *The sportsman-like acceptance of jail as the terminus of civil disobedience is fine for a football game, or for a society determined to limit reform to tokens. It does not suit a society that wants to eliminate long-festering wrongs.* [30]

In view of the history of civil disobedience, this is, indeed, a remarkable caricature. To be sure, for the classical disobedient the acceptance of jail may be "the terminus of civil disobedience," but that is far from saying that it is "the end of protest." If one means by "accepting the verdict" that one goes to jail, the civil disobedient accepts the verdict, but he does not thereby "cheerfully" accept defeat. True, he accepts jail as a (significant) gesture, but no, this does not mean that he accepts a (mere) token. Accepting punishment does not imply the permanent acquiescence in intolerable evil. Nor, as we have said, does the practice of civil disobedience, as described here, preclude the eventual resort to stronger measures.

The Citizen Dissents

I submit that an individual who breaks a law that conscience tells him is unjust, and willingly accepts the penalty by staying in jail to arouse the conscience of the community over its injustice, is in reality expressing the very highest respect for law.

Martin Luther King, Jr.

(Above left) Paul Revere's engraving of the Boston Massacre; (above right) demonstrator for women's rights; (below) Mahatma Gandhi, after spending sixteen months in jail for his protests against the British government; (opposite) Civil War draft riot in New York City

(Right) Rosa Parks, whose refusal to obey a Jim Crow law and move to the rear of a bus touched off the 1955 Montgomery bus boycotts, is fingerprinted following her arrest; (below) woman waiting to be taken to jail after being arrested for her part in a restaurant sit-in protesting segregation; (opposite top) Dr. Martin Luther King, Jr., civil rights leader; (opposite bottom) black and white demonstrators in New York City demanding welfare reforms

(Above) Columbia University student take-over, April 1969; (right) antiwar demonstrators ransacking the office of a Silver Spring, Maryland, draft board, May 1969. The demonstrators poured ''blood''on the draft records, overturned cabinets, and smashed typewriters. (Opposite) Coast Guard vessel escorting yacht *The Golden Rule* back into Honolulu harbor, May 1958, after the yacht's four crewmen attempted to sail into the Eniwetok nuclear weapons test area to protest forthcoming tests

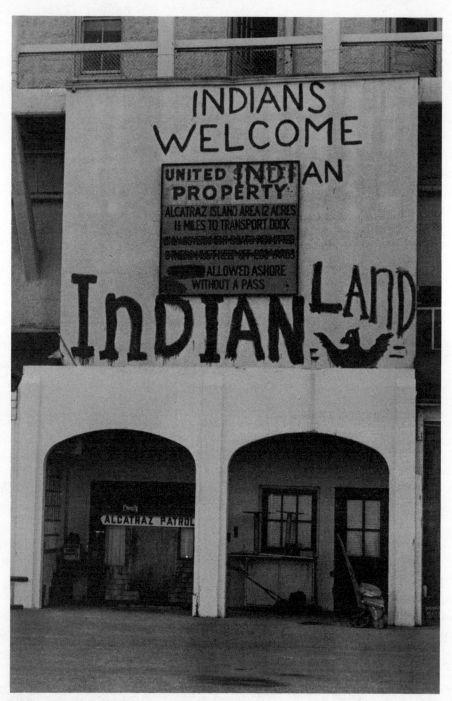

Alcatraz Island, former federal prison site, was home and cultural center for American Indians who occupied the land from 1969 until the federal government reclaimed it in 1971

Surely all this is clear from a consideration of the tradition of civil disobedience. Going to jail does not "end" one's civil disobedience; on the contrary, it is a crucial part of that disobedience. It is crucial in characterizing the disobedience as being of a certain historically intelligible sort, and this, it is hoped, will have a special effect. For the fact that the disobedient displays his fidelity to law and strictly minimizes his deviation from it, as well as the fact that he is willing to suffer for his views, is meant to reassure and to move the majority. That this is at least sometimes possible is plain from the careers of Gandhi and of Martin Luther King. Gandhi, in any number of his satyagraha campaigns, and King, writing from the Birmingham City Jail, were immensely effective.[31] Surely, they cannot be dismissed as having made "gestures" or as having "cheerfully" acquiesced in the evils they were protesting. I wish that as much could be said for Zinn's talk about "toppling the government."

The civil disobedient may commit illegal actions, but in the view of Gandhi and of King such actions ought to be nonviolent in nature. Gandhi and King were, of course, committed to nonviolence quite generally and as a matter of religious principle. Their views in this matter are therefore unconvincing to those who are willing to contemplate the use of violence in certain circumstances. If one does not oppose violence on principle one can, nevertheless, argue that it is incompatible with the distinctive purposes of civil disobedience. Indeed, John Rawls, to whom these remarks are very much indebted, argues that violent actions are incompatible with the nature of civil disobedience because they will be understood as threats, not as appeals.[32] And it is possible to add that the fear of violence (or of sudden death) puts men beyond the reach of rational and moral persuasion. There is a time for violence in human affairs, but when it arrives, civil disobedience is no longer an appropriate form of political activity.

Rawls's suggestion is persuasive, and especially so when it restricts the prohibition on violence to a prohibition on violence against other persons. It is less convincing when violence against property is in question. For the violation of symbolically important public property may be a dramatic and not very dangerous way of lodging effective protests, and the razing of the slums has been understood as a cry of despair as often as it has been perceived as a declaration of war. The argument against violence is at its weakest in the case of violence against the self. A sacrifice like Norman Morrison's, far from frustrating the purposes of civil disobedience, realized them in a peculiarly impressive and moving way. If it inspired fear, it was not the fear of sudden death but the fear of eternal wrath, and that is a fear that often brings men to their moral senses.

Civil disobedience is, then, an appeal to the public to alter certain laws or policies that the minority takes to be incompatible with the fundamental principles of morality, principles that it believes the majority accepts. If the minority is mistaken and the majority does not in fact accept such principles, civil disobedience will undoubtedly prove a pointless form of political activity, but it will not, for that reason, be an unjustifiable one. The moral duty to obey the laws of the state derives, ultimately, from the duty to support institutions that realize the principles of freedom and justice, and it lapses when, and insofar as, the state violates them. These principles of political morality normally find expression in the public morality of the state, and given the circumstances of the modern democracies, they guarantee to citizens the basic freedoms (including freedom to participate in the political life) and also a minimum of justice (by which I understand not only the disinterested administration of justice but also a fair share of the benefits of the common life). In addition, they prohibit inflicting pain and suffering on innocent persons, and they require fidelity to the idea of justice between nations. These principles are adumbrated, and often find remarkably full expression, in the constitutions of modern states, although the constitution, especially the constitution as interpreted by the courts, may be an imperfect expression of them. Thus, our own public morality, as articulated in our own Constitution, makes very broad guarantees of freedom and justice in the First, the Fifth, and the Fourteenth Amendments, and Article VI makes treaties part of the supreme law of the land. The treaties to which we are in fact a party define the rights of foreign peoples in considerable detail, and they enumerate the legitimate grounds and acceptable methods of war.

I have little doubt that, at the present time, the government of the United States is violating these principles of political morality and providing dissenters with legitimate grounds for civil disobedience. It is important to recall, however, that the public morality of our society, especially as it is articulated in the federal Constitution, gives voice to these very principles, and we must now examine the consequences of this fact for the traditional theory of civil disobedience. On the traditional view, a man who commits civil disobedience believes that he is, in fact, violating a legally valid (if morally insupportable) law or order. But in a constitutional democracy like our own, those who are asked to conform to laws that they think immoral will normally be in a position to claim, and if they are legally well advised they will claim, that the laws in question are unconstitutional nullities, not laws at all.[33]

The altered position I have described was, of course, the position of Martin Luther King and his disciples in the civil rights movement. As one would expect, they rarely, if ever, pleaded guilty to violating the laws under which they were charged. Rather, they argued that the laws were themselves in violation of the federal Constitution and that they were, in consequence, invalid and without legal effect. In a remarkable number of cases (when federal legislation had not already rendered the issues moot) the courts agreed with them.

Despite the fact that they did not believe themselves to be violating the law, King and his followers continued to refer to themselves as civil disobedients. Former Justice Fortas has fallen in with their usage, and this fact has, I believe, contributed to his wholly undeserved reputation for having a liberal and even a concessive position on the issue of civil disobedience.[34] For it is one thing to endorse "civil disobedience" of the type practised by King, and quite another thing to endorse civil disobedience in the stricter, traditional and more serious sense. Certainly, Justice Fortas has not endorsed civil disobedience in this more traditional sense. In fact, his liberalism comes to nothing more than this: the dissenter is granted a moral right to test, or to try to test, the validity of a law that he considers immoral and believes to be unconstitutional. It finds its consummation in a proposition that Vice-President Agnew would hardly contest: if the courts agree that the law is invalid, the dissenter was within his legal rights in refusing to obey it.

The fact that Justice Fortas has not endorsed anything like the classical conception of civil disobedience becomes apparent when we consider his attitude toward the "disobedient" who does not win in the courts. For on Justice Fortas's view, the man who loses in court is under a moral as well a legal obligation to refrain from any further disobedience (he has had his day in court), and he is morally as well as legally obliged to suffer the punishment prescribed by law (that is the way we play the game). Surely, this is a rigid and untenable view; indeed, Justice Fortas implies on occasion that even he does not really accept it. If Congress passed a law requiring Negroes to observe a discriminatory curfew, to confine themselves to certain restricted geographical areas (as former Ambassador George Kennan has hinted might be a good idea), and to go naked through the streets if they wished to apply for welfare, few would suppose that they had a moral obligation to do so. The fact that the courts could ultimately sustain such a law would not alter the situation in any serious way. But it is hardly necessary to seek examples that may seem fantastic or purely theoretical. After all, the Court on which Justice Fortas sat once decided the Dred Scott case, and it is hard to believe that Justice Fortas or anyone else is going to say (at least at this late date) that in the period following the Fugitive Slave Act and the Dred Scott decision, abolitionists had a moral obligation to return slaves to their owners or that slaves had an obligation to return of their own free will.

Even if we were to assume that the Court's interpretation of the Constitution in the Dred Scott case was defensible, it would not follow that we had a moral obligation to acquiesce in its decision. For the Constitution itself would then have been in violation of the fundamental principles of political morality, and one does not have a moral obligation to abide by such a constitution. Of course, there is good reason to doubt that the Constitution did in fact mean what the Court said it meant, and it is important, now, to challenge the view that the Constitution, or that the law, is inevitably what the courts say it is. For the doctrine gives a false view of the nature of law and of what it means to obey it.

The English school of Hobbes and Austin held that the law is to be identified with the command of the sovereign, and, insofar as he delegates authority to them, with the decisions and orders of his courts. The American legal realists have associated the law and the courts even more closely. For Holmes the law is "nothing more pretentious" than a prophecy of what the courts will do; for Fortas "the rule of law" requires nothing more ignoble than acquiescing in whatever they may have commanded. The objections to such views are powerful, indeed, and a far more persuasive and commonsense tradition holds that the law is to be identified not with the holdings of courts but with the authorized rules and principles that the courts interpret and apply. Of course, the interpretations and holdings of courts must be considered in determining the state of the law (the doctrine of precedent has an important place in our jurisprudence), but these interpretations and decisions must not be identified with the law. For one thing, the courts can misinterpret the law, and their decisions are often mistaken. When this is so it would be foolish and harmful to identify these dubious interpretations and questionable decisions with the law itself. Certainly the courts do not do so. It may have taken the Union armies to "reverse" the Dred Scott case, but the courts often admit that they have been in error and agree to reverse themselves. Indeed, the Supreme Court has reversed itself in such momentous cases as *Erie R.R. Co.* v. *Tomkins, Brown* v. *Board of Education,* and *West Virginia State Board of Education* v. *Barnette.*

This fact is of importance to the dissenter for a number of reasons. In the first place, it may strengthen the case for disobedience on purely moral grounds. For as Dworkin has observed,[35] it is one thing for a man to sacrifice his principles (or to violate his conscience) when it is plain that the law requires him to do so. But it is another thing (though it may still be legally required) for him to do so when the law, or the court's view of it, is of questionable validity. In addition to making a moral difference, the fact that the courts may be wrong makes a practical difference as well. One of the disobedient's aims is to change the existing law, and the most effective way of doing so in a constitutional democracy will often be to persuade the courts that the obnoxious legislation is unconstitutional. Continued defiance of the law may be the only practical way for the dissenter to obtain a rehearing of the questions at issue. Even when other methods are available, the disobedient's willingness to face criminal punishment in defense of his beliefs may help the court to see that it has misjudged the strength and perhaps the nature of his interests.

For this reason it is possible to agree with Dworkin's claim that the Jehovah's Witnesses behaved properly in refusing to observe Justice Fortas's canons of correct behavior after the Court found against them in the first "flag-salute" case.[36] As they saw it, the law denied them a basic religious freedom, and they were thus being asked to violate their fundamental religious convictions on the basis of dubious constitutional doctrine. Continued defiance did not require them to injure the interests, or abridge the rights, of others in any serious way, and in the end it probably helped to convince the Court that its original decision had been mistaken. In any event, the Court did reverse itself in the well-known case of *West Virginia State Board of Education* v. *Barnette* only a few years later. As it now viewed the matter, the intransigent Witnesses had only been exercising their constitutional rights all along. The moral is plain. It is often those who insist on their legal rights, rather than those who acquiesce in the fallible (and occasionally supine and even corrupt) opinions of courts, who strengthen the "rule of law" that Justice Fortas is so anxious to defend.

If the argument for civil disobedience is strengthened when there is reason to believe that the courts are in error, it is strengthened still more when there is reason to believe that the courts will refuse to adjudicate the issues at all. This is, of course, precisely what they have refused to do in the crucial cases arising out of the war in Vietnam. In the Spock case the trial court invoked the "political question" doctrine and denied its jurisdiction to hear any issues concerning the legality of the war or of its conduct. And in the cases of David Mitchell (who refused to report for induction) and the Fort Hood Three (who refused to report for service in Vietnam), the Supreme Court simply denied certiorari. It has been suggested that when the courts invoke the "political question" doctrine and refuse to adjudicate the crucial issues the disobedient wishes to raise, their action is tantamount to finding that the executive is legally free to perform the very actions that are being protested.[37] But it is far more plausible to argue that when they invoke this doctrine they assume a wholly agnostic position on the issues involved and simply enforce as law the determinations of the "political" branches. In the case of the Fort Hood Three, this agnostic attitude is assumed toward questions that Justice Stewart and Justice Douglas consider, and that plainly are, "of great magnitude."[38] In his dissent to the Court's decision denying certiorari in the case of the Fort Hood Three, Justice Stewart indicates that these questions include the following, among others:

I. Is the present United States military activity in Vietnam a "war" within the meaning of Article I, Section 8, Clause 11 of the Constitution?

II. If so, may the Executive constitutionally order the petitioners to participate in that military activity, when no war has been declared by the Congress?

III. Of what relevance to Question II are the present treaty obligations of the United States?

> IV. Of what relevance to Question II is the joint Congressional ("Tonkin Bay") Resolution of August 10, 1964?
>
> A. Do present United States military operations fall within the terms of the Joint Resolution?
>
> B. If the Joint Resolution purports to give the Chief Executive authority to commit United States forces to armed conflict limited in scope only by his own absolute discretion, is the Resolution a constitutionally impermissible delegation of all or part of Congress' power to declare war?

"These," he continues, "are large and deeply troubling questions. Whether the Court would ultimately reach them depends, of course, upon the resolution of serious preliminary issues of justiciability. We cannot make these problems go away simply by refusing to hear the case of three obscure Army privates. I intimate not even tentative views upon any of these matters, but I think the Court should squarely face them by granting certiorari and setting this case for oral argument."

In turn, I do not wish to intimate any views on the "political question" doctrine or on the Court's unwillingness to review the actions of the executive and legislative branches in these sensitive areas. But it is important to recognize that the Court's refusal to consider these matters can only increase the weight that the three obscure army privates, and others like them, must give to their own appraisal of the issues.[39] Certainly, a very formidable body of opinion supports the view that the government's behavior is in many particulars both illegal and unconstitutional. And there is little doubt, I believe, that it has frequently violated the principles of international law and morality. The case for disobedience in these circumstances is very strong.

The discussion has concentrated, so far, on what Gandhi called "defensive" and others have called "direct" disobedience. In such cases the law the dissenter violates is the very law he regards as immoral. But it is important to recognize the existence of another form of disobedience, called by Gandhi "offensive" and by others "indirect" disobedience. For in this type of disobedience the dissenter violates a law (usually a traffic law or the law of trespass) that he finds unobjectionable in itself in order to protest still other laws, policies, or orders that he thinks immoral or even wicked.

In Mortimer Adler's view, the distinctive feature of civil disobedience as practised by Thoreau and Gandhi is its commitment to the doctrine of "indirect" disobedience. This commitment he thinks unfortunate, for the kind of disobedience to which it leads strikes him as a form of "revolutionary" action, even as it impresses Justice Fortas as a form of "warfare" against society.[40] Adler contrasts such action with the legitimate, classical doctrine of civil disobedience that he finds in the writings of St. Thomas and John Locke. As I see it, this reading of history is mistaken. In fact, the classical tradition of Aquinas and Locke did not possess a theory of civil disobedience at all. Rather, it alternated between a doctrine of conscientious refusal and one of revolution pure and simple. Even in Thoreau the idea of civil disobedience was not clearly disengaged from the ideas of conscientious refusal and of revolution. In fact, in its main emphasis Thoreau's essay is an apology for conscientious refusal. And, insofar as this line of interpretation is honored, his refusal to pay taxes cannot be interpreted as an act of civil disobedience—certainly not as an act of indirect disobedience. Yet there are passages in the essay that support Adler's reading of Thoreau as a modern civil disobedient—and, indeed, his suspicion that the modern disobedient is an incipient revolutionary. These passages permit us to view Thoreau's act of tax refusal as an act of political protest and as an example of "indirect" disobedience, among other things. After defending these historical observations, I will offer a brief defense of Thoreau's practice and of the idea of indirect civil disobedience generally.

According to St. Thomas, a law is an ordinance of reason, for the common good, made by him who has the care of the community, and promulgated. As such, it is binding in conscience on the good man.[41] But there may be a defect in the authority of those who promulgate laws, or a defect in the nature of the laws themselves, which invalidates their claim to authority. In such cases the duty of obedience is put in doubt. Thus, the authority of the lawgiver may be defective, either because he is personally unworthy or because he has obtained power in an illegitimate manner—say through simony, or by violence. In the case of one who (like Caesar) "possessed himself of power through violence, either against the will of his subjects or by compelling their consent, and where there was no possibility of appeal to a higher authority who could pass judgment on such an act," there was no obligation to submit to his authority. In fact, in such a case "one who liberates his country by killing a tyrant is to be praised and rewarded."[42] Surely there is no doctrine of civil disobedience here, nor is there one, it would seem, where the defect is not in the manner in which power is obtained but in the way it is exercised. For according to St. Thomas, one does not have an obligation to obey where the law's object is not to advance the common good (a defect in its end), or where, although issued with a view to the common good, the law is defective in the way it distributes burdens (a defect in its form). Neither, according to Thomas, does one have an obligation to obey laws that are issued in excess of jurisdiction. In such cases, Thomas says, these orders are "acts of violence rather than laws," and they do not bind in conscience "except perhaps in order to avoid scandal or disturbance, for which cause a man should even yield his right." Here prudence may be the better part of wisdom, but the only alternative to biding one's time that Thomas suggests is the kind of forceful resistance that is appropriate to "violent acts."

If the "authorities" can act contrary to natural law, they can equally well act contrary to divine law. They might, for instance, require the worship of idols, and such requirements must be resisted, as they were by the Christian martyrs. But, again, these are not cases of what is here called civil disobedience. Rather, they are paradigm cases of conscientious refusal. The martyrs manifest an absolute unwillingness to act in violation of the dictates of conscience, but their acts are not political acts undertaken with the intention, or with the expectation, of altering the law. I conclude, then, that although St. Thomas does, of course, allow that illegitimate authorities and unjust laws need not be obeyed—in these respects his arguments are in some ways more radical than those presented here—he does not specify any particular mode of protest against such laws that is comparable to the modern conception of civil disobedience.

Similar observations apply to Locke, although he, in his *Letter Concerning Toleration,* does make some remarks that have been taken to adumbrate the modern conception of civil disobedience. He raises the question of what a man should do if the magistrate's decree orders something that seems unlawful to the conscience of a private person, and he answers as follows:

> If the commonwealth is governed in good faith, and the counsels of the magistrate are really directed to the common good of the citizens, this will seldom happen. But if it should chance to happen, I say that such a private citizen should abstain from the action which his conscience pronounces to be unlawful, but undergo the punishment which it is not unlawful for him to bear. For the private judgment of any person concerning a law enacted in political matters, and for the public good, does not take away the obligation of that law, nor does it deserve toleration. But if the law concerns things which lie outside the magistrate's province, as for example that the people, or any part of it, should be compelled to embrace a strange religion and adopt new rites, those who disagree are not obliged by that law because political society was instituted only to preserve for each private man his possession of the things of this life, and for no other purpose.[43]

It must not be thought, however, just because Locke urges the citizen whose conscience is violated to refuse obedience and accept punishment, that he is proposing a doctrine of civil disobedience. On the contrary, it looks as though what Locke has in mind here is something more closely related to conscientious refusal. Certainly, he is not proposing a course of political action. He allows that the citizen may act to preserve his conscience, but at the same time Locke thinks that he should acknowledge his obligations and defer to the magistrate and the magistrate's assessment of the common good. Locke is not proposing a technique of protest against, or appeal from, the magistrate's decision.

In this passage from *A Letter Concerning Toleration,* Locke implies that conscientious objection exhausts a man's remedies when the magistrate acts within the boundaries of politics. It appears that only when the magistrate acts "outside" the province of politics, as when he attempts to regulate religious matters, does the citizen's obligation of obedience lapse, and when it does we can only understand Locke to be suggesting that an appeal to Heaven is in order. In fact, however, we know from the *Treatise* that Locke allows the appeal to Heaven in what are ostensibly political matters as well, and even in the *Letter* he echoes this more liberal doctrine. Thus he writes, in a remarkably prescient passage:

> *Suppose religion were left out of account and that physical characteristics were made the basis of distinctions, and that those with black hair or grey eyes were treated differently from the rest of the citizens, so that they could not buy and sell freely, and were forbidden to practice their trades; that parents were deprived of the education and care of their children; that the law-courts were either closed to them or biased against them: why do not you think the magistrate would have as much to fear from these, who shared nothing in common except persecution and the color of their hair and eyes, as from others who associated together for religion?* [44]

This would be, as Locke suggests, simple tyranny, the exercise of power beyond right. "And," as he writes in the *Treatise,* "where the body of the people, or any single man is deprived of their right, or is under the exercise of a power without right, and have no appeal on earth, there they have a liberty to appeal to Heaven." [45]

So, the only alternative to conscientious refusal that Locke has to suggest in this imaginary case is the revolutionary appeal to Heaven. Yet the situation that Locke imagines here inevitably puts us in mind of the kind of discrimination that Martin Luther King protested in his civil disobedience campaigns, even as the religious discrimination that is Locke's main topic in the *Letter* reminds us of the evils Gandhi protested in some of his most notable satyagraha campaigns. These similarities help us to see that neither Locke nor Aquinas was in fact able to envisage anything like Gandhi's conception of civil disobedience.

Thoreau, in his classic essay, does adumbrate the idea. [46] But, as I have suggested, he by no means clearly articulates it or disengages it from the ideas of conscientious refusal or revolution. The words *civil disobedience* appear nowhere in his essay, and the essay in fact appeared with the title "Civil Disobedience" only when it was republished four years after his death. It was first delivered at the Concord Lyceum in January 1848, under the title "On the Relation of the Individual to the State." Thoreau spoke at the Lyceum to justify his successive refusals to pay state taxes, which, as he explained, began in 1842 and culminated in his arrest and confinement in the Concord jail in July 1846.[47] It was therefore well over a year after his arrest and many years after the first episode of tax refusal when he undertook to offer a public explanation of his actions. No doubt he hoped that arrest would come sooner, but the lack of publicity he gave to his actions arouses the suspicion, confirmed by other evidence, that Thoreau may usefully be regarded as a conscientious refuser. He puts little emphasis on the view that his actions constitute a specific form of politics (and he certainly does not imagine himself at the head of a mass movement of the sort that Gandhi and King were to lead). Nor does he view his actions as a form of protest against an unjust lapse from a fundamentally acceptable political order. Indeed, he often sounds the anarchist note. He is clearly not, as Gandhi claimed to be, a philanthropist and a friend of the state. On the contrary, he insists that "that government is best that governs not at all." He is not inclined to view his disobedience as an act of last resort but thinks, simply, that the methods the government provides for remedying an evil "take too much time." If he follows the authorized procedures "a man's life will be gone." Democratic methods fill him with contempt—voting is a sort of gaming, and voting for the right is *doing* nothing for it. Similarly, constitutional litigation of the sort that King pursued is beside the point, for in Thoreau's view the constitution—any constitution—is itself the fundamental evil. If Gandhi thought that only those who had demonstrated their active loyalty and respect for law should offer satyagraha, Thoreau believed that it was not desirable to cultivate respect for the law so much as for the right. Indeed, far from acknowledging the obligations imposed upon a citizen by the decisions of a democratic majority, Thoreau claimed that "the only obligation which I have a right to assume, is to do what I think right." Viewed from this perspective, Thoreau's refusal to pay the head tax is purely and simply an attempt to do what he thinks right independently of what his fellows think about the matter. His refusal is an attempt to dissociate himself from a wicked government, an expression of his unwillingness to be "an agent of injustice" to another.

As he recognizes no obligation to the majority or to the government, his willingness to go to jail cannot be understood as an attempt to acknowledge an obligation that he unfortunately cannot discharge, nor can it be seen as an attempt to express his fundamental fidelity to law. Certainly, it is no Gandhian attempt to convert others through his own sacrifice and suffering. Rather, going to jail is simply the outward and visible sign of his inner integrity and grace. In a land that practises slavery, jail is the appropriate place for a free man to be, and going to jail is the only tax a conscientious man ought to pay. When he leaves jail, Thoreau's reaction to his fellow townsmen is that they are a distinct race (a sentiment

Gandhi and King would never permit themselves) as unlike himself as Malays or Chinese. The struggle for brotherhood, and for *swaraj* in the deepest sense, is an eternal struggle, yet Thoreau, within a half hour of his release, after a single night in jail, is off huckleberrying, "on one of our highest hills, two miles off, and the State was no where to be seen." This is Thoreau the conscientious refuser, the man whose object is to keep his hands clean, or, if they should be stained, then only by the huckleberry. This is not the theorist of a sophisticated and dedicated form of politics, at once respectful of the state and of one's fellow men yet appealing, in a special way, and as a civil last resort, to their sense of justice.

Nevertheless, there are strains of the civil disobedient in Thoreau, and it is no accident that Gandhi and King were inspired by his essay and took its later title for their theme. Thoreau does, however intermittently, consider the public dimensions and the moral resonance of his act of tax refusal.

His view that he encounters the state but once a year, and then in the form of the tax collector, is no doubt naïve, but he does take the encounter to provide him with occasion for a direct confrontation with the state. On this occasion he can force the state, in its most palpable form, to consider whether it will treat him as "a neighbor and a well-disposed man" or "as a maniac and a disturber of the peace." Despite his perhaps momentary view of his neighbors as a distinct race (this was, after all, his view immediately upon emerging from jail), he implies that the state cannot but know what the right view is. Furthermore, he has no doubt that if others would follow his example and force the state to choose between putting all just men in prison and perpetuating the war and slavery, war and slavery would be abandoned. If he is not a Martin Luther King about to organize a movement and lead his followers into jail, he is nevertheless a transcendentalist with a sense of the power of the exemplary. "I know this well"—and it is worth noting that Gandhi quotes and endorses these words—"that if one thousand, if one hundred, if ten *honest* men whom I could name—if these honest men only—oh, if one Honest Man, in the State of Massachusetts, ceasing to hold slaves were actually to withdraw from this co-partnership and be locked up in the county jail therefore, it would be the abolition of slavery in America." Thoreau's action is not, then, simply intended to keep his own hands clean. And he is not unaware of civic obligations: he has never refused to pay the school tax, and he is educating even now. Indeed, he sees "that appeal is possible, first and instantaneously, from them to the Maker of them, and secondly, from them to themselves." He is making a Gandhian attempt to persuade and to educate; he is mounting an appeal to a common sense of justice. Going to jail is appealing to the conscience of others; it is protesting in the name of "the rights of man."

There is, then, a distinct strain of the civil disobedient in Thoreau, and when he is considered in this way his disobedience may be construed as of the "direct" type. It will not do to argue, as Adler and others have argued, that since paying taxes is itself a neutral activity, we must understand tax refusal, not as a direct refusal to conform to an immoral law, but as an indirect form of disobedience, a symbolic protest, like certain traffic violations or technical trespasses. To be sure, paying a tax may be to perform a morally neutral act, but to pay a burdensome or unfair tax may be to suffer a great injustice (Gandhi's Bardoli satyagraha was directly disobedient to such a tax),[48] or it may be to give practical support to injustice, it may be to "abet" injustice. Thoreau refuses to pay the tax, at least in part, because it helps to provide a soldier who sheds innocent blood. Refusing to pay the tax is not simply protesting an injustice, it is refusing to participate in the injustice. It is violating a law that is in itself far from neutral, in order to protest the law itself. And viewed in this way, Thoreau's tax refusal becomes an act of disobedience, and of direct disobedience at that.

But it is not simply that, and Adler is right to regard it as a case of indirect disobedience as well. For, plainly, Thoreau sees his action not only as a case of staying off another man's back but also as a form of protest against other laws, policies, and acts of government. It is a protest against the Mexican war, slavery, and the oppression of the Indian population.

If it is possible to see Thoreau's tax refusal as, among other things, an act of indirect disobedience, I do not think that such acts are, by their very nature, "revolutionary" acts. To be sure, Thoreau does speak the language of revolution. He sees himself as a son of '75, a descendant of Washington and Franklin. His tax refusal is a way of "refusing allegiance," and this is, he thinks, a time to revolutionize and rebel. If a little blood is spilled, it is spilled, in any case, when conscience is violated. This is the Thoreau who will endorse John Brown's exploits without qualm or reservation.[49] Indeed, in this mood he describes his tax refusal as "a declaration of war" against the state.

And it can be argued that tax refusal is, among forms of indirect civil disobedience, one of the most revolutionary in its implications. Taxation is the "sanguinification" of the state, as Hobbes observed, and Gandhi is well aware of the fact that the widespread withholding of taxes (as opposed to the withholding of discrete unjust taxes as in the Bardoli satyagraha) is an extreme form of noncooperation and coercion, not a typical or acceptable form of civil disobedience. So, if Thoreau's act is a revolutionary one, it is so because it is an act of tax refusal, not because it is an act of indirect civil disobedience. For symbolic traffic violations and technical trespasses, the typical forms of indirect civil disobedience, do not constitute revolutionary threats to the state. Nor, in plain fact, did Thoreau's highly personal gesture.

Justice Fortas and Mr. Adler may find some confirmation for their view that indirect disobedience is warlike and revolutionary in some of Thoreau's rhetorical extravagances. But it is worth noting that Thoreau acknowledged on occasion that he worked for a "peaceful" revolution and that he declared war "quietly." I think we can reasonably read Thoreau, and certainly the possibilities inherent in the idea of indirect disobedience, as being safely within the limits of civil disobedience as it is here set forth.

Indirect disobedience is, then, both justifiable and necessary. It is justified, as all civil disobedience is justified, as a solemn protest against important violations of moral principle, and it is necessary because there is often no alternative form of protest at a comparable level of depth. In particular, it must not be supposed that wherever the government violates the principles of political morality, it does so by enacting a positively wicked law that dissenters can protest "directly." For instance, the object of protest may well be the government's failure to pass a law, or to enforce one. Thus, Ralph Abernathy's violation of the law of trespass was meant to protest the government's failure to enact an adequate poverty program, and the obstruction of segregated sites is a familiar technique for protesting the government's failure to enforce fair employment practice statutes that have long been part of the law.[50] Even when the object of protest is a wicked law, there may be no way of protesting it directly, as Thoreau had no way of directly protesting the legal provision that a man might own slaves. Then, too, the object of protest may be a governmental policy or order rather than a law, strictly speaking. It would have made no sense to ask Thoreau to "violate" the government's policy of conducting a war against Mexico or its policy of oppressing the Indian population. And it makes no sense today to speak of violating the government's policy of intervening in the affairs of foreign states. Certainly, the ordinary citizen is in no position to defy orders issued to military personnel. It is for this reason that Thoreau employed the technique of tax refusal to protest the Mexican war, and it is for this reason that dissenters today engage in sit-ins at draft boards and mount demonstrations at the Pentagon to protest the government's intervention in Vietnam. It is peculiarly appropriate (the indirect disobedient looks for symbolically appropriate, if he cannot find directly accessible, laws to violate) that men have endured even self-immolation to protest the military's use of fire bombs against a defenseless civilian population, and it is unfortunate that these acts of disobedience are the acts of "warfare" that Justice Fortas finds it important to protest.

I should argue that those who have undertaken illegal but civil protests against the Vietnam war are far more persuasive patrons of law, and far more effective enemies of war, than those—like Justice Fortas—who have presented one-sided defenses of "the rule of law" and simpleminded condemnations of civil disobedience as "warfare" against society.

1 John Locke, *Two Treatises of Government,* ed. Peter Laslett (London: Cambridge University Press, 1967). See *GBWW,* Vol. 35, pp. 23–81.

2 Ibid., p. 366; *GBWW,* Vol. 35, p. 52d.

3 W. G. Runciman, *Social Science and Political Theory* (London: Cambridge University Press, 1969), pp. 97ff.

4 J. P. Plamenatz, *Consent, Freedom and Political Obligation* (New York: Oxford University Press, 1968), pp. 170–71.

5 Hannah Arendt, "Civil Disobedience," *New Yorker,* September 12, 1970, pp. 94ff.

6 Locke, *Two Treatises,* p. 351; *GBWW,* Vol. 35, p. 47c.

7 Ibid., p. 371; *GBWW,* Vol. 35, p. 54d.

8 Hanna Pitkin, "Obligation and Consent—I," *American Political Science Review* 59 (1965): 996.

9 M. K. Gandhi, *Non-Violent Resistance,* ed. Bharatan Kumarappa (New York: Schocken Books, 1961).

10 This paragraph, and other sections of the present essay, first appeared in "Civil Disobedience in a Constitutional Democracy," *Massachusetts Review* 10 (1969): 211–26.

11 Bertrand Russell, "Civil Disobedience and the Threat of Nuclear Warfare," reprinted in *Civil Disobedience: Theory and Practice,* comp. H. A. Bedau (New York: Pegasus, 1969), p. 157.

12 Charles E. Wyzanski, Jr., "On Civil Disobedience and Draft Resistance," reprinted in Bedau, *Civil Disobedience,* p. 199.

13 Oliver Wendell Holmes, Jr., "The Path of the Law," *Harvard Law Review* 10 (1897): 457ff.

14 H. L. A. Hart, *The Concept of Law* (Oxford: Clarendon Press, 1961), p. 39.

15 The Vykom Temple Road satyagraha was undertaken to protest the prohibition on use by untouchables of the roadways passing the temple. After Gandhi negotiated the removal of a police barricade and cordon, the satyagrahis refrained from entering the road until the Brahmans were fully persuaded of the "truth" and the government had declared acceptance of the untouchables' use of the road. In the autumn of 1925 the Brahmans declared, "We cannot any longer resist the prayers that have been made to us, and we are ready to receive the untouchables." For an account of the Vykom Temple Road satyagraha *see* Joan V. Bondurant, *Conquest of Violence: The Gandhian Philosophy of Conflict* (Berkeley and Los Angeles: University of California Press, 1965), pp. 46–52.

16 The Ahmedabad labor satyagraha was undertaken by the textile laborers against the mill owners of Ahmedabad in 1918 in order to achieve a 35 percent increase in the cost-of-living allowance or submission of the dispute to arbitration. Gandhi undertook a fast to stiffen the resolve of the laborers. As a satyagrahi he believed that he should not fast against the mill owners "but ought to leave them free to be influenced by the mill hands' strike alone." Yet he recognized that, given his close relations with the mill owners, his fast would inevitably affect and even coerce them. As a result of the satyagraha campaign, the issue went to arbitration, and the laborers achieved their objectives. *See* Bondurant, *Conquest of Violence,* pp. 65–73.

17 Albert Bigelow, "Why I Am Sailing This Boat Into the Bomb-Test Area," reprinted in Bedau, *Civil Disobedience,* pp. 146–52.

18 Albert Camus, *The Rebel,* trans. Anthony Bower (New York: Vintage Books, 1956), pp. 135–44.

19 Plato, *Apology* and *Crito,* in *Euthyphro, Apology, Crito,* trans. F. J. Church and R. D. Cumming (Indianapolis and New York: Liberal Arts Press, 1956). See *GBWW,* Vol. 7, pp. 200–219.

20 Kai Nielsen, "Remarks on Violence and Paying the Penalty," in *Philosophic Exchange,* Summer 1970 (Brockport, 1970), pp. 113–19; Howard Zinn, *Disobedience and Democracy* (New York: Random House, 1968), pp. 27–31.

21 Plato, *Crito,* pp. 61–62; *GBWW,* Vol. 7, p. 217c–d.

22 A. D. Woozley, "Socrates on Disobeying the Law," in *The Philosophy of Socrates,* ed. G. Vlastos (Garden City, N.Y.: Doubleday & Co., 1971), pp. 299–318.

23 Plato, *Crito,* p. 60; *GBWW,* Vol. 7, p. 216d.

24 Nielsen is Professor of Philosophy at the University of Calgary. Although his views are in general close to those expressed in this essay, he is critical of the claim that it is generally appropriate for the civil disobedient to accept punishment. *See* Nielsen,

"Remarks on Violence," p. 114. Howard Zinn, Professor of Government at Boston University, is a leading critic of the Vietnam war, and of American society generally. He argues, in a well-known book, that Justice Abe Fortas's *Concerning Dissent and Civil Disobedience* is guilty of nine serious fallacies. The view that the disobedient ought to accept punishment is one of them. Although I do not accept Justice Fortas's position, I am skeptical of many of the arguments Professor Zinn employs in criticizing them. See Zinn, *Disobedience and Democracy*, pp. 27–31.

25 Nielsen, "Remarks on Violence," p. 114.

26 Ronald M. Dworkin, formerly Wesley N. Hohfeld Professor of Jurisprudence and Master of Trumbull College at Yale University, is now Professor of Jurisprudence in the University of Oxford. He has offered what is perhaps the most penetrating and original treatment of the role of civil disobedience in the U.S. constitutional system. *See* his "Civil Disobedience: The Case Against Prosecution," reprinted in Noam Chomsky et al., *Trials of the Resistance* (New York: Random House, Vintage Books, 1970), pp. 50–73.

27 Nielsen, "Remarks on Violence," p. 115.

28 Dworkin, "Civil Disobedience," p. 53.

29 Zinn, *Disobedience and Democracy*, p. 30.

30 Ibid., p. 31.

31 Martin Luther King, "Letter from Birmingham City Jail," reprinted in Bedau, *Civil Disobedience*, pp. 72–89.

32 John Rawls, "The Justification of Civil Disobedience," reprinted in Bedau, *Civil Disobedience*, pp. 240–55. I have also profited from seeing an unpublished manuscript on the same subject written by Professor Rawls.

33 Irving Kristol is, therefore, either being obtuse or supercilious when he writes that "those who are morally committed to civil disobedience can properly claim that the law which arrests them, or the law that punishes them, is so perverse as to be without authority. What they may not do in good conscience is to practice civil disobedience and then hire a clever lawyer to argue that it wasn't a violation of the law at all, but rather the exercise of some kind of a right." *See* "A Symposium on Civil Disobedience and the Vietnam War," reprinted in Bedau, *Civil Disobedience*, p. 208.

34 Abe Fortas, *Concerning Dissent and Civil Disobedience* (New York: World Publishing Co., Meridian Books, 1968).

35 Dworkin, "Civil Disobedience."

36 Ibid., pp. 60ff.

37 Graham Hughes, "Civil Disobedience and the Political Question Doctrine," *New York University Law Review* 43 (1968): 15–16.

Professor Hughes regards the executive as legally free because, under the political question doctrine, the courts will not adjudicate the claim that he is subject to a legal duty. I would hold, however, that the president may be subject to a legal duty even though the courts will not offer an opinion on the matter. Nor does it follow from the fact that the courts invoke the political question doctrine that the constitutional provisions in question are hortatory. If to say so is simply to repeat that the courts will not adjudicate certain issues arising under these constitutional provisions, it is an odd way of saying it; if it means, however, that the executive is merely encouraged, but not required, to conform to these provisions, the suggestion is false. Professor Hughes's use of the distinction between the unconstitutional and the illegal is inadvisable for related reasons. The Constitution is, after all, the supreme law of the land, and to criticize (or to oppose) the president because he has acted unconstitutionally is, at very least, to criticize him because he has acted illegally. And to do so is not simply to criticize him for doing what he is urged to do or for doing what, from a moral point of view, he ought to do. Furthermore, to judge that the executive (or that anyone else) has a legal duty, or that he has violated one, is by no means the exclusive prerogative of the courts. The president, the Congress, and even the public may, and often must, make such judgments. In the case of private citizens, these judgments may become the ground for acts of civil disobedience. By speaking as though the president is legally free, when he may in fact be legally bound, Professor Hughes risks obscuring the motives and the justification for such acts.

Professor Hughes has replied to these remarks in "Response to Professor Marshall Cohen," in *Philosophic Exchange*, Summer 1970 (Brockport, 1970), pp. 121–25.

38 *Mora et al.* v. *McNamara, Secretary of Defense, et al.*, 389 U.S. 934 (1967).

39 Michael Katz has objected to this contention as it was formulated in the *Massachusetts Review* version of this article, and I have replied to it in *Massachusetts Review* 11 (1970): 172–75.

40 Mortimer Adler, *The Common Sense of Politics* (New York: Holt, Rinehart & Winston, 1971), chap. 18 and notes thereto. Mr. Adler has kindly allowed me to see the relevant sections of his book in proof. Unfortunately, I have not been able to see the entire work at the time of writing. I have also profited from seeing his lecture "Law, Coercion, and Dissent," delivered at St. John's College, December 1970.

41 St. Thomas Aquinas, *Summa Theologica*, Prima Secundae, Qu. 90–97, in *Selected Political Writings*, ed. A. Passerin d'Entrèves, trans. J. G. Dawson (Oxford: Basil Blackwell & Mott, 1959), pp. 109–47; *GBWW*, Vol. 20, pp. 205–39.

42 St. Thomas Aquinas, *Commentary on the Sentences of Peter Lombard*, Bk. II, Dist. 44, Qu. 2, Art. 2, in Passerin d'Entrèves, *Selected Political Writings*, p. 185.

43 John Locke, *Epistola de tolerantia* [A letter on toleration], ed. Raymond Klibansky, English trans. J. W. Gough (Oxford: Clarendon Press, 1968), pp. 127–28; *GBWW*, Vol. 35, p. 16d.

44 Ibid., pp. 139ff; *GBWW*, Vol. 35, p. 19b–c.

45 *Two Treatises of Government*, ed. Laslett, p. 397; *GBWW*, Vol. 35, p. 64b.

46 Henry David Thoreau, "Civil Disobedience," reprinted in Bedau, *Civil Disobedience*, pp. 27–48; *GGB*, Vol. 6, pp. 695–713.

47 Bedau, *Civil Disobedience*, p. 15. I have very much profited from Bedau's introductory comments on Thoreau's essay and, indeed, from all the commentary that is to be found in his excellent anthology.

48 In the course of the Bardoli satyagraha, concluded in August 1928, the peasants refused (among other things) to pay what they regarded as the unjust enhancement of the land revenue assessment. As a result of the satyagraha campaign, an Enquiry Committee was appointed which recommended a revision of the assessment. For an account of the Bardoli satyagraha, *see* Bondurant, *Conquest of Violence*, pp. 53–64.

49 Thoreau, "The Last Days of John Brown," in *The Portable Thoreau*, ed. Carl Bode (New York: Viking Press, 1964), pp. 676–82.

50 It is worth noting the view of the present U.S. Solicitor General (and former Dean of the Harvard Law School) on a related point. Mr. Griswold writes that he "cannot distinguish in principle the legal quality of the determination . . . to block a workman from entering a segregated job site from the determination to fire shots into a civil rights leader's home to protest integration." If all Mr. Griswold means by his fine periphrastic expression ("cannot distinguish in principle the legal quality") is that both actions are illegal, few will dispute his point. If he means anything else—perhaps that they are equally serious violations of the law—it is all to his credit that he couldn't quite bring himself to say so. *See* Erwin N. Griswold, "Dissent—1968 Style," the George Abel Dreyfus Lecture on Civil Liberties, given at the Tulane University School of Law, New Orleans, Louisiana, April 16, 1968.

NOTE TO THE READER

The matters discussed by Professor Cohen are taken up by many of the authors of *GBWW*. They are cited in the *Syntopicon* in Chapter 31 on GOVERNMENT, Chapter 46 on LAW, Chapter 74 on PUNISHMENT, and Chapter 80 on REVOLUTION. In particular, *see* the entries at GOVERNMENT 1a, having to do with the origin and necessity of government and the issue concerning anarchy; at LAW 6a and 6c, which deal with the relation between law and the individual involving either obedience or rebellion; at PUNISHMENT 4a, about the necessity of sanctions for lawbreaking; and at REVOLUTION 6a, concerned with the right of rebellion and the circumstances that justify civil disobedience or violent insurrection.

Thoreau's essay on "Civil Disobedience" and his "Plea for Captain John Brown" are reprinted in *GGB*, Vol. 6.

PART THREE

The Contemporary Status of a Great Idea

I. A. Richards

I. A. Richards is widely known for his
writings on Basic English, a subject he
had a substantial part in inventing and one
in which he deeply believes. But his other
productions have been equally distinguished. *The Meaning of Meaning* (1923),
which he wrote with C. K. Ogden, was an
early and important study in semantics;
his *Principles of Literary Criticism* (1924)

and *Practical Criticism* (1929) are classics
in their field; his *Coleridge on Imagination* (1934) is a standard work. Born in
England and educated at Cambridge,
where for a time he taught, Richards served
briefly (1929–30) on the faculty of Tsinghua
University, Peking, as the following pages
indicate. In 1944 he came to Harvard,
where at the time of his retirement in 1963
he was University Professor. Among his
recent works is a play about Hector that
was produced at the Loeb Drama Center,
Cambridge, Massachusetts, last spring.

Sources of Our Common Thought:
Homer and Plato

Confession is no doubt good for the soul: for the confessing soul and sometimes for some of the souls to whom the admissions are made. It may be well, then, to begin by a mention of what happened in me when I first really resolutely attempted to immerse myself in the *Iliad*. I was by no means completely ignorant of it. There had been some large volumes of the Earl of Derby's verse translation on a reachable shelf when I was a little boy—wide and spacious pages of verse as I seem to recall them—and there had been a Bohn translation in laborious prose rather later: both no more than desultorily dipped into. And I suppose that I would have professed some sort of knowledge of the chief characters and of the action by the time my first serious attempt to read it properly was made. This was, as I now see it, strangely late. I was in my middle thirties and had been a university teacher at Cambridge for some time.

If I linger a little before coming out with the truth here, that should be forgivable. I felt then, and have been more and more conscious of it since, the need for excuses. Perhaps the occasion was too unsuitable. I needed a book—preferably something pocketable—to be absorbed in through a Trans-Siberian Railway journey from Moscow to Vladivostok lasting about twelve days. The *Iliad*, I hoped, would take care of that. There were, it is true, not a few distractions. But thinking of the reading Napoleon managed on his visit to Russia, that did not seem a plea that would stand up. There was also the version I chose: Lang, Leaf and Myers. It bristled with *thees* and *thous*, *thereofs*, *wherebys*, *haths*, *doths*, and *-eths* throughout—a "grievous bane" indeed; but, nonetheless and despite all that, how could I have remained untouched by what—however oddly—the pages still were saying? The sad fact I must now be candid about is that I got nowhere, though I spent plenty of hours as the train jolted along, and came out from my reading even more empty-minded than I went in. And with the failure there perked up, I recall, quite ridiculous misconceptions and suspicions of and revolts against I don't know how much of tradition.

In view of what the *Iliad* was to become for me later, and of what it still offers me to pursue, this sheer unmitigated defeat deserves to be recorded. It is worth pondering. Among the adventures that minds may meet, few, it is likely, might better repay observation and reflection than the initial encounters with works that are as yet beyond their measure. What may go wrong, and how could some fruitful transmission be helped? More than is currently imagined may turn upon such inquiries. Looking back now, some random lines from a parody of "Old Man's Comforts" I once read (about 1902 it would be) recur to me. They were written to satirize the inept early conduct of the Boer War; *Clara in Blunderland* was the title of the book, and Balfour's government its target:

> *In my youth, said John Bull, t'was ever my plan*
> *To win victory after defeat;*
> *And I certainly thought that the worse I began*
> *The better my chances to beat!*

However this may be, it is not imprudent to expect that things that may in time come to matter for one profoundly will at first be felt as not only unpromising but as actually repellent, even perhaps corruptive. The early impression is often a measure of the degree of change required in the reader.

When it comes to the new world embodied in a great book, a newcomer's eye has to learn to see. That ordinarily requires not a little active exploration. And the seeing as it develops is going to entail considerable readjustments. These are indeed the sources of its growing attraction.

> *Great things are done when Men and Mountains meet;*
> *This is not done by Jostling in the Street,*

wrote William Blake, without stopping to polish up the second line.[1] (Many who recall it substitute "seen when" for that "done by.") It is safe to say that these Mountains are not those that put their spell upon the modern climber. They are metaphorical and have more to do with Horeb, or Sinai, than with Everest and the Eiger. The great things there done occur

> *In your Imagination, of which this World of Mortality is but a*
> *Shadow.*[2]

We shall see below how radically Platonic Blake's conception here is.

Not all the new worlds that great books offer us entail for all readers so much challenge, though many and perhaps most do. There are, of course, a happy few among readers who can sometimes enter a fresh demesne at once and without labor. With Homer and these Mountains of the Imagination together on this page, we may well think of Keats standing in stout Cortez's shoes,

Silent upon a peak in Darien.

Chapman, though, however "loud and bold" he may be, is, as sampling can soon show, far indeed from making Homer plain sailing for a modern reader.

Having confessed my own humbling repulse, I must in fairness tell the rest of the story. It is bound up with much else concerning the making of the key ideas in great books as widely available as may be. That very Trans-Siberian journey, which was so unfruitful as regards Homer, took me to Peking to teach English literature—to extremely able Chinese students—and to begin myself to learn some of the elementary facts that were to make me, in time, recognize such teaching as a truly impracticable undertaking. The sheer incomprehensibility to my audiences of what I had to offer forced me by degrees back into considering—as I had hardly done before—how I myself had, so I thought, come to comprehend whatever I did of what I was trying to put before them. Though I had been lecturing on English Literature at Cambridge for ten years and writing books largely about meanings and how we may mistake them, I had not, I note now, attempted any at all searching account of what understanding depends on. It was no doubt something to have read for the Moral Sciences Tripos, concentrating on psychology, linguistics, learning theory, and especially on the grounds for assent and belief, but none of that had prepared me at all usefully for what I met. It had not as yet taught me to see how much there was in human learning to be thought about and how little of it all I had noticed.

My Chinese students' difficulties throughout were cultural rather than linguistic. Their troubles in understanding what English-using authors were trying to do sprang from their almost complete unfamiliarity with the ideas, attitudes, feelings, hopes, doubts, wishes, aims, and so forth, on and through which those authors worked. It was not that the students did not know enough words or could not put them together in more or less our sentence forms. They had, in fact, an astounding power of acquiring them. They picked up vocabulary and structure as good flypaper collects flies. But the acquisitions just stuck. They could not grow; they were not alive. They could be used, as a mechanical device for maneuvering meanings, but, alas, the meanings so managed were Chinese and, as a rule, not at all those with which the English work was concerned.

As this sad—and terrifyingly dangerous—situation became clearer, it was natural to ask why there was no comparable obstacle to Chinese advances in the sciences. There was none. As we have seen since then, the Chinese can well keep pace with any nation in techniques: notably, those needed for our joint destruction. What unhappily they cannot do is comprehend the moral-political-philosophical ideas that are commonly regarded in the Western world as our prime cultural treasure, that by which we live. They fail in this just as we fail to comprehend the Chinese moral-political-philosophical principles: *their* prime cultural treasure, that by which *they* live. In terms of conduct, careful, informed and impartial observers can be found to maintain that—by and large and circumstances allowed for—the Chinese are traditionally more moral, more responsible and law-abiding, better citizens, more dependable, and far less given to casual violence than most Western peoples. But these are tricky comparisons; our powers of estimating our own and our fellows' judgments in such matters are, as yet, inadequate.

However, what became apparent as more and more concrete and harrowing illustrations accumulated of the very things I had, in academic abstractedness, been writing about in Cambridge (for instance, in a book called *Science and Poetry,* published in 1926) and as the lessons sank home, was that I must somehow try:

(1) to do something to ease, in time, the task set the Chinese people and the Western peoples of understanding better one another's positions for living, and
(2) by the same means help forward and speed up a supply of persons more competent to meet what were clearly going to be the ever more overtaxing problems of our planet.[3]

(These resolutions took shape early in 1931 when I was passed from Peking to Cambridge, England, through Harvard—serving my first term there as Visiting Lecturer. *Ulysses, The Possessed,* and *The Secret Agent* were, I recall, my themes. I was also, with [my] *Mencius on the Mind,* doing what I could to show how Chinese and Western cultures could be so mutually incommunicable.) As it happened—though this was not as yet at all clearly realized by me—I had a substantial part of what was to become a program as to (1) and (2) already to hand.

Basic English

While C. K. Ogden and I were enjoying ourselves scribbling out *The Meaning of Meaning (The Beading of Beading,* we called it, because we had so many heavy head colds as it progressed through 1918–21), some of the best fun we had was with its chapter 6, on Definition. In the course of this we realized that a relatively small number of words could, theoretically and within describable limits of exactitude, deputize for the rest of the Dictionary. If so, a suitably chosen selection would yield a general-purpose, minimum-cost, but maximum-utility English that could bridge innumerable linguistic gulfs. The huge task of that selection and the provision of a comparably simplified syntax were to become a large part of Ogden's lifework through the next ten years. When I got back to Cambridge, England, from Cambridge, Massachusetts, in 1931, he had his recommendations ready. He had labeled them *Basic English* (*basic* was then an almost unused word) and was ready to launch his project.

Someday a historian may try to tell what happened. My own account would be that much went amazingly well until World War Two swept away successful and expanding developments in many countries: China, India, Russia, Greece among them. Then, toward the end of the war, Churchill and Roosevelt took up the project. That, for a couple of decades or so, consigned it to the doghouse. Fantastic misdescriptions were concocted and zealously spread by people who knew next to nothing about it. What it had already done and had shown itself able to do were ignored. It became a taboo topic in linguistic and educational circles.

There is much here to interest students of the ways in which professional opinion can resist for a while (even for a long while) possibilities that may disturb their routines. Anyone who reflectively inquires into Basic English[4] will find in Ogden's work a superlatively ingenious, thorough, exact, and comprehensive piece of linguistic engineering, boldly original, scrupulously consistent, and speculatively stimulating in the highest degree. It is indeed one of the most impressive intellectual achievements and its inventor one of the outstanding wits and polymaths of a notable generation. And yet how many who have never bothered to look into it have been content to echo the misrepresentations of others as little acquainted with it as themselves. This tide of fashion, however, has now turned. The needs that Basic was designed to meet have now become too great to be any longer ignored. Yet partisan opposition continues.

For our purposes—making as widely available as possible all over the world the best that has been thought and said—Basic English or variants equally deriving from its fundamental design can serve in three ways, one direct and obvious, the others less so:

(1) By supplying a more economical way into English, giving a greater return and earlier, with less expenditure of time and effort
(2) By enabling the key question: *What should be learned before what?* to be submitted to new types of experimental inquiry
(3) By offering a clear model or paradigm of the development of the meanings of which a culture consists.

To take these one by one, the first is the obvious advantage. As with other technical matters, its effectiveness can only be discovered through trying it out, but those who do this must study and follow the directives. The point of number two is that with few enough words and minimal necessary constructions, the optimal *order of acquisition* becomes an explorable problem. Find the sequence in which what is learned earlier best prepares for what should be learned later: that is the assignment. With

Basic, one can experiment in the design of learning sequences in ways not practicable in less controlled languages. In all development—from an embryo's first stages on up to the discrimination of meanings—sequence becomes increasingly the key principle. This should hardly be surprising: "Not only speech, but all skilled acts seem to involve the same problems of serial ordering, even down to the temporal coordination of muscular contractions in such a movement as reaching and grasping."[5] What is true of performance is equally true of growth. And as what is to happen mounts in complexity, we can reasonably expect due sequence, serial order, to become ever more important. Grasping a meaning in a book is an immeasurably more complex achievement than reaching out and taking up a pencil. This is a spelling out of the implications of *until*. Innumerable steps in the growth of organs cannot succeed *until* the necessary earlier steps have been taken. And the acquisition of a language is a growth of an organ, literally as well as metaphorically. So too is the acquisition and development of the concepts that the language enables us to handle.

The third advantage of Basic derives from the fact that most meanings are modifications of earlier meanings, restructurings within them. Robert Hutchins quotes Jean Cocteau as saying that "each great work in Western thought arises as a contradiction of one that precedes it."[6] *Contradiction* here is too strong a word, reflecting a contentious rather than dialectic spirit. It is better to say with Hutchins at the foot of his page, "Every statement calls for explanation, correction, modification, expansion, or contradiction." Of these, contradiction is likely to be least helpful. We may say of it what Alexander Bain said of osculation: "The occasion should be adequate and the actuality rare." Often we will not understand what is being meant unless we can see both what it is a departure from and what it is guarding itself from becoming. A good dictionary is a partial record of these differentiations and interrelationships. All etymology and all history of usage bear this out. Properly speaking, we cannot understand any word by itself. We have to sense how it stands to other words, what it will do when put into sentences with them, which words it can cooperate with and which it must keep away. These things we somehow learn without more than occasionally seeing at all clearly how we learn them. But unless we have learned them, the needed understanding will not occur. And this, which is obvious as it is recorded in dictionaries, is equally true of ideas in the larger sense in which they are what great books embody, organize, and can convey. Indeed it is true, throughout, of the interactions and oppositions among meanings, as is magnificently made clear in the *Syntopicon,* that monumental outcome of superlative discernment, industry, collaboration, and organization.[7] This work shows, as no slighter indication and exposition could, how dependent upon one another are the myriad components of our culture. As its Preface remarks: "each of the great ideas is directly or remotely related to many others—perhaps to all—through a network of connections radiating from each idea as a point of origin."[8] Could a comparable analysis and presentation be achieved for the Chinese tradition, similar connexities would appear there. And if the fearsome tasks of comparison that translation must raise were faced, man's future would look more secure. The reason the Chinese and the Western people do not understand one another is that the affiliations and resistances, the requirements and exclusions within each of the two cultures are in too many ways too radically different.

My class in Tsinghua University burst into loud applause when the black flag went up telling that Tess of the D'Urbervilles had been hanged. (I was reading the page aloud to them.) They had been waiting all through the book for the lack of respect Tess had shown for her father to be suitably punished. What Hardy had in mind in writing the book could make no sort of sense whatsoever to them, though, as the applause showed, they were doing their best to admire it.

"The President of the Immortals had ended his sport with Tess." Consider that sentence and how Hardy is able here to use the peculiar forces of its terms. Thanks to its history, a range of possible uses has come to *President* that no word with another history can offer. So too with *Immortals* and with *sport*. It is not, of course, the case that the user need wittingly know these histories. Even Hardy, even his best reader imaginable, may not think of, may not even be in any way aware of, important parts of these histories. The words can work, can exert their powers, without any of that philological knowledge being present and active in writer's or reader's mind. The contexts in which the words have been met, the situations through which their users have learned what the words may do, can operate perfectly without those concerned having any inkling of how it all happens. It is, of course, very unlikely that Hardy and many good readers will not more or less consciously *feel* that Zeus and the Olympians are being brought up-to-date, and that the irony of the contrast between their triviality and the tragic fate of the mortals grows the bitterer when that malcontent family and court is turned into a Corporation. Similarly, many, and Hardy included, may consciously recall,

> As flies to wanton boys, are we to the gods,
> They kill us for their sport.[9]

But the force of the word can be felt without Shakespeare coming to mind, just as, for him, the *Iliad* need not have been consciously alluded to. The point is that great ideas and their derivatives have innumerable other channels which bypass the chief forming loci of their use. Needless to say, this does *not* diminish the usefulness of the knowledge of such loci or of an explicit awareness of how great utterances shape and are shaped by later utterances that echo, apply, support, or oppose them. Such explicit knowledge, conveyable through the *Syntopicon* and perhaps through less exacting instruments for which it will serve as a model, may be our best means, indeed perhaps our only means, of restoring the availability of man's intellectual and moral resources at a time when the innumerable other channels mentioned above seem to be (as dismaying evidence often suggests) clogging up.

However this may be, it is certain that my Chinese students, having met *President, Immortals,* and *sport* only through supposed Chinese "equivalents," inevitably with different histories, could have no sense of how explosive the conjunction of the three English words could be. Their Immortals are not ours—though a formal definition: "not liable to death," might be the same. Sports, for them and for us, in view of the Hunting Parks in which the Son of Heaven could enjoy diversion, may be more alike—but not deeply. And as to *President,* a foreign importation, as concept and as title, and from the first—with Yüan Shih-k'ai and Sun Yatsen—subject to new and peculiar Chinese uses and vicissitudes, it had no means of linking up with, say, the Yellow Emperor.[10]

Toward a basic text

To return, however, to the *Iliad,* concerning which this account of my experience in Peking and the development of Basic English will serve to explain how it was that I came to feel I must do something, and could, to reduce what seemed to be the unintelligibilities of the Homeric story: of course I should add, before going into details of that undertaking, that it required some thought of a more analytical kind before I could commence it. Indeed, I had to come, or at least I did gradually come, to an overall view of the poem and of some of the relations it bears to its descendants, its moral and intellectual offspring, chief among which is the *Republic,* on which, as it happened, I began work first.

It is not too much to say that no one can really see the point or feel the force of the *Republic* to whom the *Iliad* is not a living and familiar presence. It is our best starting point in many more senses than one. It was, as Plato said, "the educator of the Greeks," giving them the education against which he conducted the revolt. *Iliad* and *Republic* require one another, as *here* requires *there,* as figure requires ground. Much of the *Republic* (and much else in Plato) is explicit in its rejection of what the *Iliad,* as he thought, was doing to Greece. But much else in Plato is equally that revulsion implicitly directing the influences he was generating. One of the published reasons for Socrates' trial was his being a maker of new gods and not believing in the old ones: those of the *Iliad* and their worse predecessors. In Plato's version of his defense he is made very explicit and as provocative as he knew how to be on this point. It is as though he wished his death to come to him for believing in, and obeying, the god of Delphi.

> *And so, men of Athens, if you were to say to me, "Socrates, we will let you off, on condition you give up this questioning game of yours; but if you go on with it, we'll put you to death," I would answer "Men of Athens, I respect and love you, but I will do what the god says, not what you say. While I live I won't stop pointing out the truth to anyone of you I meet. I'll go on saying, 'Look, you are a citizen of the greatest city on earth. Aren't you ashamed to be giving all your mind to money-making and getting on in the world while you don't care a bit about wisdom or truth or the good of your soul?' "*
>
> *If by saying these things I corrupt the young, then these things must be corrupting. Anyhow I don't say anything else. And so, men of Athens, acquit me or not, but know that I won't change my ways; not if I had to die again and again.*[11]

Little indeed of Plato would have been at all what it is without Homer; just as, without Plato, less than we easily suppose in our own thinking—and whether we know this or not—could be as it is. Emerson's story makes the point sharply. He lent a copy of the *Republic* to a farmer who returned it remarking: "That man has a good many of my ideas."

It was, I think, that farmer's reported remark that led me to lay other things aside while I tried to make as intelligible and accessible a version as I could of the *Republic*.[12] That and a realization of the gap between such a farmer—capable of getting so far into himself and into Plato—and most of the newcomers to whom I might lend, say, a Jowett. It was coming home to me that a drop in general sagacity had been occurring, a decline in concern for and power to grasp, reflect on, and use moral ideas. The gulf between the intelligent reader and the traditions by which he still has to live seemed to me to be growing, and too rapidly not to become very soon intolerable. (What has been happening since has not exactly convinced me that I was mistaken.) It was not only the Chinese who could not benefit from Plato. The common man and the average undergraduate seemed to be in almost as distressing a state of need. And I had to doubt whether any of the remedies being tried were powerful enough. To experiment (at first via Basic and then in a slightly enlarged and suppler derivative) toward a more comprehensible *Republic* was, at least, work soothing to the conscience. It made me feel more equal to facing up to the great resolution of Godwin when he said: "The remainder of my time I determined to devote to the pursuit of such attainments as afforded me the best promise to render me useful."[13]

Looking more closely into the *Republic* sent me to the *Iliad* again and made me realize more and more fully what a part Homer had in its making. Not only as to its theology and politics. Almost every aspect of human living presented in the *Iliad* comes up in Plato for question and for radical revision, often indeed for sheer reversal. The traits in its heroes that had most successfully invited awed admiration were those that in Plato's eyes most deserved the sternest condemnation. The excessiveness of Achilles, his willfulness, his temerity, his impiety, the scale of his passions, his momentum as of a mass too vast for any control: all this makes him the perfect image of the opposite of Plato's favorite virtue, *sophrosyne*, so easily misrepresented by the English word *temperance*. (As Taylor well put it, we must "take care to remember that it is part of the virtue itself that it is not the imperfect self-restraint of the man who holds himself in check ungracefully and with difficulty, but the easy and natural self-restraint of the man who enjoys being temperate.")[14] What is happening in the *Republic* and in much of the rest of Plato is the replacement of a traditional model of man by a new model in most essential respects precisely its contrary. To say that Socrates is Achilles turned upside down, an inverted projection of him, would grossly underrate Plato's depth as a dramatist. And it would risk turning one of the greatest of all uncompleted revolutions—the creation of that inexhaustible revolutionary, Socrates—into a sort of trick. Nonetheless, their contrarieties are instructive. Each of these immense and enigmatic figures becomes for us more fully himself by comparison with the other.

These contrarieties, I have no doubt, were largely responsible for my attempt, after making what I hoped was a more easily penetrable version of the *Iliad—The Wrath of Achilles*[15]—to fashion an actable play of the trial and death of Socrates: *Why So, Socrates?* But I must tell of that in its due place in this complex story of what resulted from those days of defeat in that Trans-Siberian train. For in spite of worrying about East-West and other communicative distortions, which led me to do a good deal of writing in the following years, and notwithstanding that I worked away at the simplified *Republic,* it was some time before I began on these other projects.

The next determinative moment came when, in the expansive mood that followed the end of the Second World War, I was invited to join the Harvard Committee on the Objectives of a General Education in a Free Society. What lovely people were there to work with, and work well together we did! President Conant's Introduction and the committee's *Letter of Transmittal* show well what the participants imagined they were doing. A somewhat wry recognition of the disaccord between the hopes and aims there expressed and the actualities of the worldwide situation in the universities of 1970 belongs to my theme. For me the phrase "a Free Society" had come to mean the sort of thing Socrates describes at the end of Book 9 of the *Republic*. He has been making up his mythic image of the component powers in man: the many-headed beast, the lion, and the guardian man himself. He comes to its application:

> *Only when a man is too feeble to control the beasts but has to work for them and please them, only then do we say that he had better be slave to some other man, a man in whom godlike wisdom rules. And this is to give him the same sort of government. It isn't, as Thrasymachus thought, ruling him to his own loss. No, the best is for everyone to be ruled by a wise and godlike power, if possible seated in his own heart; if not, let it act upon him from without; in order that we may all be, as far as possible, like one another and friends, being all guided by the same pilot.*[16]

Then follows what is both a founding charter for Western education and the foundation—dependent upon that—of the ideal state; a state, as Glaucon puts it, "whose being is in ideas only, for I do not believe it can have any existence on earth." To which Socrates replies:

> *Well, maybe its pattern is already there in heaven for him to see who so desires; and seeing it he makes himself its citizen. And the question of its present or future existence makes no difference. He who sees it will live by its laws and by no other.*[17]

These are the laws to which the first citizen of this state listens at the close of the *Crito;* they are what he hears "as the worshippers hear the flutes." And this music sounds so within him that he can hear nothing else.

In reality, as was not surprising, the starry-eyed program our committee concocted and prescribed had little relation to the actual courses presented. Some of these were splendid, but very different from what the committee had proposed; their outcomes were thus unappraisable. For me there was a terrifying resultant—responsibility for Humanities 1: "Sources of Our Common Thought," which meant, to begin with, *Iliad, Republic,* Old Testament. There I was—back, in my imagination, in that Trans-Siberian train—committed to helping whomsoever I could to derive some profit from the *Iliad.*

By this date I had, I supposed, learned an iota or so about it. I had made, very laboriously, my Basic English version of the *Republic*—with many of the most lucid English translations propped up around me and a specialist in the *Republic,* a most resourceful, understanding pupil of Werner Jaeger, at my elbow, and the master, Jaeger himself, to consult when we became too uncertain. That had helped. So too did the propping up of various translations of the *Iliad.* (Since then I have found that the largest available lazy Susan, with the various versions displayed, open at the right pages, can be convenient: a device borrowed from Sir Christopher Wren's installations in the Library in Trinity College, Cambridge.) But it was an enormous class—up to or over a thousand students —with which I had to deal. I knew, I think—if I did not, I soon learned— that for Homer to be at all Homer, with so vast an audience, what you tried to read aloud had to be readable. The rivalry, otherwise—even in those good old times—of naughts and crosses, the *Crimson,* the *New York Times,* the whodunits and the didn't-oughter's, became oppressive. I had, it is true, a resource that greatly helped: a huge screen on which I would always project any passage that to me seemed to deserve especial attention. The screen reminds of the movies and thereby attracts. Moreover, those eye-minded undergraduates were *compulsively* readers. Any scrap of print could close their ears to whatever. Even so, I found that projecting for them Lang, Leaf and Myers—or even Samuel Butler— would not, often enough, keep them going. I accompanied, of course, the screen display of (alas!) only typescript with my uttermost endeavors in reading. I found out so, how hard most texts are even to read aloud, let alone to listen to. So it came home to me that I must find a version that I could—self- and audience-respectingly—read aloud, and even read with something of the confidence that a rhapsode could enjoy and an Ion[18] exhibit. I began to try out—with my experience of the *Republic* behind me—selected passages.

Selected passages? Here, sadly and reluctantly, I had to seem to dissent from or at least qualify the policy so insisted on by that impressive Advisory Board in the preface to *The Great Conversation.*[19] But I was being unfair. Their recommendations concerned a set of books. My task was a classroom application. Nonetheless, "digested" and "mutilated" are strong words with, in at least the second case, highly pejorative implications. Given the levels of preparedness I found in my students, I had to conclude that for them the attempt to read the whole *Iliad* and *Republic* resulted in sheer stultification. Selection is after all the fundamental principle in living. Without it we get nowhere. That integral texts should be available is obviously right. But equally it seemed right that in their approach to such great works, newcomers should be helped in their selection. For students being *introduced* to a strange and great new author, more than half his utterance can be to them a hindrance rather than a help. Selection, therefore, is a necessity—indeed, the only hope. (Of course, anyone who has published an abridgment knows too well the nonpurchaser who self-flatteringly declares, "*I* need the complete book!"— which he then does not open twice.) Still, selected passages! What an abandonment that can be of the main aim: the transmission, namely, of what the originator had it in him to say! It is the *connexity,* the *wholeness,* of his utterance that most matters, the *action* (in Aristotle's large sense), the plot (in which each item gets the major part of its meaning from its relations to the rest). Abridgment, then, in a critical sense—selection operating with the most sensitive discernment of relations it can achieve—may reasonably claim to be no mutilation, to be indeed a necessary clarification. Necessary, above all, if we are thinking in terms of billions of readers, instead of some guide-conducted dozen.

Here, as had happened hearteningly with the *Republic,* help came from an unexpected quarter. I had supposed that I would be fighting my original throughout—a daunting prospect. Instead, I found Homer strangely ready, passage by passage, to collaborate. It was as though those alternations of rhapsodes—whose chanted competitive contributions somehow got written down—were, or their audience was, in cahoots with me: what really mattered was rarely in doubt; essential linked up with essential; I had only to drop, almost never to twist even by a degree. The continuity obtainable without strain, merely by omission, often astonished me. From selected passages—as passage reached out to passage—the dream of a single consecutive unitary action began to dominate the design. Could it be, if the right intrusions, excursions, supplements were omitted, that some semblance of an integral, original *Wrath of Achilles* would appear?

Whether it does or not in the translation I ultimately made, I am the last who could decide. The final drafts settled down during what was for me a strangely symbolic reflex of that first Trans-Siberian defeat. I was on an obsolescent victory-ship (happily, filled with a cargo of unsinkable timber) making a twenty-one day crossing from Vancouver to Hong Kong; it was midwinter, and we were several days hove to in mid-Pacific with a number-eleven gale howling and the salt spray freezing where it fell, while the pumps valiantly labored. And—that was the best of it—I was on my way back to Peking. This was in 1950, with the Chinese showing Mao what the sons of Han could again be. The last touches were given and the introduction written high on the Peak in Hong Kong.

Still later, back again in Peking, I found that the cleanup was in full swing. Down in the Forbidden City's drains, clogged by a hundred years of neglect from corrupt officials, and equally up in the very ventricles of the citizens' brains and hearts, the new hope was making its way:

Bliss was it in that dawn to be alive.[20]

Where brutalized War Lords' police had beaten and kicked, a New Order officer gently helped the old water seller whose barrow got stuck in a rut. Something had to be done to calm one's overflowing spirits. The British Council quarters had a spacious court. But its officials were still waiting unhappily for their permits in Hong Kong. Why not try the *Iliad* out in a public reading, newly posted off to the publisher though the top copy was? It was then, in trying to compress its action into two hours, that I found that the poem has five acts and—still more striking—conforms, when so compressed, strictly to the canons of tragedy. Indeed, as so reshaped—with a chorus of alternating rhapsodes to weave in the connective descriptions—the temptation to try to find actors and actresses and essay a dramatic performance was strong. More of this below. For the moment, a one-voice reading had to suffice. In that full courtyard, as the evening light of spring lingered, it was comforting to find that my vocal chords could last out.

Together with this simplified *Iliad,* I had brought with me my near-Basic version of the *Republic.* Its reception by my Chinese students was even more thought-provoking. I took early occasion in my lectures to read key passages. The response from the large class—newly attired in the official student uniforms of Mao's regime—was more than gratifying. Might they, an editorial group came up to request, print what I had read to them in the College issue of "Texts of the Week"? By all mans, I replied, but had they not better first check with the Director about it? Why, of course they would! I still remember their pained bewilderment when they came back to tell me that Plato was on the Index. They could not divine why. Plato had said so entirely, so forcefully, what they were hoping to live by. Why should they be forbidden to read expositions of their duties to the State which coincided so well with so much that Mao was teaching them? Could I explain it? I wished I could. Under the circumstances there was nothing I could do to help. If their Director couldn't tell them why they must not read Plato, how should I?

(This episode came back to me some years later during an audience granted me by Kwame Nkrumah. I had taken along as a commemorative token an inscribed copy of that version of the *Republic.* I thought it might help to show what a selected English could do for Ghana and indeed for all Africa. Things had been going well; Nkrumah was displaying all his unmatchable charm. But at the mention of Plato there fell a perceptible chill, as though his name alone constituted a threat. That amazing politician's antennae sensed instantly then where danger lay. His instinct had not served him so well when he set up that more than life-size graven image of himself in Accra. On its plinth: "Seek ye first the political Kingdom and all things shall be added unto you." Today, like Shelley's Ozymandias, the statue lies in fragments in the dust. The inscription bears it witness still.)

The touchstone quality that Emerson noticed in the *Republic* may be borne in mind when Plato is accused of being the first totalitarian, the inventor of the police state, and so on. With wrenched texts this view can be given not a little color. But the more any reader can take in the book *as a whole,* the less can he credit such partial views of it. The concepts of Man and Justice that it presents are in fact those that best protect us from oppression, from whatever side it may come and not least from tyrant trends within ourselves. And this is the chief reason for working toward a version that will best help as many minds as may to see it *as a whole:* to see it, in its own term—its title being *On Justice*—justly; that is, with its parts in due relation to one another. It will be fitting therefore to consider some of the obstacles that have so often prevented readers from forming this *just* view of it and what can be done to remove them. Chief among them must be mentioned its great scale and its extreme complexity. But before looking into these, let us, as with the *Iliad,* step back for a few moments and try to estimate this extraordinary thing and its place among the powers shaping mankind.

The *Republic*

No book—except the Bible—has had so much influence, so pervasive and so various, upon the peoples who—since the Middle Ages and until very recently—have been regarding themselvs, with some reason, as the appointed leaders of the planet. In a very real sense they have been its creatures. What they have called their ideas have come to them, through whatever channels and in whatever disguises, from its pages. Socrates' words at the close of Book 9, quoted above, have been a true prophecy. These peoples have made themselves citizens of his ideal state and chosen to profess, at least, to live by its laws. By its principles they have attempted or pretended to govern themselves and others. "The greatest invention of the Greeks," wrote Jaeger, "was man." Western man, this is, of course. Other cultures have had their other and very different image makers. The Chinese had Confucius and Mencius to do for them what Plato did for us: give us our model of our true selves. We come short of it, endlessly, but it is of Plato's guardian mind that we come short.

Though we may never have read a word of Plato, or even heard of him, this can still ·be true. Most of our most serious thoughts have echoes in them of his. Every successful reader of Plato comes to feel that later literature is a whispering gallery. A successful reader is one who, through his reading, knows more about the good and more about himself. And this increased knowledge is Plato's thought living again in him.

It will be granted that to read Plato successfully is not easy. We may recall Whitehead: "If it were easy, the book ought to be burned; for it cannot be educational." [21] But we must distinguish necessary from avoidable difficulties. Part of the avoidable difficulty of the *Republic* is due to the superbly elaborate pedagogy employed. It was superlatively well designed for its purpose. It worked admirably for the scholar-disciples for whom it was written. But, though we are disciples, witting or unwitting, we are not those scholars. The very spaciousness of the book, the broad introductory sketches, the anticipatory hints, the figurative indications, the minor parallels, the skillful arrangements of correspondences and contrasts, the contrived disappointments, the gambits and recapitulations, the returns to deeper levels after withdrawals—all this art can wholly fail, for the modern reader, to have its due effect. Many, for example, have thrown the *Republic* down toward the end of its first book, unaware that the main ingredient of their dissatisfaction is something

that Plato meant them to feel. The long interventions of Glaucon and
Adeimantus that open Book 2 show this clearly. They are drawing the
bow for the rest of the discussion. The arguments closing Book 1 *are* thin,
and Thrasymachus *is* overcome too easily. But when the place of these
passages in the whole design becomes clear, they are seen to be but a prelude introducing, in summary, much that is to come.

Again, as Plato develops the great parallel between society and mind—
the capitals and lower case with which Socrates starts off his reply to
Plato's brothers[22]—how many realize that Socrates is going to say of all
his figures: "We shall never reach the truth this way." [23] It is a parallel
that has shaped many societies and many minds and, with the help of today's and tomorrow's physiology and linguistics, it may well have a vastly
expanded future: we go on to compare a language with an organism and
both with a state. But its service is in being *explicitly, self-admittedly,* an
analogy, and protected, we should hope, by this from being mistaken for
an argument. As figures of speech, such analogies are perpetually necessary. They are invaluable as means of exploration, misleading only if supposed to be offered as proofs. The modern sociologist is apt to take his
own analyses and arguments so seriously that he may overlook or under-
estimate Plato's account of method[24] and his hints that in "these things"
even a Glaucon (surely the best audience any speaker could have) must
be content with no more.[25]

As yet another example of the *Republic*'s complexity, we may note the
persistent ambivalences of Socrates' position as to the possibility of
knowledge. In "these things" must even a Socrates too be content with
no more? Must an analogy, a parallel, suffice? Books 6 and 7 present
an "outline only" of a program of studies for this first of all Universities
that Plato is founding. It is so extensive that it can be read as forefiguring
all inquiries ever since, and yet Glaucon is teased and twitted again and
again for naïvely taking it as more than a sketch, and a sketch of some
preliminaries only. Real knowledge and "the likely story" are deliberately
balanced. Probably we are to hold them so—eschewing certainty as
guardedly as we avoid crippling doubt. In answering such questions are
we not to exercise the very reserves we are asking about? Any recommendation in these matters should remember that it applies to itself.

It should be evident that positions so poised raise especial difficulties
for translators. Perhaps it is not too much to say that the *Republic,* as it
stands in the English versions of the best scholars, is ineffective today for
the very reasons that have made it effective in Plato's Greek. The main
lines of its thought can so easily become lost among the qualifications
and preparations and the polite and (to the Greek) persuasive
indirections.

The very familiarity, too, of so many of its ideas collaborates in preventing us from seeing their everlasting novelty. They are like our hands
and feet: only now and then do we realize them and how much they do

for us. Of all media that could guard us from this awakening shock, a translator's English that attempts to follow the Greek meticulously in minor detail and social tone is the most absorbent. Plato's syle deployed endless exquisite devices for meeting attitudes and expectations in his readers that sprang from their milieu. These attitudes and expectations do not arise in us; we have our own. A dummy discourse in English does nothing for either set, however well it is trained to ape the alien delicacies of the Greek. Nor does it help us in taking what Plato said to heart. Versions in nineteenth-century idiom did perhaps help the nineteenth century to realize itself. Today they have the uncanny effect of making Plato seem mid-Victorian. We hardly know which of two remote worlds we are exploring.

This is unfair both to Plato and to Jowett. But the source of these troubles lies even deeper than in the perennial moral strife between intellectual generations. It is the effort to get *all* of Plato's meaning into our English—just that meaning and nothing else—that befogs the translator's prose. It is a wholly admirable effort and ambition from the point of view of scholarship *in Greek*. To try to say it in English *is* one of the best means of exploring what the Greek says, though a dangerous means whenever the translator thinks his English has said it. What is needed here is a Socratic inquiry into the words *translate* and *say*. What does a sentence say, the thing the speaker had in mind or the thing some hearer gets? A typical hearer, an ideal hearer, an average hearer, an idiolectic hearer? Such an inquiry would show how hard it is for any translator to know what he is doing, and how he should attempt to direct (and therefore to limit) this "meaning" he deals with. The meaning, the whole meaning, and nothing but the meaning: that is unattainable, though scholarship rightly makes it an ideal. But when we pass from understanding the Greek as best we can to uttering something partially parallel in English for general readers, the situation is different and another ideal becomes more relevant. We have to realize that different purposes will be best served by different types of versions.

Any version whatever that in a different age is conceived in a different language must depart from that ideal exact meaning. The readings of Plato's friends in his own lifetime departed from it, do what they would, though there was no such refracting linguistic veil between them and his words. Ours must depart far more, at more points and in more dimensions. We can understand this and some of the probable departures more or less clearly. By such understanding we may correct our view. This is what modern scholarship attempts. The fatal thing in this approach is to forget the gulfs.

But there is another means of interpreting our traditional sources, a much more traditional method. And *here* interpreting means spreading out, as in irrigation. It is done by willfully overlooking the gulfs. In all ages Platonists have done this, more or less consciously. They have found in Plato a revealing mirror of their own selves and have made him say for them what they saw. It is this that formerly made him (with the Bible) the field-determinant of the Western mind. Modern historical philology, like other simplifications (or inventions, if you like) that came to power in the eighteenth century, has been extremely subversive in professing to present to us "the full facts." It has buried Plato in the dead leaves of a wood that has vanished into trees.

To recover him—our traditional mirroring sun, not any animated waxwork of a historical reconstruction—we have to recognize what we are doing and take, as the philologist likewise does, only what suits our purpose. But our prime purpose, which was Plato's, is saving society and our own souls. This, as the *Republic,* along with other great books, can teach us, is the most inclusive and demanding of all purposes. This should ignore no mode of knowledge, nor should it let any more special mode of knowledge impose its more limited scope. What the greatest school book of all time can teach us, if we let it, is what sort of knowledge it is that can most help us in the conduct both of ourselves and of the state.

All such talk sounds hollow; nonetheless, this is the preeminently searching knowledge that is only arrived at through divergencies, developments, and reconciliations of Reflection. And that capitalized Reflection which Coleridge describes was formulated by him (first as a schoolboy) primarily from Plato, derivatively from Plotinus. In Aphorism 9 of his *Aids to Reflection,* his debt to *Republic,* Book 6, shows very clearly. It is a debt compounded, of course, with an equal or greater debt to the New Testament:

> *None then, not one of human kind, so poor and destitute, but there is provided for him, even in his present state,* a house not built with hands. *Aye, and spite of the philosophy (falsely so called) which mistakes the causes, the conditions, and the occasions of our becoming* conscious *of certain truths and realities for the truths and realities themselves—a house gloriously furnished. Nothing is wanted but the eye, which is the light of this house, the light which is the eye of this soul. This* seeing *light, this* enlightening *eye, is Reflection. It is more, indeed, than is ordinarily meant by that word; but it is what a Christian ought to mean by it, and to know too, whence it first came, and still continues to come— of what light even this light is but a reflection. This, too, is THOUGHT; and all thought is but unthinking that does not flow out of this, or tend towards it.*

If we hark back to Blake's use of Shadow quoted above, we shall see that Blake's Imagination and Coleridge's Reflection equally derive from Plato. In reading both we have only to beware of "unthinking."

What such echoes from the *Republic* have to tell us about ourselves, other echoings can tell us about the state. Jefferson, who failed strangely in his reading of the *Republic* and blamed Plato for it, declared that "a Democracy can be preserved only by frequent returns to fundamentals."[26] These fundamentals are here in the *Republic,* which laid them down. Here are both the conditions upon which alone a democracy is possible *and* the most damaging description ever written of the dangers to which all democracies are exposed. That this description amounts to a portrait of Hitler[27] is no accident. These things are perpetual, being the price we pay for our failure to become in actuality more nearly what we are in essence. As Pindar put it, "May you become as you have learned you are!"

A version of the *Republic* for the general reader interested in these things may be more faithful to what mattered most to Plato if it restricts its rendering of other things that Plato is caring for. When the lingo that a strict conformity with the Greek forces upon a translator has become so familiar that its strangeness is no longer noticed; when the formulas and constructions translators must use have become by habit a code we decode at sight; when we expect most sentences to read like:

> *Tell me, in heaven's name, do you not think that such a person would make a strange instructor?*

or

> *I for one most certainly anticipate that a consideration of this question will help us.*

—when these elaborately articulated garments of simple enough thoughts have come to feel like our skin, then perhaps we will be ready to perceive through English the niceties of Plato's *tones.* But I doubt it. I believe the scholar responds to the Greek behind these sentences and that the Greekless get little or nothing of this interplay. English—except through rare and happy accidents—cannot help travestying Greek when it tries to reproduce such things by literal means. Thought, on the other hand, as opposed to tone, can be reproduced to the limits of understanding. Feeling too is relatively manageable: how Socrates or Adeimantus feels about a large matter. But not *tone:* the intricacies of their attitudes to what has just been said and to its speaker we can guess from content and context, but English refuses to let us be explicit about them without using palpably un-English forms, which for the Greekless defeat the purpose.

What can be done? The resource with which versions must experiment if they are to do what is needed is to omit this attempt, to concentrate on the thought, leaving tone to be surmised as concomitant to the thought.

This is the mode of the English of the Bible, of Bacon and Bunyan, and of modern general colloquial.

The result of shrinking one of the most literal of contemporary translations (Davies and Vaughan) from

> *Shall you have any answer to make to that objection, my clever friend?*
>
> *It is not very easy to find one at a moment's notice; but I shall apply to you, and I do so now, to state what the arguments on our side are, and to expound them for us.*

into

> *What's your answer to that?*
> *I haven't one right now. What* are *we able to answer?*

and so on throughout, is to shorten our version by about one-third. As this experiment in simplification develops, the bones, as it were, of the book show up so much more clearly that Plato's careful prefaces, progress reports, and summaries become no longer necessary. They become, in fact, barriers to readers who fail to distinguish the prefaces from the statements. It is possible to streamline the argument still further by cutting out all but its active movements; and when we are once launched on that operation the ideal naturally comes up of a *Republic* that would keep whatever has made history but nothing else, and of putting that into an English *as clear to everyone as possible*.

Such a version can be no synopsis or digest. It must keep the dramatic movement, the give and take of the dialectic, the Platonic unction, Socrates' disclaimers of knowledge, the hints of his fate, all his ironies and surprises—for these are what have made and still will make history. However simplified, this must be a *Republic,* and without these it would be nothing of the sort. In practice it proves possible to retain the entire argument, all its essential explanations and defenses, and every detail that has hitherto generated philosophic as well as other discussion, contentious and expository, in agreement and in opposition, and still to reduce its volume to something under one-half.

Why read Plato at all if you are in such a hurry? Well, most readers are in a hurry anyhow, more is the pity. That is what the curriculum and the examination system do to them. Perhaps arranging Plato so that he can be more easily read may help us to become less hurried hereafter. It is not hard, however, to imagine the comments of certain sorts of scholars. This is tampering with Holy Writ with a vengeance, and the vengeance is not unlikely to fall.[28] But if Plato's thought flows again more freely in more readers through such a version, its boldness will be justified enough. And if we will think less of that ideal "exact meaning" to which the scholar properly aspires and think more of the "actual understandings" to which living and largely baffled readers attain, Socrates himself, I believe, would be ready to clear such adjustments from charges of impiety. But to be fully useful, this pruned and adapted version should not only make it easier for a *new reader* to see what Plato was saying. It should help even the student who has worked faithfully through a complete translation with notes. With minor points absent, the great limbs of the argument should show the more clearly.

Whoever attempts such abridgment must feel pang after pang of regret for what he leaves out for the sake of the clearer movement of the whole. But our aim (as Plato might say) is not to make our rendering of this or that phase or section or interest especially happy but to make the whole thing as good an exposition as possible of the arts of ruling and being ruled.

Misunderstandings in matters as important as those with which the *Republic* deals can be dangerous. Readers who have not realized that the book is an inquiry into justice, or who agree at heart with Thrasymachus, are very ready to call it reactionary. But more comprehending readers know better. They have seen Socrates set up the very concepts of Man and of Justice that we most need when liberty is threatened either from without or from within. Lacking these concepts—though like Boëthius we forget what we are—we should be defenseless, for example, against the manipulations of a blind social science[29] and its servants among the educators. But these defenses now need an active existence in every mind. What was written for aristocrats of a city-state has in fact become the prime text for world citizenship. Other versions—valuable and indeed essential for other purposes—need to be supplemented by a version given the clearest, most universally open form attainable.

The *Iliad*

Plato on the *Iliad* had, I think, prepared me for what I found, among my undergraduates in the Humanities 1 course, to be an extremely widespread response to Achilles. It was best expressed by: "God! How I hate that man!" as one of them put it. Wildly unjust, of course, imperceptive and undiscerning; nonetheless as deep-seated as it was frequent. To attempt some redress—with Plato on Achilles coming up within a month— was a good way of engaging newcomers to both in useful self-explorations. I expect I tried a good many different lines, direct and indirect. These General Education students were, all but a very few, unfamiliar with such reading. Most of them were very soon even as lost with it as I had been in that train. What they needed first and *most* was controlled exercise in thoughtful skipping. How to construct a catena of passages through which an overall *action* could come alive for them: that was the prime task. It had to be an action they could follow both intellectually and emotionally, one that would allow Achilles—as the first truly mysterious man, the first problem-character in our tradition—to grow in them.

I have written at length—in the preface to *The Wrath of Achilles*—on some of the aspects and the outcomes of this search. I can avoid repetition here by using a device for selecting and presenting synopses that I did not hit upon till much later when I had to have it for that two-hour *Wrath of Achilles* reading in Peking. It is that of looking for, selecting, and extracting a minimal dramatic form, an irreducible framework of plot on which might be hung such other selected episodes as would not obscure (but would heighten) the essential indispensable action. But before embarking on this somewhat complex analysis and construction, this adventure in the playwright's craft, let me say something more about other strains of response in my Harvard undergraduates and in other readers.

Not all were repelled by Achilles. Some identified with him and exulted in just what antagonized the others. And some, of course, found themselves of two minds—shrinkingly sympathizing with his slaughterer's heart. Most people, I suppose, are simultaneously of all ages: have a long series of past selves, can be infants, small fry, youthful, mature, aging, at any moment, their past and future personae ready to pop up (as with Plato's Many-Headed Beast) at call and not in any manageable fashion. Certainly the *Iliad* showed itself to be "one man's meat and another man's poison," and sometimes it was that in the same mind at all but the same moment. I do not have "protocols" available recording my students' responses. I did not foresee occasion to use them. I have however a collection of phrases from final-examination blue books written by freshmen after a term's work at Harvard, much of it on the *Iliad* and *Republic* read in various uncut and unsimplified versions. I noted them down as evidence of what seems an almost customary response, a cultural habit of blaming the text, its editors and publishers, as well as its teachers, if there is anything in its pages that "fails to hold the attention," "is not immediately intelligible," "requires thought," or "doesn't make sense right away," and so on. Among them they give an impression that more of these entrants to higher academic studies than we may suppose are torn between a belief acquired from their schoolwork that everything ought *somehow* to have been made easy for them—failure in this being a sort of fraudulent betrayal—and a shrewd, native, almost biologic conviction that everything (apart from the exam game) *really* is an utterly uncrackable combination, either arbitrary—formed by an unknown, unpredictable will—or irrational: put together by forces ungoverned by intelligence. In any case the widespread resentment that difficulty arouses is remarkable.

These responses to Lang, Leaf and Myer's *Iliad* or to Paul Shorey's

Republic may be compared with an account of how *The Wrath* has been taken when read by younger people and discussed in school classes. For example, I have this from a white beginning teacher, wished into a forty-three-teacher all-black school in Alabama. She is reporting to her college instructor:

> *My ninth-grade English class had about the most wonderful literature book possible, and included in it was I. A. Richards' version of the* Iliad. *Because of all kinds of reasons hingeing on this being a Negro school in the South, these students were far behind any kind of national or even Southern ninth-grade par, so it took all the way until late spring to get up my guts and the confidence of the class to attack such a problem as the* Iliad. *But they loved it. Even the people who couldn't read were fascinated enough, while the rest were talking about what was going on, to be quiet and listen and then were able to retell the stories themselves. Gosh, and I just sat there amazed, listening to people talk about whatever book they had read the night before.*
>
> *First of all, they loved the gods and goddesses and loved it when they could pronounce all those big new names without a hitch. And the most wonderful thing was that they just totally accepted them. They didn't have any hang-ups about how gods didn't really exist in the world—like I was afraid I was going to have to figure out and explain what Aphrodite really meant in all men's lives. But not at all. They were just mad at old mean Athene for telling Diomedes not to dare fight with any of the other gods, but he could wound Aphrodite if he wanted to, and were sad and happy when Aphrodite ran to her mother and Dione wiped the wound away and comforted her. They didn't find it a bit unbelievable for gods to come pick men up off the battlefield or appear to men in different forms. I guess the only "philosophical conceptions we came to terms with" were how mortals hate Hades the most because he never changes his mind and how gods and mortals both hate Ares because he doesn't care what side he's fighting on, just so he's fighting.*
>
> *Another thing were epithets. I never said a word about them in class. I'm sure no one even knows what the word "epithet" means. And yet, whenever they were writing in class, books closed, they would automatically use them; that is, the five or six really turned-on people would—man-killing Hector (that was their favorite), thunder-throwing Zeus, and even ox-eyed Hera.*
>
> *When we first started reading it, I made a pretty big deal of similes—what exactly were being compared to what and why— because that seemed a good way to make a "more-aware reader"*

and they liked racing to see who could figure it out correctly first. Well, by about Book 16 I never had to mention the word simile again. . . . For the rest of the year, no matter what they were writing about—whether it was about something that happened to them last summer or a story using as many forms of "lie, lay, sit, set" as possible or describing a trip—there would always be in almost every paper something compared to a hungry lion, or a raging river, or a man coming upon a snake. (Back reading the Iliad, *they'd always find that simile "very funny.")*

You made me love the Iliad *in Hellenic Heritage and I guess I read it, I mean, I can even remember reading it and thinking how wonderful it was, but I think I thought that because you'd already convinced me that it was wonderful. But this year it seemed incredible that I'd ever read it before, and I certainly didn't respond to much then, except what you said.*

The big problem teaching here was that in every class there were maybe 10 people who could read fine, 10 on fourth- to sixth-grade level, and 10 who couldn't read at all, so the problem was keeping all these different levels interested and behaving at one time. They were just sitting there misbehaving in my classes, though ready to read and write and think once they got the idea it was fun.

It is a nice question whether these ninth-grade Alabamians or our recent exegetical Homerists more truly represent the *Iliad*'s audiences throughout the ages. Possibly Homer has never been understood (as opposed to enjoyed) before our times. If so, we may picture him in Elysium consulting with Shakespeare, Milton, and others about such a new turn of events.

Let us now see what a minimal plot for a *Wrath of Achilles* might be like, keeping both the scholar and the newcomer in view. In essentials, it is the same sort of inquiry as that needed in reducing the *Republic* to an accessible form or that of making a dramatic presentation of *Euthyphro, Apology, Crito, Phaedo*,[30] attempted in my *Why So, Socrates?*—to which, after discussing a nuclear *Iliad*, I will turn. But the *Wrath* (as I will call it) aims at a more dramatic elimination of all but necessities. The episodes, movements, nuances, touches omitted—for the sake of bringing out the indispensables of the *plot* with the maximal clarity—will be regarded as being, for purpose, audience, or occasion, possibilities of *dramatic* enrichment. The minimal form can thus be conceived as a nucleus, a central core or, better, stem, out from which various *dependent* activities or branches may, if dramatic gain outweighs risk of confusion, be developed. Diagrammatically, it might look something like this:

The *etc.* represents the total *Iliad.* Of course to the unifying Homerist of today hardly a phrase in all that will be without its important contribution.

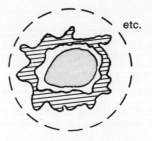

By setting our problem up this way, we gain, I believe, certain advantages: (1) freedom; (2) clarification as to what we are attempting; (3) spotlighting of the *choices* we are considering; (4) reminders of the audiences to which our efforts are addressed. As Reuben Brower well says, "We read from a particular point in space and time."[31]

To set to work. Let us suppose that our minimal plot turns out to have five acts, each act having one or more scenes. The *pausing* of the action between the acts and between the scenes will be as significant as pauses are in all utterances. These pauses do, in fact, determine how the play is divided. The action—*praxis,* in Aristotle's term[32]—and its necessary *unity,* on which Aristotle so much insisted, are what this inquiry seeks to clarify. Each choice-point will bring up that *reference to the rest of the action,* that mutual relevance of components, which Aristotle also stressed with his "organic" metaphors. "Plot," he says, "is the first principle, and, as it were, the soul of a tragedy."[33] If we recall that Aristotle selects as "the transcendent excellence" of Homer this very unity of action, studying what it stems from will seem worth more than usual trouble. My references are to books and lines in the Loeb Classical Library *Iliad,* and the quotations are from *The Wrath of Achilles.*

Act one

The Greeks are in council. To them enters Chryses, priest of Apollo, to ransom his daughter, Chryseis (1. 17–21). The Greeks shout assent, but Agamemnon sends him harshly away. He withdraws in silence to pray to Apollo, who looses shafts of the plague on the Greeks—"till the fires of the dead were burning night and day." On the tenth day Achilles (not Agamemnon) calls the Greeks together, proposing that they ask some seer why Apollo is doing this. Kalchas says he will tell them, if Achilles will protect him from Agamemnon. Achilles replies that he can and will. Kalchas then declares that Agamemnon must return Chryseis to her father, without a ransom. Agamemnon furiously refuses, unless the Greeks give him an equivalent prize of honor. Achilles proposes that they do so when they have taken Troy. Agamemnon then demands Achilles' own prize of honor, the girl, Briseis. Achilles threatens, if so, to sail away home, and Agamemnon then declares that he will come to Achilles' hut and himself take away Briseis.

The first choice-point now arises: should we include in the minimal action the following episode?

Achilles is putting his hand to his sword to end Agamemnon (and the *Iliad*) when Athene, unseen by others, arrives and seizes Achilles by his golden hair. She orders him to put up with it but to tell Agamemnon what he thinks. Achilles obeys; as regards the gods he is notably docile.

Splendid though this is, it seems to me an episode, not a movement in the main action. It belongs to a numerous class of Olympian interventions, most of which yield an action different from, wider and far more intricate than, the *minimal* plot. Certain of these interventions, by Zeus and by gods and goddesses who are acting as his messengers (Hermes and Iris), and by Apollo in sending the plague, do belong essentially to the action. As to those of Thetis, that Achilles' mother is a goddess is an essential element in his *character*. He would not be the same man, and the action of which he is the prime source would not be the same, if her role were to be omitted. But her dealings with Zeus (and Hephaestus) need not be included.

To continue with this summary of the action: Achilles reviles Agamemnon and commits himself to withdrawal from the war. Nestor attempts to make peace between them, but without effect. Achilles returns to his hut. Agamemnon does not, significantly, go there himself but sends two heralds to take Briseis, and unwillingly she goes with them. And there (in 1. 348) ends, I suggest, what I am calling Act One.

Act two

This, I suggest, consists essentially of the embassy in Book 9. The Rhapsode describes the council and Agamemnon's weeping as he rises to propose that they give up the war and sail home. Diomede declares that whatever Agamemnon does, he and Sthenelos will stay on and take Troy. Then Nestor intervenes, reminding Agamemnon of what he did in Act One and of the need to win Achilles back. Agamemnon agrees and declares his readiness to return Briseis along with adequate gifts. Nestor selects, as the best ambassadors, Ajax and Odysseus. With them goes Phoenix, Achilles' tutor.

They find (and this could be Scene Two) Achilles playing the lyre and singing of heroes to Patroclus, who sits in silence waiting for him to end (9. 191). Achilles greets them most cordially and hospitably. (A remarkable amount of eating and drinking takes place that night. Much of it, no doubt, is ritual: ambassadors will sympathize.) When the moment for speeches arrives, Ajax (the "beef-witted lord" of Shakespeare's Thersites, in *Troilus and Cressida*)[34] signs to Phoenix to begin. But Odysseus knows better. His great speech has ever since been *the* model of diplomatic approach and suasion. Throughout he is watching the effect of his every sentence on Achilles, changing his note accordingly. He was there (with Nestor in an earlier embassy) when Peleus sent Achilles (with

Patroclus) to join Agamemnon's war. He heard what Peleus then said and tries that. When he sees that the list of Agamemnon's offered gifts is not working, he reverts swiftly to the piteous plight of the Greeks and to what Achilles could do to the vaunting Hector.

Achilles' reply is, of course, one of the greatest master passages in all poetry and as probing a search for self-knowledge as can be found, endlessly repaying study. It begins with a stiff rejection of the diplomatic art: "Zeus-born son of Laërtes, man of many designings, now I must say what I have in mind and what I will do, so that you may not sit before me and argue this way and that. I hate—like the gates of Hades—a man who says one thing and has another in his heart" (9. 309–14). There follows the negation of the very value of honor which turns (so wounded he is in his own self-esteem) to speaking of Briseis, his prize of honor, as though she were his wife. "Why has Agamemnon brought all these fighters here? Because of fair-haired Helen? Are Agamemnon and Menelaus the only ones who love their wives? Does not every man in his right mind love his dear one—as I loved mine with all my heart, even though I took her with my spear?" (9. 338–42). In view of what I suggest could be the last line of the *Wrath,* "Achilles in the innermost room, with fair-faced Briseis at his side," this must be allowed some weight among the confluents of the action. Now comes savagely ironic mockery of the Greeks and a disdainful glance at Hector—all but anticipating what is to be his end. Then wounded honor strikes up again: scornful refusal of Agamemnon's gifts, with his offer of one of his daughters in marriage ironically treated again: "No, let him give her to another, to some man like himself and more of a king than I am!" (9. 392). His twofold fate—long happy years in his homeland, but without honor, or an early death with immortal fame—hangs in balance before him. He ends by advising the Greeks to sail home too. But it is clear that he does not know his own mind.

They sit in silence, and here another choice-point comes up: should the long speech from Phoenix that now follows be included in the action? It tells us much of the spoilt childhood of Achilles and has the great passage on Prayers that walk in the footsteps of Sin. Nonetheless, for a *minimal* action it can be omitted, though certainly it should be one of the first enrichments to be added.

Ajax sums up. The "beef-witted lord" shows himself to be a diagnostician: "Let us go, for Achilles has worked up his anger. Any man will take a great enough price whatever the wrong done him. As for you, Achilles, you have made your heart hard because of one girl only, when we are offering you seven, the best there are." Achilles, surprisingly, almost agrees: "But my heart swells with anger to think what Agamemnon did to me before everybody. . . . I will not take up my arms again till Hector comes to my own ships with fire. Then, I think, he will be stopped, however much of a fighter he may be."

Act three

Our selected minimal action resumes when Achilles, watching from his great ship how badly things are going for the Greeks, sees Nestor drive by in his chariot with Machaon, the surgeon, wounded (11. 599). That moves him. "A surgeon is of more value than many fighting men" (11. 514). He sends Patroclus running to Nestor's hut to verify and report. Nestor, at the end of a speech which makes him a prototype of Polonius, suggests that Patroclus put Achilles' armor on and take the Myrmidons out to drive the Trojans back to Troy. Patroclus runs back weeping, exactly as Agamemnon weeps at the outset of Act Two (Book 16, opening). This distresses Achilles, who asks what can be the matter? Is there bad news from home? Can it be the Greeks he is sorrowing for—being killed, all for their own fault? Patroclus (in many ways the most attaching character in the *Iliad*) rebukes Achilles grandly and asks for the armor in which to go out against the Trojans in Achilles' place. Achilles replies with what he has said already about "What Agamemnon did to me before everybody. . . ." Then he pretends he has ended his anger and grants Patroclus his wish. "But take this to heart. Come back again when you have cleared the ships. Do not go up against Troy or you will make my honor less." Then, *Homerically*—there is no other word for it—he foresees what is to happen: "One of the gods that are forever may come down from Olympus against you—for dearly does Phoebus Apollo love them." Now occurs the supreme instance of *hubris,* the type specimen of it: "O father Zeus, and Athene and Apollo, O would that not one of the Trojans, not one of them all—*nor one of the Greeks*—might escape death, if only we two together might throw down the sacred walls of Troy" (16. 97–100). He is beside himself. More extreme alienation can hardly be imagined.

The worst then naturally happens. The feats of Patroclus and his end—at Apollo's hand—can be briefly recounted by a Rhapsode. Then Antilochus, Nestor's son, brings the crushing news to Achilles (opening of Book 18). Achilles' behavior when he receives it may be described by the Rhapsode while the actor representing Achilles mimes it. It is this behavior that is selected by the Socrates of the *Republic* both in Book 3 and in Book 10[35] to illustrate what a man struck by terrible news should *not* do. A good man guided by reason will take such blows of fate less hardly than other people. It is best to keep quiet as far as possible because we are not certain what is good or bad in such things, and to take them hardly does not make them any better. The Achilles of the action of the *Wrath,* however, moans so loudly that his mother, Thetis, hears him. She comes up from the sea bottom, takes her son's head in her hands, and asks, "Has not Zeus done as you prayed?" Achilles tells her that Patroclus is dead, that Hector has his armor, that his own heart will not let him live on. But first he must kill Hector. She replies: "You will be short-lived, then, my son: for after Hector's death, yours will come quickly."

Here, in the middle of Act Three, comes what Aristotle called the *peripeteia*. In the *Poetics* he defines a Complex action as one in which the change is accompanied by Reversal of the Situation (*peripeteia*) or by Recognition or by both,[36] and he goes on to describe Reversal of the Situation as a change by which the action veers round to its opposite. Recognition, he says, "as the name indicates, is a change from ignorance to knowledge, producing love or hate between persons destined by the poet for good or bad fortune. The best form of Recognition is coincident with Reversal of the Situation, as in the *Oedipus*."[37] His account equally well fits this crucial turning point in the *Iliad*. Indeed, we may wonder, in view of his immense admiration for Homer, that he did not use this illustration. Recognition combined with Reversal, he remarks, will produce either pity or fear. These two are, of course, his defining marks for tragedy. Previously he has spoken of "pity and fear" together.[38] Here he separates them.

It has become customary, in discussing tragedy, to tie these up together, to relate pity with fear, as joint necessary components in the tragic effect, and to make the "proper purgation" an outcome of their combination and opposition. Certainly here, with Achilles down in the dust, the set and direction of his energies veering as he recognizes what he has been and what a change must now come, pity and fear are very intimately conjoined. Antilochus in tears holding Achilles' hands for fear he will cut his throat, the women crying aloud around him, and Thetis, too, feel both together. And in scene after scene that follows (Achilles' Lycaon speech is perhaps the clearest single example), there is the same tension between them. This is indeed the pervasive quality of the *Iliad*.

In this moment of reversal (or should we call it here *redirection*) it is interesting to note how deeply symbolic Achilles' armor can seem: "Patroclus is dead whom I honored as no other, even as my own self. And Hector, who killed him, has taken his armor—armor that the gods gave to Peleus on the day you were married to him." The armor can represent Achilles' very being, including his semidivine prowess. Hector, in killing Patroclus and in taking the armor, has deprived Achilles of his own self. That his own death will come quickly after Hector's seems fitting to him. "Let it come, then, for I was not there to help Patroclus . . . *or any of my brothers-in-arms that Hector has killed*" (this is indeed a new Achilles speaking), "but was here by the ships, a useless weight on the earth: I that in war am such as no other of the Greeks." Because of all this, "now would that war itself might end among gods and men, and anger that sweeter far than drops of honey swells like smoke in men's breasts. Even so did Agamemnon anger me." That anger is passed, swept aside and replaced by a greater anger: "But now I will go to look for Hector, who killed the man I loved. . . ." His goddess mother reminds him of his new sense of responsibilities—"It is well to save your friends from destruction"—and of his need for armor: "In the morning I will have new armor for you, made by Hephaestus."

In the morning she brings the armor: shield, breastplate, helmet, and leg guards. She puts the arms down before Achilles, and they ring loudly in their glory. All the Myrmidons shake with fear, and no man has the courage to look upon them. But when Achilles sees them, rage for battle comes on him again, and his eyes burn like flame. The wish "that war itself might end among gods and men" is forgotten. All through the *Iliad,* "evil war" turns to "joy of battle" as lightly as an aspen leaf trembles.

By the side of the sea Achilles goes shouting loudly, and the Greeks come to the place of meeting, happy because Achilles is coming back into the war. Among them are the wounded Diomede and Odysseus—helping themselves with their spears—who sit in front. Last of all comes Agamemnon, wounded too. This is the physical image of the turning point in the action. Achilles rises and speaks: "How was it better for us, Agamemnon, for you and for me, to rage in such high anger about a girl. Why did not Artemis kill her among the ships with an arrow on the day that I took her at Lernessus?"

Agamemnon, too weak to rise, answers from where he sits. He too has not been himself. He was not to blame, but "Zeus and Fate and Erinys that walks in the dark. Here in the place of meeting they made me blind on the day I took his prize of honor from Achilles." And he offers his gifts again. Achilles replies, "This is no time for talk. There is work to be done." But Odysseus wants to make sure. So he takes men, goes to Agamemnon's hut, and brings them to Achilles' ship, all of them, with the seven women skilled in needlework; and the eighth is fair-faced Briseis. And she, when she sees Patroclus dead, throws herself upon him. "Patroclus, friend to my unhappy heart. You were living when I went from this hut and now I find you dead. So evil comes upon evil. My husband, to whom my father and queenly mother gave me, I saw cut down before our city, and my three dear brothers with him. But when swift Achilles killed him you would have stopped my tears. You said you would make me Achilles' wife and that he would take me in his ships to Phthia to a marriage feast among the Myrmidons. Endlessly I cry aloud for your death for you were ever kind." And the other women add their cries. For Patroclus truly they cry, but each for her own sorrows too.

With this, Act Three, the Act of reversal and return, ends.

Act four

The next great movement of the action—through the death of Hector—opens with the going out of Achilles. Achilles' implacable fury mounts and mounts. Nothing can assuage it, as he kills Trojan after Trojan. Old Priam's youngest and dearest son, Polydorus, is the first to be named.

There he is, foolish boy, letting everyone see how swiftly he can run, when Achilles takes him with his spear point. Just how much of the horrors of this slaughter should be included presents us with another choice-point. If actors mime these episodes as the Rhapsode narrates them, the degree of realism they are permitted would be a matter to be watched. Homer spares us little. Here with Polydorus: "Through him went the spear and he fell to his knees moaning and a dark cloud came over him as he held his bowels to him with his hands." (There are almost no two woundings alike in all the *Iliad:* a remarkable feature in so formulaic a composition.)

Achilles cuts the Trojan armies in two. One part he sends running back to Troy. The other "like locusts before a grass fire flying into water" come to the banks of the deep river Xanthus and leap in. Achilles leans his spear against a tree and follows them with his sword. When tired of killing, he takes twelve young men living out of the water to be a blood price for Patroclus. And then he meets Lycaon, another of Priam's sons, coming up out of the water. Lycaon runs in under Achilles' lifted spear and prays to him with words feathered like an arrow. He has been taken earlier by Achilles and ransomed, and his prayers should be sacred. "Hear me out and do not kill me. My mother was not Hector's mother. I am only the half-brother of the man who killed your friend."

But the voice that replies is pitiless. "Fool, offer me no such words. Till Patroclus fell, it was my pleasure to have pity on the Trojans and many of them I took and sold overseas. But now, not one of them may escape death, least of all any of the sons of Priam. No, friend, you die with them. Why do you sorrow so? Patroclus died, who was better far than you. And do you not see what sort of man I am—how beautiful and tall . . . but over me too hang death and fate. There will come a dawn or eve or midday when some man will take my life in battle—with the spear or an arrow from the string." Achilles hits him on the collarbone by the neck, and all the two-edged sword goes in. Then he takes Lycaon by the foot and throws him into eddying Xanthus to go on his way.

These are preludes to the death of Hector, but they seem to me essential to the action. Much immediately preceding Hector's death, famous and deeply moving though it is, seems episodic, as regards the *Wrath.* One can imagine a play with an action centering on Hector to which his full meditation, the flight round Troy, and Athene's trickery would be indispensables. But to the action of the *Wrath* belongs, I suggest, chiefly, that deadly fate holds Hector outside Troy, while the defeated Trojans, like helpless fauns, are wiping the sweat off them within the city, as the Greeks approach. It is the old Priam who first sees Achilles running, like a prizewinning horse, toward Troy. "And to Priam he seemed like the star which comes out at harvest time—bright are his rays among the armies of the night—the star men name the Dog of Orion. Brightest of all, he is but a sign of evil." This belongs, as building up Priam toward

311

his part in Act Five. How much of it is needed or is dispensable enrichment is a director's problem. Priam beseeches Hector to enter the city, but Hector is lost in self-accusations. It is almost as in a dream that he sees Achilles coming upon him in his waving helmet with the great Pelian spear lifted. Away he runs, with swift-footed Achilles behind him. The heartbreaking list of Hector's most familiar landmarks of childhood, culminating with "the wide stone basins where the wives and daughters of the Trojans washed their clothes, of old in time of peace before the Greeks came to Troyland" would have to be given by a Rhapsode as Chorus. "By these they run—a good man in front but a far stronger man at his heels. And the prize they run for is no bull's skin, or common prize for the swift-footed, but the life of horse-taming Hector."

We omit the Olympians' discussion, seething with irony though it is. And the details of the chase. Also, and with anguish: "When they came a fourth time to the springs, Zeus lifted up his golden balance and Hector's fate went down; and Phoebus Apollo left him!" How that has echoed on! Also and most regretfully, Athene's ruthless and abominable cunning in taking on the semblance of Deiphobus, Hector's brother, come out to help him, and letting him sickeningly down at the turn of the fight. But their preliminary exchange must be included: *Hector:* "I will run from you no longer, Achilles, but kill you now or be killed. Let this be our agreement before all the gods as witnesses" (all the gods *are* there witnessing all): "if Zeus lets me outlive you and take your life, I will give your body back to the Greeks, after taking your armor. And you will do the same." *Achilles:* "Talk not to me of agreements, Hector. Between lions and men there is no swearing of oaths. . . . Now you must pay for all my sorrows for my friends you have killed." (Perhaps, for Achilles' sake, we should substitute Patroclus for those friends.)

At the climax of the fight: "As a star comes out among the stars of the night, star of evening, the most beautiful of the stars of heaven, even so came the light from the bronze of Achilles' spear as he lifted it looking for the place most open to the blow." Hector is in Achilles' own armor taken from Patroclus, and Achilles knows it well. There is an opening where the collarbones come into the neck, and through that Achilles strikes. They have their final exchange: *Achilles:* "Little you thought, you fool, of me when you took that armor from Patroclus. . . . The Greeks will give him his funeral but throw you to the dogs and birds." *Hector:* "By your life and knees and parents take the gifts my father and mother will offer you and send my body back so that the Trojans and their wives may give me to the fire after my death." *Achilles:* "Pray me not, dog, by knees and parents. O that I could make myself cut up your flesh and eat it raw myself. . . . There is no man living who can keep the dogs from your head, Hector." *Hector:* "I know you for what you are, and knew it before. The heart in your breast is of iron. See that I do not bring the anger of the gods down upon you on the day when Paris and Apollo kill you, strong though you are, at the Scaean gate." He dies; his spirit goes from him down to the house of Hades, crying out sadly. Then *Achilles:* "Lie dead there; I am ready for my own death whenever Zeus and the other immortals send it."

One last movement completes Act Four. Achilles takes that armor off Hector. The Greeks run up to wonder at Hector's beauty. And all who come near wound him with their spears saying one to another, "Hector is softer to handle now than when he burned our ships." *Achilles:* "This man has done us more damage than all the rest together. But what am I thinking of? Patroclus waits at the ships for his funeral. Even if in the house of Hades men forget their friends, even there I will not forget him. Back, sons of the Greeks, to the ships, but we will take this man with us." So, with a huntsman's knack, he cuts the backs of Hector's heels, puts thongs of leather through and ties them to his chariot. Dust goes up from Hector's dark hair outstretched and his head that was so beautiful; for now Zeus has given him over to be shamefully handled in his own land where he was born.

Act five

Scene One, the burning pyre of Patroclus. Achilles among his Myrmidons lies moaning by the side of the sounding sea in an open place where the waves wash in. He falls asleep and dreams: the ghost of Patroclus stands at his head and says: "You sleep and have no more thought for me, Achilles. Not in my life were you unmindful of me; but now in my death. . . . You too, godlike Achilles, are fated to be killed under the walls of Troy. Hear now, if you will, my request. Let our bones lie together as we were brought up together in your house." Achilles answers: "Why, my brother, do you come to tell me this? I will do all. But stand nearer. Though it is but for a little, let us throw our arms about one another and give full way to our sorrow." He stretches out his arms, but the spirit, like a mist, goes under earth, feebly moaning. Achilles leaps up clapping his hands together. "See you! Even in the house of Hades, the spirit is something—though the life is not in it. He was wonderfully like his living self!" He falls asleep again beside the pyre. Enter Agamemnon and other chiefs who waken Achilles. *Achilles:* "First put out the burning pyre with wine. Then take up the bones of Patroclus, separating them carefully from the rest." (There is need for this; many have been the sheep and cattle burned with Patroclus. Four strong horses Achilles has killed and flung upon the pyre, moaning as he did so. And two of Patroclus' nine house dogs, and, as climax, the twelve brave sons of the Trojans he had taken out of Xanthus and killed with the sword—"evil work of his heart's designing," comments the Rhapsode. There might be a temptation to mime and describe some of this; it belongs to the action.) Achilles goes on: "Then let us place his bones in a golden urn with a double roll of fat around them till the time when I go myself down to the house of Hades.

But build no great mound till then. Later you may, those of you left among the ships when I am gone."

The others go off to supper and sweet sleep, but not Achilles. All night he turns this way and that by the side of the waves, ceaselessly moaning, and, as Dawn comes on the water, he takes out his horses and chariot and drags Hector three times round the pyre.

Scene Two, Olympus, gods and goddesses in council. Apollo speaks: "Hard-hearted and cruel you gods are. Has Hector never burned thighs of bulls for you? Have you no care to save him, dead though he is, for his father Priam and his people who would burn him in the fire and give him his funeral? No, it is Achilles you would help, a man out of his mind, without pity or shame in his heart. . . . Let him beware that we do not become angry with him." Zeus sends Thetis to Achilles. She takes a motherly view. "My child, how long will you go on eating your heart out with sorrow. Good for you would be even a woman's arms. You have not long now to live. I come from Zeus who says that the gods are angered with you, he more than all, because you have not given Hector back. Give him up now and take a ransom for the dead." *Achilles:* "So be it; let the ransom-bringer take him, if so the Olympian will." Zeus has sent Iris with orders and comforting words to old Priam. He is to go—with a herald only, an old man to drive the mule wagon—to Achilles' hut.

There are many inviting scenes here. One between Priam and Hecuba. She upbraids him; he must be out of his mind. Another between Priam and his remaining sons; he rages at them in a vein that vividly reminds one of streams of abuse in *Kim.* These might be of use to build up Priam, but a good actor would not need them. They belong rather to another play which would present a purely Trojan action centered on Hector. In the present action, Priam, with Hermes' help, comes to Achilles' hut.

In this final scene, Priam, alone, goes in and finds Achilles with two Myrmidons waiting upon him. He has just finished a meal, and the table still stands at his side. (It might all have been designed for acting, so clear and adroit are the stage directions.) Priam comes in without being seen, kneels and clasps Achilles' knees and kisses the terrible hands that have killed so many of his sons. Achilles wonders as he sees Priam, and the two Myrmidons also wonder and look at one another. Then Priam, in prayer: "Think of your father, O god-like Achilles, of your father who is even as I am, at the sad doorway of old age. It may be that those who live near him trouble him and that he has no one to keep war and destruction from him. Still, when he hears that you are living. . . . But I—unhappy I am. My sons were the bravest in all Troy, and the last of them and the bravest, Hector, that himself guarded Troy, you killed but now as he fought for his country. So I have come to the Greek ships to win his body back with a ransom too great to be counted. Achilles, fear the anger of Heaven, think of your own father and take pity on me. . . . I have made myself do what no other man has done and stretched out my hands to the face of him who killed my sons."

In Achilles this wakens a desire to sorrow aloud for his father, and he takes the old man's hands and gently puts him aside. The two then sorrow together: Priam for Hector and Achilles for his own father and now again for Patroclus. And the sound of their moaning goes up through the house.

Achilles' three following speeches show us a supremely dramatic transformation. It comes, though, by stages. At the end of the first, which contains "How did you have the heart to come to meet my eyes? Your heart truly must be of iron" as well as the "two urns stand on the floor of Zeus"[39] passage which Plato reprehends,[40] he tries to soothe Priam: "You too, Priam, we hear were happy in times past. . . . But give the pain in your heart some rest. . . ." Priam answers: "Say not to me, Achilles, be seated" (he is still at Achilles' feet), "while Hector lies uncovered among the huts. Give him back to me quickly and let me look upon him. . . ." That nearly blows up everything. "Anger me no more, old man!" cries Achilles, with eyes of flame. "I am minded myself to give Hector back, for from Zeus the word came to me by my mother. And well I know that it was not without help from some god that you came here. No mortal man would be brave enough. So move my heart no more, or I may still sin against the will of Zeus and not even here under my roof will you be safe, for all your prayers." He is still barely in control, though he is coming to know himself better.

He springs out like a lion to attend to matters: to look after Priam's horses, take care of the herald and bring the ransom in, and have the women wash and oil Hector's body, keeping it out of Priam's view. Otherwise Priam might cry out on seeing it, and Achilles then might be moved to anger again and kill him.

Achilles' last long speech, made when all is ready and the body in the wagon, is to persuade Priam to supper. "Even Niobe, tired out with weeping, took food at last. Somewhere now high up in the lonely mountains where the rocks are, where, they say, the nymphs sleep, there, though turned to a stone, she still thinks of what the gods did. So now, father, let us take food. You may weep over your dear son, later, as much as you will, in Troy." Then they look and wonder at one another: one so beautiful and tall, the other so kingly.

Priam and the herald are put to bed in the place of honor. One last question: "How many days do you want for Hector's funeral? How long must I hold back the Greeks?" Priam asks for eleven days—to get enough wood in, sorrow, give the funeral, let the people feast and build the mound. "All this, old Priam, will be as you have said." Achilles is whole again. *Sophrosyne* has returned. "I will hold back the battle for as long as you want."

He takes the old man's right hand in his to keep him from any fear, and they go to their rest: Priam and the herald in the front part of the house with wise thoughts in their hearts; but Achilles in the innermost room, with fair-faced Briseis at his side.

The action of the *Wrath* is ended.

Such approximately was the two-hour version of the *Iliad* I read and mimed as best I could that spring evening in Peking to that crowded courtful of Chinese, for all of whom it was utterly new. I had opportunity to work it over again later. The Ford Foundation gave Harvard a TV professorship, which I was invited to occupy for two terms. Eight fifteen-minute spells, one each week, had to take care of the whole poem. (The second term I tried readings of eight great English poems with the words on the screen.) I have never worked harder in my life. So much planning, so much measuring, so much practising of various voices, so many concomitants, so much adjustment to camera, lighting, settings, and continuity. I suppose it was worthwhile, for even now, twenty years later, I meet complete strangers who speak of that TV *Iliad* excitedly without recalling who did it. I used for the characters, archaic Greek sculpture. They held the eye and relevantly helped me to make clear who was speaking. How I longed at the time for the relative freedom and the experimental flexibility of film. Possibilities of trying a film reading—enriched and relaxed, with a variation of voices—or even of making an acted film presentation hung in the air for some time. But the local NET station, WGBH (Boston), went up in flames, and one of the two kinescope copies that had been made of my readings helped to feed them. The other, which had been sent to Harvard for their files, proved unfindable when I inquired about it. This account, here presented, is my somewhat delayed attempt to explore the problem again. I am more than ever persuaded that the *Iliad* contains an action (if not a second Trojan plot as well), and that working this out is, at least, a useful exercise. Classroom discussion of what belongs or not to a central Achillean action is as good a way as I can imagine into deeper investigation of the *Iliad*. I am inclined to believe that on this at least Aristotle would be in agreement.

The same, with significant differences, would, I believe, be true of a parallel attempt to construct an action for Hector. That brings out sharply the wide differences between the ethos of the Greek camp and the ethos of the well-ordered city with its rich domestic and familial concerns. It is perhaps a commonplace to remark that Homer's women seem our contemporaries as compared with his men. Andromache and Hecuba support this and, however different she is from them, so does Helen: the other character in the *Iliad* as enigmatic as Achilles, concerned with self-discovery, though infinitely more self-critical throughout than he. By contrast, Paris, as a character, is extremely well understood by Hector. There is nothing very deep in him except his luck and charm—too deep to be plumbed—and Aphrodite's passion for him, divinely inexplicable.

It seems fitting that it should be frivolous, pleasure-loving Paris who—though after the ending of the *Iliad*—sped the "arrow from the string" causing Achilles' death. He has Apollo's help, as though Apollo had had his further intentions when he deserted Hector.

Why So, Socrates?

A very different Apollo this from Socrates' god of Delphi, god of the swans which Socrates evokes an hour or so before his death. Any bout of dramatic analysis and construction whets the appetite for another. I think it was the overwhelming fun I had had fumbling with threads of plots in the *Iliad*—that and an awareness of the significant contrasts and mutual relevances—that set me to making, if I could, a four-act play: *Why So, Socrates?* from *Euthyphro, Apology, Crito, Phaedo.* The general conditions of the problem were the same. Add nothing whatever to the original. Only find in it—without, I could hope, distortion—an *action* with beginning, middle, and end, such as would have an Aristotelian unity and closure. And also to present it in a version linguistically simplified enough to be serviceable in school classrooms, as well as for radio or film or TV cassette presentations to forthcoming world populations. (Designs, these, that most educators, I find, shake off as easily as ducks do the raindrops. But such remarks may not be the best way to further these projects!)

One merit of such a play would come from the tension with the *Iliad* it could set up, if taken as a due sequel. I had the *Republic,* in simple form, already, as a staging of the main clashes between them. But the *Republic* called for a more dramatic presentation of Socrates; in fact, for the crucial Socratic action to balance that of Achilles. I could not, of course, explicitly and consciously look for these things in dissecting out the action. Otherwise there would be many risks of wrenchings. I had to let the greatest familiarity I could achieve of the full texts combine of itself with my best dramatic sense of what, in Aristotle's terms, could with most plausible possibility, follow from and prepare for what. Especially, I had to beware of stretching interpretations, even more than of importations.

As before, with the *Iliad* and the *Republic,* help came most from the books themselves. As one came a little nearer to what appeared to be their essentials, these seemed, more and more, to link up, join hands, and participate. The action I sought was there, offering itself for presentation if I could only disengage it. And what I must disengage it from clung to it so because—once the action was disengaged—so much of the rest could be enrichment. But let me come now to detail.

I suppose I thought I knew the *Euthyphro* fairly well. I had found it, off and on through decades, a somewhat baffling sequence of tricky maneuvers and remained unconvinced that Socrates, where the argument appears to become really strict, was clarifying much. Then coming back to it from the *Apology*—for which a *performable* version had not been too hard to make—reading the *Euthyphro* as a designed prelude to Socrates' trial changed everything. Socrates' interlocutor then becomes a superficial, insensitive, and breathtakingly vain foil to a Socrates resigned to facing—with his unbreakable courage—a situation of the utmost danger. So far from this visit to the King Archon's office being merely a setting for a philosophical discussion on holiness and piety, it provides a deeply penetrating contrast between two sincerities and two types of religion, between a Socratic and a fanatical (one might say a more than Deuteronomic) piety. The argument is not designed to show anything beyond the fact that two such sincerities—one so complex and so self-searching, the other so simple and so unacquainted with doubts—cannot meet. Each of the definitions over which Socrates perplexes Euthyphro can be taken in at least two very different senses: one trivial and silly, the other profoundly suggestive. The silly sense Euthyphro uses, the profound sense Socrates could entertain. But not in this dialogue. Here Socrates is strangely playful throughout. It is as though the prospect of his coming encounter with his 501 judges were raising his spirits. He is clearly under no illusions whatever as to the risk he runs. Perhaps he has just freshly resolved not in any way, on any account, by any concession, to reduce it. Perhaps he already sees in this grand climactic encounter with the Great Beast an opportunity to be more himself than ever. Curiously, he can remind us of Achilles going out in his new armor. There is an "impetuous valor" and a moral joy of battle.

Here, from Book 6 of the *Republic,* is Plato's description of what happens

> *when the masses crowd together in public meetings, in the Assembly, at a trial, in the theatre or the camp, crying out full throated that some of the things done are bad and others good. At such times will not a young man's heart, as the saying is, be moved within him? What private teaching won't be washed away by such a river? Taken up by its current he will say as they say, do as they do, be as they are.*
>
> Adeimantus: *There is no help for it, Socrates.*
>
> Socrates: *And, moreover, we haven't yet pointed out the chief force at work.*
>
> Adeimantus: *What is it?*
>
> Socrates: *What these trainers and Sophists, the public, back up their words with if the words alone haven't the desired effect: punishment, fines, loss of rights and death.*[41]

Need we doubt that in writing this, Plato would look back to Socrates' trial, at which he was present and doing what he could, terrified and amazed, perhaps exalted, at the way in which his hero was behaving? That behavior was precisely the reverse of what the Socrates of the *Republic* goes on to describe. Instead of placating the Great Beast, the historic Socrates flouted and annoyed it.

> Socrates: *As things are, if anyone anywhere comes to good, that must be through some sort of heavenly inspiration. For there is not, never has been, and never will be any keeping to true values and virtues for a soul which gets the opposite education public meetings give. It is as if a man were learning the impulses and desires of some great strong beast, which he had in his keeping, how to come near it and touch it, and when and by what it may be made most violent or most gentle. Yes, and the cries it makes under which conditions, and what sounds from its keeper and others make it angry or quiet. And after getting this knowledge by living with the great beast long enough, he names it "wisdom" and makes up a system and art, and gives that as his teaching—without any knowledge as to which of these opinions and desires is beautiful or ugly, good or bad, just or unjust. But he fixes all these words by the tastes of the great beast, and names what pleases it "good," and the things which made it angry "bad," having no other account to give of them. And what is necessary he names "just" and "high," never having seen how very different are what must be and what should be. So he is not able to make that clear to another. By heaven, won't such a man give the young a strange education? Have you ever heard an argument to the effect that whatever the public praises is good and beautiful, which wouldn't make you simply laugh?*
> Adeimantus: *No, and I am not looking for one.*[42]

This passage may help to bring out a relevance of the *argument* of the *Euthyphro* to what Socrates is going to do before his judges. That the gods approve it does not make an act holy any more than being pleasing to the Great Beast makes it good. And in the *Crito* and *Phaedo* the same point is pressed home in an increasingly dramatic fashion. What is so, is to be settled, not by what people say, but by what the careful, critical, responsible thinker can *see* to be true—in that strangely safe and simple sense in which we *see* that it is beauty that *makes* beautiful things be beautiful. This is the intellectual vision that Coleridge's Aphorism 9[43] is speaking of.

There are opportunities here, of course, for the greatest and most continuing mistakings in the history of philosophy, for all the differings that have made the Doctrine of Ideas a battleground. *Why So, Socrates?*, as a play intended for every sort of performance via all available media, does not pretend to resolve any controversy. It couldn't. But no presentation of Plato's Socrates could possibly omit what is, in these four dialogues, their kingbolt. The *Euthyphro* is nominally and explicitly a quest for the Idea, the form, the universal, the essence, of holiness, piety, religion, spoken of as a single ἰδέα (principle),[44] then as an εἶδος (idea),[45] and an οὐσία (essence).[46] As Taylor points out, Euthyphro (not a philosophic mind) understands all this without any need for explanation, though it is talked of in the technical language of "theory of Forms." Taylor concludes that "from the very first Plato represented Socrates as habitually using language of this kind and being readily understood by his contemporaries."[47]

There is, however, a safe and simple and familiar sense for such words, which can be used without (perhaps) committing ourselves to anything more recondite than an evident fact which all will allow. This is that things and events recur; they can be the same and not the same, the same in some ways and not in other ways; they can be instances; we can ask what they are instances of and be intelligibly answered. For instance, in the last sentence the word *they* recurred. It (the word *they*) appears there three times. Three *they*s occurred. What is that *it?* What are these *they*s? Common sense is content and at ease with a division between occurrences (which we can note and count, compare, distinguish between, contrast and relate) and what they are occurrences of. We need not, and most thinking does not, try to go further, though we are well aware that we can only note, count, and compare occurrences by *somehow* using something of another order of being, something they are occurrences of. But, as it is so well brought out in Chapter 96 of the *Syntopicon,* on the Universal and the Particular,[48] if we try to go beyond that *somehow,* we step onto the philosophic battleground and are involved at once in what "seems to have the character of a professional secret." It is as if we were to try our hand with the spear against Hector. The safe and simple and familiar sense keeps well this side of that *somehow.* It is the sense that Euthyphro so readily understands.

For dramatic purposes, this sense is all that is needed. What the last paragraph has presented are points we can *see* in the sense in which we see that beauty makes beautiful things beautiful and whiteness makes whites be white. Nothing (perhaps) follows from this evident, allowable fact. But for Socrates—and friends of the Ideas, in general—enormously important outcomes have seemed to ensue: promise of immortality and at the least a new scale of intellectual and moral ambition.

It is usually assumed that to understand a play we do not *need* to adhere to, actually believe in, accept and assent to any of the philosophical positions of any of the characters.[49] Nor need we actually participate in their emotions and disturbances. Some sort and degree of imaginative entertainment is normally sufficient and necessary. Given that, a source of our respect for good drama is the balanced conduct of response and reflection it invites. There is to be *sophrosyne* in the good reader, in the good playgoer, whether the characters exhibit that virtue or not. And what became clear as I tried to bring the four dialogues together into one continuous Aristotelian action was that, with Socrates as the overwhelmingly dominant character, the theme of the play would be maintenance of *sophrosyne* itself, and the action, as a result, would be Simple. I need look for no Reversal of the Situation and for no Recognition. Socrates knows himself too well for redirective changes to take place. In fact, the force of Act Three, the *Crito,* comes from Socrates' calm resistance to very strong pressure for Reversal. As regards Recognition, we may be less certain. Socrates, in Plato's pages, never stops thinking; there is development throughout the *Phaedo.* The nearness of his death gives a living freshness to his view of the philosopher's attitude to it, as well as a heightened awareness that he is likely to be indulging in idle talk to encourage himself and his friends. Naturally the friends want to moan—the Achillean "desire to sorrow aloud" is strong within them. Parts of Socrates' discourse—stretches omitted in my play as dramatically inoperative—were probably a means chiefly of diverting if not distracting them. I had to cut them to let the action develop.

So too in Act Two, the *Apology:* I had to cut anything that could not be conveyed dramatically or that requires special knowledge if it is to be understood, such as the bulk of the cross-examination of Meletus. Most of these decisions did not seem doubtful or difficult; there were more than enough dramatically valid motions waiting to be used.

Time pressure, however, was troublesome. Total performance time for an unrehearsed reading over Station WGBH with parts distributed among eight readers was 73 minutes. My recollection is that some of it went too fast. Separate Acts, *read* and in a measure mimed, have been, I am told, fairly successful. As I took Socrates myself, I am in a poor position to judge. I have lively memories of doing Act One, the *Euthyphro,* with Dan Seltzer in the pulpit of the Old North Church in Boston. A lady afterward accused us of presenting an *irreligious* play. Local schools have seen readings of the other Acts: Two and Three are the easiest. I recall that, in my inexperience, I did not anticipate the queer sensations that nearly overcame me when I had drunk the poison.

Two topics in *Why So, Socrates?* invite comment: Socrates' attitudes to suicide and to Apollo.

In the *Phaedo* he comes very near to giving his audience at least a strong hint that he has deliberately used the verdict of the judges as a means for ending his life: "Maybe it is not unreasonable to say that a man must not kill himself until God sends some sort of compulsion on him like this that is upon me now." Certainly his behavior at the trial seems calculated to bring that verdict about. Even if Xenophon's explanation, forty years afterward, that Socrates provoked his own execution in order to escape the infirmities of old age be "absurd" (Taylor's description), it nonetheless shows that there had been people who wanted some such story. Infirmities, no, but there might be other reasons. Taylor and John Burnet hold that Socrates forced the judges' hands and point to the words that follow his sentence: "You are really killing me because I wouldn't say the sort of things you would have liked to hear. . . . I had much rather die after such a defense than live on after the other sort of defense. . . ." Something about this may remind us of Achilles on his twofold fate (indeed, a current Homerist presents Achilles as virtually willing his own death[50]). When the first judgment of the Court was announced, Socrates could see clearly that he had only to be modest and reasonable (in the judges' eyes) to have some light penalty replace that of death. Instead, his counterproposal was so infuriating that the balance against him leaped by eighty votes.

> Socrates: *I am not pained, men of Athens, that the vote has gone against me. For many reasons. Among them is the fact that I was not surprised. I am more surprised that there were not more votes against me. It seems that if thirty votes had gone the other way, I would have been acquitted.*
>
> *My accusers propose the punishment of death. What ought I to propose in its place? What I deserve, isn't that right? Well, what do I deserve? What ought I to undergo or pay—for never resting; for turning away from what most men care for: money and property, military office and public life; for keeping out of things in which I should have been no use to you or to myself and for giving myself up completely to doing the greatest possible good to every one of the citizens? I tried to make each of you care more about becoming better and wiser, than about what he can get, and to care more for the state itself than for its possessions. And what does a man like that deserve—a poor man too who needs time and support to do this for you? How about giving him his meals free in the Prytaneum as if he were a winner in the Olympic Games? That would be more to the point for me than for one of you who may have come in first in a chariot race. You don't need free meals, but I do. So if I am to suggest something to match what I deserve, here it is.*[51]

This is certainly asking for it. Why? The gentlest suggestion is devotion to a cause: in Socrates' eyes a cause so great and so sacred and so exacting that any accommodation, however slight, to the Great Beast would have seemed its betrayal. "Be soople, Davie, in things eemmaterial!" so his mentor advised David Balfour. To Socrates what happened at his trial was too material to admit of any yielding.

Just how serious Socrates is being is uncertain enough at enough points to make most judgments feel hazardous. It seems fitting to be in two minds, then, about his attitude to Delphi. No doubt his audience, and men of Athens generally, had good reasons for not regarding the oracle

with friendly or with trustful feelings. If so, the great play Socrates makes
with its answer to Chaerephon's question would be a sharp preliminary
irritant. Indeed his introductory injunction: "Don't cry out now and shut
me up if I tell you a very strange thing," shows that he knew he would
anger them. On the other hand, what he does to test the oracle—"Why
does he say I am the wisest of men? He can't be lying. Apollo can't do
that"—the tone of his references to his mission—"Men of Athens, I respect and love you, but I will do what the god says, not what you say"—
and other passages suggest that he feels in some peculiarly close relation
to Apollo. At the beginning of the *Phaedo*, when his friends visit him, it
appears that he has been writing verses, among them an ode to Apollo.
Later, at the central crisis of the discussion, when Simmias and Cebes are
whispering together,

> Socrates (noticing it all): *If you have difficulties, don't shrink
> from coming out with them and take me along with you, if you
> think I can help at all.*
> Simmias: *Socrates, here is the truth. For some time Cebes and I
> have been in doubt and each of us has been trying to get the other
> to ask you a question. We want your answer, but we didn't want
> to trouble you in view of your present misfortune.*
> Socrates (laughing gently): *Ah, Simmias, a hard time I would
> have with other people if I can't make even you two believe that
> this isn't to me a misfortune. You seem to think that I am more
> irritable than usual today. Evidently you take me as much less of
> a prophet than any swan, who, when he feels that he is going to
> die, sings his best in his joy at going to the god whose servant he
> is. Silly death-fearing men say the swans sing for sorrow, mourning
> their death. But no bird sings because it is hungry or cold or in
> trouble—no, not even the nightingale or the swallow, who, men
> say, sing for grief. No more do the swans. Being Apollo's birds,
> they have prophetic vision. And I myself, I think, am a fellow
> servant of the swans, belonging, I too, to Apollo. And I go out
> from life with as little sorrow. So ask what questions you please,
> for as long as the officers of the Athenians will allow it.*[52]

"Belonging, I too, to Apollo." Simmias clearly does not think this
merely whimsical. He says: "Either we must discover the truth, or, if that
is impossible, we must take whatever doctrine seems soundest and ride
through the seas of life on it as on a raft. That is, if we cannot sail more
safely upon some divine revelation."[53] Prophetic vision? Divine revelation? Some sort of heavenly inspiration? Socrates makes no further comment here and concerns himself with the arguments that Simmias and
Cebes advance. But there is the libation to some deity he would like to
pour. That might be what we could call mere piety: the sort of thing

Euthyphro knew all about. It hardly seems likely. And there are his last words: "Crito, we owe a cock to Asclepius. Don't forget!"[54] Asclepius, god of medicine (who may be curing Socrates of the disease of life), was son of Apollo, and the cock was sacred to both. These ritual acts can remind us, moreover, of the Homeric background from which the life and death of Socrates were so deeply a revolt and a departure.

---

1 *Gnomic Verses,* i.

2 William Blake, *Jerusalem.*

3 For a fuller discussion of this situation, *see* I. A. Richards, *Design for Escape,* paperback (New York: Harcourt, Brace & World, 1968).

4 C. K. Ogden, *Basic English: International Second Language,* ed. E. C. Graham (New York: Harcourt, Brace & World, 1968), includes his *Basic English, The ABC of Basic English,* and *The Basic Words.* E. C. Graham, ed., *Basic Dictionary of Science* (New York: Macmillan Co., 1966), published in England as *The Science Dictionary in Basic English* (London: Evans Brothers, 1965), and C. K. Ogden, comp., *The General Basic English Dictionary* (London: Evans Brothers, 1960) are invaluable resources in work with restricted forms of English.

5 K. S. Lashley, "The Problem of Serial Order in Behavior," in *The Hixon Symposium,* ed. Lloyd A. Jeffress (New York: John Wiley & Sons, 1951), pp. 121–22.

6 *GBWW,* Vol. 1, p. 76.

7 *GBWW,* Vols. 2–3. One would have thought that the virtues of this work, as pointing the way to—and, in fact, enabling—arrangements for making all wisdom available to all genuine inquirers, as the computer age advances, would have been by now far more widely and more effectively recognized than they are. How slow the world is to accept and take advantage of the help it most needs!

8 *GBWW,* Vol. 2, p. xxiv.

9 William Shakespeare, *King Lear,* act 4, sc. 1; *GBWW,* Vol. 27, p. 269d.

10 It is indeed, even in United States use, rather an odd term with odd episodes in its history and can serve as an illustration of my point above that a word's history can shape its powers without its users knowing that history. Harvard—then more a school than a college or a university—was looking for a successor to its first "Professor" (Nathaniel Eaton, sadistic tyrant, who had decamped with the funds: a grimly rich story for which consult chapter 17 of Samuel Eliot Morison's *The Founding of Harvard College* [Cambridge, Mass.: Harvard University Press, 1935]; on titles then current, *see* p. 200). Johann Amos Comenius (1592–1670) was the man chosen. He took too long, however, to make up his mind about it, and Harvard asked Henry Dunster of Magdalene College, Cambridge, to serve as a stopgap. He couldn't be "Professor" or "Master" (in case Comenius accepted), so another title was sought. At Magdalene we have a President whose duty in those days was to defend the Fellows against possibly tyrannic interferences from the Master. (He still supervises guests asked to the High Table and, theoretically, the Master only dines there by the President's invitation.) So Dunster became "President" of Harvard. He did so well in the end that this title was continued. People forgot why he was so styled, and in time it was only natural that the United States should follow Harvard in having a President. Whence so many other Presidents. No one, however, need know anything of this while recognizing the possible subtleties in uses of the word and the important role in Government that sitting can confer (and where you sit and on what: compare Chairman and Throne and the Stool of the African chief).

11 I. A. Richards, *Why So, Socrates?* A dramatic version in simple English of Plato's dialogues *Euthyphro, Apology, Crito, Phaedo* (Cambridge: The University Press, 1964), pp. 23–24.

12 After various revisions, through decades, finally published as *Plato's Republic* (Cambridge: The University Press, 1966). "It is usually assumed from the start that, keeping an original text in mind, there is going to be *something* queer about a version of it, whether a French version, or a shortened one, or a version leaning strongly

toward the views of Professor von Braun, or even a garbled version" (from John Hollander's delightfully discerning discussion, "Versions, Interpretations, Performances," in *On Translation,* ed. Reuben A. Brower [Cambridge, Mass.: Harvard University Press, 1959], p. 221). He adds (p. 222), "Whenever we accept or reject a version of a statement or text, we do so in full recognition of its particular bias or 'limited authority,' and never make the fact of the existence of such a bias a point of attack against it." I do hope this is so.

13 William Godwin, "Autobiographical Fragment," quoted in C. Kegan Paul, *William Godwin,* 2 vols. (1876), 1:76.

14 Alfred E. Taylor, *Plato, the Man and His Work* (New York: Dial Press, 1936), p. 48.

15 *The Wrath of Achilles: The Iliad of Homer,* paperback (New York: W. W. Norton & Co., 1950).

16 *Republic* 9. 590; cf. *GBWW,* Vol. 7, p. 426c.

17 *Republic* 9. 592; Ibid., p. 427b.

18 See *GBWW,* Vol. 7, pp. 142–48.

19 "One of the policies upon which the Advisory Board insisted most strongly was that the great writers should be allowed to speak for themselves. They should speak with their full voice and not be digested or mutilated by editorial decisions" (*GBWW,* Vol. 1, p. xx).

20 William Wordsworth, *The French Revolution, as It Appeared to Enthusiasts;* also in *The Prelude* 11. 1. 121.

21 Quoted in *GBWW,* Vol. 1, p. 47.

22 *Republic* 2. 368; *GBWW,* Vol. 7, p. 316a.

23.*Republic* 4. 435; Ibid., p. 350c.

24 *Republic* 6. 510–11; Ibid., p. 387a–d.

25 *Republic* 7. 533; Ibid., p. 397c–d.

26 Quoted in *The Practical Cogitator,* ed. Charles P. Curtis and Ferris Greenslet, (Boston: Houghton Mifflin Co., 1945), p. 553.

27 *Republic* 8. 565–69; *GBWW,* Vol. 7, pp. 413d–416a.

28 In fact, the worst that has come so far was from no less a figure than Sir Richard Livingstone himself (cf. *GBWW,* Vol. 1, p. 48). He wrote me, in a kind and most indulgent letter, that I was playing Beethoven on the harmonium. I was not alarmed or surprised. My version had been doing a thousand things which in terms of scholarly and pedagogical orthodoxy in these days are not done.

29 *Republic* 6. 506; *GBWW,* Vol. 7, p. 385a.

30 *GBWW,* Vol. 7, pp. 191–251.

31 "Seven *Agamemnons*" in *On Translation,* ed. Reuben A. Brower, p. 171. His essay demonstrates this dependence most persuasively. Many other essays in his volume are highly pertinent to our theme. And it has an admirable bibliography.

32 *Poetics* 6; *GBWW,* Vol. 9, p. 684b.

33 *Poetics* 6; Ibid., p. 684d.

34 *GBWW,* Vol. 27, pp. 103–41.

35 *GBWW,* Vol. 7 pp. 325b–326a and 432b–433c.

36 *Poetics* 10; *GBWW,* Vol. 9, p. 686d.

37 *Poetics* 11; Ibid., p. 687a.

38 *Poetics* 6; Ibid., p. 684a.

39 *GBWW,* Vol. 4, p. 176d.

40 *Republic* 2. 379; *GBWW,* Vol. 7, p. 322b.

41 *Republic* 6. 492–93; Ibid., pp. 377d–378a.

42 *Republic* 6. 493; Ibid., p. 378b–c.

43 See p. 298 above.

44 *Euthyphro* 5; *GBWW,* Vol. 7, p. 193a.

45 *Euthyphro* 6; Ibid., p. 193c.

46 *Euthyphro* 11; Ibid., p. 196a–b.

47 Taylor, *Plato, the Man and His Work,* p. 149.

48 *GBWW,* Vol. 3, pp. 957–64.

49 I am by no means securely convinced that this is true for most of the meanings of *adhere* and its synonyms, and I would hold the matter to be philosophically indeterminate unless and until these meanings become far clearer. There are, of course, schools and movements in the theater that will think such remarks much out-of-date.

50 "It is safe to say that the baffling vision of self-destruction with eternal glory was native to Greek air, and that Homer was the first to frame it in the symbols of poetry and canonize it for the succeeding ages of the Hellenic, and especially the Athenian mind" (Cedric Whitman, *Homer and the Heroic Tradition* [Cambridge: Harvard University Press, 1958], p. 220).

51 *Apology* 36; *GBWW*, Vol. 7, p. 209b–c.

52 *Phaedo* 84–85; Ibid., pp. 234d–235a.

53 *Phaedo* 85; Ibid., p. 235b.

54 *Phaedo* 118; Ibid., 251d.

NOTE TO THE READER

Most of the articles that appear in *GIT* are to some extent commentaries on the Great Books. This essay by I. A. Richards recounts one man's experience in reading certain of those books and tells us of his efforts as a teacher to make them intelligible and appealing to others. Richards's view of Homer and the way to render him is not as different as it may first seem from that of Matthew Arnold, which appears elsewhere in this volume. Both the Arnold and the Richards pieces may be compared with Virginia Woolf's essay "How Should One Read a Book?" and with Sainte-Beuve's "What Is a Classic?" both of which are reprinted in *GGB*, Vol. 5.

PART FOUR

Additions to the Great Books Library

Robert M. Hutchins

Preliminary Draft of a
World Constitution

Editor's Introduction

At the end of the Second World War, after two atomic bombs had been used to destroy the Japanese cities of Hiroshima and Nagasaki, certain members of the faculty of the University of Chicago, mindful of the crucial role the university had played in the development of such weapons—a role manifest in, among other things, the existence of its Institute for Nuclear Studies—proposed to the chancellor of the university, Robert M. Hutchins, that a parallel Institute for World Government be established. "The intellectual courage that split the atom should be called upon to unite the world," they wrote. As a result of their suggestion, what became known as the Committee to Frame a World Constitution was formed and given the task indicated by its name. Besides Hutchins himself, who acted as chairman, the members of this committee, all but one of whom ultimately signed the document that follows, included six members of the Chicago faculty: G. A. Borgese, who served as committee secretary, Mortimer J. Adler, Richard McKeon, Wilber G. Katz, Robert Redfield, and Rexford Guy Tugwell. There were also five members from other institutions: Stringfellow Barr (St. John's College), Albert L. Guérard (Stanford), Harold Innis (Toronto), Erich Kahler (Cornell), and Charles McIlwain (Harvard). Among the disciplines represented were anthropology (Redfield), law (Katz), government (McIlwain), history (Barr), letters (Guérard), and philosophy (Adler and McKeon). In addition, Innis brought special knowledge of the British Commonwealth, Tugwell wide experience in economic planning.

The committee met in various parts of the country for two or three days at a time on thirteen different occasions between November 1945 and July 1947. With the help of a staff of associates, it produced at least 150 working papers, amounting in all to perhaps 4,500 pages, which were circulated among its members. Of these papers, the 141st, considered at the thirteenth and last meeting of the committee as a whole, was in substance the draft that was finally accepted. This was published in the magazine *Common Cause* in March 1948, was immediately reprinted by the *Saturday Review of Literature* and the *Bulletin of the Atomic Scientists,* and subsequently appeared in various editions and in several languages throughout the world.

While the members of the committee sought to frame and did frame the model of single world federation, and while this required that their work embody principles to which the whole human race could at least in theory subscribe, no attempt was made to reconcile differences among existing regimes and constitutions. Indeed, care was taken to avoid the appearance of imposing a single political system upon mankind. The committee did not seek to replace all national and local governments, even hypothetically, but to transcend them. The one absolute and comprehensive change it contemplated in human affairs was the abolition of war.

Predictably, perhaps, the chief criticism leveled against the draft upon its publication, apart from questions that were raised about particular features of it, was that the whole scheme seemed utopian: it was said that the idea was a good one but that the times were not ripe for a federation of the sort that was envisaged. There were those, too, who protested that even if such a government were possible, it would violate hallowed concepts of sovereignty and nationhood as well as traditional parliamentary institutions.

The members of the committee did not suppose their work would be accepted fully. As Hutchins wrote, they "never thought that they could be remembered some day as the Committee that Framed *the* World Constitution." Rather, he said:

> *Their ambition or hope was and is to do their part in taking down to earth or, so to speak, spelling out, the general movement for World Government that has been growing, not always in definite shape, during these years. The problems of World Government are hard and intricate. The Committee felt that these problems can be best clarified in a constitutional design, intended as a concrete picture to show what a Federal Republic of the World, under certain conceivable circumstances, might look like.*

The document they produced is reprinted here because it is relevant to the discussion of the World Community in Part One, and because it is referred to at some length in the essay by Jacques Maritain that follows. For commentary on the draft's provisions, the reader is invited to consult an earlier reprint edited by Elisabeth Mann Borgese and published by the Center for the Study of Democratic Institutions under the title *A Constitution for the World* (1965).

CONTENTS

---

* Disappearing clauses and articles, on pp. 335, 336, 337, 338, 342, and 344, are within brackets.

Preliminary Draft of a World Constitution

Preamble

The people of the earth having agreed
　　that the advancement of man
in spiritual excellence and physical welfare
is the common goal of mankind;
　　that universal peace is the prerequisite
for the pursuit of that goal;
　　that justice in turn is the prerequisite of peace,
and peace and justice stand or fall together;
　　that iniquity and war inseparably spring
from the competitive anarchy of the national states;
　　that therefore the age of nations must end,
and the era of humanity begin;

the governments of the nations have decided
　　to order their separate sovereignties
in one government of justice,
to which they surrender their arms;
　　and to establish, as they do establish,
this Constitution
as the covenant and fundamental law
of the Federal Republic of the World.

Declaration of Duties and Rights

A

The universal government of justice as covenanted and pledged in this Constitution is founded on the Rights of Man.

The principles underlying the Rights of Man are and shall be permanently stated in the Duty

of everyone everywhere, whether a citizen sharing in the responsibilities and privileges of World Government or a ward and pupil of the World Commonwealth:

to serve with word and deed, and with productive labor according to his ability, the spiritual and physical advancement of the living and of those to come, as the common cause of all generations of men;

to do unto others as he would like others to do unto him;

to abstain from violence,

except for the repulse of violence as commanded or granted under law.

B

In the context therefore of social duty and service, and in conformity with the unwritten law which philosophies and religions alike called the Law of Nature and which the Republic of the World shall strive to see universally written and enforced by positive law:

it shall be the right of everyone everywhere to claim and maintain for himself and his fellowmen:

release from the bondage of poverty and from the servitude and exploitation of labor, with rewards and security according to merit and needs;

freedom of peaceful assembly and of association, in any creed or party or craft, within the pluralistic unity and purpose of the World Republic;

protection of individuals and groups against subjugation and tyrannical rule, racial or national, doctrinal or cultural, with safeguards for the self-determination of minorities and dissenters;

and any such other freedoms and franchises as are inherent in man's inalienable claims to life, liberty, and the dignity of the human person, and as the legislators and judges of the World Republic shall express and specify.

C

The four elements of life—earth, water, air, energy—are the common property of the human race. The management and use of such portions thereof as are vested in or assigned to particular ownership, private or corporate or national or regional, of definite or indefinite tenure, of individualist or collectivist economy, shall be subordinated in each and all cases to the interest of the common good.

Grant of Powers

1

The jurisdiction of the World Government as embodied in its organs of power shall extend to:

a) The control of the observance of the Constitution in all the component communities and territories of the Federal World Republic, which shall be indivisible and one;

b) The furtherance and progressive fulfillment of the Duties and Rights of Man in the spirit of the foregoing Declaration, with their specific enactment in such fields of federal and local relations as are described hereinafter [Art. 27 through 33];

c) The maintenance of peace; and to that end the enactment and promulgation of laws which shall be binding upon communities and upon individuals as well,

d) the judgment and settlement of any conflicts among component units, with prohibition of recourse to interstate violence,

e) the supervision of and final decision on any alterations of boundaries between states or unions thereof,

f) the supervision of and final decision on the forming of new states or unions thereof,

g) the administration of such territories as may still be immature for self-government, and the declaration in due time of their eligibility therefor,

h) the intervention in intrastate violence and violations of law which affect world peace and justice,

i) the organization and disposal of the federal armed forces,

j) the limitation and control of weapons and of the domestic militias in the several component units of the World Republic;

k) The establishment, in addition to the Special Bodies listed hereinafter [Art. 8 and 9], of such other agencies as may be conducive to the development of the earth's resources and to the advancement of physical and intellectual standards, with such advisory or initiating or arbitrating powers as shall be determined by law;

l) The laying and collecting of federal taxes, and the establishment of a plan and a budget for federal expenditures,

m) the administration of the World Bank and the establishment of suitable world fiscal agencies for the issue of money and the creation and control of credit,

n) the regulation of commerce affected with federal interest,

o) the establishment, regulation, and where necessary or desirable, the operation of means of transportation and communication which are of federal interest;

p) The supervision and approval of laws concerning emigration and immigration and the movements of peoples,

q) the granting of federal passports;

r) The appropriation, under the right of eminent domain, of such private or public property as may be necessary for federal use, reasonable compensation being made therefor;

s) The legislation over and administration of the territory which shall be chosen as Federal District and of such other territories as may be entrusted directly to the Federal Government.

2

The powers not delegated to the World Government by this Constitution, and not prohibited by it to the several members of the Federal World Republic, shall be reserved to the several states or nations or unions thereof.

The Federal Convention, The President, The Legislature

3

The sovereignty of the Federal Republic of the World resides in the people of the world. The primary powers of the World Government shall be vested in:

a) the Federal Convention,

b) the President,

c) the Council and the Special Bodies,

d) the Grand Tribunal, the Supreme Court, and the Tribune of the People,

e) the Chamber of Guardians.

4

The Federal Convention shall consist of delegates elected directly by the people of all states and nations, one delegate for each

million of population or fraction thereof above one-half million, with the proviso that the people of any extant state, recognized as sovereign in 1945, and ranging between 100,000 and 1,000,000, shall be entitled to elect one delegate, but any such state with a population below 100,000 shall be aggregated for federal electoral purposes to the electoral unit closest to its borders.

The delegates to the Federal Convention shall vote as individuals, not as members of national or otherwise collective representations; [except as specified hereinafter, Art. 46, paragraph 2, and Art. 47].

The Convention shall meet in May of every third year, for a session of thirty days.

5

The Federal Convention shall subdivide into nine Electoral Colleges according to the nine Societies of kindred nations and cultures, or Regions, wherefrom its members derive their powers, such Regions being:

1) the continent of Europe and its islands outside the Russian area, together with the United Kingdom if the latter so decides, and with such overseas English- or French- or Cape Dutch-speaking communities of the British Commonwealth of Nations or the French Union as decide to associate (this whole area here tentatively denominated *Europa*);

2) the United States of America, with the United Kingdom if the latter so decides, and such kindred communities of British, or Franco-British, or Dutch-British, or Irish civilization and lineage as decide to associate (*Atlantis*);

3) Russia, European and Asiatic, with such East-Baltic or Slavic or South-Danubian nations as associate with Russia (*Eurasia*);

4) the Near and Middle East, with the states of North Africa, and Pakistan if the latter so decides (*Afrasia*);

5) *Africa*, south of the Sahara, with or without the South African Union as the latter may decide;

6) *India*, with Pakistan if the latter so decides;

7) China, Korea, Japan, with the associate archipelagoes of the North- and Mid-Pacific (*Asia Major*);

8) Indochina and Indonesia, with Pakistan if the latter so decides, and with such other Mid- and South-Pacific lands and islands as decide to associate (*Austrasia*);

9) the Western Hemisphere south of the United States (*Columbia*).

Each Electoral College shall nominate by secret ballot not more than three candidates, regardless of origin, for the office of President of the World Republic. The Federal Convention in plenary meeting, having selected by secret ballot a panel of three candidates from the lists submitted, shall elect by secret ballot one of the three as President, on a majority of two-thirds.

If three consecutive ballots have been indecisive, the candidate with the smallest vote shall be eliminated and between the two remaining candidates a simple majority vote shall be decisive.

6

Each Electoral College shall then nominate by secret and proportional ballot twenty-seven candidates, originating from the respective Electoral Area or Region, for the World Council; with the proviso that one-third and not more than one-third of the nominees shall not be members of the Federal Convention; and the nine lists having been presented to the Federal Convention, the Federal Convention in plenary meeting shall select by secret and proportional ballot nine Councilmen from each list, with the same proviso as above.

The Federal Convention shall also elect by secret and proportional ballot, on nominations, prior to the opening of the Convention, by such organizations, of worldwide importance and lawfully active in more than three Regions, as shall be designated [for the first election by the United Nations Assembly and subsequently] by the Council, eighteen additional members, regardless of origin; and the total membership of the World Council shall be thus ninety-nine.

7

The primary power to initiate and enact legislation for the Federal Republic of the World shall be vested in the Council.

The tenure of the Council shall be three years.

The Council shall elect its Chairman, for its whole tenure of three years.

Councilors shall be re-eligible.

8

Within the first three years of World Government the Council and the President shall establish three Special Bodies, namely:

a) a House of Nationalities and States, with representatives from each, for the safeguarding of local institutions and autonomies and the protection of minorities;

b) a Syndical or functional Senate, for the representation of syndicates and unions or occupational associations and any other corporate interests of transnational significance, as well as for mediation or arbitration in non-justiciable issues among such syndicates or unions or other corporate interests;

c) an Institute of Science, Education, and Culture;

each of the three bodies with such membership and tenures and consultative or preparatory powers as shall be established by law and with no prejudice to the establishment of other advisory or technical agencies in accordance with the purposes stated hereinbefore [Art. 1, *k*].

9

Within its first year the World Government shall establish a Special Body, to be named Planning Agency, of twenty-one members appointed by the President, subject to vetoes by two-thirds of the Council, for tenures of twelve years, [except that the terms for the initial membership shall be staggered by lot, with one-third of it, seven members, ceasing from office and being replaced every fourth year].

It shall be the function of the Planning Agency to envisage the income of the Federal Government and to prepare programs and budgets for expenditures, both for current needs and for long-range improvements. These programs and budgets shall be submitted by the President, with his recommendations, to the Council, as provided hereinafter [Art. 13].

Plans for improvement of the world's physical facilities, either public or private, and for the productive exploitation of resources and inventions shall be submitted to the Agency or to such Development Authorities or regional subagencies as it may establish. The Agency shall pass judgment on the social usefulness of such plans.

Members of the Planning Agency shall not be re-eligible nor shall they, during their tenure in the Agency, have membership in any other federal body.

10

The executive power, together with initiating power in federal legislation, shall be vested in the President. His tenure shall be six years.

The President shall not have membership in the Council.

The President shall not be re-eligible. He shall not be eligible to the Tribunate of the People until nine years have elapsed since the expiration of his term.

No two successive Presidents shall originate from the same Region.

11

The President shall appoint a Chancellor. The Chancellor, with the approval of the President, shall appoint the Cabinet.

The Chancellor shall act as the President's representative before the Council in the exercise of legislative initiative. The Chancellor and the Cabinet members shall have at any time the privilege of the floor before the Council.

But no Chancellor or Cabinet member shall have a vote or shall hold membership in the Council, nor, if he was a member of the Council at the moment of his executive appointment, shall he be entitled to resume his seat therein when leaving the executive post unless he be re-elected at a subsequent Convention.

No one shall serve as Chancellor for more than six years, nor as Cabinet member for more than twelve, consecutive or not.

No three Cabinet members at any one time and no two successive Chancellors shall originate from the same Region.

The Council shall have power to interrogate the Chancellor and the Cabinet and to adopt resolutions on their policies.

The Chancellor and the Cabinet shall resign when the President so decides or when a vote of no confidence by the absolute majority of fifty or more of the Council is confirmed by a second such vote; but no second vote shall be taken and held valid if less than three months have elapsed from the first.

12

The sessions of the Council, as well as those of the Grand Tribunal and the Supreme Court, shall be continuous, except for one yearly recess of not more than ten weeks or two such recesses of not more than five weeks each, as the body concerned may decide.

13

The budget of the World Government, upon recommendation by the Planning Agency, shall be presented every three years by the President to the Council, which shall pass it, or reject it in whole titles, by majority vote; the same procedure to apply when at other intervals the President requests additional appropriations or approval of changes.

14

Any legislation of the Council can be vetoed by the President within thirty days of its passage. But the Council can overrule the veto if its new vote, by a majority of two-thirds, finds support, within sixty days of the President's action, in the majority of the Grand Tribunal; [and no such support shall be required during the tenure of the first President].

15

The President can be impeached on grounds of treason to the Constitution, or usurpation of power, or felony, or insanity, or other disease impairing permanently his mind.

The vote of impeachment shall be final when three-quarters of the Council and three-quarters of the Grand Tribunal concur and the majority of the Supreme Court validates the legality of the proceedings.

If a President is impeached or resigns or dies in the interval between two sessions of the Federal Convention, the Chairman of the Council shall become Acting President until the new Convention elects a new President; and the Council shall elect a new Chairman.

The Grand Tribunal and The Supreme Court

16

The supreme judiciary power of the World Republic shall be vested in a Grand Tribunal of sixty Justices, with the President of the World Republic as Chief Justice and Chairman, and the Chairman of the Council as Vice-Chairman ex officio.

The President as Chief Justice shall appoint the Justices of the Grand Tribunal and fill the vacancies, subject to vetoes by the Council on majorities of two-thirds. He shall have power to overrule any such veto if he finds support in a two-thirds majority of the Justices in office, [except that no

such power shall be vested in the first President].

No one, except the Chairman of the Council, shall hold membership at the same time in the Council and the Tribunal; nor shall a Chancellor or Cabinet member hold membership in the Tribunal or be eligible to it until six years have elapsed from the termination of his executive office.

17

The tenure of the Chief Justice and Chairman and of the Vice-Chairman of the Grand Tribunal shall be the time of their tenure of office respectively as President of the World Republic and as Chairman of the Council.

The President shall have power to appoint an Alternate, subject to approval by the Grand Tribunal, for the exercise of such of his functions in the judiciary branch and for such a time within his tenure as he may decide.

The tenures of the sixty Justices shall be fifteen years, [except that the terms for the initial membership shall be staggered by lot, with one-fifth of it, twelve Justices, ceasing from office and being replaced every third year].

Justices of the Grand Tribunal shall not be re-eligible, except that a Justice appointed as Chancellor or Cabinet member, having resigned his membership in the Tribunal, shall be re-eligible to it for the unfulfilled portion of his tenure when six years have elapsed from the termination of his executive office.

18

The sixty Justices shall be assigned twelve to each of five Benches:

the First Bench to deal with constitutional issues between the primary organs and powers of the World Government as well as with all issues and cases in which the Tribune of the People shall decide to appear in his capacity of World Attorney and defender of the Rights of Man;

the Second Bench to deal with issues and

conflicts between the World Government and any of its component units, whether single states or unions thereof or Regions, as well as with issues and conflicts of component units of the World Republic among themselves;

the Third Bench to deal with issues and conflicts between the World Government and individual citizens or corporations or unions or any other associations of citizens;

the Fourth Bench to deal with issues and conflicts among component units, whether single states or unions of states or Regions, and individual citizens or corporations or unions or any other associations of citizens when such issues and conflicts affect the interpretation or enactment of federal law;

the Fifth Bench to deal with issues and conflicts, when they affect the interpretation and enactment of federal law, either among individual citizens or among corporations, unions, syndicates, or any other collective organizations of citizens and interests.

Each Region shall be represented in each Bench by at least one member and not more than two.

19

The Supreme Court shall be of seven members: five representing one each Bench, with the Chief Justice as their Chairman and the Chairman of the Council as their Vice-Chairman ex officio; and the active membership of the Benches shall thus remain of eleven each.

No two members of the Supreme Court shall originate from the same Region.

The representatives of the Benches in the Supreme Court shall be elected by secret vote of the Grand Tribunal in plenary session, with each Justice casting a ballot for five candidates, one from each Bench, and with those candidates elected who have obtained the largest vote, except that any presumptive electee shall be held ineligible whose assignment to the Court would duplicate the representation therein of any one Region or Bench.

If the first vote fails to fill all seats, the vote shall be repeated according to the same regulations.

The tenures of the members of the Supreme Court shall be: for the Chairman and Vice-Chairman the same as their tenures of office respectively as President of the World Republic and as Chairman of the Council, and for the other members six years, at the end of which each of the five elected by the Grand Tribunal may be re-elected or shall be restored to the Bench whereof he was the delegate; but no Justice shall sit in the Court beyond his regular term of membership in the Tribunal; and when the latter term expires before the regular six-year term in the Court is completed, or when an elective member of the Court resigns or dies, the Grand Tribunal shall fill the vacancy for the unfulfilled portion of the term by secret partial election in plenary session, with the same proviso as above in regard to the representation of Regions.

Regions which have not been represented in the Supreme Court for two successive six-year terms shall have mandatory precedence in the elections for the third term.

20

The Supreme Court shall distribute the cases among the five Benches of the Grand Tribunal according to competences as specified hereinbefore [Art. 18].

Cases where competences overlap or are otherwise doubtful shall be referred to such Bench or Benches jointly as the Supreme Court shall decide.

The Supreme Court shall have power to modify the rules of assignment for the five Benches as specified in Art. 18, subject to approval by the majority of the Council and by a two-thirds majority of the Grand Tribunal concurrently.

21

It shall be the office and function of the Supreme Court to review the decisions of the Benches, within three months of their issuance, said decisions to become effective upon registration by the Court, or, when annulled, to be returned for revision each to the Bench which judged the case, or to another, or to others jointly as the Court may decide; annulment to be pronounced in cases of unfair trial or faulty procedure, and also for reasons of substance when final appeal was filed by the losing party, if the Court at its own discretion choose to take cognizance thereof, or by the Tribune of the People, whose demand shall be mandatory.

22

The Grand Tribunal, with the approval of the Supreme Court, shall establish Lower Federal Courts in such number and places as conditions in the component units of the World Republic shall require, and a Federal Appellate Court in each Region. It shall also determine the rules and competences of such courts and appoint their officials on the basis of competitive examinations.

23

The President or his Alternate and the Chairman of the Council shall not sit as judges in cases affecting the solution of conflicts between the President and the Council.

The President or Acting President or Alternate, or a Justice or the Chairman of the Council in his capacity of Justice, shall not sit as a judge in cases involving his appointment or impeachment or demotion or tenure or in any other way affecting his particular interest.

24

No member of the Council or the Grand Tribunal shall be liable to removal from office until a criminal sentence on charges of felony or grave misdemeanor is final. But he shall be suspended from office, pending last recourse to the Grand Tribunal, when a sentence of guilty, issued by a lower court, has been confirmed by a Federal Appellate Court.

The Supreme Court shall pronounce final judgment on the legality of the proceedings. It shall also pronounce final judgment on

the legal validity of elections and appointments to the Council and the Tribunal, and to the offices of President and of Tribune of the People.

25

The President in his capacity of World Chief Justice shall have power of pardon over sentences passed under federal law.

The Tribune of the People and The World Law

26

The Federal Convention, after electing the Council, shall elect by secret ballot the Tribune of the People as a spokesman for the minorities, this office to be vested in the candidate obtaining the second largest vote among the eligible candidates; ineligible to the office of Tribune being any candidate having also been nominated by any Electoral College for the office of President in the current Convention, or having been a President or Acting President or Alternate or a member of the Grand Tribunal at any time in the nine years preceding said Convention, or originating from the same Region as the President simultaneously in office.

The Tribune of the People shall not have membership in the Council.

The tenure of the Tribune of the People shall be three years. He shall have power to appoint a Deputy, subject to the same ineligibilities as above, with tenure to expire not later than his own.

He shall not be re-eligible, nor shall he be eligible to the office of President or Alternate or Justice of the Grand Tribunal, until nine years have elapsed from the expiration of his present term.

The Tribune, or his appointed Deputy, shall have the privilege of the floor before the Grand Tribunal and, under such regulations as shall be established by law, before the Supreme Court; but no vote in either; and he shall not be present when a vote is taken.

27

It shall be the office and function of the Tribune of the People to defend the natural and civil rights of individuals and groups against violation or neglect by the World Government or any of its component units; to further and demand, as a World Attorney before the World Republic, the observance of the letter and spirit of this Constitution; and to promote thereby, in the spirit of its Preamble and Declaration of Duties and Rights, the attainment of the goals set to the progress of mankind by the efforts of the ages.

28

No law shall be made or held valid in the World Republic or any of its component units:

1) inflicting or condoning discrimination against race or nation or sex or caste or creed or doctrine; or

2) barring through preferential agreements or coalitions of vested interests the access on equal terms of any state or nation to the raw materials and the sources of energy of the earth; or

3) establishing or tolerating slavery, whether overt or covert, or forced labor, except as equitable expiation endured in state or federal controlled institutions and intended for social service and the rehabilitation of the convicted criminal; or

4) permitting, whether by direction or indirection, arbitrary seizure or search, or unfair trial, or excessive penalty, or application of ex post facto laws; or

5) abridging in any manner whatsoever, except as a punishment inflicted by law for criminal transgression, the citizen's exercise of such responsibilities and privileges of citizenship as are conferred on him by law; or

6) curtailing the freedom of communication and information, of speech, of the press, and of expression by whatever means, of peaceful assembly, of travel;

paragraphs 5 and 6 to be subject to sus-pension according to circumstances, universally or locally, in time of emergency imperiling the maintenance and unity of the World Republic; such state of emergency, world-wide or local, to be proposed by the Chamber of Guardians and proclaimed concurrently by a two-thirds majority of the Council and a two-thirds majority of the Grand Tribunal for a period not in excess of six months, to be renewable on expiration with the same procedure for successive periods of six months or less but in no case beyond the date when the time of emergency is proclaimed closed, on the proposal of the Chamber of Guardians by simple majority votes of the Council and of the Grand Tribunal concurrently or, if the Guardians' proposal is deemed unduly delayed, by three-quarters majority votes of the Council and of the Grand Tribunal concurrently.

29

Capital punishment shall not be inflicted under federal law.

30

Old age pensions, unemployment relief, insurance against sickness or accident, just terms of leisure, and protection to maternity and infancy shall be provided according to the varying circumstances of times and places as the local law may direct.

Communities and states unable to provide adequate social security and relief shall be assisted by the Federal Treasury, whose grants or privileged loans shall be administered under federal supervision.

31

Every child from the age of six to the age of twelve shall be entitled to instruction and education at public expense, such primary six-year period to be obligatory and further education to be accessible to all without discrimination of age or sex or race or class or creed.

Communities and states unable to fulfill this obligation shall be assisted by the Federal Treasury with the same proviso as in Art. 30.

32

All property or business whose management and use have acquired the extension and character of a federal public service or whereon restrictive trade practices have conferred the character and power of a transnational monopoly, shall become the property of the Federal Government upon payment of a just price as determined by law.

33

Every individual or group or community shall have the right of appeal against unjust application of a law, or against the law itself, gaining access through the inferior courts, local or federal, to the superior and the Grand Tribunal, and securing the counsel and support of the Tribune of the People when the Tribune so decides; and, if a law or statute is found evidently in conflict with the guarantees pledged in the foregoing articles or irreparably in contradiction with the basic principles and intents of the World Republic as stated in the Preamble to this Constitution and in its Declaration of Duties and Rights, the Grand Tribunal shall have power to recommend to the Supreme Court that such law or statute be declared, and the Supreme Court shall have power to declare it, null and void.

34

The Tribune of the People cannot be impeached except on the same grounds and with the same procedure as specified for the President in Art. 15.

If the Tribune of the People is impeached or resigns or dies, his substitute for the unfulfilled portion of his tenure shall be the candidate to the Tribunate who was next in line in the last Federal Convention, with the same provisos in regard to eligibility as in Art. 26, first paragraph.

The Chamber of Guardians

35

The control and use of the armed forces of the Federal Republic of the World shall be assigned exclusively to a Chamber of Guardians under the chairmanship of the President, in his capacity of Protector of the Peace. The other Guardians shall be six Councilmen elected by the Council and the Grand Tribunal in Congress assembled, for terms of three years. [But the Grand Tribunal shall not participate in the first election.]

One former President shall also sit in the Chamber of Guardians, the sequence to be determined term for term, or, if he resign or die, for the fractional term, according to seniority in the presidential office; he shall have the privilege of the floor in the deliberations of the Chamber, but no vote in its decisions.

Officers holding professional or active rank in the armed forces of the Federal Republic, or in the domestic militia of any component unit thereof, shall not be eligible as Guardians.

36

The election of the six elective Guardians shall be by secret and proportional vote, with each Elector casting a ballot of six names or less; but no three Guardians of the seven, including the President and excluding the ex-President, shall originate from the same Region; and any presumptive electee whose election would contravene this norm shall be declared ineligible and replaced by the candidate fulfilling the norm and having obtained the next largest vote.

Regions which have not been represented among the seven Guardians referred to above, for two successive three-year terms, shall have mandatory precedence in the subsequent elections; but the Guardian or Guardians originating from a nation or Region where sedition against the World Republic is actual or, according to the majority of the Chamber, imminently expected, shall cease from office and be replaced; unless the other Guardians decide unanimously otherwise.

No Guardian can be impeached or in any way suspended or removed from office for any other reason, except on such grounds and with such procedure as specified for the President and the Tribune of the People hereinbefore [Art. 15 and 34], and for the Guardians hereinafter [Art. 38].

If a Guardian resigns or dies or is in any way suspended or removed, his substitute for the unfulfilled portion of the term shall be chosen by partial election, with the same rules and provisos as in the first two paragraphs of this article, each elector casting a ballot of one or more names as the number of vacancies may be.

37

The Chancellor shall have access to the Chamber of Guardians as Deputy of the President, whose vote he shall cast by proxy if the President so decides.

38

Appropriations for the budget of Peace and Defense, under control of the Chamber of Guardians, as proposed by the Chamber at the beginning of each term for the whole duration thereof, shall be submitted by the President to the Council, in conformity with Art. 13. But if a state of emergency is declared, in the manner and limits as specified hereinbefore [Art. 28, last paragraph], the Chamber shall have power to demand and appropriate such additional funds as the emergency demands, subject to auditing and sanction by the Council when the emergency is closed; whereafter, if sanction is denied, the Guardians responsible shall be liable to impeachment and prosecution for usurpation of power with the same procedure as specified for the President and the Tribune of the People hereinbefore [Art. 15 and 34].

39

The Chamber shall have power to propose by absolute majority, subject to approval by two-thirds majority votes of the Council and of the Grand Tribunal concurrently, extraordinary powers, world-wide or local, to be conferred on the President beyond those assigned to him by this Constitution, when a state of emergency, as provided in Art. 28, is proclaimed; such powers not to be granted for periods exceeding six months each and to be relinquished before the expiration of any such period as soon as the state of emergency, in conformity with Art. 28, is proclaimed closed.

40

The Chamber of Guardians shall answer interrogations from the Council on its general and administrative directives, but no vote shall be taken after discussion thereof, except as otherwise provided in Art. 28 and 39; and the decisions of the Chamber in matters technical and strategic shall be final, and withheld from publicity when the Chamber so decides.

41

The Chamber of Guardians, assisted by a General Staff and an Institute of Technology whose members it shall appoint, shall determine the technological and the numerical level that shall be set as limits to the domestic militias of the single communities and states or unions thereof.

Armed forces and the manufacture of armaments beyond the levels thus determined shall be reserved to the World Government.

The Federal Capital and Federal Language and Standards

42

Within one year of its foundation the World Republic shall choose a Federal Capital, or a site therefor, with eminent domain over it and an adequate Federal District.

43

Within three years of its foundation the Federal Government shall designate one language, which shall be standard for the formulation and interpretation of the federal laws; and for analogous purposes, relative to communication, taxation and finances, it shall establish in its first year a federal unit of currency with a federal system of measures and a federal calendar.

The Amending Power

44

Amendments to this Constitution, recommended concurrently by a two-thirds majority of the Council and of the Grand Tribunal, shall be in force when approved by a two-thirds majority of the Federal Convention in the Constitutional Session following the recommendation.

Constitutional Sessions, of thirty days or less, as the discussion may require and the majority may decide, shall be held immediately after the ordinary electoral session in the third Federal Convention and thereafter every ninth year.

[But no amendment altering the electoral units as listed in Art. 5, or the assignment to them of seats in the Council and the other federal bodies, shall be recommended to the first of such Sessions.]

[Ratification and Preliminary Period

45

The first Federal Convention shall be the Founding Convention.

The ratio of representation therein shall be based on the world population figures as ascertained or authoritatively approximated in 1948.

The ways and means for the convocation of the Founding Convention, and the regulations for its inaugural and voting procedures, shall be determined by the General Assembly of the United Nations.

46

The thirty-day electoral session of the Founding Convention shall be preceded by a preliminary session of thirty days or less for the discussion and approval of this Constitution, such preliminary session to be extended for thirty additional days or less as the discussion may require and the majority may decide.

The delegates to the Founding Convention shall vote individually, and not by delegations; except on the assignment to the nine Electoral Colleges or Regions of such optional states or zones as listed hereinbefore [Art. 5]; in which matter the vote of the majority, within the delegation from the state or zone concerned, shall be binding upon the minority; and Art. 5 shall be adjusted accordingly.

47

The Founding Convention having discussed and approved by individual majority vote this Constitution, ratification by collective majorities within as many delegations of states and nations as represent two-thirds of the population of the earth, shall be sufficient for the establishment of the Federal Republic of the World.]

THE COMMITTEE TO FRAME A WORLD CONSTITUTION

ROBERT M. HUTCHINS, *President*
G. A. BORGESE, *Secretary*

MORTIMER J. ADLER
STRINGFELLOW BARR
ALBERT GUÉRARD

HAROLD A. INNIS
ERICH KAHLER
WILBUR G. KATZ
CHARLES H. MCILWAIN
ROBERT REDFIELD
REXFORD GUY TUGWELL

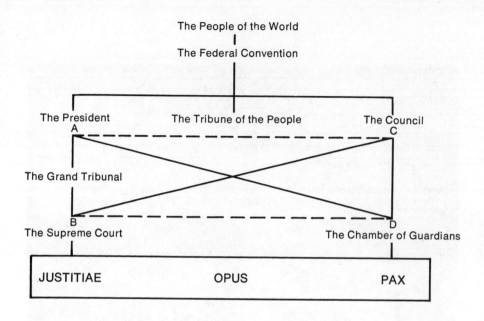

Dotted line *AC* symbolizes intervention of Council in tenure of the President's Cabinet and Acting Presidency of the Chairman of the Council during vacancies in the Presidency.

Diagonal *AD* symbolizes Chairmanship of the President in the Chamber of Guardians.

Diagonal *CB* symbolizes Council's veto power on appointments to the Judiciary and membership of the Chairman of the Council in the Tribunal and Supreme Court.

Dotted line *BD* symbolizes intervention of the Judiciary in elections to the Chamber of Guardians.

The Problem of World Government

Jacques Maritain

Editor's Introduction

The work on world government by Jacques Maritain that is reprinted here was originally one of the Charles R. Walgreen Foundation Lectures given at the University of Chicago in 1949. In published form it appeared as the seventh and concluding chapter of Maritain's book *Man and the State*, published by the University of Chicago Press in 1951 (pp. 188–216). As the reader will see, the French Christian philosopher's reflections on the problem were inspired in large part by the *Preliminary Draft of a World Constitution*, printed above (pp. 328–45).

The essay stands on its own, although it also forms a fitting close to a book that is the ripest expression of Maritain's political philosophy. At the time he wrote it, Maritain was sixty-seven years old and just completing his closest involvement in the great political issues of his time. In the conflicts of the 1930s and the war years, he had gained fame as a clear and strong proponent and defender of democracy. In the United States during the Nazi occupation of France, he was a staunch supporter from the beginning of De Gaulle's Free France. Through his writings as well as by his personal influence, he served as elder statesman for the parties of Christian Democracy that emerged in strength in Western Europe after the war. French ambassador to the Vatican from 1945 to 1948, he was also the French delegate to UNESCO and took a leading part in the drawing up of the United Nations Universal Declaration of Human Rights.

Maritain devoted many works to problems of political and social philosophy. The most important of these, besides the one reprinted here, are *True Humanism* (1936), *Education at the Crossroads* (1943), *Scholasticism and Politics* (1940), *On the Philosophy of History* (1957).

Maritain's writings and activities were by no means limited to the field of politics. He first gained prominence, especially in America, for his essays on art and poetry. His *Art et scholastique* (1920) was first translated into English in 1923. He was then and remained thereafter the friend and intimate of many painters, poets, and musicians. His concern with the arts finds its fullest expression in *Creative Intuition in Art and Poetry* (1953), based on the A. W. Mellon Lectures in the Fine Arts that he gave at the National Gallery of Art in Washington in 1952.

Maritain has also written widely in the more technical fields of philosophy. He found his intellectual vocation while a student at the Sorbonne.

inspired especially by Henri Bergson's lectures at the Collège de France. Converted to Catholicism, largely through the influence of the novelist Léon Bloy, he undertook a long and profound study of the works of Thomas Aquinas and his leading commentators. Since then, all of Maritain's work may be viewed as an attempt to explore and work out the implications and applications of the promise of the Gospel and the principles of St. Thomas. As the titles of many of his books indicate, Maritain considers himself a follower of the Scholastics in theology and philosophy.

In the theory of knowledge, his greatest book, and some would say his most lasting claim to fame, is undoubtedly *The Degrees of Knowledge* (1932). It is a large work in which he endeavors to distinguish and relate all the kinds of knowledge and in particular to justify the methods and achievements of philosophy and theology. During the years in which he was teaching at the Institut Catholique in Paris, where he began in 1913, he produced a series of works that constitutes in effect an entire course in systematic philosophy: an introduction to philosophy, logic, the philosophy of nature, the theory of knowledge, metaphysics, and moral philosophy.

Throughout his long career, Maritain has constantly been concerned with the problems of the church in the world. Before and during the war, he wrote extensively against those who thought that Catholicism, if not also Christianity, is incompatible with democracy. As an avowed Catholic and scholastic thinker, he argued for the liberalization of the church and thus became one of the most powerful voices calling for the *aggiornamento* introduced by Pope John XXIII. But, while welcoming the new liberties and the spirit of unity and brotherhood that have resulted, Maritain has been deeply disturbed and distressed by other aspects of the Catholic "renewal." In a book entitled *The Peasant of the Garonne* (1966) he criticized and attacked what he calls "chronolatry" and the turning away from, if not the actual denial of, many of the traditional values in philosophy that he considers to be permanent truths of the Scholastic tradition.

Maritain was born in Paris, in 1882, of a Protestant, liberal, anticlerical family and was raised in that tradition. In 1904 he married Raïssa Oumansoff, who remained his close companion and was a collaborator on several of his books until her death in 1960. After a period of study in Heidelberg with the biologist Hans Driesch in 1906–08, he returned to Paris and became closely associated with its literary and artistic world at the time he began teaching at the Institut Catholique. In the 1930s he began lecturing in the United States and Canada and thereafter was closely associated with the Pontifical Institute of Mediaeval Studies in Toronto and with the universities of Columbia, Chicago, Princeton, and Notre Dame.

Since 1961 Maritain has been living with Les Petit Frères de Jesus at Toulouse, on the Garonne river, where he has just completed another book, this one on the holiness of the church.

The Problem of World Government[1]

Jacques Maritain

I The alternative

In 1944, Mr. Mortimer Adler published a book entitled *How to Think About War and Peace,* in which he advocated in a conclusive manner World Government as the only means of ensuring peace. This book was written just on the eve of the advent of what they now call the atomic age— that's a proof that philosophers do not need to be stimulated by the atomic bomb in order to think. Yet the advent of the atomic bomb is a strong invitation to think, directed both to the States, which, having no soul of their own, find it a harder matter to think than mechanical brains do, and to the peoples, which, as long as they are not atomized, still have human brains.

The problem of World Government—I would prefer to say, of a genuinely political organization of the world—is the problem of lasting peace. And in a sense we might say that the problem of lasting peace is simply the problem of peace, meaning that mankind is confronted today with the alternative: either lasting peace or a serious risk of total destruction.

I need not emphasize the reality and significance of this alternative, which results from the fact that modern wars are world wars, and total wars, involving the whole of human existence, with regard to the deepest structures of social life as well as to the extent of the population mobilized by war, and threatened by it, in every nation.

What I should like is rather to seek for the reasons for this alternative.

---

[1] In this essay I consider the problem of world government from the point of view of political philosophy and not from that of immediate practical activity. Furthermore, I aim in my discussion to clarify the positions of the particular group whose approach to the problem is most closely concerned, in my opinion, with the philosophical issues involved; I refer to the group at the University of Chicago.

As a result, (1) the development of my own views on the philosophical theory of world government being my main purpose, no attempt has been made to analyze the huge diversity of conflicting views with which a complete practical discussion of the matter would have had to deal; (2) as regards the material quoted, I have restricted myself to a few books from the Chicago group which happen to be more closely linked with the topic of my discussion. In order to ward off the reproach of provincialism which such an approach might seem to de-

serve (if the reader were mistaken about the author's actual aim), I should like to lay stress here on the importance and interest of the various contributions that have come from other quarters, and more especially from such authorities in the matter as Messrs. MacIver, Carr, Clarence Streit, Cord Meyer, Kelsen, Herbert Hoover, Culbertson, Goodrich, Hambrò, Woodward, and the Shotwell Commission—without forgetting the strong objections made by Messrs. Walter Lippmann and Reinhold Niebuhr. I should like also to mention Julia E. Johnsen's books: *United Nations or World Government* ("The Reference Shelf," Vol. XIX, No. 5 [April, 1947]) and *Federal World Government* ("The Reference Shelf," Vol. XX, No. 5 [September, 1948]), as well as the general survey undertaken by Duke University, under the direction of Professor Hornell Hart. See also J. Warburg, *Faith, Purpose and Power* (New York, 1950), chap. v.

The basic fact is the henceforth unquestionable interdependence of nations, a fact which is not a token of peace, as people for a moment believed in their wishful thinking, but rather a token of war: why? because that interdependence of nations is essentially an economic interdependence, not a politically agreed-upon, willed, and built up interdependence, in other words, because it has come to exist by virtue of a merely technical or material process, not by virtue of a simultaneous genuinely political or rational process.

Quoting a statement of Mr. Emery Reves, Mortimer Adler, in his chapter on "The Economic Community," points out that "the technical developments which render the world smaller, and its parts more interdependent, can have two consequences: '1) a political and economic rapprochement, or 2) fights and quarrels more devastating than ever, precisely because of the proximity of men to each other. Which one of these two possibilities will occur depends on matters essentially nontechnical.'" And he rightly adds: "Both will occur within the next great historic epoch, but the second before the first."[2]

An essentially *economic* interdependence, without any corresponding fundamental recasting of the *moral* and *political* structures of human existence, can but impose by material necessity a partial and fragmentary, growing bit by bit, political interdependence which is reluctantly and hatefully accepted, because it runs against the grain of nature as long as nations live on the assumption of their full political autonomy. In the framework and against the background of that assumed full political autonomy of nations, an essentially economic interdependence can but exasperate the rival needs and prides of nations; and the industrial progress only accelerates the process, as Professor John Nef has shown in his book *La Route de la guerre totale* [The Road to Total War].[3] Thus it is that we have the privilege of contemplating to-day a world more and more economically one, and more and more divided by the pathological claims of opposed nationalisms.

At this point we may make two remarks. In the first place, both economic life and political life depend on *nature* and *reason*, I mean *nature* as dominated by material forces and laws and by deterministic evolution, even when the human mind interferes in the process with its technical discoveries—and on *reason* as concerned with the ends of human existence and the realm of freedom and morality, and as freely establishing, in consonance with Natural Law, an order of human relations. In the second place, it is nature and matter that have the upper hand in the economic process; and it is reason and freedom that have the upper hand in the political, the genuinely political process.

As a result, it is permissible to say that the spectacle we are contemplating today is but an instance of that unfortunate law that in human history matter goes faster than the spirit. The human intellect is always getting winded in catching up with the advance of matter. It is probable that with the discovery of fire the cave-man had to face predicaments not unlike those which our civilization is facing now. The question is whether human conscience and moral intelligence, teamed with the effort of creative energies, will be able to make the Machine a positive force in the service of mankind—in other words, to impose on man's instinctive greed, with its unsurpassable technical equipment, a collective reason grown stronger than instinct—without a period of trial and error more terrible to our kind than the prehistoric eras.[4]

---

2 Mortimer J. Adler, *How to Think About War and Peace* (New York: Simon & Schuster, 1944), pp. 228–29. Mr. Emery Reves's quotation is taken from his *Democratic Manifesto.*

3 John U. Nef, *La Route de la guerre totale* (Paris: Armand Colin, 1949).

4 Cf. [my] *France, My Country* (New York: Longmans, Green & Co., 1941), p. 108.

Now the preceding considerations are not enough. Another factor must be considered, which plays a far-reaching part in the development of that alternative: *either lasting peace or a serious risk of total destruction,* the reasons for which we are seeking.

This factor is the modern State, with its false pretense to be a person, a superhuman person, and to enjoy, as a result, a right of absolute sovereignty.

In a remarkable essay, entitled "The Modern State: a Danger for Peace,"[5] the Belgian jurist Fernand de Visscher offers this primary fact for our consideration: the fundamental amorality of the foreign policy of modern States; a fundamental amorality whose unique rule and principle is the *raison d'État,* which raises the particular interest of a State to a supreme law of its activity, especially as to its relations with the other States. And the same author goes on to explain that the root of this evil is the false assumption that the State is a person, a supreme person, which consequently has its supreme justification, supreme reason for being and supreme end in itself, and possesses a supreme right to its own preservation and growth in power by any means whatever.

Mr. de Visscher calls this assumption a political "heresy," and thinks that it derives from a fatal misunderstanding, by virtue of which a mere metaphor, technically useful in the language of jurists—the notion of "juridical personality"—has been mistaken for a reality, and has given birth in this way to "one of the most baneful myths of our times." As we have seen, such a myth has much deeper roots, I would say Hegelian roots. Hegel did not invent, he gave full metaphysical expression to the idea of the State as a superhuman person.* The modern States were Hegelian in practice long before Hegel and his theory. The modern State, heir of the kings of old, has conceived of itself as a person superior to the body politic, and either dominating the body politic from above or absorbing the body politic

in itself. Now, since the State in actual fact is not a person, but a mere impersonal mechanism of abstract laws and concrete power, it is this impersonal mechanism which will become suprahuman, when that vicious idea comes to develop its whole potentialities; and as a result the natural order of things will be turned upside down: the State will be no longer in the service of men, men will be in the service of the peculiar ends of the State.

Let us not forget, moreover, that this trend toward supreme domination and supreme amorality, which has fully developed and is in full swing in the totalitarian States, is by no means inherent in the State in its real nature and its true and necessary functions, but depends on a perverted notion which preys upon the modern State, and of which democracy, if it is to survive, will get clear.

Let us also observe with de Visscher that this trend of modern States toward supreme domination and supreme amorality, which runs against the nature of the genuinely democratic State and can but impair its most beneficial initiatives, is constantly thwarted, in democratic nations, as concerns especially the *internal or domestic* activity of the State. Because in democratic nations the basic idea of justice, law, and common welfare, on which the State itself is grounded, the rights and freedom of the citizens, the constitution and the free institutions of the body politic, the control exercised by the assemblies of the representatives of the people, the pressure of public opinion, the freedom of expression, freedom of teaching and freedom of the press, tend of themselves to check the vicious trend in question and keep, somehow or other, the State within its proper and natural limits.

But as concerns the *external or foreign*

5 Fernand de Visscher, *L'État moderne: Un Danger pour la paix: Extrait de la revue Le Flambeau* (1940–47).

* *GBWW,* Vol. 46, pp. 80–108.

activity of the State, that is, its relations with the other States, there is nothing to check the trend of modern States—to the extent to which they are infected with the Hegelian virus—toward supreme domination and supreme amorality, nothing except the opposite force of the other States. For there is no more powerful control, no organized international public opinion, to which these States can be submitted. And as to the superior law of justice, they deem it to be embodied in their own supreme interests. I by no means disregard the work which international institutions like the late League of Nations or the present United Nations Organization were or are performing in order to remedy that situation. Yet this work cannot touch the root of the evil, and remains inevitably precarious and subsidiary, from the very fact that such institutions are organs created and put into action by the sovereign States, whose decisions they can only register. As a matter of fact, modern States, with respect to international relations, are acting in a kind of vacuum, as supreme and adamantine, transcendent, absolute entities. While the modern State grows inevitably stronger as regards its supervision over national life, and the powers with which it is armed more and more dangerous for the peace of nations, at the same time the external relations of foreign policy between nations are strictly reduced to relations between those supreme entities in their harsh mutual competition, with an only remote participation of the people—their human aspirations and their human wills—in the course of fateful events developing above them in an unattainable Jupiterian heaven.

II Discarding the so-called sovereignty of the State

From all that I have said it appears that the two main obstacles to the establishment of a lasting peace are, first, the so-called absolute sovereignty of modern States; second,

the impact of the economic interdependence of all nations upon our present irrational stage of political evolution, in which no world political organization corresponds to world material unification.

As concerns the so-called absolute sovereignty of modern States, I am not unaware of the fact that we may use, and we often use, the expression "sovereignty of the State" to mean a genuine political concept, namely the full independence or autonomy of the body politic. Unfortunately, "sovereignty of the State" is exactly the wrong expression for that concept, because the subject involved is not the State but the body politic, and because the body politic itself is not genuinely sovereign. The right name is autonomy. No less unfortunately, this very autonomy of the body politic no longer exists in full: as a matter of fact, the nations are no longer autonomous in their economic life; they are even only half autonomous in their political life, because their political life is impaired by the lasting threat of war and interfered with, in domestic affairs, by the ideology and pressure of other nations. Now I say that it is not enough to remark that modern bodies politic have ceased in actual fact to be "sovereign" in that improper sense which means full autonomy. It is also not enough to request from sovereign States limitations and partial surrenders of their sovereignty, as if it were only a matter of making more or less restricted in its extension a privilege genuinely and really inherent in the State, and as if, moreover, sovereignty could be limited in its own sphere.

That is not enough. We must come down to the roots, that is, we must get rid of the Hegelian or pseudo-Hegelian concept of the State as a person, a suprahuman person, and understand that the State is only a *part* (a topmost part, but a part) and an *instrumental agency* in the body politic—thus bringing the State back to its true, normal, and necessary functions as well as to its genuine dignity. And we must realize that the State is not and has never been sovereign, because sovereignty means a *natural* right (which does not belong to the State but to the body politic as perfect society) to a supreme power and independence which are supreme *separately from* and *above* the whole that the sovereign rules (and of which neither the State nor the body politic is possessed). If the State were sovereign, in the genuine sense of this word, it could never surrender its sovereignty, nor even have it restricted. Whereas the body politic, which is not sovereign, but has a right to full autonomy, can freely surrender this right if it recognizes that it is no longer a perfect society, and decides to enter a larger, truly perfect political society.

III   Necessity for a world political society

As concerns the second main obstacle to the establishment of a lasting peace, namely the present state of political *inorganization* of the world, well, here we are getting to the core of the problem we have to discuss.

If we place ourselves in the perspective of rational necessities, neglecting for a moment the factual entanglements of history, and if we transfer ourselves to the final conclusions made clear by the logical requirements of the issue, then we shall see how cogently the advocates of World Government, or of a *one world* politically organized, make out their case.

Suffice it briefly to recall the arguments they have developed to substantiate their contention.

Distinguishing from the various causes which are incitations to war (and which are epitomized in human nature and its need for material goods) the basic structural condition presupposed by war, Mr. Mortimer Adler states that "the only cause of war is anarchy," that is, "the condition of those who try to live together without government." "Anarchy occurs wherever men or nations try to live together without each surrendering their sovereignty." [6] As

a result, if a time arrives in which war is made impossible, this will be a time in which anarchy between nations has been suppressed, in other words, a time in which world government has been established.

In a similar line of reasoning, Mr. Stringfellow Barr, having described *The Pilgrimage of Western Man,* writes: "The problem which confronted the generation of Armistice Two, the first generation of the Atomic Age, was clearly the oldest political problem of all: how to find government for a community that lacked it, even if each fraction of the community already lived under a government of its own. It had been solved by tribes that had merged to form a village, by villages that had merged to form city-states like those of Renaissance Italy, by city-states that had merged to form empires or to form sovereign nation-states. Now it was nation-states, not villages, that were the governed fractions of an ungoverned community. What was terribly new about the problem was that this time the community was world-wide, bound together for weal or woe by modern science, modern technology, and the clamorous needs of modern industry." Thus man today, broadening his imagination, has to grasp with respect to a whole planet the force of the argument of Alexander Hamilton in the first of the *Federalist Papers,** that is to say, as Stringfellow Barr puts it, "that the price of peace is justice, the price of justice is law, that the price of law is government, and that government must apply law to men and women, not merely to subordinate governments." [7]

Finally, Mr. Hutchins has admirably shown, in his lecture on *St. Thomas and the World State,* [8] that the concept of a plu-

---

6 Adler, op. cit., p. 69.

7 Stringfellow Barr, *The Pilgrimage of Western Man* (New York: Harcourt, Brace & Co., 1949), p. 341.

8 Robert M. Hutchins, *St. Thomas and the World State* (Aquinas Lecture, 1949 [Milwaukee: Marquette University Press, 1949]).

* *GBWW,* Vol. 43.

ralist world-wide political society perfectly squares with the basic principles of Thomas Aquinas' political philosophy.* For Thomas Aquinas as well as for Aristotle,† self-sufficiency (I do not say total self-sufficiency, I say real, if relative, self-sufficiency) is the essential property of *perfect society*, which is the goal to which the evolution of political forms in mankind tends; and the primary good ensured by a perfect society—a good which is one indeed with its very unity and life—is its own internal and external peace. As a result, when neither peace nor self-sufficiency can be achieved by a particular form of society, like the city, it is no longer that particular form, but a broader one, for instance the kingdom, which is perfect society. Hence we are entitled to conclude, following the same line of argumentation: when neither peace nor self-sufficiency can be achieved by particular kingdoms, nations, or states, they are no longer perfect societies, and it is a broader society, defined by its capacity to achieve self-sufficiency and peace—therefore, in actual fact, with reference to our historical age, the international community politically organized—which is to become perfect society.

According to the same principles, it was on a merely moral ground, reinforced as far as possible by legal and customary bonds born of mutual agreement, in other words, it was by virtue of *natural law* and *jus gentium* or the common law of civilization, that kingdoms and States, as long as they answered in an approximate yet sufficient manner the concept of perfect society, had to fulfil their obligations toward that "community of the whole world," that international society whose existence and dignity have always been affirmed by Christian doctors and jurists, as well as by the common consciousness of mankind. And God knows how the obligations in question were fulfilled in the absence of the sword of the law. But when the particular bodies politic, our so-called national States, grown incapable of achieving self-sufficiency and assuring peace, definitely recede from the concept of perfect society, then the picture necessarily changes: since it is the international society which must become henceforth the perfect society, it is not only on a *moral,* but on a fully *juridical* ground that the obligations of the particular bodies politic, once they have become parts of a politically organized whole, will have to fulfil their obligations toward this whole: not only by virtue of *natural law* and *jus gentium,* but also by virtue of the *positive laws* which the politically organized world society will establish and which its government will enforce.

In the transitional period, or as long as a world government has not yet been founded by the only normal and genuine process of generation of political societies, that is, through the exercise of freedom, reason, and human virtues, it is obvious, as Mr. Hutchins points out, that the foundation of a World State by force, as well as any attempt by one State forcibly to impose its will upon another, should be opposed as contrary to Natural Law. As long as a pluralist world political society has not yet been founded, the particular bodies politic shaped by history remain the only political units in which the concept of perfect society, though they are now falling short of it, has been carried into effect: be they great or small, powerful or weak, they keep their right to full independence, as well as that right to make war and peace which is inherent in perfect society, and in the exercise of which moral law demands of them today more self-restraint than ever.

Yet the final aim is clearly determined. Once the perfect society required by our historical age, that is the world political society, has been brought into being, it will be bound in justice to respect to the greatest possible extent the freedoms—essential

---

* *GBWW,* Vol. 20, pp. 205–337.

† *GBWW,* Vol. 9, pp. 445–552.

to the common good of the world—of those invaluable vessels of political, moral, and cultural life which will be its parts; but the particular States will have surrendered their full independence, much more indeed in their external than in their internal sphere of activity, and the World State will have to enjoy, within the strict limits and the well-balanced modalities proper to such a completely new creation of human reason, the powers naturally required by a perfect society: legislative power, executive power, judicial power, with the coercive power necessary to enforce the law.

I should like to add that the Constitution in which the rights and duties and the governmental structures of such a World State will perhaps be defined some day can only be the fruit of the common efforts, experiences, and hard trials met with by present and future history; but that the *Preliminary Draft of a World Constitution* which is known as the Chicago Plan, or Hutchins Plan, appears as a particularly valuable inception.* If this *Preliminary Draft* is understood, according to the purpose of its authors, as a merely tentative "proposal to history, to promote further study and discussion," it seems to me to be both the best among the many plans of international organization which are being elaborated today, and the most comprehensive and well-balanced ideal pattern that prominent political scientists could work out in order to exasperate frowning realists, and to prod the thought and meditation of men of good will and far-sighted ingenuousness.

*   *   *

A good many objections have been raised, of course, to the idea of a World Government. I should like only to allude to the most conspicuous one, which insists that the idea is fine and beautiful, but utterly impossible of realization, and therefore most dangerous, for it runs the risk of di-

verting toward a brilliant utopia efforts which should be directed toward more humble but possible achievements. The reply is that if the idea is grounded, as we believe, on true and sound political philosophy, it cannot be impossible *in itself*. Therefore it is up to human intelligence and energy to make it, in the long run, not impossible *with respect to* the enormous yet contingent obstacles and impediments that the sociological and historical conditions which lie heavy on mankind have piled up against it.

At this point I must confess that in my capacity as an Aristotelian I am not much of an idealist. If the idea of a world political society were only a beautiful idea, I would not care much for it. I hold it to be a great idea, but also a sound and right idea. Yet the greater an idea is with respect to the weakness and entanglements of the human condition, the more cautious one must be in handling it. And the more attentive one must be in *not* demanding its immediate realization (a warning which, if I may be allowed to say, sounds especially distasteful in a generous country where good ideas are looked upon as something to be immediately applied and seem worthy of interest only to that extent). It would not be good, either for the cause of the idea or for the cause of peace, to use the idea of World Government as a weapon against the limited and precarious international agencies which for the time being are the only existing political means at the disposal of men to protract the truce among nations. Moreover the supporters of the concept of World Government perfectly know—Mr. Mortimer Adler has especially stressed that aspect of the question—that this concept can be brought into being only after many years of struggle and effort. They know, therefore, that their solution for a future perpetual peace has surely no more efficacy for the precarious peace to be

---

* *See* pp. 328–45.

ensured today than the work of the agencies to which I just alluded. The pros and cons, in the issue of World Government, do not concern our day, but the generations to come.

IV· Fully political vs. merely governmental theory

So far I have dealt with the most general aspects of the problem. Perhaps I could be tempted to end my essay here; so at least I would spare the patience of the reader. Yet further consideration seems to me to be needed. My discussion is not finished, and it is necessary to set forth a new series of considerations.

The reason for this is that the problem has been posed in terms of its ultimate solution, and in terms of world government—therefore, first of all in terms of *State* and *government.* Now, if we reflect upon the distinction between *state* and *body politic,* we shall see that the very idea of world government can be conceived in two opposite ways.* The question, therefore, is: in which way should a sound political philosophy conceive of world government? A first possible manner of conceiving world government would reduce the whole matter to the *sole and exclusive* consideration of the *state and government.* Let us call it the *merely governmental* theory of world organization. The second possible manner of conceiving world government envisages the matter under the universal or integral consideration of the *body politic* or *political society.* Let us call it the *fully political* theory of world organization.

I think that the *fully political* theory is the good one, and that a *merely governmental* theory would be wrong and disastrous. I do not know of anybody having ever taken a stand in its behalf. But sins of omission are to be avoided like the others. My point is that it is necessary to clarify the issue, in order to brush aside any possibility of mistaking one theory for the other, and to get rid of misunderstandings quite detrimental to the very idea of world political organization.

Let me emphasize once again that the basic political reality is not the State, but the body politic with its multifarious institutions, the multiple communities which it involves, and the moral community which grows out of it. The body politic is the people organized under just laws. The State is the particular agency which specializes in matters dealing with the common good of the body politic, it is therefore the topmost political agency, but the State is a part, not a whole, and its functions are merely instrumental: it is for the body politic and for the people that it sees to the public order, enforces laws, possesses power; and being a part in the service of the people, it must be controlled by the people.

What is called in French *le gouvernement,* and here the Administration or the administrative officials, that is, the men who are in charge of the common good, are part both of the body politic and of the State; but because they are the head of the people, and deputies for the people with respect to whom they exercise a vicarious function, and by whom, in a democratic régime, they are chosen, their governing function is rooted in the body politic, not in the State; it is not because their function is rooted in the State that they are part of the body politic; it is because their function is rooted in the body politic that they are part of the State.

---

* "These . . . differ from each other as a part differs from the whole. The *Body Politic* or the *Political Society* is the whole. The *State* is a part—the topmost part—of this whole." (Maritain, *Man and the State* [University of Chicago Press, 1951], pp. 9–10.) "The State is only that part of the body politic especially concerned with the maintenance of law, the promotion of the common welfare and public order, and the administration of public affairs. . . . [It] is but an agency entitled to use power and coercion, and made up of experts or specialists in public order and welfare, an instrument in the service of man." (Ibid., pp. 12, 13.)

Since that is how things are, we might better say, as I observed at the start, the *Problem of the World's Political Organization* than the *Problem of World Government*. The whole issue is not simply *World Government*. It is *World Political Society*.

What I just called a *merely governmental* theory would consider the whole thing, Existence and Nature of World Government, as well as Passage from the present state of affairs to the World Government, in the perspective of the State and government *separately* from that of the body politic. As a result, we would have to contemplate a process developed artificially, and against the grain of nature, resulting in a State without a body politic or a political society of its own, a world brain without a world body; and the World Government would be an absolute Superstate, or a superior State deprived of body politic and merely *superimposed* on and interfering with the life of the particular States—even though it were born of popular election and representation. For this procedure is of course the only authentic one—it is not through delegation from the various governments, it is through the free suffrage of men and women that the World State is to be founded and maintained—but this necessary procedure is a merely technical or juridical one and would be entirely insufficient to change in any way the fact that I am pointing out.

Just, then, as the ambition to become a sovereign person was transferred from the Holy Germanic Emperor to the kings—at the time when the French kings refused obedience to the Holy Empire—and from the kings to the States, so this same ambition would be transferred from the States to the World Superstate. So that by a tragic inconsistency, while putting an end to the modern myth of the State as regards all the particular States, men would again find this myth, the myth of the State as person and sovereign person and suprahuman person, enthroned at the top of the universe. All the consequences involved in the Hegelian conception of the State could then spread over humanity with irresistible power.

The quest of such a Superstate capping the nations is nothing else, in fact, than the quest of the old utopia of a universal Empire. This utopia was pursued in past ages in the form of the Empire of one single nation over all others. The pursuit, in the modern age, of an absolute World Superstate would be the pursuit of a democratic multinational Empire, which would be no better than the others.

* * *

What I have just characterized as a merely governmental theory of world government is the exact opposite of what all of us who support the idea of world government are thinking, and, in particular, of the political philosophy of the Chicago Plan's authors. But other people may come along, and be in a hurry, and be mistaken. And the more we insist on the right way, the more we must be aware of, and point out, the dangers of the wrong one. A *merely governmental* theory of world organization would go the wrong way, because from the very start it would pursue the analogy between *State with respect to individuals* and *World State with respect to particular States* in the mere perspective of the topmost power.

The *fully political* theory of world organization goes the right way, because it pursues the same analogy in the perspective of the basic requirements of political life and freedom. As Adler and Hutchins have repeatedly pointed out, the problem is to raise international community to the condition of a perfect society, or of a politically organized international society.

At this point I should like to make a few remarks on the comparison which suggests itself, and which, quoting Mr. Stringfellow Barr, I used in the first part of this discussion, between the passage from the tribe to the village, from the village to the city, from the city to the kingdom or to the modern political society, and the passage from our present political society to a world political society. The processes in question are only analogical, of course, and took place in multiple and exceedingly various fashions. Mr. Max Ascoli has sharply criticized that comparison,[9] and accused of utter naïveté the notion that our present political societies, ripened by history, could or should develop into a world political society by a so-to-speak mechanical process of broadening in extension. This criticism, in my opinion, applies to the manner in which things would be conceived in a merely governmental theory. It does not apply to the manner in which things are conceived in the fully political theory of world organization.

From another point of view, Henri Bergson, distinguishing *closed societies,* which are temporal and terrestrial, from *open society,* which is spiritual, insisted that that kind of friendship which unites members of the village or the city can broaden from a closed society to another, larger, closed society, but that when it comes to love for all men, then it is a question of passing from one order to another; from the realm of closed societies to the realm, infinitely different, of open and spiritual society, in which man is united with that very Love which has created the world.[10] All that is true. But here also the mere consideration of extension is only accidental. If men are to pass from our present political societies to a world political society, they will pass to a larger *closed* society, as large as the whole company of nations, and civic friendship will have to broaden in the same manner. Civic friendship will still remain infinitely different from charity, just as the world society will remain infinitely different from the Kingdom of God.

Yet these remarks make us aware of a crucial point. The passage of which we are speaking implies a change not only in the dimension of extension, but first of all in the dimension of depth: a change in the inner structures of man's morality and sociality.

In the past epochs of history the will of men to live together, which is basic in the formation of political societies, was as a rule—with the splendid exception of this country—brought into being by any kind of means, save freedom. It has been enforced even by war; for, it is sad to say, wars have been the most general means—because they are the most primitive and brutal—of mixing and brewing peoples together and forcing them to know each other and to live with one another, conqueror and conquered, in the same place, and in the long run to develop between each other a kind of unhappy congeniality. Later on civic friendship could occur.

That time is past, at least as concerns democratic principles and the requirements of justice. Now, if a world political society is some day founded, it will be by means of freedom. *It is by means of freedom that the peoples of the earth will have been brought to a common will to live together.* This simple sentence makes us measure the magnitude of the moral revolution—the *real* revolution now proposed to the hopes and virtues of mankind—on the necessity for which Mr. Mortimer Adler laid stress in his book.

Living together does not mean occupying the same place in space. It does not mean, either, being subjected to the same physical or external conditions or pressures or to the same pattern of life; it does not mean *Zusammenmarschieren* [keeping in step]. Living together means sharing as men, not

---

[9] Cf. Max Ascoli, *The Power of Freedom* (New York: Farrar, Straus, 1949), Part III, chap. iv.

[10] Cf. Henri Bergson, *Les deux sources de la morale et de la religion* (Paris: Alcan, 1932), chap. iv. "De la société close à la société ouverte, de la cité à l'humanité, on ne passera jamais par voie d'élargissement. Elles ne sont pas de la même essence" (p. 288). [One does not make a closed society into an open one by enlarging it, any more than one can arrive at the idea of mankind by increasing the number of people in a group. Such things are of different orders.]

as beasts, that is, with basic free acceptance, in certain common sufferings and in a certain common task.

The reason for which men will to live together is a positive, creative reason. It is not because they fear some danger that men will to live together. Fear of war is not and never has been the reason for which men have wanted to form a political society. Men want to live together and form a political society for a given task to be undertaken in common. When men will have a will to live together in a world-wide society, it will be because they will have a will to achieve a world-wide common task. What task indeed? The conquest of freedom. The point is to have men become aware of that task, and of the fact that it is worthy of self-sacrifice.

Given the human condition, the most significant synonym of *living together* is *suffering together*. When men form a political society, they do not want to share in common suffering out of love for each other. They want to accept common suffering out of love for the common task and the common good. The will to achieve a world-wide common task must therefore be strong enough to entail a will to share in certain common sufferings made inevitable by that task, and by the common good of a world-wide society. What sufferings indeed? Sufferings due to solidarity. Suffice it to observe that the very existence of a world-wide society will inevitably imply deep changes in the social and economic structures of the national and international life of peoples, and a serious repercussion of these changes on the free business of a number of individuals, who are not the most numerous in the world, but the most attached to profit-making. The very existence of a world-wide society will also inevitably imply a certain—relative no doubt, yet quite serious and appreciable—equalization of the standards of life of all individuals. Let us put it in crude terms: perhaps, if the issue were made sufficiently clear to them, people in occidental nations would be ready to accept, for the sake of peace and of a world political organization ensuring lasting peace, a serious lowering of their standards of life in order to provide people on the other side of the iron curtain with an equivalent raising of their standards of life. Yet this would suppose a kind of moral heroism, for which, I deem, we are badly prepared. People are unhappy, and it will be necessary for them to confront new obligations and sacrifices, connected with the life of other men at the other end of the world, in order to promote in the long run peace, happiness, and freedom for all.

We can meditate in this connection two far-reaching sentences of Mr. John Nef: "Science and machinery," he wrote, "have enabled humanity to command the material resources of the planet in ways which have made world government indispensable. At the same time science and machinery are depriving individuals and societies of the vision and of the control over themselves, which alone might make world government human and worth having."[11] And: "The price of peace is the renunciation, to a large extent, of success as the principal driving force in thought, work and politics."[12] The matter is nothing less than having science perfected by wisdom, and the criterion of success superseded by the criterion of good and devotion to the good.

One body politic is *one* organized people. Of course the unity of a world body politic would be quite different from the unity which characterizes kingdoms or nations, and to which our thought is accustomed. It would be not even a federal unity, but rather, let me say, a *pluralist unity,* taking place only through the lasting diversity of the particular bodies politic, and fostering

---

11 From a chapter, "Renewal (1950)," in an unpublished book, "French Civilization and Universal Community."

12 Nef, *La Route de la guerre totale*, p. 161: "Le prix de la paix . . . est l'abandon, dans une large mesure, du succès comme principe à la fois de la pensée, du travail et de la politique."

that diversity. The fact remains that when we say that the community of nations must form *one* body politic, even taking into account the qualifications to which such a unity would be subject, we are saying that the community of peoples must form *one* people, even taking into account the qualifications to which such a pluralist unity would be subject. That means that among all peoples the sense of the common good of that *one people* should develop, and supersede the sense of the common good peculiar to each body politic. A sense of civic friendship as large as that one people should also and simultaneously develop, since civic love or friendship is the very soul or animating form of every political society. To insist that this sense of a world-wide civic friendship and a world-wide common good is a prerequisite condition for the foundation of a world political society would be putting the cart before the horse. Yet some beginnings should actually take shape in the peoples; moreover the sense of the common good of the community of peoples, with the mood of good will and fellow-feeling it implies, is implicitly and virtually involved in the freely developed will to live together, which *is* the basic condition prerequired for the foundation of a world political society coming into existence by means of freedom.

*   *   *

We see, therefore, that the birth of a world political society would result from a growing, vital process, in which the work of all official and private institutions interested in any form of international rapprochement and cooperation would participate, but in which the essential part would be played by the will of the people, in every nation, to live together, in the world. I mean a will growing so powerful as to sweep away the obstacles caused by the myth of the States as sovereign persons or by the bias of governments, and the obstacles, still greater, caused in the people themselves by

misfortune and fatigue, slowness of reason, and natural self-interest.

We also see in this way how the World State would have a body politic of its own: this pluralist world body politic would be made up, not only of the international and supra-national institutions required by the world government, but also, and first of all, of the particular bodies politic themselves, with their own political structures and lives, their own national and cultural heritages, their own multifarious institutions and communities—all this being enveloped, treasured and held sacred by the same will which would tend, beyond all this, to a world-wide living together, and which would have achieved this aim by the foundation of a world political society.

At this point it is advisable for us to elaborate a new concept, the concept of *imperfect* political society—I mean, of course, as *part* of a kind of perfect society that the Ancients did not know, and in which, because of its very extension, the functions and properties inherent in self-sufficiency are divided between a multiplicity of particular bodies politic and a central common organism. In a world political society the nations would become *by right* and with the guarantees of a superior juridical order what they already are in fact, but anarchically, namely non-self-sufficient or imperfect bodies politic; and the World State, considered separately from them, and only in its supra-national institutions and life, would also be an imperfect political society. Only the world society taken as a whole both with the supra-national State and the multiplicity of nations, would be a perfect political society.

By the same token we may realize that the independence of nations would not be jeopardized—it would rather be better assured—by the creation of a world political society. The States would have to surrender their privilege of being sovereign persons, that is, a privilege which they have never possessed. They would have to give up their full independence, that is, something which they have lost. They would have to give up something which they have now, but the use of which has become more detrimental than profitable to them, to the nations, and to the world, namely the property of each one of enjoying *top* independence. Yet in their mutual interdependence the nations could achieve a degree of real, though imperfect, independence higher than that they possess now, from the very fact that their inner political life, being freed from the threat of war and from the interference of rival nations, could become more autonomous in actual fact than it is at present.

Some people are afraid that making the concern for justice, as the Chicago draft does, the chief duty of the World State, would result in extending over everything the celestial power of the world government.[13] They are thinking of a State without a body politic. Ensuring justice by law, which is the main function of the State, should obviously be the main function of the World State; but presupposing and needing all the other channels—legal, customary, social, moral, even merely vegetative—through which justice is ensured, somehow or other, in the infinitely diversified existence of nations. Limping as human justice is, justice is the primary need of the human community. And in this respect it is hard to say that our present world suffers from overnutrition.

V A supra-national advisory council

As to practical application, a conclusion follows from all the preceding considerations: namely, that the passage to a world political society presupposes a will to live together developed in all the peoples, especially all great peoples in the world; any effort to found a World State in the absence of such a universal basis, thus creating a half-universality to be extended progressively to the whole, would, I am afraid, invite war rather than peace.

A second conclusion is that the passage to a one world politically organized can only occur after a long time. I know that time is relative, not only in the sense that a long time with respect to our experience is a short time with respect to history, but also in the sense that time runs faster in proportion as human history goes on. Nevertheless the period of maturation will seem very long to our unhappy race.

It is regrettable that perpetual peace cannot be established immediately after the discovery of the atomic bomb. This is no more regrettable than the fact that it *was necessary* to discover the atomic bomb; this is no more regrettable than the fact that, twenty centuries after the good tidings in Bethlehem, mankind is still in a prehistoric age with regard to the application of the Gospel in actual life. Now the business of human history is not in a stage of free creative development, rather it reckons up its losses; we are paying century-old historical debts. Ancient Israel, in such moments, turned to God in self-accusation and hope. We are more proud, and less hopeful. I have often expressed the opinion that our major problems cannot be decisively settled before the time of great crisis and great reconciliation announced by St. Paul.

Yet the creative process, visibly or invisibly, is always at work in history; and the saddest periods are often the most fecund ones. If nations have still to extricate themselves, in a most precarious and far from brilliant way, from the dangers of universal destruction, and if the foundation of a politically organized community of the world is only to be expected in a distant future, this is but reason to hope for that foundation more strongly, and to undertake, right now, with greater energy, the task of preparing it, and of awakening common consciousness to the imperative necessity of moving toward it.

---

13 Cf. McGeorge Bundy, "An Impossible World Republic," *Reporter*, November 22, 1949.

This task, as we well know, has already been undertaken by the most courageous and far-seeing pioneers—in Chicago especially it was undertaken six days after the first atomic bomb dropped on Hiroshima. Such a task will obviously develop first of all as a deep and continuing task of education and enlightenment, discussion and study. It will also develop through the efforts, limited as they may be, of the diverse cooperative agencies of the United Nations, and through all the various efforts that have been started everywhere to promote the federal idea, and which are especially valuable, in my opinion, when they tend to well defined objectives actually achievable in one partial field or another, and are on their guard, at the same time, against the risk of only creating new and larger patterns for the world competition they are trying to eliminate.

But is there no means whatever of inserting in the present structure of the world a germ, however small it may be, or a first beginning, however weak it may be, which would have a chance of proving useful, if, some day, better times make possible the *political preparation* for the foundation of a world political society? Everyone's imagination can exert itself in this regard. Well, at this point may I also be permitted to make, in the most tentative way, a suggestion of my own?

My own suggestion is that a new superior agency, which would be deprived of any *power* whatsoever, but endowed with unquestionable *moral authority*, would perhaps have a chance of being accepted by the States, and would also have a chance of becoming the first beginning of which I just spoke.

Let us suppose a kind of world council whose function would be only a function of ethical and political wisdom, and which would be made up of the highest and most experienced authorities in moral and juridical sciences. Let us suppose that the members of this supreme advisory council would

be picked from the nations of the world according to some equitable method of apportionment, and would be directly elected by the people of all nations, among men previously proposed by the highest institutions and the governments of every State. But let us suppose that, once elected, they would lose their national citizenship and would be given world citizenship, so as to become independent of any government and completely free in the exercise of their spiritual responsibility.

Let us suppose that they would be materially disarmed, without any other means of action than their own pronouncements, and only protected by the mutual commitments of the States. And let us suppose that they would be deprived of any powers, even, in contradistinction to the present International Court of Justice, of any judicial power. No government could appeal to them to make any decision, they would have no juridical connection with the United Nations, they would be simply free to tell the governments and the nations what they held to be just.

In proportion as such a supreme advisory council acted in a really wise, independent, and firm manner, and resisted the pressures exerted upon it, its moral authority would grow stronger, as well as its influence on public opinion. It would give a voice to the conscience of the peoples.

I think that being really a world institution, shielded by its constitution from the interference of any government; being, at the same time, deprived of powers; and exercising a merely moral function, it would have a chance of disarming the fears—fears of manoeuvres, of encirclement, of loss of prestige, etc.—which spoil the activities of international organizations; as a result, and taking into account the lip service which even the most cynical governments deem it necessary to pay to the moral factor, I think that some day, perhaps after new ordeals shall have made the situation more desperate, the idea of such a supreme advisory council could perhaps have a chance of being accepted by all States and governments.

What makes me fond of that idea is the fact that by this means a possibility could be offered for the coming into being of something indispensable and badly needed—namely an organized international opinion.

It is also the fact that, by this means, people could be enlightened and helped with regard to the most intricate temporal problems which concern the common good of the world, and on which, in democratic nations, they have to make a decision. Some of such problems are even of a nature to put their consciences on the rack—I am thinking especially of the problem of just war. People know that participating in an unjust war is sharing in homicide. They are told, on the other hand, that things have become so obscure and entangled that they lack competence to bear judgment on each particular case: am I bound, then, to share in what is *perhaps* a crime, because my government is a better judge than I on the matter, even if I were a German at the time of the Hitlerian war? On the opposite side, systematic conscientious objection is a tragic illusion, no less harmful to justice than blind obedience. The old standards with respect to which a war was to be considered just or unjust are outworn, and

nevertheless the fact of giving up the distinction between the just and the unjust, in the case of war as in any other case, would boil down to a simple abdication of moral reason. It would be good if, in given and especially serious international conjunctures, a senate of wise men were to tell people where, in their opinion, the road to justice was.

But first and foremost, if such a senate of wise men existed, it would be the first token of the possibility of a really supra-national world organization, and it would foster in the consciousness of the peoples that great movement of intelligence and will on which depends the genuine and constructive revolution needed by our historical age, the foundation of a world community politically organized.

I am afraid that in expressing at the end of this essay a practical suggestion of my own, I have perhaps yielded to the old temptation of philosophers, who would have reason, through the instrumentality of certain wise men, be accepted as an authority in human affairs. After all, this would be less serious an illusion, I suppose—and in any case a less frequent one—than the conviction treasured by so many fatalists, that any reliance on reason has to be carefully avoided in the conduct of *Man, and the State.*

NOTE TO THE READER

As Maritain indicates, the problem of world government revolves around the ideas of state and of government. Both ideas, the reader may be reminded, constitute distinct and whole chapters in the *Syntopicon*. Chapter 31 is devoted to GOVERNMENT, Chapter 90 to STATE, which also includes the analysis and indexing of discussions of the general idea of society. In these chapters, in their introductory essays, and in the discussions in *GBWW* which their references cite, the reader will find a wealth of material to aid the analysis and understanding of these ideas and of the issues in which

they are involved.

In particular, the reader will find in STATE 10f, the ideal of a world state, references to discussions that are relevant to the problem of world government. GOVERNMENT 2e, the ideal form of government, cites passages bearing on the distinction between practicable and utopian ideals.

The reader also should not forget that *GGB* contains materials dealing with the world political society, particularly Dante's *De Monarchia*, Vol. 7, pp. 379–99, and Kant's *Perpetual Peace*, Vol. 7, pp. 437–75.

On the Formation of Coral-Reefs

Charles Darwin

Editor's Introduction

In 1831, when Charles Darwin was twenty-two, he was to all appearances merely an agreeable young English gentleman, with abilities not as yet developed in any particular direction, who seemed chiefly to be fond of hunting. Despite his failure to make anything of either the classical studies that were prescribed for him as a schoolboy, the medical training he subsequently received at Edinburgh, or the three years he spent after that at Cambridge with the idea that he might enter the ministry, it was just possible to see that he had definite interests and talents. But as these were all in the area of natural history, where he had received no formal education, they had manifested themselves in nothing much more systematic than a passion for collecting beetles. He had not himself guessed the significance of the fact that the books he found most interesting were all works of natural science, that he was good at zoology when he got a chance one summer to work at it, and that his closest friend and mentor at Cambridge, J. S. Henslow, was a professor of botany and learned besides in entomology, chemistry, mineralogy, and geology. Thus when Henslow, who had arranged for Darwin to go on a field trip through Wales in the summer of 1831, told him on his return of an opportunity to sail as a naturalist on the impending survey voyage of H.M.S. *Beagle,* Darwin almost turned it down, in deference to his father's objections. He was persuaded to change his mind only by his uncle—Josiah Wedgwood, the son of the famous potter—who convinced his father also that it was the thing for the young man to do.

The *Beagle,* a vessel of about five hundred tons (fully loaded), carried seventy-four officers and men around the world, from England to Tierra del Fuego and back by way of the South Sea Islands and the Indian Archipelago. The voyage took five years, from 1831 to 1836, and constituted, as Darwin afterward said, "by far the most important event in my life." Not only did he gain experience beyond that of any naturalist of his day; he brought back masses of notes and observations, the material for a lifetime of study. Unhappily, he also, though he did not know it, contracted a tropical disease (as the evidence now suggests) that made him a chronic invalid.

From his notebooks and a diary he kept, Darwin eventually put together an account of the cruise that was first published in 1839 and appeared thereafter in various editions with different titles, coming to be known at last merely as *The Voyage of the Beagle*. An immediate success, it has always been the best liked of his books, as it was the one that gave him most satisfaction. In its description of how he sought out, noted, examined, compared, and reflected upon plants, animals, fish, bones, and fossils—a myriad of living things and their remains—it provides a wholly engaging picture of a great naturalist at work.

Besides this volume, two important scientific insights grew out of the voyage. One became the theory of evolution, the idea that the species we can distinguish among creatures both living and extinct are not fixed forms but such as have adapted to their environment; they represent a natural selection, the theory says, from among other kinds less able to survive. Darwin wrote of this, perhaps the best known of all scientific hypotheses, in *The Origin of Species* (1859). The particular evidence for it, which he understood only years later, was in the strange birds, tortoises, and lizards he observed in the Galápagos Islands—creatures not found elsewhere, as he knew, and ones that he gradually realized were the descendants of mainland species modified by their habitat. They exhibited the evolutionary process clearly, without the confusion that the abundance and variety of mainland species at various stages of development tend to create.

The other insight the voyage inspired was one that Darwin arrived at even before he got home. This was that coral reefs and atolls, which ring so many of the Pacific islands, have built up around the shores of partially submerged volcanic peaks that gradually sink as the ocean floor subsides, and are not growths upon sedimentary platforms deposited by the ocean on peaks long since submerged. Darwin explained why he thought this was so in a portion of *The Voyage of the Beagle* that is reprinted here, as well as in a separate volume called *The Structure and Distribution of Coral Reefs*. His theory was for a long time disputed, and it remained at best a plausible though highly interesting guess until after the Second World War, when drillings were made through the hard coral of the Pacific atolls that hit the volcanic rock—not sediment—which Darwin had assumed would be there. It was the vindication of one of the most remarkable bits of observation and one of the choicest pieces of reasoning in scientific literature.

On the Formation of Coral-Reefs

Charles Darwin

I will now give a very brief account of the three great classes of coral-reefs; namely, Atolls, Barrier, and Fringing-reefs, and will explain my views on their formation. Almost every voyager who has crossed the Pacific has expressed his unbounded astonishment at the lagoon-islands, or as I shall for the future call them by their Indian name of atolls, and has attempted some explanation. Even as long ago as the year 1605, Pyrard de Laval well exclaimed, "C'est une merville de voir chacun de ces atollons, environné d'un grand banc de pierre tout autour, n'y ayant point d'artifice humain." [It is a marvel to see these atolls, each surrounded by a great stone parapet which has nothing to do with any human artifice.] The accompanying sketch [Fig. 1] of Whitsunday Island in the Pacific, copied from Capt. Beechey's admirable Voyage, gives but a faint idea of the singular aspect of an atoll: it is one of the smallest size, and has its narrow islets united together in a ring. The immensity of the ocean, the fury of the breakers, contrasted with the lowness of the land and the smoothness of the bright green water within the lagoon, can hardly be imagined without having been seen.

The earlier voyagers fancied that the coral-building animals instinctively built up their great circles to afford themselves protection in the inner parts; but so far is this from the truth, that those massive kinds, to whose growth on the exposed outer shores the very existence of the reef depends, cannot live within the lagoon, where other delicately-branching kinds flourish. Moreover, on this view, many species of distinct genera and families are supposed to combine for one end; and of such a combination, not a single instance can be found in the whole of nature. The theory that has been most generally received is, that atolls are based on submarine craters; but when we consider the form and size of some, the number, proximity, and relative positions of others, this idea loses its plausible character: thus, Suadiva atoll is 44 geographical miles in diameter in one line, by 34 miles in another line; Rimsky is 54 by 20 miles across, and it has a strangely sinuous margin; Bow atoll is 30 miles long, and on an average only 6 in width; Menchicoff atoll consists of three atolls united or tied together. This theory, moreover, is totally inapplicable to the northern Maldiva atolls in the Indian Ocean (one of which is 88 miles in length, and between 10 and 20 in breadth), for they are not bounded like ordinary atolls by narrow reefs, but by a vast number of separate little atolls; other little atolls rising out of the great central lagoon-like spaces. A third and better theory was advanced by Chamisso, who thought that from the corals growing more vigorously where exposed to the open sea, as undoubtedly is the case, the outer edges would grow up from the general foundation before any other part, and that this would account for the ring or cup-shaped structure. But we shall immediately see, that in this, as well as in the crater-theory, a most important consideration has been over-

[Fig. 1]

looked, namely, on what have the reef-building corals, which cannot live at a great depth, based their massive structures?

Numerous soundings were carefully taken by Captain Fitz Roy on the steep outside of Keeling atoll, and it was found that within ten fathoms, the prepared tallow at the bottom of the lead invariably came up marked with the impressions of living corals, but as perfectly clean as if it had been dropped on a carpet of turf; as the depth increased, the impressions became less numerous, but the adhering particles of sand more and more numerous, until at last it was evident that the bottom consisted of a smooth sandy layer: to carry on the analogy of the turf, the blades of grass grew thinner and thinner, till at last the soil was so sterile, that nothing sprang from it. From these observations, confirmed by many others, it may be safely inferred that the utmost depth at which corals can construct reefs is between 20 and 30 fathoms. Now there are enormous areas in the Pacific and Indian oceans, in which every single island is of coral formation, and is raised only to that height to which the waves can throw up fragments, and the winds pile up sand. Thus the Radack group of atolls is an irregular square, 520 miles long and 240 broad; the Low archipelago is elliptic-formed, 840 miles in its longer, and 420 in its shorter axis: there are other small groups and single low islands between these two archipelagoes, making a linear space of ocean actually more than 4000 miles in length, in which not one single island rises above the specified height. Again, in the Indian Ocean there is a space of ocean 1500 miles in length, including three archipelagoes, in which every island is low and of coral formation. From the fact of the reef-building corals not living at great depths, it is absolutely certain that throughout these vast areas, wherever there is now an atoll, a foundation must have originally existed within a depth of from 20 to 30 fathoms from the surface. It is improbable in the highest degree that broad, lofty, isolated, steep-sided banks of sediment, arranged in groups and lines hundreds of leagues in length, could have been deposited in the central and profoundest parts of the Pacific and Indian oceans, at an immense distance from any continent, and where the water is perfectly limpid. It is equally improbable that the elevatory forces should have uplifted throughout the above vast areas, innumerable great rocky banks within 20 to 30 fathoms, or 120 to 180 feet, of the surface of the sea, and not one single point above that level; for where on the whole face of the globe can we find a single chain of mountains, even a few hundred miles in length, with their many summits rising within a few feet of a given level, and not one pinnacle above it? If then the foundations, whence the atoll-building corals sprang, were not formed of sediment, and if they were not lifted up to the required level, they must of necessity have subsided into it; and this at once solves the difficulty. For as mountain after mountain, and island after island, slowly sank beneath the water, fresh bases would be successively afforded for the growth of the corals. It is impossible here to enter into all the necessary details, but I venture to defy any one to explain in any other manner, how it is possible that numerous islands should be distributed throughout vast areas—all the islands being low—all being built of corals, absolutely requiring a foundation within a limited depth from the surface.[1]

Before explaining how atoll-formed reefs acquire their peculiar structure, we must turn to the second great class, namely, Barrier-reefs. These either extend in straight lines in front of the shores of a continent or of a large island, or they encircle smaller islands; in both cases, being separated from the land by a broad and rather deep channel of water, analogous to the lagoon within an atoll. It is remarkable how little attention has been paid to encircling barrier-reefs; yet they are truly wonderful structures. The following sketch [Fig. 2] represents part of the barrier encircling the island of Bolabola in the Pacific, as seen from one of the central peaks. In this instance the whole line of reef has been converted into land; but usually a snow-white line of great breakers, with only here and there a single low islet crowned with cocoa-

nut trees, divides the dark heaving waters of the ocean from the light-green expanse of the lagoon-channel. And the quiet waters of this channel generally bathe a fringe of low alluvial soil, loaded with the most beautiful productions of the tropics, and lying at the foot of the wild, abrupt, central mountains.

Encircling barrier-reefs are of all sizes, from three miles to no less than forty-four miles in diameter; and that which fronts one side, and encircles both ends, of New Caledonia, is 400 miles long. Each reef includes one, two, or several rocky islands of various heights; and in one instance, even as many as twelve separate islands. The reef runs at a greater or less distance from the included land; in the Society archipelago generally from one to three or four miles; but at Hogoleu the reef is 20 miles on the southern side, and 14 miles on the opposite or northern side, from the included islands. The depth within the lagoon-channel also varies much; from 10 to 30 fathoms may be taken as an average; but at Vanikoro there are spaces no less than 56 fathoms or

---

[1] It is remarkable that Mr. Lyell, even in the first Edition of his "Principles of Geology," inferred that the amount of subsidence in the Pacific must have exceeded that of elevation, from the area of land being very small relatively to the agents there tending to form it, namely, the growth of coral and volcanic action.

[Fig. 2]

336 feet deep. Internally the reef either slopes gently into the lagoon-channel, or ends in a perpendicular wall sometimes between two and three hundred feet under water in height: externally the reef rises, like an atoll, with extreme abruptness out of the profound depths of the ocean. What can be more singular than these structures? We see an island, which may be compared to a castle situated on the summit of a lofty submarine mountain, protected by a great wall of coral-rock, always steep externally and sometimes internally, with a broad level summit, here and there breached by narrow gateways, through which the largest ships can enter the wide and deep encircling moat.

As far as the actual reef of coral is concerned, there is not the smallest difference, in general size, outline, grouping, and even in quite trifling details of structure, between a barrier and an atoll. The geographer Balbi has well remarked, that an encircled island is an atoll with high land rising out of its lagoon; remove the land from within, and a perfect atoll is left.

But what has caused these reefs to spring up at such great distances from the shores of the included islands? It cannot be that the corals will not grow close to the land; for the shores within the lagoon-channel, when not surrounded by alluvial soil, are often fringed by living reefs; and we shall presently see that there is a whole class, which I have called Fringing-reefs from their close attachment to the shores both of continents and of islands. Again, on what have the reef-building corals, which cannot live at great depths, based their encircling structures? This is a great apparent difficulty, analogous to that in the case of atolls, which has generally been overlooked. It will be perceived more clearly by inspecting the following sections [Fig. 3], which are real ones, taken in north and south lines, through the islands with their barrier-reefs, of Vanikoro, Gambier, and Maurua; and they are laid down, both vertically and horizontally, on the same scale of a quarter of an inch to a mile.

It should be observed that the sections might have been taken in any direction through these islands, or through many other encircled islands, and the general features would have been the same. Now bearing in mind that reef-building coral

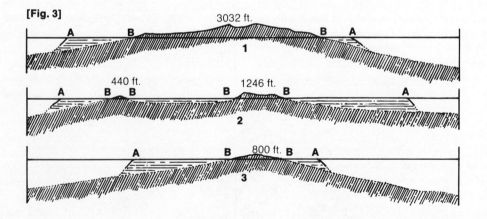

[Fig. 3]

3032 ft.

1

440 ft.   1246 ft.

2

800 ft.

3

1. Vanikoro.   **2.** Gambier Islands.   **3.** Maurua.
The horizontal shading shows the barrier-reefs and lagoon-channels. The inclined shading above the level of the sea **(A)** shows the actual form of the land; the inclined shading below this line shows its probable prolongation under water.

cannot live at a greater depth than from 20 to 30 fathoms, and that the scale is so small that the plummets on the right hand show a depth of 200 fathoms, on what are these barrier-reefs based? Are we to suppose that each island is surrounded by a collar-like submarine ledge of rock, or by a great bank of sediment, ending abruptly where the reef ends? If the sea had formerly eaten deeply into the islands, before they were protected by the reefs, thus having left a shallow ledge round them under water, the present shores would have been invariably bounded by great precipices; but this is most rarely the case. Moreover, on this notion, it is not possible to explain why the corals should have sprung up, like a wall, from the extreme outer margin of the ledge, often leaving a broad space of water within, too deep for the growth of corals. The accumulation of a wide bank of sediment all round these islands, and generally widest where the included islands are smallest, is highly improbable, considering their exposed positions in the central and deepest parts of the ocean. In the case of the barrier-reef of New Caledonia, which extends for 150 miles beyond the northern point of the island, in the same straight line with which it fronts the west coast, it is hardly possible to believe that a bank of sediment could thus have been straightly deposited in front of a lofty island, and so far beyond its termination in the open sea. Finally, if we look to other oceanic islands of about the same height and of similar geological constitution, but not encircled by coral-reefs, we may in vain search for so trifling a circumambient depth as 30 fathoms, except quite near to their shores; for usually land that rises abruptly out of water, as do most of the encircled and non-encircled oceanic islands, plunges abruptly under it. On what then, I repeat, are these barrier-reefs based? Why, with their wide and deep moat-like channels, do they stand so far from the included land? We shall soon see how easily these difficulties disappear.

We come now to our third class of Fring-ing-reefs, which will require a very short notice. Where the land slopes abruptly under water, these reefs are only a few yards in width, forming a mere ribbon or fringe round the shores: where the land slopes gently under the water the reef extends further, sometimes even as much as a mile from the land; but in such cases the soundings outside the reef always show that the submarine prolongation of the land is gently inclined. In fact the reefs extend only to that distance from the shore, at which a foundation within the requisite depth from 20 to 30 fathoms is found. As far as the actual reef is concerned, there is no essential difference between it and that forming a barrier or an atoll: it is, however, generally of less width, and consequently few islets have been formed on it. From the corals growing more vigorously on the outside, and from the noxious effect of the sediment washed inwards, the outer edge of the reef is the highest part, and between it and the land there is generally a shallow sandy channel a few feet in depth. Where banks of sediment have accumulated near to the surface, as in parts of the West Indies, they sometimes become fringed with corals, and hence in some degree resemble lagoon-islands or atolls; in the same manner as fringing-reefs, surrounding gently-sloping islands, in some degree resemble barrier-reefs.

No theory on the formation of coral-reefs can be considered satisfactory which does not include the three great classes. We have seen that we are driven to believe in the subsidence of these vast areas, interspersed with low islands, of which not one rises above the height to which the wind and waves can throw up matter, and yet are constructed by animals requiring a foundation, and that foundation to lie at no great depth. Let us then take an island surrounded by fringing-reefs, which offer no difficulty in their structure; and let this island with its reef, represented by the unbroken lines in the woodcut [Fig. 4], slowly subside. Now as the island sinks down,

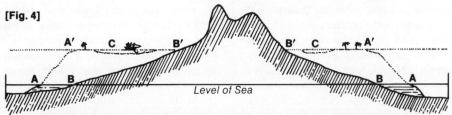

[Fig. 4]

Level of Sea

A. Outer edges of the fringing-reef, at the level of the sea. **B.** The shores of the fringed island.

A′. Outer edges of the reef, after its upward growth during a period of subsidence, now converted into a barrier, with islets on it. **B′.** The shores of the now encircled island. **C.** Lagoon-channel.

Note: In this and the following woodcut, the subsidence of the land could be represented only by an apparent rise in the level of the sea.

either a few feet at a time or quite insensibly, we may safely infer, from what is known of the conditions favourable to the growth of coral, that the living masses, bathed by the surf on the margin of the reef, will soon regain the surface. The water, however, will encroach little by little on the shore, the island becoming lower and smaller, and the space between the inner edge of the reef and the beach proportionally broader. A section of the reef and island in this state, after a subsidence of several hundred feet, is given by the dotted lines. Coral islets are supposed to have been formed on the reef; and a ship is anchored in the lagoon-channel. This channel will be more or less deep, according to the rate of subsidence, to the amount of sediment accumulated in it, and to the growth of the delicately branched corals which can live there. The section in this state resembles in every respect one drawn through an encircled island: in fact, it is a real section (on the scale of .517 of an inch to a mile) through Bolabola in the Pacific. We can now at once see why encircling barrier-reefs stand so far from the shores which they front. We can also perceive that a line drawn perpendicularly down from the outer edge of the new reef, to the foundation of solid rock beneath the old fringing-reef, will exceed by as many feet as there have been feet of subsidence, that small limit of depth at which the effective corals can live—the

little architects having built up their great wall-like mass, as the whole sank down, upon a basis formed of other corals and their consolidated fragments. Thus the difficulty on this head, which appeared so great, disappears.

If, instead of an island, we had taken the shore of a continent fringed with reefs, and had imagined it to have subsided, a great straight barrier, like that of Australia or New Caledonia, separated from the land by a wide and deep channel, would evidently have been the result.

Let us take our new encircling barrier-reef [Fig. 5], of which the section is now represented by unbroken lines, and which, as I have said, is a real section through Bolabola, and let it go on subsiding. As the barrier-reef slowly sinks down, the corals will go on vigorously growing upwards; but as the island sinks, the water will gain inch by inch on the shore—the separate mountains first forming separate islands within one great reef—and finally, the last and highest pinnacle disappearing. The instant this takes place, a perfect atoll is formed: I have said, remove the high land from within an encircling barrier-reef, and an atoll is left, and the land has been removed. We can now perceive how it comes that atolls, having sprung from encircling barrier-reefs, resemble them in general size, form, in the manner in which they are grouped together, and in their arrangement in single or double lines; for they may be called rude outline charts of the sunken islands over which they stand. We can further see how it arises that the atolls in the Pacific and Indian oceans extend in lines parallel to the generally prevailing strike of the high islands and the great coast-lines of those oceans. I venture, therefore, to affirm, that on the theory of the upward growth of the corals during the sinking of the land,[2] all the leading features in those wonderful structures, the lagoon-islands or atolls, which have so long excited the attention of voyagers, as well as in the no less wonderful barrier-reefs, whether encircling small islands or stretching for hundreds of miles along the shores of a continent, are simply explained.

It may be asked whether I can offer any direct evidence of the subsidence of barrier-reefs or atolls; but it must be borne in mind how difficult it must ever be to detect a movement, the tendency of which is to hide under water the part affected. Nevertheless, at Keeling atoll I observed on all sides of the lagoon old cocoa-nut trees undermined and falling; and in one place the foundation-posts of a shed, which the inhabitants asserted had stood seven years before just above high-water mark, but now was daily washed by every tide: on inquiry I found

that three earthquakes, one of them severe, had been felt here during the last ten years. At Vanikoro, the lagoon-channel is remarkably deep, scarcely any alluvial soil has accumulated at the foot of the lofty included mountains, and remarkably few islets have been formed by the heaping of fragments and sand on the wall-like barrier-reef; these facts, and some analogous ones, led me to believe that this island must lately have subsided and the reef grown upwards: here again earthquakes are frequent and very severe. In the Society archipelago, on the other hand, where the lagoon-channels are almost choked up, where much low alluvial land has accumulated, and where in some cases long islets have been formed on the barrier-reefs—facts all showing that the islands have not very lately subsided—only

---

[2] It has been highly satisfactory to me to find the following passage in a pamphlet by Mr. Couthouy, one of the naturalists in the great Antarctic Expedition of the United States: "Having personally examined a large number of coral-islands, and resided eight months among the volcanic class having shore and partially encircling reefs, I may be permitted to state that my own observations have impressed a conviction of the correctness of the theory of Mr. Darwin." The naturalists, however, of this expedition differ with me on some points respecting coral formations.

[Fig. 5]

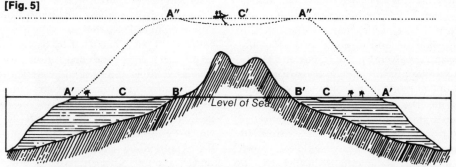

A'. Outer edges of the barrier-reef at the level of the sea, with islets on it. **B'.** The shores of the included island. **C.** The lagoon-channel.

A''. Outer edges of the reef, now converted into an atoll. **C'.** The lagoon of the new atoll.

Note: According to the true scale, the depths of the lagoon-channel and lagoon are much exaggerated.

feeble shocks are most rarely felt. In these coral formations, where the land and water seem struggling for mastery, it must be ever difficult to decide between the effects of a change in the set of the tides and of a slight subsidence: that many of these reefs and atolls are subject to changes of some kind is certain; on some atolls the islets appear to have increased greatly within a late period; on others they have been partially or wholly washed away. The inhabitants of parts of the Maldiva archipelago know the date of the first formation of some islets; in other parts, the corals are now flourishing on water-washed reefs, where holes made for graves attest the former existence of inhabited land. It is difficult to believe in frequent changes in the tidal currents of an open ocean; whereas, we have in the earthquakes recorded by the natives on some atolls, and in the great fissures observed on other atolls, plain evidence of changes and disturbances in progress in the subterranean regions.

It is evident, on our theory, that coasts merely fringed by reefs cannot have subsided to any perceptible amount; and therefore they must, since the growth of their corals, either have remained stationary or have been upheaved. Now it is remarkable how generally it can be shown, by the presence of upraised organic remains, that the fringed islands have been elevated: and so far, this is indirect evidence in favour of our theory. I was particularly struck with this fact, when I found to my surprise, that the descriptions given by MM. Quoy and Gaimard were applicable, not to reefs in general as implied by them, but only to those of the fringing-class; my surprise, however, ceased when I afterwards found that, by a strange chance, all the several islands visited by these eminent naturalists, could be shown by their own statements to have been elevated within a recent geological era.

Not only the grand features in the structure of barrier-reefs and of atolls, and of their likeness to each other in form, size, and other characters, are explained on the theory of subsidence—which theory we are independently forced to admit in the very areas in question, from the necessity of finding bases for the corals within the requisite depth—but many details in structure and exceptional cases can thus also be simply explained. I will give only a few instances. In barrier-reefs it has long been remarked with surprise, that the passages through the reef exactly face valleys in the included land, even in cases where the reef is separated from the land by a lagoon-channel so wide and so much deeper than the actual passage itself, that it seems hardly possible that the very small quantity of water or sediment brought down could injure the corals on the reef. Now, every reef of the fringing-class is breached by a narrow gateway in front of the smallest rivulet, even if dry during the greater part of the year, for the mud, sand, or gravel, occasionally washed down, kills the corals on which it is deposited. Consequently, when an island thus fringed subsides, though most of the narrow gateways will probably become closed by the outward and upward growth of the corals, yet any that are not closed (and some must always be kept open by the sediment and impure water flowing out of the lagoon-channel) will still continue to front exactly the upper parts of those valleys, at the mouths of which the original basal fringing-reef was breached.

We can easily see how an island fronted only on one side, or on one side with one end or both ends encircled by barrier-reefs, might after long-continued subsidence be converted either into a single wall-like reef, or into an atoll with a great straight spur projecting from it, or into two or three atolls tied together by straight reefs—all of which exceptional cases actually occur. As the reef-building corals require food, are preyed upon by other animals, are killed by sediment, cannot adhere to a loose bottom, and may be easily carried down to a depth whence they cannot spring up again, we need feel no surprise at the reefs both of atolls and barriers becoming in parts imperfect. The great barrier of New Caledonia is thus imperfect and broken in many parts; hence, after long subsidence, this great reef would not produce one great atoll 400 miles in length, but a chain or archipelago of atolls, of very nearly the same dimensions with those in the Maldiva archipelago. Moreover, in an atoll once breached on opposite sides, from the likelihood of the oceanic and tidal currents passing straight through the breaches, it is extremely improbable that the corals, especially during continued subsidence, would ever be able again to unite the rim; if they did not, as the whole sank downwards, one atoll would be divided into two or more. In the Maldiva archipelago there are distinct atolls so related to each other in position, and separated by channels either unfathomable or very deep (the channel between Ross and Ari atolls is 150 fathoms, and that between the north and south Nillandoo atolls is 200 fathoms in depth), that it is impossible to look at a map of them without believing that they were once more intimately related. And in this same archipelago, Mahlos-Mahdoo atoll is divided by a bifurcating channel from 100 to 132 fathoms in depth, in such a manner, that it is scarcely possible to say whether it ought strictly to be called three separate atolls, or one great atoll not yet finally divided.

I will not enter on many more details; but I must remark that the curious structure of the northern Maldiva atolls receives (taking into consideration the free entrance of the sea through their broken margins) a simple explanation in the upward and outward growth of the corals, originally based both on small detached reefs in their lagoons, such as occur in common atolls, and on broken portions of the linear marginal reef, such as bounds every atoll of the ordinary form. I cannot refrain from once again remarking on the singularity of these complex structures—a great sandy and generally concave disk rises abruptly from the unfathomable ocean, with its central expanse studded, and its edge symmetrically bordered with oval basins of coral-rock just lipping the surface of the sea, sometimes clothed with vegetation, and each containing a lake of clear water!

One more point in detail: as in two neighbouring archipelagoes corals flourish in one and not in the other, and as so many conditions before enumerated must affect their existence, it would be an inexplicable fact if, during the changes to which earth, air, and water are subjected, the reef-building corals were to keep alive for perpetuity on any one spot or area. And as by our theory the areas including atolls and barrier-reefs are subsiding, we ought occasionally to find reefs both dead and submerged. In all reefs, owing to the sediment being washed out of the lagoon or lagoon-channel to leeward, that side is least favourable to the long-continued vigorous growth of the corals; hence dead portions of reef not unfrequently occur on the leeward side; and these, though still retaining their proper wall-like form, are now in several instances sunk several fathoms beneath the surface. The Chagos group appears from some cause, possibly from the subsidence having been too rapid, at present to be much less favourably circumstanced for the growth of reefs than formerly: one atoll has a portion of its marginal reef, nine miles in length, dead and submerged; a second has only a few quite small living points which rise to the surface; a third and fourth are entirely dead and submerged; a fifth is a mere wreck, with its structure almost obliterated. It is remarkable that in all these cases, the dead reefs and portions of reef lie at nearly the same depth, namely, from six to eight fathoms beneath the surface, as if they had been carried down by one uniform movement. One of these "half-drowned atolls," so called by Capt. Moresby (to whom I am indebted for much invaluable information), is of vast size, namely, ninety nautical miles across in one direction, and seventy miles in another line; and is in many respects eminently curious. As by our theory it follows that new atolls will generally be formed in each new area of subsidence, two weighty objections might have been raised, namely, that atolls must be increasing indefinitely in number; and secondly, that in old areas of subsidence each separate atoll must be increasing indefinitely in thickness, if proofs of their occasional destruction could not have been adduced. Thus have we traced the history of these great rings of coral-rock, from their first origin through their normal changes, and through the occasional accidents of their existence, to their death and final obliteration.

In my volume on "Coral Formations" I have published a map, in which I have coloured all the atolls dark-blue, the barrier-reefs pale-blue, and the fringing-reefs red. These latter reefs have been formed whilst the land has been stationary, or, as appears from the frequent presence of upraised organic remains, whilst it has been slowly rising: atolls and barrier-reefs, on the other hand, have grown up during the directly opposite movement of subsidence, which movement must have been very gradual, and in the case of atolls so vast in amount as to have buried every mountain-summit over wide ocean-spaces. Now in this map we see that the reefs tinted pale and dark blue, which have been produced by the same order of movement, as a general rule manifestly stand near each other. Again we see that the areas with the two blue tints are of wide extent; and that they lie separate from extensive lines of coast coloured red, both of which circumstances might naturally have been inferred, on the theory of the nature of the reefs having been governed by the nature of the earth's movement. It deserves notice, that in more than one instance where single red and blue circles approach near each other, I can show that there have been oscillations of level; for in such cases the red or fringed circles consist of atolls, originally by our theory formed during subsidence, but subsequently upheaved; and on the other hand, some of

the pale-blue or encircled islands are composed of coral-rock, which must have been uplifted to its present height before that subsidence took place, during which the existing barrier-reefs grew upwards.

Authors have noticed with surprise, that although atolls are the commonest coral-structures throughout some enormous oceanic tracts, they are entirely absent in other seas, as in the West Indies: we can now at once perceive the cause, for where there has not been subsidence, atolls cannot have been formed; and in the case of the West Indies and parts of the East Indies, these tracts are known to have been rising within the recent period. The larger areas, coloured red and blue, are all elongated; and between the two colours there is a degree of rude alternation, as if the rising of one had balanced the sinking of the other. Taking into consideration the proofs of recent elevation both on the fringed coasts and on some others (for instance, in South America) where there are no reefs, we are led to conclude that the great continents are for the most part rising areas; and from the nature of the coral-reefs, that the central parts of the great oceans are sinking areas. The East Indian archipelago, the most broken land in the world, is in most parts an area of elevation, but surrounded and penetrated, probably in more lines than one, by narrow areas of subsidence.

I have marked with vermilion spots all the many known active volcanoes within the limits of this same map. Their entire absence from every one of the great subsiding areas, coloured either pale or dark blue, is most striking; and not less so is the coincidence of the chief volcanic chains with the parts coloured red, which we are led to conclude have either long remained stationary, or more generally have been recently upraised. Although a few of the vermilion spots occur within no great distance of single circles tinted blue, yet not one single active volcano is situated within several hundred miles of an archipelago, or even small group of atolls. It is, therefore,

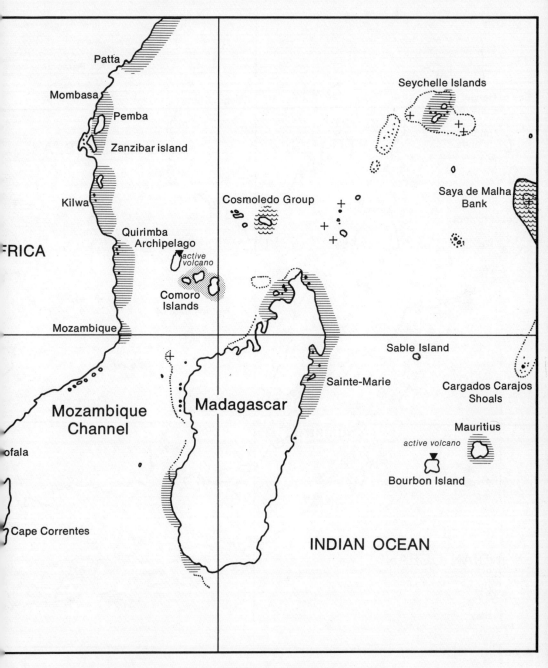

Patta

Mombasa

Pemba

Zanzibar island

Kilwa

Quirimba
Archipelago

active
volcano

FRICA

Comoro
Islands

Mozambique

Mozambique
Channel

ofala

Cape Correntes

Madagascar

Sainte-Marie

Cosmoledo Group

Seychelle Islands

Saya de Malha
Bank

Sable Island

Cargados Carajos
Shoals

Mauritius

active volcano

Bourbon Island

INDIAN OCEAN

〰〰〰〰 ATOLLS OR LAGOON ISLANDS (DARWIN'S TEXT—DARK BLUE)
░░░░░ BARRIER-REEFS (DARWIN'S TEXT—PALE BLUE)
═════ FRINGING-REEFS (DARWIN'S TEXT—RED)
   + SMALL ELEVATED LAND FORMATIONS

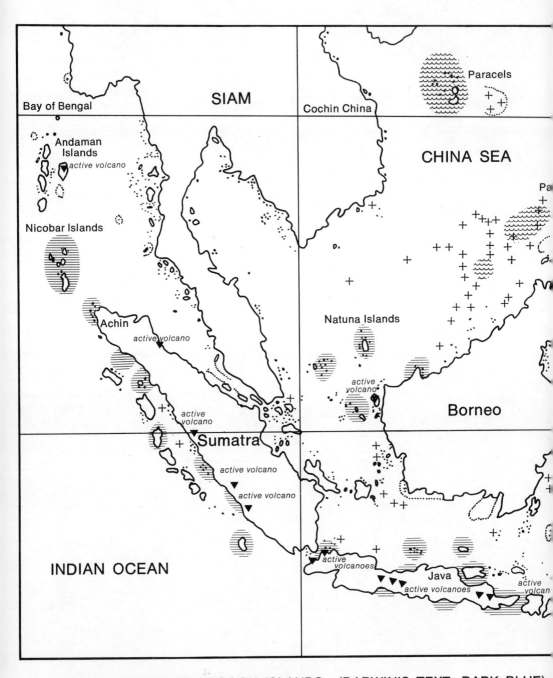

Bay of Bengal

SIAM

Cochin China

Paracels

CHINA SEA

Pa

Andaman
Islands
active volcano

Nicobar Islands

Achin
active volcano

Natuna Islands

active
volcano

Borneo

active
volcano

Sumatra

active volcano

active volcano

active volcano

Java
active volcanoes

active
volcan

INDIAN OCEAN

active
volcanoes

ATOLLS OR LAGOON ISLANDS   (DARWIN'S TEXT—DARK BLUE)
BARRIER-REEFS   (DARWIN'S TEXT—PALE BLUE)
FRINGING-REEFS   (DARWIN'S TEXT—RED)
+   SMALL ELEVATED LAND FORMATIONS

a striking fact that in the Friendly Archipelago, which consists of a group of atolls upheaved and since partially worn down, two volcanoes, and perhaps more, are historically known to have been in action. On the other hand, although most of the islands in the Pacific which are encircled by barrier-reefs, are of volcanic origin, often with the remnants of craters still distinguishable, not one of them is known to have ever been in eruption. Hence in these cases it would appear that volcanoes burst forth into action and become extinguished on the same spots, according as elevatory or subsiding movements prevail there. Numberless facts could be adduced to prove that upraised organic remains are common wherever there are active volcanoes; but until it could be shown that in areas of subsidence, volcanoes were either absent or inactive, the inference, however probable in itself, that their distribution depended on the rising or falling of the earth's surface, would have been hazardous. But now, I think, we may freely admit this important deduction.

Taking a final view of the map, and bearing in mind the statement made with respect to the upraised organic remains, we must feel astonished at the vastness of the areas, which have suffered changes in level either downwards or upwards, within a period not geologically remote. It would appear, also, that the elevatory and subsiding movements follow nearly the same laws. Throughout the spaces interspersed with atolls, where not a single peak of high land has been left above the level of the sea, the sinking must have been immense in amount. The sinking, moreover, whether continuous, or recurrent with intervals sufficiently long for the corals again to bring up their living edifices to the surface, must necessarily have been extremely slow. This conclusion is probably the most important one which can be deduced from the study of coral formations; and it is one which it is difficult to imagine, how otherwise could ever have been arrived at. Nor can I quite pass over the probability of the former existence of large archipelagoes of lofty islands, where now only rings of coral-rock scarcely break the open expanse of the sea, throwing some light on the distribution of the inhabitants of the other high islands, now left standing so immensely remote from each other in the midst of the great oceans. The reef-constructing corals have indeed reared and preserved wonderful memorials of the subterranean oscillations of level; we see in each barrier-reef a proof that the land has there subsided, and in each atoll a monument over an island now lost. We may thus, like unto a geologist who had lived his ten thousand years and kept a record of the passing changes, gain some insight into the great system by which the surface of this globe has been broken up, and land and water interchanged.

NOTE TO THE READER

The full text of *The Voyage of the Beagle* is available in an edition annotated with an introduction by Leonard Engel for the American Museum of Natural History and published by Doubleday Anchor Books (paperback) in 1962. *The Structure and Distribution of Coral Reefs*, with a foreword by H. W. Menard, has been reprinted by the University of California Press (also paperback). Of Darwin's other writings, *The Origin of Species* and *The Descent of Man* are in *GBWW* Vol. 49.

See also in the *Syntopicon* Chapter 36, HYPOTHESIS, especially Topic 4b, on saving the appearances, and Chapter 83, SCIENCE, Topic 5d: Induction and deduction in the philosophy of nature and natural science.

The Battle of the Books

Jonathan Swift

Editor's Introduction

Jonathan Swift was born in Dublin in 1667 and attended Trinity College there. Although he did not complete his course of studies, he managed to attain a degree. The family being in economic straits, he went to England in 1689 to enter the employ of Sir William Temple, a noted diplomat and essayist who was living in retirement at Moor Park. After Temple's death in 1699, Swift returned to Ireland to take up a church living, but the work was not satisfying. He had many friends in England, some in high places, and he visited London and wrote to them. In 1710 his friend Robert Harley became chancellor of the exchequer and Swift entered upon the most exciting period of his life, serving during the last years of Queen Anne's rule as the most influential Tory journalist in England. After the queen's death, however, his friends fell out of power, and Swift retired to the deanery of St. Patrick's, Dublin, in which position he remained for the rest of his life, dying after a long and painful illness in 1745.

The critic Herbert J. Davis has divided Swift's writings into three phases: literary satire, political satire, and moral satire. To the first phase belong *A Tale of a Tub* and *The Battle of the Books;* the former is said to have offended Queen Anne and led to her refusal to make Swift a bishop of the Anglican church. To the second phase belong his efforts in behalf of the Tory ministry and his Irish political works, which included the *Drapier's Letters.* These had the effect of hindering the English from effecting one of their periodic raids on the Irish economy. To the last phase belong *Gulliver's Travels,* published in 1726, the *Modest Proposal,* and other powerful and bitter works of this great misanthrope.

The Battle of the Books was one of the fruits of Swift's ten-year association with Temple. Probably written in 1696 or 1697, the work was not published until 1704. Temple had produced in 1690 an *Essay upon the Ancient and Modern Learning,* in which he had attempted to defend the Ancients against what he considered the presumptuous claims of modern scientists and critics. Unfortunately for Temple, he based much of his defense on two figures—Aesop, the reputed author of the famous fables, and Phalaris, a Greek tyrant who had supposedly written some political letters. But as the noted critic Richard Bentley soon showed, Aesop was more a mythical figure than not, and the *Letters of Phalaris* were outright forgeries. Swift, partly out of affection for Temple and partly out of the natural distaste of the creative writer for critics, defended his employer in the way that you see here. Bentley was a very distinguished man, and so was William Wotton, the other object of Swift's ridicule. It was of course unfair to treat them so uncivilly, but few readers, enjoying the delicious satire, have ever complained.

The work was not meant to be profound. Swift was content to make fun of various figures, among them his cousin, the poet John Dryden, who had offended him. He was not himself even a partisan, strictly speaking, of either side in the underlying controversy, which was the so-called quarrel of the Ancients and Moderns that had occupied writers in both France and England for half a century. Adherents of the Moderns affirmed the idea of progress in human affairs, while their opponents denied it, maintaining that the world's great age was in the past. Swift rejected the first of these contentions wholly and accepted the second one only as it applied to individuals. He regarded men in general as creatures of limited intellect and distinctly limited virtue who were absurd and contemptible in thinking that they could ever be better than they were, or that they ever had been. If he came down harder on the Moderns than on the Ancients in *The Battle of the Books,* it was because in taking the position they did, the Moderns inevitably claimed something for themselves. They could not assert the fact of human progress without implying that they were its result, and so they became the legitimate object of satirical attack.

The text used here combines, along with Swift's own notes, the notes of two earlier editors, John Hawkesworth ("H.") and Sir Walter Scott ("S."). Some further information, indicated by appropriate symbols, has been added.

A

Full and True Account

OF THE

BATTEL

Fought laſt *FRIDAY*,

Between the

Antient and the *Modern*

BOOKS

IN

St. *JAMES*'s

LIBRARY.

LONDON:
Printed in the Year, MDCCX.

Title page from the 1710 edition

The Bookseller to the Reader

The following Discourse, as it is unquestionably of the same author, so it seems to have been written about the same time with the former; I mean the year 1697, when the famous dispute was on foot about ancient and modern learning. The controversy took its rise from an essay of Sir William Temple's upon that subject, which was answered by W. Wotton, B.D., with an Appendix by Dr. Bentley, endeavouring to destroy the credit of Æsop and Phalaris for authors, whom Sir William Temple had, in the essay before-mentioned, highly commended. In that appendix, the doctor falls hard upon a new edition of Phalaris, put out by the Honourable Charles Boyle (now Earl of Orrery), to which Mr. Boyle replied at large, with great learning and wit; and the doctor voluminously rejoined. In this dispute, the town highly resented to see a person of Sir William Temple's character and methods roughly used by the two reverend gentlemen aforesaid, and without any manner of provocation. At length, there appearing no end of the quarrel, our author tells us, that the Books in St. James's Library, looking upon themselves as parties principally concerned, took up the controversy, and came to a decisive battle; but the manuscript, by the injury of fortune or weather, being in several places imperfect, we cannot learn to which side the victory fell.

I must warn the reader to beware of applying to persons what is here meant only of books in the most literal sense. So, when Virgil is mentioned, we are not to understand the person of a famous poet called by that name, but only certain sheets of paper, bound up in leather, containing in print the works of the said poet; and so of the rest.

The Preface of the Author

Satire is a sort of glass, wherein beholders do generally discover everybody's face but their own; which is the chief reason for that kind reception it meets in the world, and that so very few are offended with it. But if it should happen otherwise, the danger is not great; and I have learned, from long experience, never to apprehend mischief from those understandings I have been able to provoke; for anger and fury, though they add strength to the sinews of the body, yet are found to relax those of the mind, and to render all its efforts feeble and impotent.

There is a brain that will endure but one scumming; let the owner gather it with discretion, and manage his little stock with husbandry; but, of all things, let him beware of bringing it under the lash of his betters, because that will make it all bubble up into impertinence, and he will find no new supply. Wit, without knowledge, being a sort of cream, which gathers in a night to the top, and, by a skilful hand, may be soon whipped into froth; but, once scummed away, what appears underneath will be fit for nothing but to be thrown to the hogs.

The Battle of the Books

Jonathan Swift

Whoever examines with due circumspection in the the *Annual Records of Time* [1] will find it remarked, that war is the child of pride, and pride the daughter of riches. The former of which assertions may be soon granted, but one cannot so easily subscribe to the latter; for pride is nearly related to beggary and want, either by father or mother, and sometimes by both: and, to speak naturally, it very seldom happens among men to fall out when all have enough; invasions usually travelling from north to south, that is to say, from poverty upon plenty. The most ancient and natural grounds of quarrels are lust and avarice; which, though we may allow to be brethren, or collateral branches of pride, are certainly the issues of want. For, to speak in the phrase of writers upon the politics, we may observe in the Republic of Dogs (which, in its original, seems to be an institution of the many), that the whole state is ever in the profoundest peace after a full meal; and that civil broils arise among them when it happens for one great bone to be seized on by some leading dog, who either divides it among the few, and then it falls to an oligarchy, or keeps it to himself, and then it runs up to a tyranny. The same reasoning also holds place among them in those dissensions we behold upon a turgescency in any of their females. For the right of possession lying in common (it being impossible to establish a property in so delicate a case), jealousies and suspicions do so abound, that the whole commonwealth of that street is reduced to a manifest state of war, of every citizen against every citizen, till some one, of more courage, conduct, or fortune than the rest, seizes and enjoys the prize; upon which naturally arises plenty of heart-burning, and envy, and snarling against the happy dog. Again, if we look upon any of these republics engaged in a foreign war, either of invasion or defence, we shall find the same reasoning will serve as to the grounds and occasions of each, and that poverty or want in some degree or other (whether real or in opinion, which makes no alteration in the case), has a great share, as well as pride, on the part of the aggressor.

Now, whoever will please to take this scheme, and either reduce or adapt it to an intellectual state, or commonwealth of learning, will soon discover the first ground of disagreement between the two great parties at this time in arms, and may form just conclusions upon the merits of either cause. But the issue of events of this war are not so easy to conjecture at; for the present quarrel is so inflamed by the warm heads of either faction, and the pretensions somewhere or other so exorbitant, as not to admit the least overtures of accommodation. This quarrel first began (as I have heard it affirmed by an old dweller in the neighbourhood) about a small spot of ground, lying and being upon one of the two tops of the hill Parnassus; the highest and largest of which had, it seems, been time out of mind in quiet possession of certain tenants, called the Ancients, and the other was held by the Moderns. But these, disliking their present station, sent certain ambassadors to the Ancients, complaining of a great nuisance; how the height of that part of Parnassus quite spoiled the prospect of theirs, especially towards the *east;* [2] and therefore, to avoid a war, offered them the choice of this alternative—either that the Ancients would please to remove themselves and their effects down to the lower summit, which the Moderns would graciously surrender to them, and advance in their place; or else that the said Ancients will give leave to the Moderns to come with shovels and mattocks, and level the said hill as low as they shall think it convenient. To which the Ancients made answer, how little they expected such a message as this from a colony whom they had admitted, out of their own free grace, to so near a neighbourhood. That, as to their own seat, they were aborigines of it, and therefore to talk with them of a removal or surrender, was a language they did not understand. That if the height of the hill on their side shortened the prospect of the Moderns, it was a disadvantage they could not help, but desired them to consider, whether that injury (if it be any) were not largely recompensed by the shade and shelter it afforded them. That as to the levelling or digging down, it was either folly or ignorance to propose it, if they did, or did not know, how that side of the hill was an entire rock, which would break their tools and hearts, without any damage to itself. That they would therefore advise the Moderns rather to raise their own side of the hill, than dream of pulling down that of the Ancients; to the former of which they would not only give licence, but also largely contribute. All this was rejected by the Moderns with much indignation, who still insisted upon one of the two expedients; and so this difference broke out into a long and obstinate war, maintained on the one part by resolution, and by the courage of certain leaders and allies; but on the other, by the greatness of their number, upon all defeats, affording continual recruits. In this quarrel whole rivulets of ink have been exhausted, and the virulence of both parties enormously augmented. Now, it must here be understood, that ink is the great missive weapon in all battles of the learned, which, conveyed through a sort of engine called a quill, infinite numbers of these are darted at the enemy, by the val-

iant on each side, with equal skill and violence, as if it were an engagement of porcupines. This malignant liquor was compounded, by the engineer who invented it, of two ingredients, which are gall and copperas, by its bitterness and venom to suit in some degree, as well as to foment, the genius of the combatants. And as the Grecians, after an engagement, when they could not agree about the victory, were wont to set up trophies on both sides, the beaten party being content to be at the same expense, to keep itself in countenance (a laudable and ancient custom, happily revived of late, in the art of war), so the learned, after a sharp and bloody dispute, do on both sides hang out their trophies too, whichever comes by the worse. These trophies have largely inscribed on them the merits of the cause, a full impartial account of such a battle, and how the victory fell clearly to the party that set them up. They are known to the world under several names; as disputes, arguments, rejoinders, brief considerations, answers, replies, remarks, reflections, objections, confutations. For a very few days they are fixed up in all public places, either by themselves or their representatives,[3] for passengers to gaze at; from whence the chiefest and largest are removed to certain magazines they call libraries, there to remain in a quarter purposely assigned them, and from thenceforth begin to be called Books of Controversy.

In these books is wonderfully instilled and preserved the spirit of each warrior, while he is alive; and after his death his soul transmigrates there to inform them. This at least is the more common opinion; but I believe it is with libraries as with other cemeteries, where some philosophers affirm that a certain spirit, which they call *brutum hominis,* hovers over the monument till the body is corrupted and turns to dust or to worms, but then vanishes or dissolves. So, we may say, a restless spirit haunts over every book, till dust or worms have seized upon it, which to some may happen in a few days, but to others later;

and, therefore, books of controversy being, of all others, haunted by the most disorderly spirits, have always been confined in a separate lodge from the rest; and, for fear of mutual violence against each other, it was thought prudent by our ancestors to bind them to the peace with strong iron chains. Of which invention the original occasion was this—When the works of Scotus* first came out, they were carried to a certain great library and had lodgings appointed them; but this author was no sooner settled than he went to visit his master Aristotle; and there both concerted together to seize Plato by main force, and turn him out from his ancient station among the divines, where he had peaceably dwelt near eight hundred years. The attempt succeeded, and the two usurpers have reigned ever since in his stead: but to maintain quiet for the future, it was decreed, that all polemics of the larger size should be held fast with a chain.

By this expedient, the public peace of libraries might certainly have been preserved, if a new species of controversial books had not arose of late years, instinct with a most malignant spirit, from the war above-mentioned between the learned, about the higher summit of Parnassus.

When these books were first admitted into the public libraries, I remember to have said, upon occasion, to several persons concerned, how I was sure they would create broils wherever they came, unless a world of care were taken; and therefore I advised, that the champions of each side should be coupled together, or otherwise mixed, that, like the blending of contrary poisons, their malignity might be employed among themselves. And it seems I was neither an ill prophet nor an ill counsellor; for it was nothing else but the neglect of this caution which gave occasion to the terrible fight that happened on Friday last between the ancient and modern books in the King's Library. Now, because the talk of this battle is so fresh in everybody's mouth, and the expectation of the

town so great to be informed in the particulars, I, being possessed of all qualifications requisite in an historian, and retained by neither party, have resolved to comply with the urgent importunity of my friends, by writing down a full impartial account thereof.

The guardian of the regal library,[4] a person of great valour, but chiefly renowned for his humanity,[5] had been a fierce champion for the Moderns; and, in an engagement upon Parnassus, had vowed, with his own hands, to knock down two of the Ancient chiefs,[6] who guarded a small pass on the superior rock; but, endeavouring to climb up, was cruelly obstructed by his own unhappy weight, and tendency towards his centre: a quality to which those of the Modern party are extreme subject; for, being light-headed, they have in speculation a wonderful agility, and conceive nothing too high for them to mount, but in reducing to practice discover a mighty pressure about their posteriors and their heels. Having thus failed in his design, the disappointed champion bore a cruel rancour to the Ancients, which he resolved to gratify by showing all marks of his favour to the books of their adversaries, and lodging them in the fairest apartments; when, at the same time, whatever book had the boldness to own itself for an advocate of the Ancients, was buried alive in some obscure corner, and threatened, upon the least displeasure, to be turned out of doors. Besides, it so happened, that about this time there was a strange confusion of place among all the books in the library; for which several reasons were assigned. Some imputed it to a great heap of learned dust, which a perverse wind blew off from a shelf of Moderns into the keeper's eyes. Others affirmed he had a humour to pick the worms out of the schoolmen, and swallow them fresh and fasting; whereof some fell upon his spleen, and some climbed up

---

* John Duns Scotus, thirteenth-century Scholastic and theologian.

into his head, to the great perturbation of both. And lastly, others maintained, that, by walking much in the dark about the library, he had quite lost the situation of it out of his head; and therefore in replacing his books he was apt to mistake, and clap Descartes next to Aristotle; poor Plato had got between Hobbes and the Seven Wise Masters, and Virgil was hemmed in with Dryden on one side and Withers* on the other.

Meanwhile those books that were advocates for the Moderns chose out one from among them to make a progress through the whole library, examine the number and strength of their party, and concert their affairs. This messenger performed all things very industriously, and brought back with him a list of their forces, in all fifty thousand, consisting chiefly of light-horse, heavy-armed foot, and mercenaries; whereof the foot were in general but sorrily armed, and worse clad; their horses large, but extremely out of case and heart; however, some few, by trading among the Ancients, had furnished themselves tolerably enough.

While things were in this ferment, discord grew extremely high, hot words passed on both sides, and ill blood was plentifully bred. Here a solitary Ancient, squeezed up among a whole shelf of Moderns, offered fairly to dispute the case, and to prove by manifest reasons, that the priority was due them, from long possession, and in regard of their prudence, antiquity, and, above all, their great merits towards the Moderns. But these denied the premises, and seemed very much to wonder, how the Ancients could pretend to insist upon their antiquity, when it was so plain (if they went to that) that the Moderns were much the more ancient [7] of the two. As for any obligations they owed to the Ancients, they renounced them all. ''Tis true,' said they, 'we are informed, some few of our party have been so mean to borrow their subsistence from you; but the rest, infinitely the greater number (and especially we French and English) were so

far from stooping to so base an example, that there never passed, till this very hour, six words between us. For our horses are of our own breeding, our arms of our own forging, and our clothes of our own cutting out and sewing.' Plato was by chance upon the next shelf, and observing those that spoke to be in the ragged plight mentioned a while ago, their jades lean and foundered, their weapons of rotten wood, their armour rusty, and nothing but rags underneath, he laughed aloud, and in his pleasant way swore, by G—— he believed them.

Now, the Moderns had not proceeded in their late negotiation with secrecy enough to escape the notice of the enemy. For those advocates, who had begun the quarrel by setting first on foot the dispute of precedency, talked so loud of coming to a battle, that Temple happened to overhear them, and gave immediate intelligence to the Ancients, who thereupon drew up their scattered troops together, resolving to act upon the defensive; upon which, several of the Moderns fled over to their party, and among the rest Temple himself. This Temple, having been educated and long conversed among the Ancients, was, of all the Moderns, their greatest favourite, and became their greatest champion.

Things were at this crisis, when a material accident fell out. For, upon the highest corner of a large window, there dwelt a certain spider, swollen up to the first magnitude by the destruction of infinite numbers of flies, whose spoils lay scattered before the gates of his palace, like human bones before the cave of some giant. The avenues to his castle were guarded with turnpikes and palisadoes, all after the modern way of fortification.[8] After you had passed several courts, you came to the centre, wherein you might behold the constable himself in his own lodgings, which had windows fronting to each avenue, and ports to sally out, upon all occasions of

---

* George Wither (1588–1667), a minor English pamphleteer and poet.

prey or defence. In this mansion he had for some time dwelt in peace and plenty, without danger to his person by swallows from above, or to his palace by brooms from below; when it was the pleasure of fortune to conduct thither a wandering bee, to whose curiosity a broken pane in the glass had discovered itself, and in he went; where, expatiating a while, he at last happened to alight upon one of the outward walls of the spider's citadel; which, yielding to the unequal weight, sunk down to the very foundation. Thrice he endeavoured to force his passage, and thrice the centre shook. The spider within, feeling the terrible convulsion, supposed at first that nature was approaching to her final dissolution; or else that Beelzebub,[9] with all his legions, was come to revenge the death of many thousands of his subjects, whom his enemy had slain and devoured. However, he at length valiantly resolved to issue forth, and meet his fate. Meanwhile the bee had acquitted himself of his toils, and, posted securely at some distance, was employed in cleansing his wings, and disengaging them from the ragged remnants of the cobweb. By this time the spider was adventured out, when, beholding the chasms, the ruins, and dilapidations of his fortress, he was very near at his wit's end; he stormed and swore like a madman, and swelled till he was ready to burst. At length, casting his eye upon the bee, and wisely gathering causes from events (for they knew each other by sight): 'A plague split you,' said he, 'for a giddy son of a whore. Is it you, with a vengeance, that have made this litter here? Could not you look before you, and be d——d? Do you think I have nothing else to do, in the devil's name, but to mend and repair after your arse?'—'Good words, friend,' said the bee (having now pruned himself, and being disposed to droll), 'I'll give you my hand and word to come near your kennel no more; I was never in such a confounded pickle since I was born.'— 'Sirrah,' replied the spider, 'if it were not for breaking an old custom in our family, never to stir abroad against an enemy, I should come and teach you better manners.'—'I pray have patience,' said the bee, 'or you will spend your substance, and, for aught I see, you may stand in need of it all, towards the repair of your house.'— 'Rogue, rogue,' replied the spider, 'yet methinks you should have more respect to a person, whom all the world allows to be so much your betters.'—'By my troth,' said the bee, 'the comparison will amount to a very good jest, and you will do me a favour to let me know the reasons that all the world is pleased to use in so hopeful a dispute.' At this the spider, having swelled himself into the size and posture of a disputant, began his argument in the true spirit of controversy, with a resolution to be heartily scurrilous and angry, to urge on his own reasons, without the least regard to the answers or objections of his opposite, and fully predetermined in his mind against all conviction.

'Not to disparage myself,' said he, 'by the comparison with such a rascal, what art thou but a vagabond without house or home, without stock or inheritance, born to no possession of your own, but a pair of wings and a drone-pipe? Your livelihood is an universal plunder upon nature; a freebooter over fields and gardens; and, for the sake of stealing, will rob a nettle as easily as a violet. Whereas I am a domestic animal, furnished with a native stock within myself. This large castle (to show my improvements in the mathematics[10]) is all built with my own hands, and the materials extracted altogether out of my own person.'

'I am glad,' answered the bee, 'to hear you grant at least that I am come honestly by my wings and my voice; for then, it seems, I am obliged to Heaven alone for my flights and my music; and Providence would never have bestowed on me two such gifts, without designing them for the noblest ends. I visit indeed all the flowers and blossoms of the field and the garden; but whatever I collect thence enriches my-

389

self, without the least injury to their beauty, their smell, or their taste. Now, for you and your skill in architecture and other mathematics, I have little to say: in that building of yours there might, for aught I know, have been labour and method enough; but, by woful experience for us both, 'tis too plain, the materials are naught, and I hope you will henceforth take warning, and consider duration and matter as well as method and art. You boast, indeed, of being obliged to no other creature, but of drawing and spinning out all from yourself; that is to say, if we may judge of the liquor in the vessel by what issues out, you possess a good plentiful store of dirt and poison in your breast; and, though I would by no means lessen or disparage your genuine stock of either, yet I doubt you are somewhat obliged, for an increase of both, to a little foreign assistance. Your inherent portion of dirt does not fail of acquisitions, by sweepings exhaled from below; and one insect furnishes you with a share of poison to destroy another. So that, in short, the question comes all to this—Whether is the nobler being of the two, that which, by a lazy contemplation of four inches round, by an overweening pride, feeding and engendering on itself, turns all into excrement and venom, producing nothing at all, but flybane and a cobweb; or that which, by an universal range, with long search, much study, true judgment, and distinction of things, brings home honey and wax.'

This dispute was managed with such eagerness, clamour, and warmth, that the two parties of books, in arms below, stood silent a while, waiting in suspense what would be the issue, which was not long undetermined: for the bee, grown impatient at so much loss of time, fled straight away to a bed of roses, without looking for a reply, and left the spider like an orator, collected in himself and just prepared to burst out.

It happened upon this emergency, that Æsop broke silence first. He had been of late most barbarously treated by a strange effect of the regent's humanity, who[11] had tore off his title-page, sorely defaced one half of his leaves, and chained him fast among a shelf of Moderns. Where, soon discovering how high the quarrel was like to proceed, he tried all his arts, and turned himself to a thousand forms. At length, in the borrowed shape of an ass, the regent mistook him for a Modern; by which means he had time and opportunity to escape to the Ancients, just when the spider and the bee were entering into their contest, to which he gave his attention with a world of pleasure; and when it was ended, swore in the loudest key, that in all his life he had never known two cases so parallel and adapt to each other, as that in the window, and this upon the shelves. 'The disputants,' said he, 'have admirably managed the dispute between them, have taken in the full strength of all that is to be said on both sides, and exhausted the substance of every argument *pro* and *con*. It is but to adjust the reasonings of both to the present quarrel, than to compare and apply the labours and fruits of each, as the bee has learnedly deduced them, and we shall find the conclusion full plain and close upon the Moderns and us. For, pray, gentlemen, was ever anything so modern as the spider, in his air, his turns, and his paradoxes? He argues in the behalf of you his brethren and himself, with many boastings of his native stock and great genius, that he spins and spits wholly from himself, and scorns to own any obligation or assistance from without. Then he displays to you his great skill in architecture, and improvement in the mathematics. To all this the bee, as an advocate retained by us the Ancients, thinks fit to answer—that, if one may judge of the great genius or inventions of the Moderns by what they have produced, you will hardly have countenance to bear you out in boasting of either. Erect your schemes with as much method and skill as you please; yet if the materials be nothing but dirt, spun out of your own entrails (the guts of modern brains), the edifice will conclude at last in a cobweb, the duration of which, like that of other spiders' webs, may be imputed to their being forgotten, or neglected, or hid in a corner. For anything else of genuine that the Moderns may pretend to, I cannot recollect; unless it be a large vein of wrangling and satire, much of a nature and substance with the spider's poison; which, however, they pretend to spit wholly out of themselves, is improved by the same arts, by feeding upon the insects and vermin of the age. As for us the Ancients, we are content with the bee to pretend to nothing of our own, beyond our wings and our voice, that is to say, our flights and our language. For the rest, whatever we have got, has been by infinite labour and search, and ranging through every corner of nature; the difference is, that, instead of dirt and poison, we have rather chosen to fill our hives with honey and wax, thus furnishing mankind with the two noblest of things, which are sweetness and light.'

'Tis wonderful to conceive the tumult arisen among the books, upon the close of this long descant of Æsop; both parties took the hint, and heightened their animosities so on a sudden, that they resolved it should come to a battle. Immediately the two main bodies withdrew, under their several ensigns, to the farther parts of the library, and there entered into cabals and consults upon the present emergency. The Moderns were in very warm debates upon the choice of their leaders; and nothing less than the fear impending from their enemies, could have kept them from mutinies upon this occasion. The difference was greatest among the horse, where every private trooper pretended to the chief command, from Tasso* and Milton to Dryden and Withers. The light-horse[12] were commanded by Cowley† and Despréaux.[13] There came the bowmen[14] under their

valiant leaders, Descartes, Gassendi,‡ and Hobbes, whose strength was such that they could shoot their arrows beyond the atmosphere, never to fall down again, but turn, like that of Evander, into meteors, or, like the cannon-ball, into stars. Paracelsus§ brought a squadron of stink-pot-fingers from the snowy mountains of Rhætia. There came a vast body of dragoons, of different nations, under the leading of Harvey,[15] their great aga: part armed with scythes, the weapons of death; part with lances and long knives, all steeped in poison; part shot bullets of a most malignant nature, and used white powder, which infallibly killed without report. There came several bodies of heavy-armed foot, all mercenaries, under the ensigns of Guicciardini, Davila, Polydore Virgil, Buchanan, Mariana, Camden, and others.** The engineers†† were commanded by Regiomontanus and Wilkins. The rest were a confused multitude, led by Scotus, Aquinas, and Bellarmine;‡‡ of mighty bulk and stature, but without either arms, courage, or discipline. In the last place, came infinite swarms of calones,[16] a disorderly rout led by L'Estrange, rogues and ragamuffins, that follow the camp for nothing but the plunder, all without coats to cover them.

The army of the Ancients was much fewer in number; Homer led the horse, and Pindar the light-horse; Euclid was chief en-

---

* Torquato Tasso (1544–95), Italian epic poet.
† Abraham Cowley (1618–67) was an English poet and essayist. Nicolas Boileau-Despréaux (1636–1711) was a French poet and literary critic.
‡ Pierre Gassendi (1592–1655), French mathematician and philosopher, an anti-Aristotelian.
§ Paracelsus was a sixteenth-century physician and alchemist.
** These were all modern historians.
†† "Engineers" because these two moderns made or wrote about mechanical devices.
‡‡ Robert Bellarmine (1542–1621), Italian cardinal and theologian, who defended the Roman Catholic cause against Protestantism.

gineer; Plato and Aristotle commanded the bowmen; Herodotus and Livy the foot; Hippocrates the dragoons. The allies, led by Vossius* and Temple, brought up the rear.

All things violently tending to a decisive battle, Fame, who much frequented, and had a large apartment formerly assigned her in the regal library, fled up straight to Jupiter, to whom she delivered a faithful account of all that had passed between the two parties below. (For, among the gods, she always tells truth.) Jove, in great concern, convokes a council in the Milky Way. The senate assembled, he declares the occasion of convening them; a bloody battle just impendent between two mighty armies of Ancient and Modern creatures, called books, wherein the celestial interest was but too deeply concerned. Momus,[17] the patron of the Moderns, made an excellent speech in their favour, which was answered by Pallas, the protectress of the Ancients.† The assembly was divided in their affections; when Jupiter commanded the book of fate to be laid before him. Immediately were brought by Mercury three large volumes in folio, containing memoirs of all things past, present, and to come. The clasps were of silver, double gilt; the covers of celestial turkey leather; and the paper such as here on earth might almost pass for vellum. Jupiter, having silently read the decree, would communicate the import to none, but presently shut up the book.

Without the doors of this assembly, there attended a vast number of light, nimble gods, menial servants to Jupiter: these are his ministering instruments in all affairs below. They travel in a caravan, more or less together, and are fastened to each other, like a link of galley-slaves, by a light chain, which passes from them to Jupiter's great toe; and yet, in receiving or delivering a message, they may never approach above the lowest step of his throne, where he and they whisper to each other, through a long hollow trunk. These deities are called by mortal men accidents or events; but the gods call them second causes. Jupiter having delivered his message to a certain number of these divinities, they flew immediately down to the pinnacle of the regal library, and, consulting a few minutes, entered unseen and disposed the parties according to their orders.

Meanwhile, Momus, fearing the worst, and calling to mind an ancient prophecy, which bore no very good face to his children the Moderns, bent his flight to the region of a malignant deity, called Criticism. She dwelt on the top of a snowy mountain in Nova Zembla;‡ there Momus found her extended in her den, upon the spoils of numberless volumes half devoured. At her right hand sat Ignorance, her father and husband, blind with age; at her left, Pride, her mother, dressing her up in the scraps of paper herself had torn. There was Opinion, her sister, light of foot, hoodwinked, and headstrong, yet giddy, and perpetually turning. About her played her children, Noise and Impudence, Dulness and Vanity, Positiveness, Pedantry, and Ill-Manners. The goddess herself had claws like a cat; her head, and ears, and voice, resembled those of an ass; her teeth fallen out before, her eyes turned inward, as if she looked only upon herself; her diet was the overflowing of her own gall; her spleen was so large, as to stand prominent like a dug of the first rate; nor wanted excrescencies in form of teats, at which a crew of ugly monsters were greedily sucking; and, what is wonderful to conceive, the bulk of spleen increased faster than the sucking could diminish it. 'Goddess,' said Momus, 'can you sit idly here while our devout worshippers, the Moderns, are this minute entering into a cruel battle, and perhaps now lying under the swords of their enemies? Who then hereafter will ever

---

* A seventeenth-century Dutch scholar, editor of Catullus and Juvenal.

† The Moderns, who excel at satire, are led by Momus, the god of ridicule; the Ancients are led by Pallas, goddess of wisdom.

‡ Novaya Zemlya, in the Arctic Ocean.

sacrifice or build altars to our divinities? Haste, therefore, to the British Isle, and, if possible, prevent their destruction; while I make factions among the gods, and gain them over to our party.'

Momus, having thus delivered himself, stayed not for an answer, but left the goddess to her own resentment. Up she rose in a rage, and, as it is the form upon such occasions, began a soliloquy: '"Tis I,' (said she), 'who give wisdom to infants and idiots; by me, children grow wiser than their parents; by me, beaux become politicians, and school-boys judges of philosophy; by me, sophisters debate, and conclude upon the depths of knowledge; and coffeehouse wits, instinct by me, can correct an author's style and display his minutest errors, without understanding a syllable of his matter or his language. By me, striplings spend their judgment, as they do their estate, before it comes into their hands. 'Tis I who have deposed wit and knowledge from their empire over poetry, and advanced myself in their stead. And shall a few upstart Ancients dare oppose me?—But come, my aged parents and you, my children dear, and thou, my beauteous sister; let us ascend my chariot, and haste to assist our devout Moderns, who are now sacrificing to us a hecatomb, as I perceive by that grateful smell, which from thence reaches my nostrils.'

The goddess and her train having mounted the chariot, which was drawn by tame geese, flew over infinite regions, shedding her influence in due places, till at length she arrived at her beloved island of Britain; but in hovering over its metropolis, what blessings did she not let fall upon her seminaries of Gresham and Covent Garden!* And now she reached the fatal plain of St. James's Library, at what time the two armies were upon the point to engage; where, entering with all her caravan unseen, and landing upon a case of shelves, now desert, but once inhabited by a colony of virtuosos, she stayed a while to observe the posture of both armies.

But here the tender cares of a mother began to fill her thoughts, and move in her breast. For, at the head of a troop of Modern Bowmen, she cast her eyes upon her son W-tt-n; to whom the fates had assigned a very short thread. W-tt-n, a young hero, whom an unknown father of mortal race begot by stolen embraces with this goddess. He was the darling of his mother above all her children, and she resolved to go and comfort him. But first, according to the good old custom of deities, she cast about to change her shape, for fear the divinity of her countenance might dazzle his mortal sight, and overcharge the rest of his senses. She therefore gathered up her person into an octavo compass; her body grew white and arid, and split in pieces with dryness; the thick turned into pasteboard, and the thin into paper, upon which her parents and children artfully strewed a black juice, or decoction of gall and soot, in form of letters; her head, and voice, and spleen, kept their primitive form, and that which before was a cover of skin, did still continue so. In which guise she marched on towards the Moderns, undistinguishable in shape and dress from the divine B-ntl-y, W-tt-n's dearest friend. 'Brave W-tt-n,' said the goddess, 'why do our troops stand idle here, to spend their present vigour, and opportunity of this day? Away, let us haste to the generals, and advise to give the onset immediately.' Having spoke thus, she took the ugliest of her monsters, full glutted from her spleen, and flung it invisibly into his mouth, which, flying straight up into his head, squeezed out his eye-balls, gave him a distorted look, and half overturned his brain. Then she privately ordered two of her beloved children, Dulness and Ill-Manners, closely to attend his person in all encounters. Having

---

* "Seminaries" is ironic as applied to Covent Garden, where wits, poets, and men of fashion met in coffee houses and taverns, and which is here maliciously linked with Gresham College, home of the Royal Society.

thus accoutred him, she vanished in a mist, and the hero perceived it was the goddess his mother.

The destined hour of fate being now arrived, the fight began; whereof, before I dare adventure to make a particular description, I must, after the example of other authors, petition for a hundred tongues, and mouths, and hands, and pens, which would all be too little to perform so immense a work. Say, goddess, that presidest over History, who it was that first advanced in the field of battle! Paracelsus, at the head of his dragoons, observing Galen in the adverse wing, darted his javelin with a mighty force, which the brave Ancient received upon his shield, the point breaking in the second fold. . . .

Hic pauca desunt. *

They bore the wounded aga [18] on their shields to his chariot. . . .

Desunt nonnula †

Then Aristotle, observing Bacon [19] advanced with a furious mien, drew his bow to the head, and let fly his arrow, which missed the valiant Modern, and went hizzing over his head. But Descartes it hit; the steel point quickly found a defect in his head-piece; it pierced the leather and the pasteboard, and went in at his right eye. The torture of the pain whirled the valiant bowman round, till death, like a star of superior influence, drew him into his own vortex. . . . [20]

Ingens hiatus hic in MS. ‡

. . . when Homer appeared at the head of the cavalry, mounted on a furious horse, with difficulty managed by the rider himself, but which no other mortal durst approach: he rode among the enemy's ranks, and bore down all before him. Say, goddess, whom he slew first, and whom he slew last! First, Gondibert [21] advanced against him, clad in heavy armour, and mounted on a staid, sober gelding, not so famed for his speed as his docility in kneeling, whenever his rider would mount or alight. He had made a vow to Pallas that he would never leave the field till he had spoiled Homer [22] of his armour: Madman, who had never once seen the wearer, nor understood his strength! Him Homer overthrew, horse and man, to the ground, there to be trampled and choked in the dirt. Then, with a long spear, he slew Denham, [23] a stout Modern, who from his father's side derived his lineage from Apollo, but his mother was of mortal race. He fell, and bit the earth. The celestial part Apollo took, and made it a star; but the terrestrial lay wallowing upon the ground. Then Homer slew W-sl-y [24] with a kick of his horse's heel; he took Perrault by mighty force out of his saddle, then hurled him at Fontenelle, § with the same blow dashing out both their brains.

On the left wing of the horse, Virgil appeared, in shining armour, completely fitted to his body: He was mounted on a dapple-gray steed, the slowness of whose pace was an effect of the highest mettle and vigour. He cast his eye on the adverse wing, with a desire to find an object worthy of his valour, when, behold, upon a sorrel gelding of a monstrous size, appeared a foe, issuing from among the thickest of the enemy's squadrons; but his speed was less than his noise; for his horse, old and lean, spent the dregs of his strength in a high trot, which, though it made slow advances, yet caused a loud clashing of his armour, terrible to hear. The two cavaliers had now approached within the throw of a lance, when the stranger desired a parley, and, lifting up the vizor of his helmet, a face hardly appeared from within, which, after a pause, was known for that of the re-

---

* [Here a small part of the text is missing.]
† [More missing parts.]
‡ [A huge gap in the manuscript appears here.]
§ Bernard de Fontenelle (1657–1757) scientist, playwright, man of letters, etc., called by Voltaire the most universal mind of the age of Louis XIV. With Perrault, he defended the Moderns in France.

nowned Dryden. The brave Ancient suddenly started, as one possessed with surprise and disappointment together; for the helmet was nine times too large for the head, which appeared situate far in the hinder part, even like the lady in a lobster, or like a mouse under a canopy of state, or like a shrivelled beau, from within the penthouse of a modern periwig; and the voice was suited to the visage, sounding weak and remote. Dryden, in a long harangue, soothed up the good Ancient, called him father, and, by a large deduction of genealogies, made it plainly appear that they were nearly related.[25] Then he humbly proposed an exchange of armour, as a lasting mark of hospitality between them. Virgil consented (for the goddess Diffidence came unseen, and cast a mist before his eyes), though his was of gold, and cost a hundred beeves, the other's but of rusty iron.[26] However, this glittering armour became the Modern yet worse than his own. Then they agreed to exchange horses; but, when it came to the trial, Dryden was afraid, and utterly unable to mount. . . .

*Alter hiatus in MS.**

. . . Lucan† appeared upon a fiery horse of admirable shape, but headstrong, bearing the rider where he list over the field; he made a mighty slaughter among the enemy's horse; which destruction to stop, Bl-ckm-re, a famous Modern (but one of the mercenaries), strenuously opposed himself, and darted a javelin with a strong hand, which, falling short of its mark, struck deep in the earth. Then Lucan threw a lance; but Æsculapius came unseen, and turned off the point. 'Brave Modern,' said Lucan, 'I perceive some god protects you,[27] for never did my arm so deceive me before; but what mortal can contend with a god? Therefore, let us fight no longer, but present gifts to each other.' Lucan then bestowed the Modern a pair of spurs, and Bl-ckm-re gave Lucan a bridle.[28] . . .

Pauca desunt.‡

. . . Creech: but the goddess Dulness took a cloud, formed into the shape of Horace, armed and mounted, and placed in a flying posture before him. Glad was the cavalier to begin a combat with a flying foe, and pursued the image, threatening loud, till at last it led him to the peaceful bower of his father, Ogleby,§ by whom he was disarmed, and assigned for his repose.

Then Pindar slew———, and ———, and Oldham,** and ———, and Afra the Amazon,[29] light of foot; never advancing in a direct line, but wheeling with incredible agility and force, he made a terrible slaughter among the enemy's light-horse. Him when Cowley observed, his generous heart burnt within him, and he advanced against the fierce Ancient, imitating his address, and pace, and career, as well as the vigour of his horse and his own skill would allow. When the two cavaliers had approached within the length of three javelins, first Cowley threw a lance, which missed Pindar, and, passing into the enemy's ranks, fell ineffectual to the ground. Then Pindar darted a javelin so large and weighty that scarce a dozen cavaliers, as cavaliers are in our degenerate days, could raise it from the ground; yet he threw it with ease, and it went, by an unerring hand, singing through the air; nor could the Modern have avoided present death, if he had not luckily opposed the shield that had been given him by Venus.[30] And now both heroes drew their swords; but the Modern was so aghast and disordered, that he knew not where he was; his shield dropped from his hands; thrice he fled, and thrice he could not escape; at last he turned, and lifting up his hands in the posture of a suppliant: 'Godlike Pindar,' said he, 'spare my life, and

---

* [Another gap in the manuscript.]
† Roman poet (A.D. 39–65).
‡ [A small part is missing.]
§ Creech and Ogleby had translated various ancient poets.
** John Oldham (1653–83), a poet praised by Dryden, wrote odes in the style of Pindar, as did Mrs. Behn (1640?–85).

possess my horse with these arms, besides the ransom which my friends will give when they hear I am alive, and your prisoner.' 'Dog!' said Pindar, 'let your ransom stay with your friends; but your carcass shall be left for the fowls of the air and the beasts of the field.' With that he raised his sword, and, with a mighty stroke, cleft the wretched Modern in twain, the sword pursuing the blow; and one half lay panting on the ground, to be trod in pieces by the horses' feet, the other half was borne by the frighted steed through the field. This Venus[31] took, washed it seven times in ambrosia, then struck it thrice with a sprig of amaranth; upon which the leather grew round and soft, and the leaves turned into feathers, and being gilded before, continued gilded still; so it became a dove, and she harnessed it to her chariot. . . .

*Hiatus valde deflendus in MS.**

The episode of B-ntl-y and W-tt-n

Day being far spent, and the numerous forces of the Moderns half inclining to a retreat, there issued forth from a squadron of their heavy-armed foot, a captain, whose name was B-ntl-y, in person the most deformed of all the Moderns; tall, but without shape or comeliness; large, but without strength or proportion. His armour was patched up of a thousand incoherent pieces, and the sound of it, as he marched, was loud and dry, like that made by the fall of a sheet of lead, which an Etesian wind blows suddenly down from the roof of some steeple. His helmet was of old rusty iron, but the vizor was brass, which, tainted by his breath, corrupted into copperas, nor wanted gall from the same fountain; so that, whenever provoked by anger or labour, an atramentous quality, of most malignant nature, was seen to distil from his lips. In his right hand he grasped a flail, and (that he might never be unprovided of an offensive weapon) a vessel full of ordure in his left.[32] Thus completely

armed, he advanced with a slow and heavy pace where the Modern chiefs were holding consult upon the sum of things; who, as he came onwards, laughed to behold his crooked leg and hump shoulder, which his boot and armour, vainly endeavouring to hide, were forced to comply with and expose. The generals made use of him for his talent of railing, which, kept within government, proved frequently of great service to their cause, but, at other times, did more mischief than good; for at the least touch of offence, and often without any at all, he would, like a wounded elephant, convert it against his leaders. Such, at this juncture, was the disposition of B-ntl-y; grieved to see the enemy prevail, and dissatisfied with everybody's conduct but his own. He humbly gave the Modern generals to understand, that he conceived, with great submission, they were all a pack of rogues, and fools, and sons of whores, and d——d cowards, and confounded loggerheads, and illiterate whelps, and nonsensical scoundrels; that if himself had been constituted general, those presumptuous dogs,[33] the Ancients, would, long before this, have been beaten out of the field. 'You,' said he, 'sit here idle; but when I, or any other valiant Modern, kill an enemy, you are sure to seize the spoil. But I will not march one foot against the foe till you all swear to me, that, whomever I take or kill, his arms I shall quietly possess.' B-ntl-y having spoken thus, Scaliger,† bestowing him a sour look: 'Miscreant prater!' said he, 'eloquent only in thine own eyes, thou railest without wit, or truth, or discretion. The malignity of thy temper perverteth nature, thy learning makes thee more barbarous, thy study of humanity more inhuman; thy converse amongst poets, more grovelling, miry, and dull. All arts of civilizing others

---

* [A very much deplored gap in the manuscript.]

† Joseph Scaliger (1540–1609), one of the great scholars of the Renaissance, who edited many classical authors.

render thee rude and untractable; courts have taught thee ill manners, and polite conversation has finished thee a pedant. Besides, a greater coward burdeneth not the army. But never despond; I pass my word, whatever spoil thou takest shall certainly be thy own, though, I hope, that vile carcass will first become a prey to kites and worms.'

B-ntl-y durst not reply, but, half choked with spleen and rage, withdrew, in full resolution . of performing some great achievement. With him, for his aid and companion, he took his beloved W-tt-n; resolving, by policy or surprise, to attempt some neglected quarter of the Ancients' army. They began their march over carcasses of their slaughtered friends; then to the right of their own forces; then wheeled northward, till they came to Aldrovandus's* tomb, which they passed on the side of the declining sun. And now they arrived, with fear, towards the enemy's out-guards; looking about, if haply they might spy the quarters of the wounded, or some straggling sleepers, unarmed, and remote from the rest. As when two mongrel curs, whom native greediness and domestic want provoke and join in partnership, though fearful, nightly to invade the folds of some rich grazier, they, with tails depressed, and lolling tongues, creep soft and slow; meanwhile, the conscious moon, now in her zenith, on their guilty heads darts perpendicular rays; nor dare they bark, though much provoked at her refulgent visage, whether seen in puddle by reflection, or in sphere direct; but one surveys the region round, while t'other scouts the plain, if haply to discover, at distance from the flock, some carcass half devoured, the refuse of gorged wolves, or ominous ravens. So marched this lovely, loving pair of friends, nor with less fear and circumspection; when, at distance, they might perceive two shining suits of armour hanging upon an oak, and the owners not far off in a profound sleep. The two friends drew lots, and the pursuing of this adventure fell to

B-ntl-y; on he went, and in his van Confusion and Amaze, while Horror and Affright brought up the rear. As he came near, behold two heroes of the Ancients' army, Phalaris and Æsop, lay fast asleep: B-ntl-y would fain have dispatched them both, and, stealing close, aimed his flail at Phalaris's breast. But then the goddess Affright interposing, caught the Modern in her icy arms, and dragged him from the danger she foresaw; for both the dormant heroes happened to turn at the same instant, though soundly sleeping, and busy in a dream. For Phalaris[34] was just that minute dreaming how a most vile poetaster had lampooned him, and how he had got him roaring in his bull.† And Æsop dreamed that, as he and the Ancient chiefs were lying on the ground, a wild ass broke loose, ran about, trampling and kicking, and dunging in their faces. B-ntl-y, leaving the two heroes asleep, seized on both their armours, and withdrew in quest of his darling W-tt-n.

He, in the mean time, had wandered long in search of some enterprize, till at length he arrived at a small rivulet, that issued from a fountain hard by, called, in the language of mortal men, Helicon.‡ Here he stopped, and, parched with thirst, resolved to allay it in this limpid stream. Thrice with profane hands he essayed to raise the water to his lips, and thrice it slipped all through his fingers. Then he stooped prone on his breast, but, ere his mouth had kissed the liquid crystal, Apollo came, and in the channel held his shield betwixt the Modern and the fountain, so that he drew up nothing but mud. For, although no fountain on earth can compare with the clearness of Helicon, yet there lies at bottom a thick sediment of slime and

---

* Sixteenth-century Italian naturalist.

† Phalaris, whose supposed "letters" created the occasion that led Swift to write *The Battle of the Books,* was a sixth-century B.C. Sicilian tyrant of legendary cruelty who liked to roast his enemies in a brazen bull.

‡ The fountain sacred to the Muses.

mud; for so Apollo begged of Jupiter, as a punishment to those who durst attempt to taste it with unhallowed lips, and for a lesson to all not to draw too deep or far from the spring.

At the fountain-head W-tt-n discerned two heroes; the one he could not distinguish, but the other was soon known for Temple, general of the allies to the Ancients. His back was turned, and he was employed in drinking large draughts in his helmet from the fountain, where he had withdrawn himself to rest from the toils of the war. W-tt-n, observing him, with quaking knees, and trembling hands, spoke thus to himself: 'O that I could kill this destroyer of our army, what renown should I purchase among the chiefs! But to issue out against him,[35] man for man, shield against shield, and lance against lance, what Modern of us dare? For he fights like a god, and Pallas or Apollo are ever at his elbow. But, O mother! if what Fame reports be true, that I am the son of so great a goddess, grant me to hit Temple with this lance, that the stroke may send him to hell, and that I may return in safety and triumph, laden with his spoils.' The first part of his prayer, the gods granted at the intercession of his mother and of Momus; but the rest by a perverse wind sent from Fate was scattered in the air. Then W-tt-n grasped his lance, and, brandishing it thrice over his head, darted it with all his might, the goddess, his mother, at the same time, adding strength to his arm. Away the lance went hissing, and reached even to the belt of the averted Ancient, upon which lightly grazing, it fell to the ground. Temple neither felt the weapon touch him, nor heard it fall; and W-tt-n might have escaped to his army, with the honour of having remitted his lance against so great a leader, unrevenged; but Apollo, enraged that a javelin, flung by the assistance of so foul a goddess, should pollute his fountain, put on the shape of ———, and softly came to young Boyle, who then accompanied Temple. He pointed first to the lance, then

to the distant Modern that flung it, and commanded the young hero to take immediate revenge.[36] Boyle, clad in a suit of armour, which had been given him by all the gods,[37] immediately advanced against the trembling foe, who now fled before him. As a young lion in the Libyan plains or Araby desert, sent by his aged sire to hunt for prey, or health, or exercise, he scours along, wishing to meet some tiger from the mountains, or a furious boar; if chance, a wild ass, with brayings importune, affronts his ear, the generous beast, though loathing to distain his claws with blood so vile, yet, much provoked at the offensive noise which Echo, foolish nymph, like her ill-judging sex, repeats much louder, and with more delight than Philomela's song, he vindicates the honour of the forest, and hunts the noisy long-eared animal. So W-tt-n fled, so Boyle pursued. But W-tt-n, heavy-armed and slow of foot, began to slack his course, when his lover, B-ntl-y, appeared, returning laden with the spoils of the two sleeping Ancients. Boyle observed him well, and soon discovering the helmet and shield of Phalaris, his friend, both which he had lately with his own hands new polished and gilded, Rage sparkled in his eyes, and, leaving his pursuit after W-tt-n, he furiously rushed on against this new approacher. Fain would he be revenged on both; but both now fled different ways; and, as a woman[38] in a little house that gets a painful livelihood by spinning,[39] if chance her geese be scattered o'er the common, she courses round the plain from side to side, compelling here and there the stragglers to the flock; they cackle loud, and flutter o'er the champaign. So Boyle pursued, so fled this pair of friends: finding at length their flight was vain, they bravely joined, and drew themselves in phalanx. First B-ntl-y threw a spear with all his force, hoping to pierce the enemy's breast; but Pallas came unseen, and in the air took off the point, and clapped on one of lead, which, after a dead bang against the enemy's shield, fell blunted to the ground. Then Boyle, observing well his time, took a lance of wondrous length and sharpness; and as this pair of friends compacted stood close side to side, he wheeled him to the right, and, with unusual force, darted the weapon. B-ntl-y saw his fate approach, and flanking down his arms close to his ribs, hoping to save his body, in went the point, passing through arm and side, nor stopped or spent its force, till it had also pierced the valiant W-tt-n who, going to sustain his dying friend, shared his fate.[40] As when a skilful cook has trussed a brace of wood-cocks, he, with iron skewer, pierces the tender sides of both, their legs and wings close pinioned to their ribs; so was this pair of friends transfixed, till down they fell, joined in their lives, joined in their deaths, so closely joined that Charon would mistake them both for one, and waft them over Styx for half his fare. Farewell, beloved loving pair! Few equals have you left behind: and happy and immortal shall you be, if all my wit and eloquence can make you.

And, now. . . .

*Desunt cœtera.**

Finis

_____

* [The rest is missing.]

1 Riches produceth pride; pride is war's ground, &c. Vid. *Ephem. de Mary Clarke;* opt. edit. [Now called *Wing's Sheet Almanack,* and printed by J. Roberts for the Company of Stationers.—H.]

2 Sir William Temple affects to trace the progress of arts and sciences from east to west. Thus the moderns had only such knowledge of the learning of Chaldæa and Egypt as was conveyed to them through the medium of Grecian and Roman writers.—S.

3 Their title-pages.

4 Dr. Bentley was appointed Royal Librarian, December 23, 1693, upon the death of his predecessor, Mr. Justell. He had already distinguished himself by his learning and by his excellent sermons.—S.

5 The Honourable Mr. Boyle, in the preface to his edition of Phalaris, says he was refused a manuscript by the library keeper, *pro solita humanitate suâ.*—1710.

This was the sparkle which kindled so hot a flame. Dr. Bentley does not quite clear himself of having been a little churlish concerning the manuscript.—S.

6 Dr. Bentley aided Wotton in his *Reflections upon Ancient and Modern Learning,* by proving that the works of Phalaris and Æsop, authors extolled by Sir William Temple, were in reality spurious.—S.

7 According to the modern paradox [i.e., the fact that the modern world is later, and thus older, than the ancient one].

8 Fortification was one of the arts, upon the improvement of which the argument in favour of the moderns was founded by their advocates.—S.

9 Supposed to be the tutelar deity of the flies.—S.

10 The improvements in mathematical science were (very justly) urged by those who contended for the excellence of modern learning.—S.

11 Bentley, who denied the antiquity of Æsop, and the authenticity of the fables ascribed to him, which he supposed to have been composed by Maximus Planudes.—S.

12 The epic poets were presented as full-armed horsemen; the lyrical bards as light-horse.—S.

13 More commonly known by the name of Boileau.—H.

14 The philosophers, whether physical or metaphysical, are thus classed.—S.

15 The celebrated discoverer of the circulation of the blood; concerning which Sir William Temple, with very little candour, thus expresses himself: 'There is nothing new in astronomy to vie with the ancients, unless it be the Copernaean system; nor in physic, unless Harvey's circulation of the blood. But whether either of these be modern discoveries, or derived from old fountains is disputed; nay, it is so too, whether they are true or no; for though reason may seem to favour them more than the contrary opinions, yet sense can very hardly allow them; and, to satisfy mankind, both these must concur. But if they are true, yet these two great discoveries have made no change in the conclusions of astronomy, nor in the practice of physic and so have been of little use to the world, though, perhaps, of much honour to the authors.'—*Essay upon Ancient and Modern Learning.*—S. [For Harvey, see *GBWW,* Vol. 28.]

16 These are pamphlets, which are not bound or covered.—1710.

By calling this disorderly rout *calones* the author points both his satire and contempt against all sorts of mercenary scribblers, who write as they are commanded by the leaders and patrons of sedition, faction, corruption, and every evil work: they are styled *calones* because they are the meanest and most despicable of all writers, as the calones, whether belonging to the army or private families, were the meanest of all slaves or servants whatsoever—H.

Sir Roger L'Estrange was distinguished by his activity in this dirty warfare in the reigns of Charles II and James II.—S.

17 Momus is named as the presiding deity of the Moderns, probably on account of the superiority claimed for them in works of humour.—S.

18 Dr. Harvey. It was not thought proper to name his antagonist, but only to intimate that he was wounded.—H.

19 The author, in naming Bacon, does a piece of justice to modern philosophy which Temple had omitted. 'I know of no new philosophers that have made entries on that noble stage for fifteen hundred years past, unless Descartes and Hobbes should pretend to it; of whom I shall make no critique here, but only say, that by what appears of learned men's opinions in this age they have by no means eclipsed the lustre of Plato, Aristotle, Epicurus, or others of the ancients.'—*Essay on Ancient and Modern Learning.*—Neither Swift nor Temple mention the discoveries of Newton, though the *Principia* were published in 1657.—S.

20 Alluding to his absurd system.—S.

21 A heroic poem by Sir William Davenant, in stanzas of four lines.—H.

22 *Vid.* Homer.

23 Sir John Denham's poems are very un-

equal, extremely good and very indifferent; so that his detractors said he was not the real author of *Cooper's Hill*.

24 Mr. Wesley, who wrote the *Life of Christ*, in verse, &c. A wretched scribbler.—S.

25 Alluding to the Preliminary Dissertations in Dryden's Virgil.—S.

26 *Vid.* Homer.

27 His skill as a physician atoned for his dulness as a poet.—H.

28 The respect with which Swift treats Blackmore, in comparison to his usage of Dryden, shows, as plainly as his own *Ode to the Athenian Society,* that he was at this period incapable of estimating the higher kinds of poetry.—S.

29 Mrs. Aphra Behn, author of many plays, novels, and poems.—H.

30 His poem called *The Mistress.*—H.

31 I do not approve the author's judgment in this, for I think Cowley's *Pindarics* are much preferable to his *Mistress*.

32 The person here spoken of is famous for letting fly at everybody without distinction, and using mean and foul scurrilities.

33 *Vid.* Homer, de Thersites; *GBWW*, Vol. 4, p. 12b–c.

34 This is according to Homer, who tells the dreams of those who were killed in their sleep.

35 *Vid.* Homer.

36 Boyle alleges in his preface, as his principal reason for entering into the controversy about Phalaris, his respect for Sir William Temple, who had been coarsely treated by Bentley.—S.

37 Boyle was assisted in this dispute by Dean Aldrich, Dr. Atterbury, afterwards Bishop of Rochester, and other persons at Oxford, celebrated for their genius and their learning, then called the Christ-Church wits.—H.

38 *Vid.* Homer.

39 This is also after the manner of Homer; the woman's getting a painful livelihood by spinning, has nothing to do with the similitude, nor would be excusable without such an authority.

40 Notwithstanding what is here stated, Wotton was treated with much more delicacy by Boyle, than was his friend Bentley.—S.

NOTE TO THE READER

Swift's best-known work, *Gulliver's Travels,* is in *GBWW,* Vol. 36. His "Modest Proposal for Preventing the Children of Ireland from Being a Burden to Their Parents or Country," which has been called the greatest pamphlet ever written, appears with other short works by him in *GGB,* Vol. 7. *See also* in *GGB,* Vol. 5, the essay on Swift by William Hazlitt.

On Translating Homer

Matthew Arnold

Editor's Introduction

Matthew Arnold (1822–88), who was one of the three or four best Victorian poets, was also the preeminent English critic of his day, as Dr. Johnson was of an earlier time and Dryden of the time before that. No one has ever held a higher idea of the critical function than Arnold did—"a disinterested endeavor," he called it, "to learn and propagate the best that is known and thought in the world"—yet no critic has been more explicit in acknowledging that criticism is the second best thing, inferior to creation. That Arnold nevertheless devoted his later years to critical writing rather than to poetry, which he gradually ceased to produce, stemmed from a conviction that his own verse was defective when judged by the highest standard, and that this defect was in an important sense the defect of the modern world—a world, as he described it, of "sick hurry and divided aims," in which great poetry could not be written save as criticism might prepare for it by creating "a current of fresh and true ideas." To this end, in a series of essays, Arnold undertook to show how a critical intelligence might be applied not just to literature but also to history, science, politics, and religion—all the great human concerns. At the same time he sought to distinguish the qualities of mind and art that in his view had always characterized great poetry and would reveal it when it appeared again. For he thought that only when this happened would the human spirit, overwhelmed by complexity and plagued by doubt as in his century it seemed to be, acquire the serenity and strength to prevail against what he called "this strange disease of modern life."

Arnold's father was Dr. Thomas Arnold (1795–1842), the noted headmaster of Rugby school, who gave his son both a classical education and the earnest precepts of a Christian gentleman. In 1841 the younger Arnold went to Oxford, where, possibly in reaction to his earlier training (which, however, he afterward warmly upheld), he became something of a dandy and cultivated an ironic manner, but where he also won an important prize in poetry. He graduated with honors in 1844 and along with Arthur Hugh Clough was granted a fellowship the following year. In 1847 he got a job as private secretary to Lord Lansdowne, who was president of the Privy Council with certain responsibilities for public education, and four years after that, through Lansdowne's favor, Arnold was appointed inspector of schools. This position he held for the next thirty-five years, despite its tedious routine, partly because it paid him at least a small regular income, and partly because he came to believe in its importance; it did not prevent his other occupations, though it limited the time he could give to them.

In 1849 he published his first volume of verse, *The Strayed Reveller,* and in 1852 a second one, *Empedocles on Etna, and Other Poems.* A year later, poems from both these books were reprinted with others in still a third volume, with a famous preface in which Arnold explained why "Empedocles on Etna" itself, his most ambitious work to date, had been left out. It was, he said, a dramatic poem "in which the suffering finds no vent in action," in which "everything is to be endured, nothing to be done," and which he had come to feel was "inevitably morbid." He also expounded views, never afterward materially altered, on poetry in general and in particular on the classical masterpieces, which he felt should serve as models for his own age—an age of "spiritual discomfort," as he called it, that was "wanting in moral grandeur." Later editions of this volume followed, as did a classical tragedy, *Merope,* in 1858, and *New Poems* in 1867, after which Arnold wrote almost no new verse. Of all his poems, the best known are "Dover Beach," "The Scholar-Gypsy," "To Marguerite," and "Thyrsis," an elegy on the model of Milton's "Lycidas" and Shelley's "Adonaïs" inspired by the early death of his friend Clough.

Arnold's critical career began, practically speaking, with his election to the poetry chair at Oxford in 1857, a position that required formal lectures from him, and which he held for ten years. His inaugural address was "On the Modern Element in Literature," in which he considered the term *modern* as defining not merely what is contemporary (Arnold thought the Greeks were modern) but also that spirit which seeks to transcend the calamities and confusions that beset all human existence. "On Translating Homer" consisted originally of three further lectures written for this same professorship in the winter of 1860–61. With its explanation of why Arnold thought the now forgotten translation of the *Iliad* by Francis Newman was unsatisfactory, the essay constitutes one of his best and most characteristic statements about poetry and the poetic art.

His critical principles were summarized in still another Oxford lecture, "The Function of Criticism at the Present Time," which was later published in *Essays in Criticism* (1865). That volume also contained "The Literary Influence of Academies," in which Arnold argued for standards of knowledge and taste such as the French Academy existed to maintain. Other essays on literature were collected in *Essays in Criticism,* Second Series (1888), which included his famous dictum that poetry, rather than religion, is what we must turn to for an interpretation of life, for what may "console us" and "sustain us." This volume also contained notable discussions of Milton, Wordsworth, Byron, and Shelley, among other English poets.

In line with his broad conception of the critic's function, Arnold devoted a great part of his time to social questions, and ultimately, in essays that are no longer much read, to religion. What is widely regarded as his best book was *Culture and Anarchy* (1869), in which he attacked the smugness, provinciality, and materialism of Victorian England, whose society he divided into three classes: Barbarians (the aristocracy), Philistines (the middle class), and Populace. These classes were incapable, he said, either singly or together, of preventing the impending democratic revolution from arriving at anarchy, except as they might be willing to submit to a State that embodied the idea of humanity's "best self" and forced them to rise to it. The incidental result of such a development, he thought, would be that social classes cease to exist.

Arnold's influence, which was never complete or unchallenged even in his lifetime, has diminished somewhat since his death. He is more honored for something that he was than for anything he happened to think. Indeed, what he thought has been largely discounted by such a critic as T. S. Eliot—his successor, so far as he can be said to have had one, in the twentieth century—who characterized him as "a champion of 'ideas' most of which we no longer take seriously." Yet the main idea Arnold had, so far as criticism was concerned, was simply that all men have minds, which they can learn to make use of by reflecting freely and seriously upon the works—the finite number of works, as he thought it was—which the best use of the mind has managed to create. In popularizing this notion, Arnold sought to liberate the critical faculty of his contemporaries from the limitations—clerical and academic, as well as philistine and insular—that prevailed before his time (he was the first secular person to be appointed to the Oxford poetry chair, as he was the first to lecture from it in English rather than in Latin), and to show how this faculty might be capable of a high level of perception. He was thus an important background figure in the revival of liberal learning that occurred subsequently in the colleges and universities of the United States, as incidentally he is in some real sense the spiritual father not only of *The Great Ideas Today* but also of *Great Books of the Western World*.

NOTE TO THE READER

Those who have read "Sources of Our Common Thought: Homer and Plato," by I. A. Richards, which appears elsewhere in this volume (pp. 280–326), will be interested to compare it with what Arnold says here about translating Homer.

In addition, reference may be made to the *Syntopicon*, Chapter 69, on POETRY, especially Topic 4*a*, on epic and dramatic poetry; and Topic 8*b*, which is concerned with the critical standards and artistic rules that have been thought proper to poetic language. *See also* Chapter 81, RHETORIC, Topic 2*b*, on excellence in style.

On Translating Homer

Matthew Arnold

*.... Nunquamne reponam?**

I

It has more than once been suggested to me that I should translate Homer. That is a task for which I have neither the time nor the courage; but the suggestion led me to regard yet more closely a poet whom I had already long studied, and for one or two years the works of Homer were seldom out of my hands. The study of classical litera-ture is probably on the decline; but, what-ever may be the fate of this study in general, it is certain that, as instruction spreads and the number of readers increases, attention will be more and more directed to the poetry of Homer, not indeed as a part of a classical course, but as the most important poetical monument existing. Even within the last ten years two fresh translations of the *Iliad* have appeared in England: one by a man of great ability and genuine learning, Professor New-man; the other by Mr. Wright, the conscien-tious and painstaking translator of Dante. It may safely be asserted that neither of these works will take rank as the standard transla-tion of Homer; that the task of rendering him will still be attempted by other trans-lators. It may perhaps be possible to render to these some service, to save them some loss of labour, by pointing out rocks on which their predecessors have split, and the right objects on which a translator of Homer should fix his attention.

It is disputed what aim a translator should propose to himself in dealing with his origi-nal. Even this preliminary is not yet settled. On one side it is said that the translation ought to be such 'that the reader should, if possible, forget that it is a translation at all, and be lulled into the illusion that he is

reading an original work—something origi-nal' (if the translation be in English), 'from an English hand.' The real original is in this case, it is said, 'taken as a basis on which to rear a poem that shall affect our countrymen as the original may be conceived to have affected its natural hearers.' On the other hand, Mr. Newman, who states the fore-going doctrine only to condemn it, declares that he 'aims at precisely the opposite: to re-tain every peculiarity of the original, so far as he is able, *with the greater care the more foreign it may happen to be*'; so that it may 'never be forgotten that he is imitating, and imitating in a different material.' The trans-lator's 'first duty,' says Mr. Newman, 'is a historical one—to be *faithful*.' Probably both sides would agree that the translator's 'first duty is to be faithful'; but the question at issue between them is, in what faithfulness consists.

My one object is to give practical advice to a translator; and I shall not in the least concern myself with theories of translation as such. But I advise the translator not to try 'to rear on the basis of the *Iliad,* a poem that shall affect our countrymen as the original may be conceived to have affected its natural hearers'; and for this simple reason, that we cannot possibly tell *how* the *Iliad* 'affected its natural hearers.' It is probably meant merely that he should try to affect English-men powerfully, as Homer affected Greeks powerfully; but this direction is not enough, and can give no real guidance. For all great poets affect their hearers powerfully, but the effect of one poet is one thing, that of an-other poet another thing: it is our trans-lator's business to reproduce the effect of Homer, and the most powerful emotion of the unlearned English reader can never as-

*Juvenal 1.1 [Am I never to rest?].

sure him whether he has *re*produced this, or whether he has produced something else. So, again, he may follow Mr. Newman's directions, he may try to be 'faithful,' he may 'retain every peculiarity of his original'; but who is to assure him, who is to assure Mr. Newman himself, that, when he has done this, he has done that for which Mr. Newman enjoins this to be done, 'adhered closely to Homer's manner and habit of thought'? Evidently the translator needs some more practical directions than these. No one can tell him how Homer affected the Greeks; but there are those who can tell him how Homer affects *them*. These are scholars; who possess, at the same time with knowledge of Greek, adequate poetical taste and feeling. No translation will seem to them of much worth compared with the original; but they alone can say whether the translation produces more or less the same effect upon them as the original. They are the only competent tribunal in this matter: the Greeks are dead; the unlearned Englishman has not the data for judging; and no man can safely confide in his own single judgment of his own work. Let not the translator, then, trust to his notions of what the ancient Greeks would have thought of him; he will lose himself in the vague. Let him not trust to what the ordinary English reader thinks of him; he will be taking the blind for his guide. Let him not trust to his own judgment of his own work; he may be misled by individual caprices. Let him ask how his work affects those who both know Greek and can appreciate poetry; whether to read it gives the Provost of Eton, or Professor Thompson at Cambridge, or Professor Jowett here in Oxford, at all the same feeling which to read the original gives them. I consider that when Bentley said of Pope's translation, 'It was a pretty poem, but must not be called Homer,' the work, in spite of all its power and attractiveness, was judged.

'Ὡς ἄν ὁ φρόνιμος ὁρίσειεν,—'as the judicious would determine,'—that is a test to which every one professes himself willing to submit his works. Unhappily, in most cases,

no two persons agree as to who 'the judicious' are. In the present case the ambiguity is removed: I suppose the translator at one with me as to the tribunal to which alone he should look for judgment; and he has thus obtained a practical test by which to estimate the real success of his work. How is he to proceed, in order that his work, tried by this test, may be found most successful?

First of all, there are certain negative counsels which I will give him. Homer has occupied men's minds so much, such a literature has arisen about him, that every one who approaches him should resolve strictly to limit himself to that which may directly serve the object for which he approaches him. I advise the translator to have nothing to do with the questions, whether Homer ever existed; whether the poet of the *Iliad* be one or many; whether the *Iliad* be one poem or an *Achilleis* and an *Iliad* stuck together; whether the Christian doctrine of the Atonement is shadowed forth in the Homeric mythology; whether the Goddess Latona in any way prefigures the Virgin Mary, and so on. These are questions which have been discussed with learning, with ingenuity, nay, with genius; but they have two inconveniences—one general for all who approach them, one particular for the translator. The general inconvenience is that there really exist no data for determining them. The particular inconvenience is that their solution by the translator, even were it possible, could be of no benefit to his translation.

I advise him, again, not to trouble himself with constructing a special vocabulary for his use in translation; with excluding a certain class of English words, and with confining himself to another class, in obedience to any theory about the peculiar qualities of Homer's style. Mr. Newman says that 'the entire dialect of Homer being essentially archaic, that of a translator ought to be as much Saxo-Norman as possible, and owe as little as possible to the elements thrown into our language by classical learning.' Mr. Newman is unfortunate in the observance of his own theory; for I continually find in his translation words of Latin origin, which seem to me quite alien to the simplicity of Homer—'responsive,' for instance, which is a favourite word of Mr. Newman, to represent the Homeric ἀμειβόμενος:

Great Hector of the motley helm thus spake to her responsive.
But thus responsively to him spake god-like Alexander.

And the word 'celestial,' again, in the grand address of Zeus to the horses of Achilles,

You, who are born celestial, *from Eld and Death exempted!*

seems to me in that place exactly to jar upon the feeling as too bookish. But, apart from the question of Mr. Newman's fidelity to his own theory, such a theory seems to me both dangerous for a translator and false in itself. Dangerous for a translator, because, wherever one finds such a theory announced (and one finds it pretty often), it is generally followed by an explosion of pedantry; and pedantry is of all things in the world the most un-Homeric. False in itself, because, in fact, we owe to the Latin element in our language most of that very rapidity and clear decisiveness by which it is contradistinguished from the German, and in sympathy with the languages of Greece and Rome: so that to limit an English translator of Homer to words of Saxon origin is to deprive him of one of his special advantages for translating Homer. In Voss's well-known translation of Homer, it is precisely the qualities of his German language itself, something heavy and trailing both in the structure of its sentences and in the words of which it is composed, which prevent his translation, in spite of the hexameters, in spite of the fidelity, from creating in us the impression created by the Greek. Mr. Newman's prescription, if followed, would just strip the English translator of the advantage which he has over Voss.

The frame of mind in which we approach an author influences our correctness of ap-

preciation of him; and Homer should be approached by a translator in the simplest frame of mind possible. Modern sentiment tries to make the ancient not less than the modern world its own; but against modern sentiment in its applications to Homer the translator, if he would feel Homer truly—and unless he feels him truly, how can he render him truly?—cannot be too much on his guard. For example: the writer of an interesting article on English translations of Homer, in the last number of the *National Review,* quotes, I see, with admiration, a criticism of Mr. Ruskin on the use of the epithet φυσίζοος, 'life-giving,' in that beautiful passage in the third book of the *Iliad,* which follows Helen's mention of her brothers Castor and Pollux as alive, though they were in truth dead:

ὣς φάτο · τοὺς δ’ ἤδη κατέχεν φυσίζοος αἶα
ἐν Λακεδαίμονι αὖθι, φίλῃ ἐν πατρίδι γαίῃ.[1]

'The poet,' says Mr. Ruskin, 'has to speak of the earth in sadness; but he will not let that sadness affect or change his thought of it. No; though Castor and Pollux be dead, yet the earth is our mother still—fruitful, life-giving.' This is a just specimen of that sort of application of modern sentiment to the ancients, against which a student, who wishes to feel the ancients truly, cannot too resolutely defend himself. It reminds one, as, alas! so much of Mr. Ruskin's writing reminds one, of those words of the most delicate of living critics: 'Comme tout genre de composition a son écueil particulier, *celui du genre romanesque, c'est le faux*' ['Every literary genre has its own peculiar peril; that of romanticism is falsity'—Sainte-Beuve]. The reader may feel moved as

---

[1] *Iliad,* iii. 243; *GBWW,* Vol. 4, p. 21b–c. [These two lines are rendered as follows in the translation of the *Iliad* by Richmond Lattimore, University of Chicago Press, 1951, p. 106: "So she spoke, but the teeming earth lay already upon them away in Lakedaimon, the beloved land of their fathers." The epithet "life-giving," to which Arnold refers below in talking of Ruskin, is what Lattimore gives here as "teeming."]

he reads it; but it is not the less an example of 'le faux' in criticism; it is false. It is not true, as to that particular passage, that Homer called the earth φυσίζοος because, 'though he had to speak of the earth in sadness, he would not let that sadness change or affect his thought of it,' but consoled himself by considering that 'the earth is our mother still—fruitful, life-giving.' It is not true, as a matter of general criticism, that this kind of sentimentality, eminently modern, inspires Homer at all. 'From Homer and Polygnotus I every day learn more clearly,' says Goethe, 'that in our life here above ground we have, properly speaking, to enact Hell'[2]—if the student must absolutely have a keynote to the *Iliad,* let him take this of Goethe, and see what he can do with it; it will not, at any rate, like the tender pantheism of Mr. Ruskin, falsify for him the whole strain of Homer.

These are negative counsels; I come to the positive. When I say, the translator of Homer should above all be penetrated by a sense of four qualities of his author—that he is eminently rapid; that he is eminently plain and direct, both in the evolution of his thought and in the expression of it, that is, both in his syntax and in his words; that he is eminently plain and direct in the substance of his thought, that is, in his matter and ideas; and, finally, that he is eminently noble—I probably seem to be saying what is too general to be of much service to anybody. Yet it is strictly true that, for want of duly penetrating themselves with the first-named quality of Homer, his rapidity, Cowper and Mr. Wright have failed in rendering him; that, for want of duly appreciating the second-named quality, his plainness and directness of style and diction, Pope and Mr. Sotheby have failed in rendering him; that for want of appreciating the third, his plainness and directness of ideas, Chapman has failed in rendering him; while for want of appreciating the fourth, his nobleness, Mr.

[2] *Briefwechsel zwischen Schiller und Goethe,* vi. 230.

Newman, who has clearly seen some of the faults of his predecessors, has yet failed more conspicuously than any of them.

Coleridge says, in his strange language, speaking of the union of the human soul with the divine essence, that this takes place

Whene'er the mist, which stands 'twixt God and thee,
Defecates to a pure transparency;

and so, too, it may be said of that union of the translator with his original, which alone can produce a good translation, that it takes place when the mist which stands between them—the mist of alien modes of thinking, speaking, and feeling on the translator's part—'defecates to a pure transparency,' and disappears. But between Cowper and Homer —(Mr. Wright repeats in the main Cowper's manner, as Mr. Sotheby repeats Pope's manner, and neither Mr. Wright's translation nor Mr. Sotheby's has, I must be forgiven for saying, any proper reason for existing)— between Cowper and Homer there is interposed the mist of Cowper's elaborate Miltonic manner, entirely alien to the flowing rapidity of Homer; between Pope and Homer there is interposed the mist of Pope's literary artificial manner, entirely alien to the plain naturalness of Homer's manner; between Chapman and Homer there is interposed the mist of the fancifulness of the Elizabethan age, entirely alien to the plain directness of Homer's thought and feeling; while between Mr. Newman and Homer is interposed a cloud of more than Egyptian thickness—namely, a manner, in Mr. Newman's version, eminently ignoble, while Homer's manner is eminently noble.

I do not despair of making all these propositions clear to a student who approaches Homer with a free mind. First, Homer is eminently rapid, and to this rapidity the elaborate movement of Miltonic blank verse is alien. The reputation of Cowper, that most interesting man and excellent poet, does not depend on his translation of Homer; and in his preface to the second edition, he himself tells us that he felt—he had too much poetical taste not to feel—on returning to his own version after six or seven years, 'more dissatisfied with it himself than the most difficult to be pleased of all his judges.' And he was dissatisfied with it for the right reason—that 'it seemed to him deficient *in the grace of ease.*' Yet he seems to have originally misconceived the manner of Homer so much, that it is no wonder he rendered him amiss. 'The similitude of Milton's manner to that of Homer is such,' he says, 'that no person familiar with both can read either without being reminded of the other; and it is in those breaks and pauses to which the numbers of the English poet are so much indebted, both for their dignity and variety, that he chiefly copies the Grecian.' It would be more true to say: 'The unlikeness of Milton's manner to that of Homer is such, that no person familiar with both can read either without being struck with his difference from the other; and it is in his breaks and pauses that the English poet is most unlike the Grecian.'

The inversion and pregnant conciseness of Milton or Dante are, doubtless, most impressive qualities of style; but they are the very opposites of the directness and flowingness of Homer, which he keeps alike in passages of the simplest narrative, and in those of the deepest emotion. Not only, for example, are these lines of Cowper un-Homeric:

So numerous seemed those fires the banks
*   between*
Of Xanthus, blazing, and the fleet of Greece
In prospect all of Troy;

where the position of the word 'blazing' gives an entirely un-Homeric movement to this simple passage, describing the fires of the Trojan camp outside of Troy; but the following lines, in that very highly-wrought passage where the horse of Achilles answers his master's reproaches for having left Patroclus on the field of battle, are equally un-Homeric:

For not through sloth or tardiness on us
Aught chargeable, have Ilium's sons thine
*   arms*

Stript from Patroclus' shoulders; but a God
Matchless in battle, offspring of bright-haired
Latona, him contending in the van
Slew, for the glory of the chief of Troy.

Here even the first inversion, 'have Ilium's sons thine arms Stript from Patroclus' shoulders,' gives the reader a sense of a movement not Homeric; and the second inversion, 'a God him contending in the van Slew,' gives this sense ten times stronger. Instead of moving on without check, as in reading the original, the reader twice finds himself, in reading the translation, brought up and checked. Homer moves with the same simplicity and rapidity in the highly-wrought as in the simple passage.

It is in vain that Cowper insists on his fidelity: 'my chief boast is that I have adhered closely to my original'—'the matter found in me, whether the reader like it or not, is found also in Homer; and the matter not found in me, how much soever the reader may admire it, is found only in Mr. Pope.' To suppose that it is *fidelity* to an original to give its matter, unless you at the same time give its manner; or, rather, to suppose that you can really give its matter at all, unless you can give its manner, is just the mistake of our pre-Raphaelite school of painters, who do not understand that the peculiar effect of nature resides in the whole and not in the parts. So the peculiar effect of a poet resides in his manner and movement, not in his words taken separately. It is well known how conscientiously literal is Cowper in his translation of Homer. It is well known how extravagantly free is Pope.

So let it be!
Portents and prodigies are lost on me:

that is Pope's rendering of the words:

Ξάνθε, τί μοι θάνατον μαντεύεαι; οὐδέ τί σε χρή · [3]

Xanthus, why prophesiest thou my death to
*   me? thou needest not at all—*

yet, on the whole, Pope's translation of the

----

[3] *Iliad*, xix. 420; *GBWW*, Vol. 4, p. 141c.

Iliad is more Homeric than Cowper's, for it is more rapid.

Pope's movement, however, though rapid, is not of the same kind as Homer's; and here I come to the real objection to rhyme in a translation of Homer. It is commonly said that rhyme is to be abandoned in a translation of Homer, because 'the exigencies of rhyme,' to quote Mr. Newman, 'positively forbid faithfulness'; because 'a just translation of any ancient poet in rhyme,' to quote Cowper, 'is impossible.' This, however, is merely an accidental objection to rhyme. If this were all, it might be supposed, that if rhymes were more abundant Homer could be adequately translated in rhyme. But this is not so; there is a deeper, a substantial objection to rhyme in a translation of Homer. It is, that rhyme inevitably tends to pair lines which in the original are independent, and thus the movement of the poem is changed. In these lines of Chapman, for instance, from Sarpedon's speech to Glaucus, in the twelfth book of the *Iliad*:

> O friend, if keeping back
> Would keep back age from us, and death,
> and that we might not wrack
> In this life's human sea at all, but that de-
> ferring now
> We shunned death ever,—nor would I half
> this vain valor show,
> Nor glorify a folly so, to wish thee to ad-
> vance;
> But since we must go, though not here, and
> that besides the chance
> Proposed now, there are infinite fates, etc.

Here the necessity of making the line,

> Nor glorify a folly so, to wish thee to ad-
> vance,

rhyme with the line which follows it, entirely changes and spoils the movement of the passage.

οὔτε κεν αὐτὸς ἐνὶ πρώτοισι μαχοίμην,
οὔτε κέ σε στέλλοιμι μάχην ἐς κυδιάνειραν · [4]

---

[4] *Iliad*, xii. 324; *GBWW*, Vol. 4, p. 85c.

> Neither would I myself go forth to fight
> with the foremost,
> Nor would I urge thee on to enter the glori-
> ous battle,

says Homer; there he stops, and begins an opposed movement:

νῦν δ'—ἔμπης γὰρ Κῆρες ἐφεστᾶσιν θανάτοιο—

> But—for a thousand fates of death stand
> close to us always—

This line, in which Homer wishes to go away with the most marked rapidity from the line before, Chapman is forced, by the necessity of rhyming, intimately to connect with the line before.

> But since we must go, though not here, and
> that besides the chance—

The moment the word *chance* strikes our ear, we are irresistibly carried back to *advance* and to the whole previous line, which, according to Homer's own feeling, we ought to have left behind us entirely, and to be moving farther and farther away from.

Rhyme certainly, by intensifying antithesis, can intensify separation, and this is precisely what Pope does; but this balanced rhetorical antithesis, though very effective, is entirely un-Homeric. And this is what I mean by saying that Pope fails to render Homer, because he does not render his plainness and directness of style and diction. Where Homer marks separation by moving away, Pope marks it by antithesis. No passage could show this better than the passage I have just quoted, on which I will pause for a moment.

Robert Wood, whose *Essay on the Genius of Homer* is mentioned by Goethe as one of the books which fell into his hands when his powers were first developing themselves, and strongly interested him, relates of this passage a striking story. He says that in 1762, at the end of the Seven Years' War, being then Under-Secretary of State, he was directed to wait upon the President of the Council, Lord Granville, a few days before he died, with the preliminary articles of the Treaty of Paris. 'I found him,' he continues, 'so languid, that I proposed postponing my business for another time; but he insisted that I should stay, saying, it could not prolong his life to neglect his duty; and repeating the following passage out of Sarpedon's speech, he dwelled with particular emphasis on the third line, which recalled to his mind the distinguishing part he had taken in public affairs:

ὦ πέπον, εἰ μὲν γὰρ, πόλεμον περὶ τόνδε
  φυγόντε,
αἰεὶ δὴ μέλλοιμεν ἀγήρω τ' ἀθανάτω τε
ἔσσεσθ', οὔτε κεν αὐτὸς ἐνὶ πρώτοισι μαχοίμην,[5]
οὔτε κέ σε στέλλοιμι μάχην ἐς κυδιάνειραν ·
νῦν δ'—ἔμπης γὰρ Κῆρες ἐφεστᾶσιν θανάτοιο
μυρίαι, ἃς οὐκ ἔστι φυγεῖν βρότον, οὐδ'
  ὑπαλύξαι—
ἴομεν.*

His Lordship repeated the last word several times with a calm and determinate resignation; and, after a serious pause of some minutes, he desired to hear the Treaty read, to which he listened with great attention, and recovered spirits enough to declare the approbation of a dying statesman (I use his own words) "on the most glorious war, and most honourable peace, this nation ever saw." [6]

I quote this story, first, because it is interesting as exhibiting the English aristocracy at its very height of culture, lofty spirit, and greatness, towards the middle of the last century. I quote it, secondly, because it seems to me to illustrate Goethe's saying which I mentioned, that our life, in Homer's view of it, represents a conflict and a hell; and it brings out, too, what there is tonic and fortifying in this doctrine. I quote it, lastly, because it shows that the passage is just one of those in translating which Pope will be at his best, a passage of strong emotion and oratorical movement, not of simple narrative or description.

Pope translates the passage thus:

Could all our care elude the gloomy grave
Which claims no less the fearful than the
  brave,
For lust of fame I should not vainly dare
In fighting fields, nor urge thy soul to war:
But since, alas! ignoble age must come,
Disease, and death's inexorable doom;
The life which others pay, let us bestow,
And give to fame what we to nature owe.

Nothing could better exhibit Pope's prodigious talent; and nothing, too, could be better in its own way. But, as Bentley said, 'You must not call it Homer.' One feels that Homer's thought has passed through a literary and rhetorical crucible, and come out highly intellectualised; come out in a form which strongly impresses us, indeed, but which no longer impresses us in the same way as when it was uttered by Homer. The antithesis of the last two lines—

The life which others pay, let us bestow,
And give to fame what we to nature owe—

is excellent, and is just suited to Pope's heroic couplet; but neither the antithesis itself, nor the couplet which conveys it, is

---

5 These are the words on which Lord Granville 'dwelled with particular emphasis.'

* The lines quoted above in Greek from *Iliad* xii are those previously quoted by Arnold in Chapman's translation, and subsequently in Pope's. They are rendered as follows by Samuel Butler in *GBWW*, Vol. 4, p. 85c: "My good friend, if, when we were once out of this fight, we could escape old age and death thenceforward and for ever, I should neither press forward myself nor bid you do so, but death in ten thousand shapes hangs ever over our heads, and no man can elude him; therefore let us go forward and either win glory for ourselves, or yield it to another." The words in the third line of the Greek on which Granville is said to have "dwelled with particular emphasis" are those given by Butler as "press forward myself." The last word, ἴομεν, which "His Lordship repeated several times with a calm and deliberate resignation," and which Arnold later mentions in discussing Pope's translation of the same passage, is what Butler renders as "let us go forward."

6 Robert Wood, *Essay on the Original Genius and Writings of Homer,* London, 1775, p. vii.

suited to the feeling or to the movement of the Homeric ἴομεν.

A literary and intellectualised language is, however, in its own way well suited to grand matters; and Pope, with a language of this kind and his own admirable talent, comes off well enough as long as he has passion, or oratory, or a great crisis to deal with. Even here, as I have been pointing out, he does not render Homer; but he and his style are in themselves strong. It is when he comes to level passages—passages of narrative or description—that he and his style are sorely tried, and prove themselves weak. A perfectly plain direct style can, of course, convey the simplest matter as naturally as the grandest; indeed, it must be harder for it, one would say, to convey a grand matter worthily and nobly, than to convey a common matter, as alone such a matter should be conveyed, plainly and simply. But the style of Rasselas is incomparably better fitted to describe a sage philosophising than a soldier lighting his camp-fire. The style of Pope is not the style of Rasselas; but it is equally a literary style, equally unfitted to describe a simple matter with the plain naturalness of Homer.

Every one knows the passage at the end of the eighth book of the *Iliad,* where the fires of the Trojan encampment are likened to the stars. It is very far from my wish to hold Pope up to ridicule, so I shall not quote the commencement of the passage, which in the original is of great and celebrated beauty, and in translating which Pope has been singularly and notoriously fortunate. But the latter part of the passage, where Homer leaves the stars, and comes to the Trojan fires, treats of the plainest, most matter-of-fact subject possible, and deals with this, as Homer always deals with every subject, in the plainest and most straightforward style. 'So many in number, between the ships and the streams of Xanthus, shone forth in front of Troy the fires kindled by the Trojans. There were kindled a thousand fires in the plain; and by each one there sat fifty men in the light of the blazing fire. And the

horses, munching white barley and rye, and standing by the chariots, waited for the bright-throned Morning.'[7]

In Pope's translation, this plain story becomes the following:

So many flames before proud Ilion blaze,
And brighten glimmering Xanthus with
  their rays;
The long reflections of the distant fires
Gleam on the walls, and tremble on the
  spires.
A thousand piles the dusky horrors gild,
And shoot a shady lustre o'er the field.
Full fifty guards each flaming pile attend,
Whose umbered arms, by fits, thick flashes
  send;
Loud neigh the coursers o'er their heaps of
  corn,
And ardent warriors wait the rising morn.

It is for passages of this sort, which, after all, form the bulk of a narrative poem, that Pope's style is so bad. In elevated passages he is powerful, as Homer is powerful, though not in the same way; but in plain narrative, where Homer is still powerful and delightful, Pope, by the inherent fault of his style, is ineffective and out of taste. Wordsworth says somewhere, that wherever Virgil seems to have composed 'with his eye on the object,' Dryden fails to render him. Homer invariably composes 'with his eye on the object,' whether the object be a moral or a material one: Pope composes with his eye on his style, into which he translates his object, whatever it is. That, therefore, which Homer conveys to us immediately, Pope conveys to us through a medium. He aims at turning Homer's sentiments pointedly and rhetorically; at investing Homer's description with ornament and dignity. A sentiment may be changed by being put into a pointed and oratorical form, yet may still be very effective in that form; but a description, the moment it takes its eyes off that which it is to describe, and begins to think of ornamenting itself, is worthless.

---

[7] *Iliad,* viii. 560; *GBWW,* Vol. 4, p. 56d.

Therefore, I say, the translator of Homer should penetrate himself with a sense of the plainness and directness of Homer's style; of the simplicity with which Homer's thought is evolved and expressed. He has Pope's fate before his eyes, to show him what a divorce may be created even between the most gifted translator and Homer by an artificial evolution of thought and a literary cast of style.

Chapman's style is not artificial and literary like Pope's, nor his movement elaborate and self-retarding like the Miltonic movement of Cowper. He is plain-spoken, fresh, vigorous, and, to a certain degree, rapid; and all these are Homeric qualities. I cannot say that I think the movement of his fourteen-syllable line, which has been so much commended, Homeric; but on this point I shall have more to say by-and-by, when I come to speak of Mr. Newman's metrical exploits. But it is not distinctly anti-Homeric, like the movement of Milton's blank verse; and it has a rapidity of its own. Chapman's diction, too, is generally good, that is, appropriate to Homer; above all, the syntactical character of his style is appropriate. With these merits, what prevents his translation from being a satisfactory version of Homer? Is it merely the want of literal faithfulness to his original, imposed upon him, it is said, by the exigencies of rhyme? Has this celebrated version, which has so many advantages, no other and deeper defect than that? Its author is a poet, and a poet, too, of the Elizabethan age; the golden age of English literature, as it is called, and on the whole truly called; for, whatever be the defects of Elizabethan literature (and they are great), we have no development of our literature to compare with it for vigour and richness. This age, too, showed what it could do in translating, by producing a masterpiece—its version of the Bible.

Chapman's translation has often been praised as eminently Homeric. Keats's fine sonnet in its honour every one knows; but Keats could not read the original, and therefore could not really judge the translation.

Coleridge, in praising Chapman's version, says at the same time, 'It will give you small idea of Homer.' But the grave authority of Mr. Hallam pronounces this translation to be 'often exceedingly Homeric'; and its latest editor boldly declares that by what, with a deplorable style, he calls 'his own innative Homeric genius,' Chapman 'has thoroughly identified himself with Homer'; and that 'we pardon him even for his digressions, for they are such as we feel Homer himself would have written.'

I confess that I can never read twenty lines of Chapman's version without recurring to Bentley's cry, 'This is not Homer!' and that from a deeper cause than any unfaithfulness occasioned by the fetters of rhyme.

I said that there were four things which eminently distinguished Homer, and with a sense of which Homer's translator should penetrate himself as fully as possible. One of these four things was the plainness and directness of Homer's ideas. I have just been speaking of the plainness and directness of his style; but the plainness and directness of the contents of his style, of his ideas themselves, is not less remarkable. But as eminently as Homer is plain, so eminently is the Elizabethan literature in general, and Chapman in particular, fanciful. Steeped in humours and fantasticality up to its very lips, the Elizabethan age, newly arrived at the free use of the human faculties after their long term of bondage, and delighting to exercise them freely, suffers from its own extravagance in this first exercise of them, can hardly bring itself to see an object quietly or to describe it temperately. Happily, in the translation of the Bible, the sacred character of their original inspired the translators with such respect that they did not dare to give the rein to their own fancies in dealing with it. But, in dealing with works of profane literature, in dealing with poetical works above all, which highly stimulated them, one may say that the minds of the Elizabethan translators were *too* active; that they could not forbear importing so much of their own, and this of a most peculiar and Elizabethan character, into their original, that they effaced the character of the original itself.

Take merely the opening pages to Chapman's translation, the introductory verses, and the dedications. You will find—

An Anagram of the name of our Dread
  Prince,
My most gracious and sacred Mæcenas,
Henry, Prince of Wales,
Our Sunn, Heyr, Peace, Life—

Henry, son of James the First, to whom the work is dedicated. Then comes an address—

To the sacred Fountain of Princes,
Sole Empress of Beauty and Virtue, Anne,
  Queen
    Of England, etc.

All the Middle Age, with its grotesqueness, its conceits, its irrationality, is still in these opening pages; they by themselves are sufficient to indicate to us what a gulf divides Chapman from the 'clearest-souled' of poets, from Homer; almost as great a gulf as that which divides him from Voltaire. Pope has been sneered at for saying that Chapman writes 'somewhat as one might imagine Homer himself to have written before he arrived at years of discretion.' But the remark is excellent: Homer expresses himself like a man of adult reason, Chapman like a man whose reason has not yet cleared itself. For instance, if Homer had had to say of a poet that he hoped his merit was now about to be fully established in the opinion of good judges, he was as incapable of saying this as Chapman says it—'Though truth in her very nakedness sits in so deep a pit, that from Gades to Aurora, and Ganges, few eyes can sound her, I hope yet those few here will so discover and confirm that the date being out of her darkness in this morning of our poet, he shall now gird his temples with the sun,' —I say, Homer was as incapable of saying this in that manner, as Voltaire himself would have been. Homer, indeed, has actually an affinity with Voltaire in the unri-

valled clearness and straightforwardness of his thinking; in the way in which he keeps to one thought at a time, and puts that thought forth in its complete natural plainness, instead of being led away from it by some fancy striking him in connection with it, and being beguiled to wander off with this fancy till his original thought, in its natural reality, knows him no more. What could better show us how gifted a race was this Greek race? The same member of it has not only the power of profoundly touching that natural heart of humanity which it is Voltaire's weakness that he cannot reach, but can also address the understanding with all Voltaire's admirable simplicity and rationality.

My limits will not allow me to do more than shortly illustrate, from Chapman's version of the *Iliad,* what I mean when I speak of this vital difference between Homer and an Elizabethan poet in the quality of their thought; between the plain simplicity of the thought of the one, and the curious complexity of the thought of the other. As in Pope's case, I carefully abstain from choosing passages for the express purpose of making Chapman appear ridiculous: Chapman, like Pope, merits in himself all respect, though he too, like Pope, fails to render Homer.

In that tonic speech of Sarpedon, of which I have said so much, Homer, you may remember, has:

εἰ μὲν γὰρ, πόλεμον περὶ τόνδε φυγόντε,
αἰεὶ δὴ μέλλοιμεν ἀγήρω τ' ἀθανάτω τε
ἔσσεσθ'—

if indeed, but once this battle avoided,
We were for ever to live without growing
  old and immortal.

Chapman cannot be satisfied with this, but must add a fancy to it:

        if keeping back
Would keep back age from us, and death,
  and that we might not wrack
In this life's human sea at all;

and so on. Again; in another passage which I have before quoted, where Zeus says to the horses of Peleus,

τί σφῶϊ δόμεν Πηλῆϊ ἀνάκτι
θνητῷ; ὑμεῖς δ' ἐστὸν ἀγήρω τ' ἀθανάτω τε · [8]

Why gave we you to royal Peleus, to a mortal? but ye are without old age, and immortal.

Chapman sophisticates this into:

Why gave we you t' a mortal king, when immortality
And incapacity of age so dignifies your states?

Again; in the speech of Achilles to his horses, where Achilles, according to Homer, says simply, 'Take heed that ye bring your master safe back to the host of the Danaans, in some other sort than the last time, when the battle is ended,' Chapman sophisticates this into:

When with blood, for this day's fast observed, revenge shall yield
Our heart satiety, *bring us off.*

In Hector's famous speech, again, at his parting from Andromache, Homer makes him say: 'Nor does my own heart so bid me' (to keep safe behind the walls), 'since I have learned to be staunch always, and to fight among the foremost of the Trojans, busy on behalf of my father's great glory, and my own.'[9] In Chapman's hands this becomes:

The spirit I first did breathe
Did never teach me that; much less, since the contempt of death
Was settled in me, and my mind knew what a worthy was,
Whose office is to lead in fight, and give no danger pass
Without improvement. In this fire must Hector's trial shine:
Here must his country, father, friends, be in him made divine.

---

8 *Iliad,* xvii. 443; *GBWW,* Vol. 4, p. 126c.
9 *Iliad,* vi. 444; *GBWW,* Vol. 4, p. 44c.

You see how ingeniously Homer's plain thought is *tormented,* as the French would say, here. Homer goes on, 'For well I know this in my mind and in my heart, the day will be, when sacred Troy shall perish'—

ἔσσεται ἦμαρ, ὅτ' ἄν ποτ' ὀλώλῃ ῎Ιλιος ἱρή.

Chapman makes this:

And such a stormy *day shall come, in mind and soul I know,*
When sacred Troy shall shed her towers, for tears of overthrow.

I might go on for ever, but I could not give you a better illustration than this last, of what I mean by saying that the Elizabethan poet fails to render Homer because he cannot forbear to interpose a play of thought between his object and its expression. Chapman translates his object into Elizabethan, as Pope translates it into the Augustan of Queen Anne; both convey it to us through a medium. Homer, on the other hand, sees his object and conveys it to us immediately.

And yet, in spite of this perfect plainness and directness of Homer's style, in spite of this perfect plainness and directness of his ideas, he is eminently *noble;* he works as entirely in the grand style, he is as grandiose, as Phidias, or Dante, or Michael Angelo. This is what makes his translators despair. 'To give relief,' says Cowper, 'to prosaic subjects' (such as dressing, eating, drinking, harnessing, travelling, going to bed), that is to treat such subjects nobly, in the grand style, 'without seeming unreasonably tumid, is extremely difficult.' It *is* difficult, but Homer has done it. Homer is precisely the incomparable poet he is, because he has done it. His translator must not be tumid, must not be artificial, must not be literary— true: but then also he must not be commonplace, must not be ignoble. I have shown you how translators of Homer fail by wanting rapidity, by wanting simplicity of style, by wanting plainness of thought: in a second lecture I will show you how a translator fails by wanting nobility.

II

I must repeat what I said in beginning, that the translator of Homer ought steadily to keep in mind where lies the real test of the success of his translation, what judges he is to try to satisfy. He is to try to satisfy *scholars,* because scholars alone have the means of really judging him. A scholar may be a pedant, it is true, and then his judgment will be worthless; but a scholar may also have poetical feeling, and then he can judge him truly; whereas all the poetical feeling in the world will not enable a man who is not a scholar to judge him truly. For the translator is to reproduce Homer, and the scholar alone has the means of knowing that Homer who is to be reproduced. He knows him but imperfectly, for he is separated from him by time, race, and language; but he alone knows him at all. Yet people speak as if there were two real tribunals in this matter—the scholar's tribunal, and that of the general public. They speak as if the scholar's judgment was one thing, and the general public's judgment another; both with their shortcomings, both with their liability to error; but both to be regarded by the translator. The translator who makes verbal literalness his chief care 'will,' says a writer in the *National Review* whom I have already quoted, 'be appreciated by the scholar accustomed to test a translation rigidly by comparison with the original, to look perhaps with excessive care to finish in detail rather than boldness and general effect, and find pardon even for a version that seems bare and bold, so it be scholastic and faithful.' But, if the scholar in judging a translation looks to detail rather than to general effect, he judges it pedantically and ill. The appeal, however, lies not from the pedantic scholar to the general public, which can only like or dislike Chapman's version, or Pope's, or Mr. Newman's, but cannot *judge* them; it lies from the pedantic scholar to the scholar who is not pedantic, who knows that Homer is Homer by his general effect, and not by his single words, and who

demands but one thing in a translation—that it shall, as nearly as possible, reproduce for him the *general effect* of Homer. This, then, remains the one proper aim of the translator: to reproduce on the intelligent scholar, as nearly as possible, the general effect of Homer. Except so far as he reproduces this, he loses his labour, even though he may make a spirited *Iliad* of his own, like Pope, or translate Homer's *Iliad* word for word, like Mr. Newman. If his proper aim were to stimulate in any manner possible the general public, he might be right in following Pope's example; if his proper aim were to help schoolboys to construe Homer, he might be right in following Mr. Newman's. But it is not: his proper aim is, I repeat it yet once more, to reproduce on the intelligent scholar, as nearly as he can, the general effect of Homer.

When, therefore, Cowper says, 'My chief boast is that I have adhered closely to my original'; when Mr. Newman says, 'My aim is to retain every peculiarity of the original, to be *faithful,* exactly as is the case with the draughtsman of the Elgin marbles'; their real judge only replies: 'It may be so: reproduce then upon us, reproduce the effect of Homer, as a good copy reproduces the effect of the Elgin marbles.'

When, again, Mr. Newman tells us that 'by an exhaustive process of argument and experiment' he has found a metre which is at once the metre of 'the modern Greek epic,' and a metre 'like in moral genius' to Homer's metre, his judge has still but the same answer for him: 'It may be so: reproduce then on our ear something of the effect produced by the movement of Homer.'

But what is the general effect which Homer produces on Mr. Newman himself? —because, when we know this, we shall know whether he and his judges are agreed at the outset; whether we may expect him, if he can reproduce the effect he feels, if his hand does not betray him in the execution, to satisfy his judges and to succeed. If, however, Mr. Newman's impression from Homer is something quite different from that of his judges, then it can hardly be expected that any amount of labour or talent will enable him to reproduce for them *their* Homer.

Mr. Newman does not leave us in doubt as to the general effect which Homer makes upon him. As I have told you what is the general effect which Homer makes upon me —that of a most rapidly moving poet, that of a poet most plain and direct in his style, that of a poet most plain and direct in his ideas, that of a poet eminently noble—so Mr. Newman tells us his general impression of Homer. 'Homer's style,' he says, 'is direct, popular, forcible, quaint, flowing, garrulous.' Again: 'Homer rises and sinks with his subject, is prosaic when it is tame, is low when it is mean.'

I lay my finger on four words in these two sentences of Mr. Newman, and I say that the man who could apply those words to Homer can never render Homer truly. The four words are these: *quaint, garrulous, prosaic, low.* Search the English language for a word which does not apply to Homer, and you could not fix on a better than *quaint,* unless perhaps you fixed on one of the other three.

Again: 'to translate Homer suitably,' says Mr. Newman, 'we need a diction sufficiently antiquated to obtain pardon of the reader for its frequent homeliness.' 'I am concerned,' he says again, 'with the artistic problem of attaining a plausible aspect of moderate antiquity, while remaining easily intelligible.' And again, he speaks of 'the more antiquated style suited to this subject.' Quaint! antiquated!—but to whom? Sir Thomas Browne is quaint, and the diction of Chaucer is antiquated: does Mr. Newman suppose that Homer seemed quaint to Sophocles, when he read him, as Sir Thomas Browne seems quaint to us, when we read him? or that Homer's diction seemed antiquated to Sophocles, as Chaucer's diction seems antiquated to us? But we cannot really know, I confess, how Homer seemed to Sophocles: well then, to those who can tell us how he seems to them, to the living scholar, to our only present witness on this

matter—does Homer make on the Provost of Eton, when he reads him, the impression of a poet quaint and antiquated? does he make this impression on Professor Thompson or Professor Jowett? When Shakspeare says, 'The princes *orgulous*,' meaning 'the proud princes,' we say, 'This is antiquated'; when he says of the Trojan gates, that they

> *with massy staples*
> *And corresponsive and fulfilling bolts*
> Sperr *up the sons of Troy,**

we say, 'This is both quaint and antiquated.' But does Homer ever compose in a language which produces on the scholar at all the same impression as this language which I have quoted from Shakspeare? Never once. Shakspeare is quaint and antiquated in the lines which I have just quoted; but Shakspeare—need I say it?—can compose, when he likes, when he is at his best, in a language perfectly simple, perfectly intelligible; in a language which, in spite of the two centuries and a half which part its author from us, stops us or surprises us as little as the language of a contemporary. And Homer has not Shakspeare's variations: Homer always composes as Shakspeare composes at his best; Homer is always simple and intelligible, as Shakspeare is often; Homer is never quaint and antiquated, as Shakspeare is sometimes.

When Mr. Newman says that Homer is garrulous, he seems, perhaps, to depart less widely from the common opinion than when he calls him quaint; for is there not Horace's authority for asserting that 'the good Homer sometimes nods,' *bonus dormitat Homerus*? and a great many people have come, from the currency of this well-known criticism, to represent Homer to themselves as a diffuse old man, with the full-stocked mind, but also with the occasional slips and weaknesses of old age. Horace has said better things than his 'bonus dormitat Homerus'; but he never meant by this, as I

---

* *Troilus and Cressida,* Prologue; *GBWW,* Vol. 27, p. 103b.

need not remind any one who knows the passage, that Homer was garrulous, or anything of the kind. Instead, however, of either discussing what Horace meant, or discussing Homer's garrulity as a general question, I prefer to bring to my mind some style which *is* garrulous, and to ask myself, to ask you, whether anything at all of the impression made by that style is ever made by the style of Homer. The mediæval romancers, for instance, are garrulous; the following, to take out of a thousand instances the first which comes to hand, is in a garrulous manner. It is from the romance of *Richard Cœur de Lion.*

Of my tale be not a-wondered!
The French says he slew an hundred
(Whereof is made this English saw)
Or he rested him any thraw.
Him followed many an English knight
That eagerly holp him for to fight,

and so on. Now, the manner of that composition I call garrulous; every one will feel it to be garrulous; every one will understand what is meant when it is called garrulous. Then I ask the scholar—does Homer's manner ever make upon you, I do not say the same impression of its garrulity as that passage; but does it make, ever for one moment, an impression in the slightest way resembling, in the remotest degree akin to, the impression made by that passage of the mediæval poet? I have no fear of the answer.

I follow the same method with Mr. Newman's two other epithets, *prosaic* and *low.* 'Homer rises and sinks with his subject,' says Mr. Newman; 'is prosaic when it is tame, is low when it is mean.' First I say, Homer is never, in any sense, to be with truth called prosaic; he is never to be called low. He does not rise and sink with his subject; on the contrary, his manner invests his subject, whatever his subject be, with nobleness. Then I look for an author of whom it may with truth be said, that he 'rises and sinks with his subject, is prosaic when it is tame, is low when it is mean.' Defoe is emi-

nently such an author; of Defoe's manner it may with perfect precision be said, that it follows his matter; his lifelike composition takes its character from the facts which it conveys, not from the nobleness of the composer. In *Moll Flanders* and *Colonel Jack,* Defoe is undoubtedly prosaic when his subject is tame, low when his subject is mean. Does Homer's manner in the *Iliad,* I ask the scholar, ever make upon him an impression at all like the impression made by Defoe's manner in *Moll Flanders* and *Colonel Jack?* Does it not, on the contrary, leave him with an impression of nobleness, even when it deals with Thersites or with Irus?

Well, then, Homer is neither quaint, nor garrulous, nor prosaic, nor mean: and Mr. Newman, in seeing him so, sees him differently from those who are to judge Mr. Newman's rendering of him. By pointing out how a wrong conception of Homer affects Mr. Newman's translation, I hope to place in still clearer light those four cardinal truths which I pronounce essential for him who would have a right conception of Homer: that Homer is rapid, that he is plain and direct in word and style, that he is plain and direct in his ideas, and that he is noble.

Mr. Newman says that in fixing on a style for suitably rendering Homer, as he conceives him, he 'alights on the delicate line which separates the *quaint* from the *grotesque.*' 'I ought to be quaint,' he says, 'I ought not to be grotesque.' This is a most unfortunate sentence. Mr. Newman is grotesque, which he himself says he ought not to be; and he ought not to be quaint, which he himself says he ought to be.

'No two persons will agree,' says Mr. Newman, 'as to where the quaint ends and the grotesque begins'; and perhaps this is true. But, in order to avoid all ambiguity in the use of the two words, it is enough to say that most persons would call an expression which produced on them a very strong sense of its incongruity, and which violently surprised them, *grotesque;* and an expression which produced on them a slighter sense of its incongruity, and which more gently surprised them, *quaint.* Using the two words in this manner, I say that when Mr. Newman translates Helen's words to Hector in the sixth book,

Δᾶερ ἐμεῖο, κυνὸς κακομηχάνου, ὀκρυοέσσης,—[10]

*O, brother thou of me, who am a mischief-
working vixen,*
A numbing horror,—

he is grotesque; that is, he expresses himself in a manner which produces on us a very strong sense of its incongruity, and which violently surprises us. I say, again, that when Mr. Newman translates the common line,

Τὴν δ᾽ ἠμείβετ᾽ ἔπειτα μέγας κορυθαίολος
"Εκτωρ,—

*Great Hector of the motley helm then spake
to her responsive,—*

or the common expression ἐϋκνήμιδες ᾽Αχαιοί, 'dapper-greaved Achaians,' he is quaint; that is, he expresses himself in a manner which produces on us a slighter sense of incongruity, and which more gently surprises us. But violent and gentle surprise are alike far from the scholar's spirit when he reads in Homer κυνὸς κακομηχάνου, or κορυθαίολος "Εκτωρ, or ἐϋκνήμιδες ᾽Αχαιοί. These expressions no more seem odd to him than the simplest expressions in English. He is not more checked by any feeling of strangeness, strong or weak, when he reads them, than when he reads in an English book 'the painted savage,' or 'the phlegmatic Dutchman.' Mr. Newman's renderings of them must, therefore, be wrong expressions in a translation of Homer, because they excite in the scholar, their only competent judge, a feeling quite alien to that excited in him by what they profess to render.

Mr. Newman, by expressions of this kind, is false to his original in two ways. He is false to him inasmuch as he is ignoble; for a noble air, and a grotesque air, the air of the address,

---

10 *Iliad,* vi. 344; *GBWW,* Vol. 4, p. 43c.

Δᾶερ ἐμεῖο, κυνὸς κακομηχάνου, ὀκρυοέσσης,

and the air of the address,

*O, brother thou of me, who am a mischief-
working vixen,*
A numbing horror,—

are just contrary the one to the other: and he is false to him inasmuch as he is odd; for an odd diction like Mr. Newman's, and a perfectly plain natural diction like Homer's —'dapper-greaved Achaians' and ἐϋκνήμιδες ᾽Αχαιοί—are also just contrary the one to the other. Where, indeed, Mr. Newman got his diction, with whom he can have lived, what can be his test of antiquity and rarity for words, are questions which I ask myself with bewilderment. He has prefixed to his translation a list of what he calls 'the more antiquated or rarer words' which he has used. In this list appear, on the one hand, such words as *doughty, grisly, lusty, noisome, ravin,* which are familiar, one would think, to all the world; on the other hand, such words as *bragly,* meaning, Mr. Newman tells us, 'proudly fine'; *bulkin,* 'a calf'; *plump,* 'a mass'; and so on. 'I am concerned,' says Mr. Newman, 'with the artistic problem of attaining a plausible aspect of moderate antiquity, while remaining easily intelligible.' But it seems to me that *lusty* is not antiquated; and that *bragly* is not a word readily understood. That this word, indeed, and *bulkin,* may have 'a plausible aspect of moderate antiquity,' I admit; but that they are 'easily intelligible,' I deny.

Mr. Newman's syntax has, I say it with pleasure, a much more Homeric cast than his vocabulary; his syntax, the mode in which his thought is evolved, although not the actual words in which it is expressed, seems to me right in its general character, and the best feature of his version. It is not artificial or rhetorical, like Cowper's syntax or Pope's: it is simple, direct, and natural, and so far it is like Homer's. It fails, however, just where, from the inherent fault of Mr. Newman's conception of Homer, one might expect it to fail—it fails in nobleness. It presents the thought in a way which is something more than unconstrained—over-familiar; something more than easy—free and easy. In this respect it is like the movement of Mr. Newman's version, like his rhythm; for this, too, fails, in spite of some good qualities, by not being noble enough; this, while it avoids the faults of being slow and elaborate, falls into a fault in the opposite direction, and is slipshod. Homer presents his thought naturally; but when Mr. Newman has,

A thousand fires along the plain, I say, that night were burning,

he presents his thought familiarly; in a style which may be the genuine style of ballad-poetry, but which is not the style of Homer. Homer moves freely; but when Mr. Newman has,

Infatuate! O that thou wert lord to some other army,[11]

he gives himself too much freedom; he leaves us too much to do for his rhythm ourselves, instead of giving to us a rhythm like Homer's, easy indeed, but mastering our ear with a fulness of power which is irresistible.

I said that a certain style might be the genuine style of ballad-poetry, but yet not the style of Homer. The analogy of the ballad is ever present to Mr. Newman's thoughts in considering Homer; and perhaps nothing has more caused his faults than this analogy—this popular, but, it is time to say, this erroneous analogy. 'The moral qualities of Homer's style,' says Mr.

Newman, 'being like to those of the English ballad, we need a metre of the same genius. Only those metres, which by the very possession of these qualities are liable to degenerate into *doggerel,* are suitable to reproduce the ancient epic.' 'The style of Homer,' he says, in a passage which I have before quoted, 'is direct, popular, forcible, quaint, flowing, garrulous: in all these respects it is similar to the old English ballad.' Mr. Newman, I need not say, is by no means alone in this opinion. 'The most really and truly Homeric of all the creations of the English muse is,' says Mr. Newman's critic in the *National Review,* 'the ballad-poetry of ancient times; and the association between metre and subject is one that it would be true wisdom to preserve.' 'It is confessed,' says Chapman's last editor, Mr. Hooper, 'that the fourteen-syllable verse' (that is, a ballad-verse) 'is peculiarly fitting for Homeric translation.' And the editor of Dr. Maginn's clever and popular *Homeric Ballads* assumes it as one of his author's greatest and most indisputable merits, that he was 'the first who consciously realised to himself the truth that Greek ballads can be really represented in English only by a similar measure.'

This proposition that Homer's poetry is *ballad-poetry,* analogous to the well-known ballad-poetry of the English and other nations, has a certain small portion of truth in it, and at one time probably served a useful purpose, when it was employed to discredit the artificial and literary manner in which Pope and his school rendered Homer. But it has been so extravagantly over-used, the mistake which it was useful in combating has so entirely lost the public favour, that it is now much more important to insist on the large part of error contained in it, than to extol its small part of truth. It is time to say plainly that, whatever the admirers of our old ballads may think, the supreme form of epic poetry, the genuine Homeric mould, is not the form of the Ballad of Lord Bateman. I have myself shown the broad difference between Mil-

---

11 From the reproachful answer of Ulysses to Agamemnon, who had proposed an abandonment of their expedition. This is one of the 'tonic' passages of the *Iliad,* so I quote it:
Ah, unworthy king, some other inglorious army
Should'st thou command, not rule over us, whose portion for ever
Zeus hath made it, from youth right up to age, to be winding
Skeins of grievous wars, till every soul of us perish.
      Iliad, xiv. 84; *GBWW,* Vol. 4, p. 99a.

ton's manner and Homer's; but, after a course of Mr. Newman and Dr. Maginn, I turn round in desperation upon them and upon the balladists who have misled them, and I exclaim: 'Compared with you, Milton is Homer's double; there is, whatever you may think, ten thousand times more of the real strain of Homer in,

Blind Thamyris, and blind Mæonides,
And Tiresias, and Phineus, prophets old,

than in,

Now Christ thee save, thou proud porter,
Now Christ thee save and see,[12]

or in,

While the tinker did dine, he had plenty
of wine.'[13]

For Homer is not only rapid in movement, simple in style, plain in language, natural in thought; he is also, and above all, *noble*. I have advised the translator not to go into the vexed question of Homer's identity. Yet I will just remind him that the grand argument—or rather, not argument, for the matter affords no data for arguing, but the grand source from which conviction, as we read the *Iliad,* keeps pressing in upon us, that there is one poet of the *Iliad,* one Homer—is precisely this nobleness of the poet, this grand manner: we feel that the analogy drawn from other joint compositions does not hold good here, because those works do not bear, like the *Iliad,* the magic stamp of a master; and the moment you have *anything* less than a masterwork, the cooperation or consolidation of several poets becomes possible, for talent is not uncommon; the moment you have *much* less than a masterwork, they become easy, for mediocrity is everywhere. I can imagine fifty Bradies joined with as many

Tates to make the New Version of the Psalms. I can imagine several poets having contributed to any one of the old English ballads in Percy's collection. I can imagine several poets, possessing, like Chapman, the Elizabethan vigour and the Elizabethan mannerism, united with Chapman to produce his version of the *Iliad*. I can imagine several poets, with the literary knack of the twelfth century, united to produce the *Nibelungen Lay* in the form in which we have it—a work which the Germans, in their joy at discovering a national epic of their own, have rated vastly higher than it deserves. And lastly, though Mr. Newman's translation of Homer bears the strong mark of his own idiosyncrasy, yet I can imagine Mr. Newman and a school of adepts trained by him in his art of poetry, jointly producing that work, so that Aristarchus himself should have difficulty in pronouncing which line was the master's, and which a pupil's. But I cannot imagine several poets, or one poet, joined with Dante in the composition of his *Inferno,*[*] though many poets have taken for their subject a descent into Hell. Many artists, again, have represented Moses; but there is only one Moses of Michael Angelo. So the insurmountable obstacle to believing the *Iliad* a consolidated work of several poets is this: that the work of great masters is unique; and the *Iliad* has a great master's genuine stamp, and that stamp is *the grand style.*

Poets who cannot work in the grand style instinctively seek a style in which their comparative inferiority may feel itself at ease, a manner which may be, so to speak, indulgent to their inequalities. The ballad-style offers to an epic poet, quite unable to fill the canvas of Homer, or Dante, or Milton, a canvas which he is capable of filling. The ballad-measure is quite able to give due effect to the vigour and spirit which its employer, when at his very best, may be able to exhibit; and, when he is not at his best, when he is a

---

12 From the ballad of *King Estmere,* in Percy's *Reliques of Ancient English Poetry,* i. 69 (edit. of 1767).

13 *Reliques,* i. 241.

* *GBWW,* Vol. 21.

little trivial or a little dull, it will not betray him, it will not bring out his weaknesses into broad relief. This is a convenience; but it is a convenience which the ballad-style purchases by resigning all pretensions to the highest, to the grand manner. It is true of its movement, as it is *not* true of Homer's, that it is 'liable to degenerate into doggerel.' It is true of its 'moral qualities,' as it is *not* true of Homer's, that 'quaintness' and 'garrulity' are among them. It is true of its employers, as it is *not* true of Homer, that they 'rise and sink with their subject, are prosaic when it is tame, are low when it is mean.' For this reason the ballad-style and the ballad-measure are eminently *in*appropriate to render Homer. Homer's manner and movement are always both noble and powerful: the ballad-manner and movement are often either jaunty and smart, so not noble; or jog-trot and humdrum, so not powerful.

The *Nibelungen Lay* affords a good illustration of the qualities of the ballad-manner. Based on grand traditions, which had found expression in a grand lyric poetry, the German epic poem of the *Nibelungen Lay,* though it is interesting, and though it has good passages, is itself anything rather than a grand poem. It is a poem of which the composer is, to speak the truth, a very ordinary mortal, and often, therefore, like other ordinary mortals, very prosy. It is in a measure which eminently adapts itself to this commonplace personality of its composer, which has much the movement of the well-known measures of Tate and Brady, and can jog on, for hundreds of lines at a time, with a level ease which reminds one of Sheridan's saying that easy writing may be often such hard reading. But, instead of occupying myself with the *Nibelungen Lay,* I prefer to look at the ballad-style as directly applied to Homer, in Chapman's version and Mr. Newman's, and in the *Homeric Ballads* of Dr. Maginn.

First I take Chapman. I have already shown that Chapman's conceits are un-

Homeric, and that his rhyme is un-Homeric; I will now show how his manner and movement are un-Homeric. Chapman's diction, I have said, is generally good; but it must be called good with this reserve, that, though it has Homer's plainness and directness, it often offends him who knows Homer, by wanting Homer's nobleness. In a passage which I have already quoted, the address of Zeus to the horses of Achilles, where Homer has—

ἆ δειλώ, τί σφῶϊ δόμεν Πηλῆϊ ἄνακτι
θνητῷ; ὑμεῖς δ' ἐστὸν ἀγήρω τ' ἀθανάτω τε!
ἦ ἵνα δυστήνοισι μετ' ἀνδράσιν ἄλγε' ἔχητον;[14]

Chapman has—

Poor wretched beasts, *said he,*
Why gave we you to a mortal king, when immortality
And incapacity of age so dignifies your states?
Was it to haste[15] *the miseries poured out on human fates?*

There are many faults in this rendering of Chapman's, but what I particularly wish to notice in it is the expression 'Poor wretched beasts' for ἆ δειλώ. This expression just illustrates the difference between the ballad-manner and Homer's. The ballad-manner—Chapman's manner—is, I say, pitched sensibly lower than Homer's. The ballad-manner requires that an expression shall be plain and natural, and then it asks no more. Homer's manner requires that an expression shall be plain and natural, but it also requires that it shall be noble. Ἀ δειλώ is as plain, as simple as 'Poor wretched beasts'; but it is also noble, which 'Poor wretched beasts' is not. 'Poor wretched beasts' is, in truth, a little over-familiar, but this is no objection to it for the ballad-manner; it is good enough for the old En-

---

14 *Iliad,* xvii, 443; *GBWW,* Vol. 4, p. 126c.

15 All the editions which I have seen have 'haste,' but the right reading must certainly be 'taste.'

glish ballad, good enough for the *Nibelungen Lay,* good enough for Chapman's *Iliad,* good enough for Mr. Newman's *Iliad,* good enough for Dr. Maginn's *Homeric Ballads;* but it is not good enough for Homer.

To feel that Chapman's measure, though natural, is not Homeric; that, though tolerably rapid, it has not Homer's rapidity; that it has a jogging rapidity rather than a flowing rapidity; and a movement familiar rather than nobly easy, one has only, I think, to read half a dozen lines in any part of his version. I prefer to keep as much as possible to passages which I have already noticed, so I will quote the conclusion of the nineteenth book, where Achilles answers his horse Xanthus, who has prophesied his death to him.[16]

> *Achilles, far in rage,*
> *Thus answered him:—It fits not thee thus*
>   *proudly to presage*
> *My overthrow. I know myself it is my fate*
>   *to fall*
> *Thus far from Phthia; yet that fate shall fail*
>   *to vent her gall*
> *Till mine vent thousands.—These words*
>   *said, he fell to horrid deeds,*
> *Gave dreadful signal, and forthright made*
>   *fly his one-hoofed steeds.*

For what regards the manner of this passage, the words 'Achilles Thus answered him,' and 'I know myself it is my fate to fall Thus far from Phthia,' are in Homer's manner, and all the rest is out of it. But for what regards its movement, who, after being jolted by Chapman through such verse as this,

> *These words said, he fell to horrid deeds,*
> *Gave dreadful signal, and forthright made*
>   *fly his one-hoofed steeds,*

who does not feel the vital difference of the movement of Homer,

ἦ ῥα, καὶ ἐν πρώτοις ἰάχων ἔχε μώνυχας ἵππους?

To pass from Chapman to Dr. Maginn. His

Homeric Ballads are vigorous and genuine poems in their own way; they are not one continual falsetto, like the pinchbeck *Roman Ballads* of Lord Macaulay; but just because they are ballads in their manner and movement, just because, to use the words of his applauding editor, Dr. Maginn has 'consciously realised to himself the truth that Greek ballads can be really represented in English only by a similar manner'—just for this very reason they are not at all Homeric, they have not the least in the world the manner of Homer. There is a celebrated incident in the nineteenth book of the *Odyssey,* the recognition by the old nurse Eurycleia of a scar on the leg of her master Ulysses, who has entered his own hall as an unknown wanderer, and whose feet she has been set to wash. 'Then she came near,' says Homer, 'and began to wash her master; and straightway she recognised a scar which he had got in former days from the white tusk of a wild boar, when he went to Parnassus unto Autolycus and the sons of Autolycus, his mother's father and brethren.'[17] This, 'really represented' by Dr. Maginn, in 'a measure similar' to Homer's, becomes:

> *And scarcely had she begun to wash*
> *Ere she was aware of the grisly gash*
>   *Above his knee that lay.*
> *It was a wound from a wild boar's tooth,*
> *All on Parnassus' slope,*
> *Where he went to hunt in the days of his*
>   *youth*
> *With his mother's sire,*

and so on. That is the true ballad-manner, no one can deny; 'all on Parnassus' slope' is, I was going to say, the true ballad-slang; but never again shall I be able to read,

νίζε δ' ἄρ' ἆσσον ἰοῦσα ἄναχθ' ἑόν· αὐτίκα δ' ἔγνω οὐλήν,

without having the detestable dance of Dr. Maginn's—

> *And scarcely had she begun to wash*
> *Ere she was aware of the grisly gash—*

---

[16] *Iliad,* xix. 419; *GBWW,* Vol. 4, p. 141c.

[17] *Odyssey,* xix. 392; *GBWW,* Vol. 4, p. 293b.

jigging in my ears, to spoil the effect of Homer, and to torture me. To apply that manner and that rhythm to Homer's incidents, is not to imitate Homer, but to travesty him.

Lastly I come to Mr. Newman. His rhythm, like Chapman's and Dr. Maginn's, is a ballad-rhythm, but with a modification of his own. 'Holding it,' he tells us, 'as an axiom, that rhyme must be abandoned,' he found, on abandoning it, 'an unpleasant void until he gave a double ending to the verse.' In short, instead of saying,

Good people all with one accord
Give ear unto my tale,

Mr. Newman would say,

Good people all with one accord
Give ear unto my story.

A recent American writer[18] gravely observes that for his countrymen this rhythm has a disadvantage in being like the rhythm of the American national air *Yankee Doodle,* and thus provoking ludicrous associations. *Yankee Doodle* is not our national air: for us Mr. Newman's rhythm has not this disadvantage. He himself gives us several plausible reasons why this rhythm of his really ought to be successful: let us examine how far it *is* successful.

Mr. Newman joins to a bad rhythm so bad a diction that it is difficult to distinguish exactly whether in any given passage it is his words or his measure which produces a total impression of such an unpleasant kind. But with a little attention we may analyse our total impression, and find the share which each element has in producing it. To take the passage which I have so often mentioned, Sarpedon's speech to Glaucus, Mr. Newman translates this as follows:

O gentle friend! if thou and I, from this
encounter 'scaping,
Hereafter might forever be from Eld and
Death exempted

As heavenly gods, not I in sooth would fight
among the foremost,
Nor liefly thee would I advance to man-
ennobling battle.
Now—sith ten thousand shapes of Death do
any-gait pursue us
Which never mortal may evade, though sly
of foot and nimble—
Onward! and glory let us earn, or glory yield
to some one.

Could all our care elude the gloomy grave
Which claims no less the fearful than the
brave—

I am not going to quote Pope's version over again,* but I must remark in passing, how much more, with all Pope's radical difference of manner from Homer, it gives us of the real effect of

εἰ μὲν γὰρ, πόλεμον περὶ τόνδε φυγόντε—

than Mr. Newman's lines. And now, why are Mr. Newman's lines faulty? They are faulty, first, because, as a matter of diction, the expressions 'O gentle friend,' 'eld,' 'in sooth,' 'liefly,' 'advance,' 'man-ennobling,' 'sith,' 'any-gait,' and 'sly of foot,' are all bad; some of them worse than others, but all bad: that is, they all of them as here used excite in the scholar, their sole judge—excite, I will boldly affirm, in Professor Thompson or Professor Jowett—a feeling totally different from that excited in them by the words of Homer which these expressions profess to render. The lines are faulty, secondly, because, as a matter of rhythm, any and every line among them has to the ear of the same judges (I affirm it with equal boldness) a movement as unlike Homer's movement in the corresponding line as the single words are unlike Homer's words. Οὔτε κέ σε στέλλοιμι μάχην ἐς κυδιάνειραν†—'Nor liefly thee would I advance to man-ennobling battle;'—for whose ears do those two rhythms produce impressions of, to use Mr. Newman's own words, 'similar moral genius'?

---

[18] Mr. Marsh, in his *Lectures on the English Language,* New York, 1860, p. 520.

* *See* p. 413.
† *See* p. 413, editor's note.

I will by no means make search in Mr. Newman's version for passages likely to raise a laugh; that search, alas! would be far too easy. I will quote but one other passage from him, and that a passage where the diction is comparatively inoffensive, in order that disapproval of the words may not unfairly heighten disapproval of the rhythm. The end of the nineteenth book, the answer of Achilles to his horse Xanthus, Mr. Newman gives thus:

Chestnut! why bodest death to me? from thee this was not needed.
Myself right surely know also, that 't is my doom to perish,
From mother and from father dear apart, in Troy; but never
Pause will I make of war, until the Trojans be glutted.
  He spake, and yelling, held afront the single-hoofed horses.

Here Mr. Newman calls Xanthus *Chestnut,* indeed, as he calls Balius *Spotted,* and Podarga *Spry-foot;* which is as if a Frenchman were to call Miss Nightingale *Mdlle. Rossignol,* or Mr. Bright *M. Clair.* And several other expressions, too—'yelling,' 'held afront,' 'single-hoofed'—leave, to say the very least, much to be desired. Still, for Mr. Newman, the diction of this passage is pure. All the more clearly appears the profound vice of a rhythm, which, with comparatively few faults of words, can leave a sense of such incurable alienation from Homer's manner as, 'Myself right surely know also that 'tis my doom to perish,' compared with the εὖ νύ τοι οἶδα καὶ αὐτός, ὅ μοι μόρος ἐνθάδ' ὀλέσθαι of Homer.

But so deeply seated is the difference between the ballad-manner and Homer's, that even a man of the highest powers, even a man of the greatest vigour of spirit and of true genius—the Coryphæus of balladists, Sir Walter Scott—fails with a manner of this kind to produce an effect at all like the effect of Homer. 'I am not so rash,' declares Mr. Newman, 'as to say that if *freedom* be given to rhyme as in Walter Scott's poetry'— Walter Scott, 'by far the most Homeric of our poets,' as in another place he calls him— 'a genius may not arise who will translate Homer into the melodies of *Marmion*.' 'The *truly* classical and *truly* romantic,' says Dr. Maginn, 'are one; the moss-trooping Nestor reappears in the moss-trooping heroes of Percy's *Reliques*'; and a description by Scott, which he quotes, he calls 'graphic, and therefore Homeric.' He forgets our fourth axiom—that Homer is not *only* graphic; he is also noble, and has the grand style. Human nature under like circumstances is probably in all stages much the same; and so far it may be said that 'the truly classical and the truly romantic are one'; but it is of little use to tell us this, because we know the human nature of other ages only through the representations of them which have come down to us, and the classical and the romantic modes of representation are so far from being 'one,' that they remain eternally distinct, and have created for us a separation between the two worlds which they respectively represent. Therefore to call Nestor the 'moss-trooping Nestor' is absurd, because, though Nestor may possibly have been much the same sort of man as many a moss-trooper, he has yet come to us through a mode of representation so unlike that of Percy's *Reliques,* that instead of 'reappearing in the moss-trooping heroes' of these poems, he exists in our imagination as something utterly unlike them, and as belonging to another world. So the Greeks in Shakspeare's *Troilus and Cressida** are no longer the Greeks whom we have known in Homer, because they come to us through a mode of representation of the romantic world. But I must not forget Scott.

I suppose that when Scott is in what may be called full ballad swing, no one will hesitate to pronounce his manner neither Homeric nor the grand manner. When he says, for instance,

---

* *GBWW,* Vol. 27, pp. 103–41.

I do not rhyme to that dull elf
Who cannot image to himself,[19]

and so on, any scholar will feel that *this* is
not Homer's manner. But let us take Scott's
poetry at its best; and when it is at its best,
it is undoubtedly very good indeed:

Tunstall lies dead upon the field,
His life-blood stains the spotless shield;
Edmund is down,—my life is reft,—
The Admiral alone is left.

Let Stanley charge with spur of fire,—
With Chester charge, and Lancashire,
Full upon Scotland's central host,
Or victory and England's lost.[20]

That is, no doubt, as vigorous as possible,
as spirited as possible; it is exceedingly fine
poetry. And still I say, it is not in the grand
manner, and therefore it is not like Homer's
poetry. Now, how shall I make him who
doubts this feel that I say true; that these
lines of Scott are essentially neither in Homer's style nor in the grand style? I may
point out to him that the movement of
Scott's lines, while it is rapid, is also at the
same time what the French call *saccadé*, its
rapidity is 'jerky'; whereas Homer's rapidity
is a flowing rapidity. But this is something
external and material; it is but the outward
and visible sign of an inward and spiritual
diversity. I may discuss what, in the abstract,
constitutes the grand style; but that sort of
general discussion never much helps our
judgment of particular instances. I may say
that the presence or absence of the grand
style can only be spiritually discerned; and
this is true, but to plead this looks like evad-
ing the difficulty. My best way is to take
eminent specimens of the grand style, and
to put them side by side with this of Scott.
For example, when Homer says:

ἀλλά, φίλος, θάνε καὶ σύ· τίη ὀλυφύρεαι
οὕτως;

κάτθανε καὶ Πάτροκλος, ὅπερ σέο πολλὸν
ἀμείνων,[21]

that is in the grand style. When Virgil says:

Disce, puer, virtutem ex me verumque
laborem,
Fortunam ex aliis,[22]

that is in the grand style. When Dante says:

Lascio lo fele, et vo pei dolci pomi
Promessi a me per lo verace Duca;
Ma fino al centro pria convien ch' io tomi,[23]

that is in the grand style. When Milton says:

     his form had yet not lost
All her original brightness, nor appeared
Less than archangel ruined, and the excess
Of glory obscured,[24]

that, finally, is in the grand style. Now let
any one after repeating to himself these
four passages, repeat again the passage of
Scott, and he will perceive that there is
something in style which the four first have
in common, and which the last is without;
and this something is precisely the grand
manner. It is no disrespect to Scott to say
that he does not attain to this manner in
his poetry; to say so, is merely to say that he
is not among the five or six supreme poets
of the world. Among these he is not; but,
being a man of far greater powers than the
ballad poets, he has tried to give to their
instrument a compass and an elevation
which it does not naturally possess, in order
to enable him to come nearer to the effect

---

19 *Marmion*, canto vi. 38.
20 *Marmion*, canto vi. 29.

21 'Be content, good friend, die also thou!
why lamentest thou thyself on this wise? Patroclus, too, died, who was a far better man than
thou.'—*Iliad*, xxi. 106; *GBWW*, Vol. 4, p. 149b.
22 'From me, young man, learn nobleness of
soul and true effort: learn success from others.'
—*Æneid*, xii. 435; *GBWW*, Vol. 13, p. 365b.
23 'I leave the gall of bitterness, and I go for
the apples of sweetness promised unto me by
my faithful Guide; but far as the centre it be-
hoves me first to fall.'—*Hell*, xvi. 61; *GBWW*,
Vol. 21, p. 23a.
24 *Paradise Lost*, i. 591; *GBWW*, Vol. 32,
p. 106a.

of the instrument used by the great epic poets—an instrument which he felt he could not truly use—and in this attempt he has but imperfectly succeeded. The poetic style of Scott is—(it becomes necessary to say so when it is proposed to 'translate Homer into the melodies of *Marmion*')—it is, tried by the highest standard, a bastard epic style; and that is why, out of his own powerful hands, it has had so little success. It is a less natural, and therefore a less good style, than the original ballad-style; while it shares with the ballad-style the inherent incapacity of rising into the grand style, of adequately rendering Homer. Scott is certainly at his best in his battles. Of Homer you could not say this: he is not better in his battles than elsewhere; but even between the battle-pieces of the two there exists all the difference which there is between an able work and a masterpiece.

Tunstall lies dead upon the field,
His life-blood stains the spotless shield:
Edmund is down,—my life is reft,—
The Admiral alone is left.

—'For not in the hands of Diomede the son of Tydeus rages the spear, to ward off destruction from the Danaans; neither as yet have I heard the voice of the son of Atreus, shouting out of his hated mouth; but the voice of Hector the slayer of men bursts round me, as he cheers on the Trojans; and they with their yellings fill all the plain, overcoming the Achaians in the battle.'—I protest that, to my feeling, Homer's performance, even through that pale and far-off shadow of a prose translation, still has a hundred times more of the grand manner about it than the original poetry of Scott.

Well, then, the ballad-manner and the ballad-measure, whether in the hands of the old ballad poets, or arranged by Chapman, or arranged by Mr. Newman, or, even, arranged by Sir Walter Scott, cannot worthily render Homer. And for one reason: Homer is plain, so are they; Homer is natural, so are they; Homer is spirited, so are they; but Homer is sustainedly noble, and they are

not. Homer and they are both of them natural, and therefore touching and stirring; but the grand style, which is Homer's, is something more than touching and stirring; it can form the character, it is edifying. The old English balladist may stir Sir Philip Sidney's heart like a trumpet, and this is much; but Homer, but the few artists in the grand style, can do more: they can refine the raw natural man, they can transmute him. So it is not without cause that I say, and say again, to the translator of Homer: 'Never for a moment suffer yourself to forget our fourth fundamental proposition, *Homer is noble.*' For it is seen how large a share this nobleness has in producing that general effect of his, which it is the main business of a translator to *re*produce.

I shall have to try your patience yet once more upon this subject, and then my task will be completed. I have shown what the four axioms respecting Homer which I have laid down, exclude—what they bid a translator not to do; I have still to show what they supply, what positive help they can give to the translator in his work. I will even, with their aid, myself try my fortune with some of those passages of Homer which I have already noticed; not indeed with any confidence that I more than others can succeed in adequately rendering Homer, but in the hope of satisfying competent judges, in the hope of making it clear to the future translator, that I, at any rate, follow a right method, and that, in coming short, I come short from weakness of execution, not from original vice of design. This is why I have so long occupied myself with Mr. Newman's version: that, apart from all faults of execution, his original design was wrong, and that he has done us the good service of declaring that design in its naked wrongness. To bad practice he has prefixed the bad theory which made the practice bad; he has given us a false theory in his preface, and he has exemplified the bad effects of that false theory in his translation. It is because his starting-point is so bad that he runs so badly; and to save others from taking so false a starting-point, may be to save them from running so futile a course.

Mr. Newman, indeed, says in his preface, that if any one dislikes his translation, 'he has his easy remedy: to keep aloof from it.' But Mr. Newman is a writer of considerable and deserved reputation; he is also a Professor of the University of London, an institution which by its position and by its merits acquires every year greater importance. It would be a very grave thing if the authority of so eminent a Professor led his students to misconceive entirely the chief work of the Greek world; that work which, whatever the other works of classical antiquity have to give us, gives it more abundantly than they all. The eccentricity, too, the arbitrariness, of which Mr. Newman's conception of Homer offers so signal an example, are not a peculiar failing of Mr. Newman's own; in varying degrees they are the great defect of English intellect, the great blemish of English literature. Our literature of the eighteenth century, the literature of the school of Dryden, Addison, Pope, Johnson, is a long reaction against this eccentricity, this arbitrariness; that reaction perished by its own faults, and its enemies are left once more masters of the field. It is much more likely that any new English version of Homer will have Mr. Newman's faults than Pope's. Our present literature, which is very far, certainly, from having the spirit and power of Elizabethan genius, yet has in its own way these faults, eccentricity and arbitrariness, quite as much as the Elizabethan literature ever had. They are the cause that, while upon none, perhaps, of the modern literatures has so great a sum of force been expended as upon the English literature, at the present hour this literature, regarded not as an object of mere literary interest, but as a living intellectual instrument, ranks only third in European effect and importance among the literatures of Europe; it ranks after the literatures of France and Germany. Of these two literatures, as of the intellect of Europe in general, the main effort, for now many years, has been a *criti-*

cal effort; the endeavour, in all branches of knowledge, theology, philosophy, history, art, science, to see the object as in itself it really is. But, owing to the presence in English literature of this eccentric and arbitrary spirit, owing to the strong tendency of English writers to bring to the consideration of their object some individual fancy, almost the last thing for which one would come to English literature is just that very thing which now Europe most desires—*criticism.* It is useful to notice any signal manifestation of those faults, which thus limit and impair the action of our literature. And therefore I have pointed out how widely, in translating Homer, a man even of real ability and learning may go astray, unless he brings to the study of this clearest of poets one quality in which our English authors, with all their great gifts, are apt to be somewhat wanting—simple lucidity of mind.

III

Homer is rapid in his movement, Homer is plain in his words and style, Homer is simple in his ideas, Homer is noble in his manner. Cowper renders him ill because he is slow in his movement, and elaborate in his style; Pope renders him ill because he is artificial both in his style and in his words; Chapman renders him ill because he is fantastic in his ideas; Mr. Newman renders him ill because he is odd in his words and ignoble in his manner. All four translators diverge from their original at other points besides those named; but it is at the points thus named that their divergence is greatest. For instance Cowper's diction is not as Homer's diction, nor his nobleness as Homer's nobleness; but it is in movement and grammatical style that he is most unlike Homer. Pope's rapidity is not of the same sort as Homer's rapidity, nor are his plainness of ideas and his nobleness as Homer's plainness of ideas and nobleness; but it is in the artificial character of his style and diction that he is most unlike Homer. Chapman's movement, words, style, and manner are often far enough from resembling Homer's movement, words, style, and manner; but it is the fantasticality of his ideas which puts him farthest from resembling Homer. Mr. Newman's movement, grammatical style, and ideas are a thousand times in strong contrast with Homer's; still it is by the oddness of his diction and the ignobleness of his manner that he contrasts with Homer the most violently.

Therefore the translator must not say to himself: 'Cowper is noble, Pope is rapid, Chapman has a good diction, Mr. Newman has a good cast of sentence: I will avoid Cowper's slowness, Pope's artificiality, Chapman's conceits, Mr. Newman's oddity; I will take Cowper's dignified manner, Pope's impetuous movement, Chapman's vocabulary, Mr. Newman's syntax, and so make a perfect translation of Homer.' Undoubtedly in certain points the versions of Chapman, Cowper, Pope, and Mr. Newman, all of them have merit; some of them very high merit, others a lower merit; but even in these points they have none of them precisely the same kind of merit as Homer, and therefore the new translator, even if he can imitate them in their good points, will still not satisfy his judge, the scholar, who asks him for Homer and Homer's kind of merit, or, at least, for as much of them as it is possible to give.

So the translator really has no good model before him for any part of his work, and has to invent everything for himself. He is to be rapid in movement, plain in speech, simple in thought, and noble; and *how* he is to be either rapid, or plain, or simple, or noble, no one yet has shown him. I shall try to-day to establish some practical suggestions which may help the translator of Homer's poetry to comply with the four grand requirements which we make of him.

His version is to be rapid; and, of course, to make a man's poetry rapid, as to make it noble, nothing can serve him so much as to have, in his own nature, rapidity and nobleness. *It is the spirit that quickeneth;* and no one will so well render Homer's swift-flow-

ing movement as he who has himself something of the swift-moving spirit of Homer. Yet even this is not quite enough. Pope certainly had a quick and darting spirit, and he had, also, real nobleness; yet Pope does not render the movement of Homer. To render this the translator must have, besides his natural qualifications, an appropriate metre.

I have sufficiently shown why I think all forms of our ballad-metre unsuited to Homer. It seems to me to be beyond question that, for epic poetry, only three metres can seriously claim to be accounted capable of the grand style. Two of these will at once occur to every one—the ten-syllable, or so-called *heroic,* couplet, and blank verse. I do not add to these the Spenserian stanza, although Dr. Maginn, whose metrical eccentricities I have already criticised, pronounces this stanza the one right measure for a translation of Homer. It is enough to observe that if Pope's couplet, with the simple system of correspondence that its rhymes introduce, changes the movement of Homer, in which no such correspondences are found, and is therefore a bad measure for a translator of Homer to employ, Spenser's stanza, with its far more intricate system of correspondences, must change Homer's movement far more profoundly, and must therefore be for the translator a far worse measure than the couplet of Pope. Yet I will say, at the same time, that the verse of Spenser is more fluid, slips more easily and quickly along, than the verse of almost any other English poet.

By this the northern wagoner had set
His seven-fold team behind the steadfast star
That was in ocean waves yet never wet,
But firm is fixt, and sendeth light from far
To all that in the wide deep wandering are.[25]

One cannot but feel that English verse has not often moved with the fluidity and sweet ease of these lines. It is possible that it may have been this quality of Spenser's poetry which made Dr. Maginn think that the

_____
25 *The Faery Queen,* canto ii. stanza 1.

stanza of *The Faery Queen* must be a good measure for rendering Homer. This it is not: Spenser's verse is fluid and rapid, no doubt, but there are more ways than one of being fluid and rapid, and Homer is fluid and rapid in quite another way than Spenser. Spenser's manner is no more Homeric than is the manner of the one modern inheritor of Spenser's beautiful gift—the poet, who evidently caught from Spenser his sweet and easy-slipping movement, and who has exquisitely employed it; a Spenserian genius, nay, a genius by natural endowment richer probably than even Spenser; that light which shines so unexpected and without fellow in our century, an Elizabethan born too late, the early lost and admirably gifted Keats.

I say, then, that there are really but three metres—the ten-syllable couplet, blank verse, and a third metre which I will not yet name, but which is neither the Spenserian stanza nor any form of ballad-verse—between which, as vehicles for Homer's poetry, the translator has to make his choice. Every one will at once remember a thousand passages in which both the ten-syllable couplet and blank verse prove themselves to have nobleness. Undoubtedly the movement and manner of this,

Still raise for good the supplicating voice,
But leave to Heaven the measure and the
  choice,

are noble. Undoubtedly, the movement and manner of this,

High on a throne of royal state, which far
Outshone the wealth of Ormus and of Ind,

are noble also. But the first is in a rhymed metre; and the unfitness of a rhymed metre for rendering Homer I have already shown. I will observe, too, that the fine couplet which I have quoted comes out of a satire, a didactic poem; and that it is in didactic poetry that the ten-syllable couplet has most successfully essayed the grand style. In narrative poetry this metre has succeeded best

when it essayed a sensibly lower style, the style of Chaucer, for instance; whose narrative manner, though a very good and sound manner, is certainly neither the grand manner nor the manner of Homer.

The rhymed ten-syllable couplet being thus excluded, blank verse offers itself for the translator's use. The first kind of blank verse which naturally occurs to us is the blank verse of Milton, which has been employed, with more or less modification, by Mr. Cary in translating Dante, by Cowper, and by Mr. Wright in translating Homer. How noble this metre is in Milton's hands, how completely it shows itself capable of the grand, nay, of the grandest, style, I need not say. To this metre, as used in the *Paradise Lost,** our country owes the glory of having produced one of the only two poetical works in the grand style which are to be found in the modern languages; the *Divine Comedy*† of Dante is the other. England and Italy here stand alone; Spain, France, and Germany have produced great poets, but neither Calderon, nor Corneille, nor Schiller, nor even Goethe, has produced a body of poetry in the true grand style, in the sense in which the style of the body of Homer's poetry, or Pindar's, or Sophocles', is grand. But Dante has, and so has Milton; and in this respect Milton possesses a distinction which even Shakspeare, undoubtedly the supreme poetical power in our literature, does not share with him. Not a tragedy of Shakspeare but contains passages in the worst of all styles, the affected style; and the grand style, although it may be harsh, or obscure, or cumbrous, or over-laboured, is never affected. In spite, therefore, of objections which may justly be urged against the plan and treatment of the *Paradise Lost,* in spite of its possessing, certainly, a far less enthralling force of interest to attract and to carry forward the reader than the *Iliad* or the *Divine Comedy,* it fully deserves, it can never lose,

---

* *GBWW,* Vol. 32.
† *GBWW,* Vol. 21.

its immense reputation; for, like the *Iliad* and the *Divine Comedy,* nay, in some respects to a higher degree than either of them, it is in the grand style.

But the grandeur of Milton is one thing, and the grandeur of Homer is another. Homer's movement, I have said again and again, is a flowing, a rapid movement; Milton's, on the other hand, is a laboured, a self-retarding movement. In each case, the movement, the metrical cast, corresponds with the mode of evolution of the thought, with the syntactical cast, and is indeed determined by it. Milton charges himself so full with thought, imagination, knowledge, that his style will hardly contain them. He is too full-stored to show us in much detail one conception, one piece of knowledge; he just shows it to us in a pregnant, allusive way, and then he presses on to another; and all this fulness, this pressure, this condensation, this self-constraint, enters into his movement, and makes it what it is—noble, but difficult and austere. Homer is quite different: he says a thing, and says it to the end, and then begins another, while Milton is trying to press a thousand things into one. So that whereas, in reading Milton, you never lose the sense of laborious and condensed fulness, in reading Homer you never lose the sense of flowing and abounding ease. With Milton line runs into line, and all is straitly bound together: with Homer line runs off from line, and all hurries away onward. Homer begins, Μῆνιν ἄειδε, Θεά ['The wrath, sing, goddess'], at the second word announcing the proposed action. Milton begins:

Of man's first disobedience, and the fruit
Of that forbidden tree, whose mortal taste
Brought death into the world, and all our
*   woe,*
With loss of Eden, till one greater Man
Restore us, and regain the blissful seat,
*Sing, heavenly muse.**

---

* *GBWW,* Vol. 32, p. 93b.

So chary of a sentence is he, so resolute not to let it escape him till he has crowded into it all he can, that it is not till the thirty-ninth word in the sentence that he will give us the key to it, the word of action, the verb. Milton says:

O for that warning voice, which he, who saw
The Apocalypse, heard cry in heaven aloud.†

He is not satisfied, unless he can tell us, all in one sentence, and without permitting himself actually to mention the name, that the man who had the warning voice was the same man who saw the Apocalypse. Homer would have said, 'O for that warning voice, which *John* heard'—and if it had suited him to say that John also saw the Apocalypse, he would have given us that in another sentence. The effect of this allusive and compressed manner of Milton is, I need not say, often very powerful; and it is an effect which other great poets have often sought to obtain much in the same way: Dante is full of it, Horace is full of it; but wherever it exists, it is always an un-Homeric effect. 'The losses of the heavens,' says Horace, 'fresh moons speedily repair; we, when we have gone down where the pious Æneas, where the rich Tullus and Ancus are—*pulvis et umbra sumus* ["we are dust and dreams"].'[26] He never actually says *where* we go to; he only indicates it by saying that it is that place where Æneas, Tullus and Ancus are. But Homer, when he has to speak of going down to the grave, says, definitely, ἐς Ἠλύσιον πεδίον—ἀθάνατοι πέμψουσιν[27]—'The immortals shall send thee *to the Elysian plain*'; and it is not till after he has definitely said this, that he adds, that it is there that the abode of departed worthies is placed: ὅθι ξανθὸς Ῥαδάμανθυς—'Where the yellow-haired Rhadamanthus is.' Again; Horace, having to say that punishment sooner or

---

† Ibid., p. 152b.
26 *Odes,* IV. vii. 13.
27 *Odyssey,* iv. 563; *GBWW,* Vol. 4, p. 204d.

later overtakes crime, says it thus:

> *Raro antecedentem scelestum*
> *Deseruit pede Pœna claudo.*[28]
> [*Seldom does Retribution abandon its pursuit, however halting, of the guilty man, whatever his head start.*]

The thought itself of these lines is familiar enough to Homer and Hesiod; but neither Homer nor Hesiod, in expressing it, could possibly have so complicated its expression as Horace complicates it, and purposely complicates it, by his use of the word *deseruit.* I say that this complicated evolution of the thought necessarily complicates the movement and rhythm of a poet; and that the Miltonic blank verse, of course the first model of blank verse which suggests itself to an English translator of Homer, bears the strongest marks of such complication, and is therefore entirely unfit to render Homer.

If blank verse is used in translating Homer, it must be a blank verse of which English poetry, naturally swayed much by Milton's treatment of this metre, offers at present hardly any examples. It must not be Cowper's blank verse, who has studied Milton's pregnant manner with such effect, that, having to say of Mr. Throckmorton that he spares his avenue, although it is the fashion with other people to cut down theirs, he says that Benevolus 'reprieves The obsolete prolixity of shade.' It must not be Mr. Tennyson's blank verse.

For all experience is an arch, wherethrough
Gleams that untravelled world, whose distance fades
For ever and for ever, as we gaze.

It is no blame to the thought of those lines, which belongs to another order of ideas than Homer's, but it is true, that Homer would certainly have said of them, 'It is to consider too curiously to consider so.' It is no blame to their rhythm, which belongs

---

[28] *Odes,* III. ii. 31.

to another order of movement than Homer's, but it is true that these three lines by themselves take up nearly as much time as a whole book of the *Iliad.* No; the blank verse used in rendering Homer must be a blank verse of which perhaps the best specimens are to be found in some of the most rapid passages of Shakspeare's plays—a blank verse which does not dovetail its lines into one another, and which habitually ends its lines with monosyllables. Such a blank verse might no doubt be very rapid in its movement, and might perfectly adapt itself to a thought plainly and directly evolved; and it would be interesting to see it well applied to Homer. But the translator who determines to use it, must not conceal from himself that in order to pour Homer into the mould of this metre, he will have entirely to break him up and melt him down, with the hope of then successfully composing him afresh; and this is a process which is full of risks. It may, no doubt, be the real Homer that issues new from it; it is not certain beforehand that it cannot be the real Homer, as it is certain that from the mould of Pope's couplet or Cowper's Miltonic verse it cannot be the real Homer that will issue; still, the chances of disappointment are great. The result of such an attempt to renovate the old poet may be an Æson; but it may also, and more probably will be a Pelias.

When I say this, I point to the metre which seems to me to give the translator the best chance of preserving the general effect of Homer—that third metre which I have not yet expressly named, the hexameter. I know all that is said against the use of hexameters in English poetry; but it comes only to this, that, among us, they have not yet been used on any considerable scale with success. *Solvitur ambulando* [Solve by going ahead]: this is an objection which can best be met by *producing* good English hexameters. And there is no reason in the nature of the English language why it should not adapt itself to hexameters as well as the German language does; nay, the English language, from its greater rapidity, is in itself better suited than the German for them. The hexameter, whether alone or with the pentameter, possesses a movement, an expression, which no metre hitherto in common use amongst us possesses, and which I am convinced English poetry, as our mental wants multiply, will not always be content to forgo. Applied to Homer, this metre affords to the translator the immense support of keeping him more nearly than any other metre to Homer's movement; and, since a poet's movement makes so large a part of his general effect, and to reproduce this general effect is at once the translator's indispensable business and so difficult for him, it is a great thing to have this part of your model's general effect already given you in your metre, instead of having to get it entirely for yourself.

These are general considerations; but there are also one or two particular considerations which confirm me in the opinion that for translating Homer into English verse the hexameter should be used. The most successful attempt hitherto made at rendering Homer into English, the attempt in which Homer's general effect has been best retained, is an attempt made in the hexameter measure. It is a version of the famous lines in the third book of the *Iliad,* which end with that mention of Castor and Pollux from which Mr. Ruskin extracts the sentimental consolation already noticed by me. The author is the accomplished Provost of Eton, Dr. Hawtrey; and this performance of his must be my excuse for having taken the liberty to single him out for mention, as one of the natural judges of a translation of Homer, along with Professor Thompson and Professor Jowett, whose connection with Greek literature is official. The passage is short; [29] and Dr. Hawtrey's version of it is suffused with a pensive grace which is, perhaps, rather more Virgilian than Homeric; still it is the one version of any part of the *Iliad* which in some degree reproduces for me the original effect of

[29] So short, that I quote it entire:

Clearly the rest I behold of the dark-eyed sons of Achaia;
Known to me well are the faces of all; their names I remember;
Two, two only remain, whom I see not among the commanders,
Castor fleet in the car,—Polydeukes brave with the cestus,—
Own dear brethren of mine,—one parent loved us as infants.
Are they not here in the host, from the shores of loved Lacedæmon,
Or, though they came with the rest in ships that bound through the waters,
Dare they not enter the fight or stand in the council of Heroes,
All for fear of the shame and the taunts my crime has awakened!
    So said she;—they long since in Earth's soft arms were reposing,
There, in their own dear land, their Fatherland, Lacedæmon.

English Hexameter Translations, London, 1847; p. 242.

I have changed Dr. Hawtrey's 'Kastor,' 'Lakedaimon,' back to the familiar 'Castor,' 'Lacedæmon,' in obedience to my own rule that everything *odd* is to be avoided in rendering Homer, the most natural and least odd of poets. I see Mr. Newman's critic in the *National Review* urges our generation to bear with the unnatural effect of these rewritten Greek names, in the hope that by this means the effect of them may have to the next generation become natural. For my part, I feel no disposition to pass all my own life in the wilderness of pedantry, in order that a posterity which I shall never see may one day enter an orthographical Canaan; and, after all, the real question is this: whether our living apprehension of the Greek word is more checked by meeting in an English book about the Greeks, names not spelt letter for letter as in the original Greek, or by meeting names which make us rub our eyes and call out, 'How exceedingly odd!'

The Latin names of the Greek deities raise in most cases the idea of quite distinct personages from the personages whose idea is raised by the Greek names. Hera and Juno are actually, to every scholar's imagination, two different people. So in all these cases the Latin names must, at any inconvenience, be abandoned when we are dealing with the Greek world. But I think it can be in the sensitive imagination of Mr. Grote only, that 'Thucydides' [Thukydides] raises the idea of a different man from Θουκυδίδης.

435

Homer: it is the best, and it is in hexameters.

This is one of the particular considerations that incline me to prefer the hexameter, for translating Homer, to our established metres. There is another. Most of you, probably, have some knowledge of a poem by Mr. Clough, *The Bothie of Toper-na-fuosich,* a long-vacation pastoral, in hexameters. The general merits of that poem I am not going to discuss: it is a serio-comic poem, and therefore of essentially different nature from the *Iliad.* Still in two things it is, more than any other English poem which I can call to mind, like the *Iliad:* in the rapidity of its movement, and the plainness and directness of its style. The thought in this poem is often curious and subtle, and that is not Homeric; the diction is often grotesque, and that is not Homeric. Still by its rapidity of movement, and plain and direct manner of presenting the thought, however curious in itself, this poem, which, being as I say a serio-comic poem, has a right to be grotesque, is grotesque *truly,* not, like Mr. Newman's version of the *Iliad, falsely.* Mr. Clough's odd epithets, 'The grave man nicknamed Adam,' 'The hairy Aldrich,' and so on, grow vitally and appear naturally in their place; while Mr. Newman's 'dapper-greaved Achaians,' and 'motley-helmed Hector,' have all the air of being mechanically elaborated and artificially stuck in. Mr. Clough's hexameters are excessively, needlessly rough; still, owing to the native rapidity of this measure, and to the directness of style which so well allies itself with it, his composition produces a sense in the reader which Homer's composition also produces, and which Homer's translator ought to *re-produce*—the sense of having, within short limits of time, a large portion of human life presented to him, instead of a small portion.

Mr. Clough's hexameters are, as I have just said, too rough and irregular; and indeed a good model, on any considerable scale, of this metre, the English translator will nowhere find. He must not follow the model offered by Mr. Longfellow in his pleasing and popular poem of *Evangeline;*

for the merit of the manner and movement of *Evangeline,* when they are at their best, is to be tenderly elegant; and their fault, when they are at their worst, is to be lumbering; but Homer's defect is not lumberingness, neither is tender elegance his excellence. The lumbering effect of most English hexameters is caused by their being much too dactylic; the translator must learn to use spondees freely. Mr. Clough has done this, but he has not sufficiently observed another rule which the translator cannot follow too strictly; and that is, to have no lines which will not, as it is familiarly said, *read themselves.* This is of the last importance for rhythms with which the ear of the English public is not thoroughly acquainted. Lord Redesdale, in two papers on the subject of Greek and Roman metres, has some good remarks on the outrageous disregard of quantity in which English verse, trusting to its force of accent, is apt to indulge itself. The predominance of accent in our language is so great, that it would be pedantic not to avail one's self of it; and Lord Redesdale suggests rules which might easily be pushed too far. Still, it is undeniable that in English hexameters we generally force the quantity far too much; we rely on justification by accent with a security which is excessive. But not only do we abuse accent by shortening long syllables and lengthening short ones; we perpetually commit a far worse fault, by requiring the removal of the accent from its natural place to an unnatural one, in order to make our line scan. This is a fault, even when our metre is one which every English reader knows, and when he can see what we want and can correct the rhythm according to our wish; although it is a fault which a great master may sometimes commit knowingly to produce a desired effect, as Milton changes the natural accent on the word *Tirésias* in the line:

And Tiresias and Phineus, prophets old; *

---

* *Paradise Lost* iii. 36; *GBWW,* Vol. 32, p. 136a.

and then it ceases to be a fault, and becomes a beauty. But it is a real fault, when Chapman has:

By him the golden-throned Queen slept, the Queen of Deities; *

for in this line, to make it scan, you have to take away the accent from the word *Queen,* on which it naturally falls, and to place it on *throned,* which would naturally be unaccented; and yet, after all, you get no peculiar effect or beauty of cadence to reward you.

It is a real fault, when Mr. Newman has:

Infatuate! O that thou wert lord to some other army—†

for here again the reader is required, not for any special advantage to himself, but simply to save Mr. Newman trouble, to place the accent on the insignificant word *wert,* where it has no business whatever. But it is still a greater fault, when Spenser has (to take a striking instance):

Wot ye why his mother with a veil hath covered his face?‡

for a hexameter; because here not only is the reader causelessly required to make havoc with the natural accentuation of the line in order to get it to run as a hexameter; but also he, in nine cases out of ten, will be utterly at a loss how to perform the process required, and the line will remain a mere monster for him. I repeat, it is advisable to construct *all* verses so that by reading them naturally—that is, according to the sense and

legitimate accent—the reader gets the right rhythm; but, for English hexameters, that they be so constructed is indispensable.

If the hexameter best helps the translator to the Homeric rapidity, what style may best help him to the Homeric plainness and directness? It is the merit of a metre appropriate to your subject, that it in some degree suggests and carries with itself a style appropriate to the subject; the elaborate and self-retarding style, which comes so naturally when your metre is the Miltonic blank verse, does not come naturally with the hexameter; is, indeed, alien to it. On the other hand, the hexameter has a natural dignity which repels both the jaunty style and the jog-trot style, to both of which the ballad-measure so easily lends itself. These are great advantages; and, perhaps, it is nearly enough to say to the translator who uses the hexameter that he cannot too religiously follow, in style, the inspiration of his metre. He will find that a loose and idiomatic grammar—a grammar which follows the essential rather than the formal logic of the thought—allies itself excellently with the hexameter; and that, while this sort of grammar ensures plainness and naturalness, it by no means comes short in nobleness. It is difficult to pronounce, certainly, what is idiomatic in the ancient literature of a language which, though still spoken, has long since entirely adopted, as modern Greek has adopted, modern idioms. Still one may, I think, clearly perceive that Homer's grammatical style is idiomatic—that it may even be called, not improperly, a loose grammatical style. Examples, however, of what I mean by a loose grammatical style, will be of more use to the translator if taken from English poetry than if taken from Homer. I call it, then, a loose and idiomatic grammar which Shakspeare uses in the last line of the following three:

He's here in double trust:
First, as I am his kinsman and his subject,
Strong both against the deed;§

---

* The conclusion of *Iliad* I is given as "with Juno of the golden throne by his side;" *GBWW,* Vol. 4, p. 9c.

† Ulysses to Agamemnon in *Iliad* XIV; rendered as, "Wretch, you should have commanded some other and baser army," in *GBWW,* Vol. 4, p. 99a.

‡ From "Tetrastecion," in a letter to M. Gabriel Harvey, 1592.

§ *Macbeth,* act 1, sc. 7; *GBWW,* Vol. 27, p. 289b.

or in this:

> *Wit,* whither wilt?*

What Shakspeare means is perfectly clear—clearer, probably, than if he had said it in a more formal and regular manner; but his grammar is loose and idiomatic, because he leaves out the subject of the verb 'wilt' in the second passage quoted, and because, in the first, a prodigious addition to the sentence has to be, as we used to say in our old Latin grammar days, *understood,* before the word 'both' can be properly parsed. So, again, Chapman's grammar is loose and idiomatic where he says,

> *Even share hath he that keeps his tent, and*
> he to field *doth go,*

because he leaves out, in the second clause, the relative which in formal writing would be required. But Chapman here does not lose dignity by this idiomatic way of expressing himself, any more than Shakspeare loses it by neglecting to confer on 'both' the blessings of a regular government: neither loses dignity, but each gives that impression of a plain, direct, and natural mode of speaking, which Homer, too, gives, and which is so important, as I say, that Homer's translator should succeed in giving. Cowper calls blank verse 'a style further removed than rhyme from the vernacular idiom, both in the language itself and in the arrangement of it'; and just in proportion as blank verse is removed from the vernacular idiom, from that idiomatic style which is of all styles the plainest and most natural, blank verse is unsuited to render Homer.

Shakspeare is not only idiomatic in his grammar or style, he is also idiomatic in his words or diction; and here too, his example is valuable for the translator of Homer. The translator must not, indeed, allow himself all the liberty that Shakspeare allows himself; for Shakspeare sometimes uses expressions which pass perfectly well as he uses

them, because Shakspeare thinks so fast and so powerfully, that in reading him we are borne over single words as by a mighty current; but, if our mind were less excited—and who may rely on exciting our mind like Shakspeare?—they would check us. 'To grunt and sweat under a weary life'—that does perfectly well where it comes in Shakspeare; but if the translator of Homer, who will hardly have wound our minds up to the pitch at which these words of Hamlet find them, were to employ, when he has to speak of one of Homer's heroes under the load of calamity, this figure of 'grunting' and 'sweating,' we should say, *He Newmanises,* and his diction would offend us. For he is to be noble; and no plea of wishing to be plain and natural can get him excused from being this: only, as he is to be also, like Homer, perfectly simple and free from artificiality, and as the use of idiomatic expressions undoubtedly gives this effect, he should be as idiomatic as he can be without ceasing to be noble. Therefore the idiomatic language of Shakspeare—such language as 'prate of his *whereabout*'; '*jump* the life to come'; 'the damnation of his *taking-off*'; 'his *quietus make* with a bare *bodkin*'—should be carefully observed by the translator of Homer, although in every case he will have to decide for himself whether the use, by him, of Shakspeare's liberty, will or will not clash with his indispensable duty of nobleness. He will find one English book, and one only, where, as in the *Iliad* itself, perfect plainness of speech is allied with perfect nobleness; and that book is the Bible. No one could see this more clearly than Pope saw it: 'This pure and noble simplicity,' he says, 'is nowhere in such perfection as in the Scripture and Homer; yet even with Pope a woman is a 'fair,' a father is a 'sire,' and an old man a 'reverend sage,' and so on through all the phrases of that pseudo-Augustan, and most unbiblical, vocabulary. The Bible, however, is undoubtedly the grand mine of diction for the translator of Homer; and, if he knows how to discriminate truly between what will suit him and

---

* *As You Like It,* act 4, sc. 1; *GBWW,* Vol. 26, p. 618c.

what will not, the Bible may afford him also invaluable lessons of style.

I said that Homer, besides being plain in style and diction, was plain in the quality of his thought. It is possible that a thought may be expressed with idiomatic plainness, and yet not be in itself a plain thought. For example, in Mr. Clough's poem, already mentioned, the style and diction is almost always idiomatic and plain, but the thought itself is often of a quality which is not plain; it is *curious*. But the grand instance of the union of idiomatic expression with curious or difficult thought is in Shakspeare's poetry. Such, indeed, is the force and power of Shakspeare's idiomatic expression, that it gives an effect of clearness and vividness even to a thought which is imperfect and incoherent: for instance, when Hamlet says,

*to take arms against a sea of troubles,**

the figure there is undoubtedly most faulty, it by no means runs on four legs; but the thing is said so freely and idiomatically, that it passes. This, however, is not a point to which I now want to call your attention; I want you to remark, in Shakspeare and others, only that which we may directly apply to Homer. I say, then, that in Shakspeare the thought is often, while most idiomatically uttered, nay, while good and sound in itself, yet of a quality which is curious and difficult, and that this quality of thought is something entirely un-Homeric. For example, when Lady Macbeth says,

memory, the warder of the brain,
Shall be a fume, and the receipt of reason
A limbeck only,†

this figure is a perfectly sound and correct figure, no doubt; Mr. Knight even calls it a 'happy' figure; but it is a *difficult* figure: Homer would not have used it. Again, when Lady Macbeth says,

When you durst do it, then you were a man;
And, to be more than what you were, you
* would*
Be so much more the man,‡

the thought in the two last of these lines is, when you seize it, a perfectly clear thought, and a fine thought; but it is a *curious* thought: Homer would not have used it. These are favourable instances of the union of plain style and words with a thought not plain in quality; but take stronger instances of this union—let the thought be not only not plain in quality, but highly fanciful: and you have the Elizabethan conceits; you have, in spite of idiomatic style and idiomatic diction, everything which is most un-Homeric: you have such atrocities as this of Chapman:

Fate shall fail to vent her gall
Till mine vent thousands.

I say, the poets of a nation which has produced such conceit as that, must purify themselves seven times in the fire before they can hope to render Homer. They must expel their nature with a fork, and keep crying to one another night and day: 'Homer not only moves rapidly, not only speaks idiomatically; he is, also, *free from fancifulness.*'

So essentially characteristic of Homer is his plainness and naturalness of thought, that to the preservation of this in his own version the translator must without scruple sacrifice, where it is necessary, verbal fidelity to his original, rather than run any risk of producing, by literalness, an odd and unnatural effect. The double epithets so constantly occurring in Homer must be dealt with according to this rule; these epithets come quite naturally in Homer's poetry; in English poetry they, in nine cases out of ten, come, when literally rendered, quite unnaturally. I will not now discuss why this is so, I assume it as an indisputable fact that it is so; that Homer's μερόπων ἀνθρώπων comes to the reader as something perfectly natural, while Mr. Newman's 'voice-dividing mortals' comes to him as something perfectly un-natural. Well then, as it is Homer's general effect which we are to reproduce, it is to be false to Homer to be so verbally faithful to him as that we lose this effect; and by the English translator Homer's double epithets must be, in many places, renounced altogether; in all places where they are rendered, rendered by equivalents which come naturally. Instead of rendering Θέτι τανύπεπλε by Mr. Newman's 'Thetis trailing-robed,' which brings to one's mind long petticoats sweeping a dirty pavement, the translator must render the Greek by English words which come as naturally to us as Milton's words when he says, 'Let gorgeous Tragedy In sceptred pall come sweeping by.'* Instead of rendering μώνυχας ἵππους by Chapman's 'one-hoofed steeds,' or Mr. Newman's 'single-hoofed horses,' he must speak of horses in a way which surprises us as little as Shakspeare surprises when he says, 'Gallop apace, you fiery-footed steeds.'† Instead of rendering μελιηδέα θυμόν by 'life as honey pleasant,' he must characterise life with the simple pathos of Gray's 'warm precincts of the cheerful day.' Instead of converting ποῖόν σε ἔπος φύγεν ἕρκος ὀδόντων into the portentous remonstrance, 'Betwixt the outwork of thy teeth what word hath split?' he must remonstrate in English as straightforward as this of St. Peter, 'Be it far from thee, Lord: this shall not be unto thee;' or as this of the disciples, 'What is this that he saith, a little while? we cannot tell what he saith.' Homer's Greek, in each of the places quoted, reads as naturally as any of those English passages: the expression no more calls away the attention from the sense in the Greek than in the English. But when, in order to render literally in English one of Homer's double epithets, a strange unfamiliar adjective is invented—such as 'voice-dividing' for μέροψ—an improper

share of the reader's attention is necessarily diverted to this ancillary word, to this word which Homer never intended should receive so much notice; and a total effect quite different from Homer's is thus produced. Therefore Mr. Newman, though he does not purposely import, like Chapman, conceits of his own into the *Iliad,* does actually import them; for the result of his singular diction is to raise ideas, and odd ideas, not raised by the corresponding diction in Homer; and Chapman himself does no more. Cowper says: 'I have cautiously avoided all terms of new invention, with an abundance of which persons of more ingenuity than judgment have not enriched our language but encumbered it'; and this criticism so exactly hits the diction of Mr. Newman that one is irresistibly led to imagine his present appearance in the flesh to be at least his second.

A translator cannot well have a Homeric rapidity, style, diction, and quality of thought, without at the same time having what is the result of these in Homer—nobleness. Therefore I do not attempt to lay down any rules for obtaining this effect of nobleness—the effect, too, of all others the most impalpable, the most irreducible to rule, and which most depends on the individual personality of the artist. So I proceed at once to give you, in conclusion, one or two passages in which I have tried to follow those principles of Homeric translation which I have laid down. I give them, it must be remembered, not as specimens of perfect translation, but as specimens of an attempt to translate Homer on certain principles; specimens which may very aptly illustrate those principles by falling short as well as by succeeding.

I take first a passage of which I have already spoken, the comparison of the Trojan fires to the stars. The first part of that passage is, I have said, of splendid beauty; and to begin with a lame version of that would be the height of imprudence in me. It is the last and more level part with which I shall concern myself. I have already quoted Cow-

---

* *Il Penseroso; GBWW,* Vol. 32, p. 23a.
† *Romeo and Juliet,* act 3, sc. 2; *GBWW,* Vol. 26, p. 303a.

per's version of this part in order to show you how unlike his stiff and Miltonic manner of telling a plain story is to Homer's easy and rapid manner:

So numerous seemed those fires the bank between
Of Xanthus, blazing, and the fleet of Greece,
In prospect all of Troy—

I need not continue to the end. I have also quoted Pope's version of it, to show you how unlike his ornate and artificial manner is to Homer's plain and natural manner:

So many flames before proud Ilion blaze,
And brighten glimmering Xanthus with their rays;
The long reflections of the distant fires
Gleam on the walls, and tremble on the spires,

and much more of the same kind. I want to show you that it is possible, in a plain passage of this sort, to keep Homer's simplicity without being heavy and dull; and to keep his dignity without bringing in pomp and ornament. 'As numerous as are the stars on a clear night,' says Homer,

So shone forth, in front of Troy, by the bed of Xanthus,
Between that and the ships, the Trojans' numerous fires.
In the plain there were kindled a thousand fires: by each one
There sat fifty men, in the ruddy light of the fire:
By their chariots stood the steeds, and champed the white barley
While their masters sat by the fire, and waited for Morning.

Here, in order to keep Homer's effect of perfect plainness and directness, I repeat the word 'fires' as he repeats πυρά without scruple; although in a more elaborate and literary style of poetry this recurrence of the same word would be a fault to be avoided. I omit the epithet of Morning, and whereas Homer says that the steeds 'waited

for Morning,' I prefer to attribute this expectation of Morning to the master and not to the horse. Very likely in this particular, as in any other single particular, I may be wrong: what I wish you to remark is my endeavour after absolute plainness of speech, my care to avoid anything which may the least check or surprise the reader, whom Homer does not check or surprise. Homer's lively personal familiarity with war, and with the warhorse as his master's companion, is such that, as it seems to me, his attributing to the one the other's feelings comes to us quite naturally; but, from a poet without this familiarity, the attribution strikes as a little unnatural; and therefore, as everything the least unnatural is un-Homeric, I avoid it.

Again, in the address of Zeus to the horses of Achilles, Cowper has:

Jove saw their grief with pity, and his brows
Shaking, within himself thus, pensive, said.
*   'Ah hapless pair! wherefore by gift divine*
Were ye to Peleus given, a mortal king,
Yourselves immortal and from age exempt?'

There is no want of dignity here, as in the versions of Chapman and Mr. Newman, which I have already quoted; but the whole effect is much too slow. Take Pope:

Nor Jove disdained to cast a pitying look
While thus relenting to the steeds he spoke.
*   'Unhappy coursers of immortal strain!*
Exempt from age and deathless now in vain;
Did we your race on mortal man bestow
Only, alas! to share in mortal woe?'

Here there is no want either of dignity or rapidity, but all is too artificial. 'Nor Jove disdained,' for instance, is a very artificial and literary way of rendering Homer's words, and so is 'coursers of immortal strain.'

Μυρομένω δ' ἄρα τώ γε ἰδών, ἐλέησε Κρονίων—*

---

* *GBWW*, Vol. 4, p. 126c.

And with pity the son of Saturn saw them
    bewailing,
And he shook his head, and thus addressed
    his own bosom:—
    'Ah, unhappy pair, to Peleus why did
      we give you,
To a mortal? but ye are without old age
    and immortal.
Was it that ye, with man, might have your
    thousands of sorrows?
For than man, indeed, there breathes no
    wretcheder creature,
Of all living things, that on earth are breath-
    ing and moving.'

Here I will observe that the use of 'own,' in the second line, for the last syllable of a dactyl, and the use of 'To a,' in the fourth, for a complete spondee, though they do not, I think, actually spoil the run of the hexameter, are yet undoubtedly instances of that over-reliance on accent, and too frequent disregard of quantity, which Lord Redesdale visits with just reprehension.

I now take two longer passages in order to try my method more fully; but I still keep to passages which have already come under our notice. I quoted Chapman's version of some passages in the speech of Hector at his parting with Andromache. One astounding conceit will probably still be in your remembrance—

When sacred Troy shall shed her tow'rs for
    tears of overthrow—

as a translation of ὅτ᾽ ἄν ποτ᾽ ὀλώλῃ ῎Ιλιος ἱρή. I will quote a few lines which may give you, also, the keynote to the Anglo-Augustan manner of rendering this passage and to the Miltonic manner of rendering it. What Mr. Newman's manner of rendering it would be you can by this time sufficiently imagine for yourselves. Mr. Wright—to quote for once from his meritorious version instead of Cowper's, whose strong and weak points are those of Mr. Wright also—Mr. Wright begins his version of this passage thus:

All these thy anxious cares are also mine,
Partner beloved; but how could I endure
The scorn of Trojans and their long-robed
    wives,
Should they behold their Hector shrink from
    war,
And act the coward's part? Nor doth my
    soul
Prompt the base thought.

Ex pede Herculem [Hercules is known by his foot]:* you see just what the manner is. Mr. Sotheby, on the other hand (to take a disciple of Pope instead of Pope himself), begins thus:

'What moves thee, moves my mind,' brave
    Hector said,
'Yet Troy's upbraiding scorn I deeply dread,
If, like a slave, where chiefs with chiefs en-
    gage,
The warrior Hector fears the war to wage.
Not thus my heart inclines.'

From that specimen, too, you can easily divine what, with such a manner, will become of the whole passage. But Homer has neither

What moves thee, moves my mind,

nor has he

All these thy anxious cares are also mine.

῞Η καὶ ἐμοὶ τάδε πάντα μέλει, γύναι · ἀλλὰ μάλ᾽ αἰνῶς,—

that is what Homer has, that is his style and movement, if one could but catch it. Andromache, as you know, has been entreating Hector to defend Troy from within the walls, instead of exposing his life, and, with his own life, the safety of all those dearest to him, by fighting in the open plain. Hector replies:

Woman, I too take thought for this; but
    then I bethink me

---

* Herodotus History 4.82; GBWW, Vol. 6, pp. 138d–139a.

*What the Trojan men and Trojan women
     might murmur,
If like a coward I skulked behind, apart
     from the battle.
Nor would my own heart let me; my heart,
     which has bid me be valiant
Always, and always fighting among the first
     of the Trojans,
Busy for Priam's fame and my own, in spite
     of the future.
For that day will come, my soul is assured of
     its coming,
It will come, when sacred Troy shall go to
     destruction,
Troy, and warlike Priam too, and the people
     of Priam.
And yet not that grief, which then will be,
     of the Trojans,
Moves me so much—not Hecuba's grief, nor
     Priam my father's,
Nor my brethren's, many and brave, who
     then will be lying
In the bloody dust, beneath the feet of their
     foemen—
As thy grief, when, in tears, some brazen-
     coated Achaian
Shall transport thee away, and the day of
     thy freedom be ended.
Then, perhaps, thou shalt work at the loom
     of another, in Argos,
Or bear pails to the well of Messeïs, or
     Hypereia,
Sorely against thy will, by strong Necessity's
     order.
And some man may say, as he looks and sees
     thy tears falling:
See, the wife of Hector, that great pre-
     eminent captain
Of the horsemen of Troy, in the day they
     fought for their city.
So some man will say; and then thy grief
     will redouble
At thy want of a man like me, to save thee
     from bondage.
But let me be dead, and the earth be
     mounded above me,
Ere I hear thy cries, and thy captivity told of.*

The main question, whether or no this version reproduces for him the movement and general effect of Homer better than other versions[30] of the same passage, I leave for the judgment of the scholar. But the particular points, in which the operation of my own rules is manifested, are as follows. In the second line I leave out the epithet of the Trojan women ἑλκεσιπέπλους altogether. In the sixth line I put in five words, 'in spite of the future,' which are in the original by implication only, and are not there actually expressed. This I do, because Homer, as I have before said, is so remote from one who reads him in English, that the English translator must be even plainer, if possible, and more unambiguous than Homer himself; the connection of meaning must be even more distinctly marked in the translation than in the original. For in the Greek language itself there is something which brings one nearer to Homer, which gives one a clue to his thought, which makes a hint enough; but in the English language this sense of nearness, this clue, is gone; hints are insufficient, everything must be stated with full distinctness. In the ninth line Homer's epithet for Priam is ἐϋμμελίω— 'armed with good ashen spear,' say the dictionaries; 'ashen-speared,' translates Mr. Newman, following his own rule to 'retain every peculiarity of his original,'—I say, on the other hand, that ἐϋμμελίω has not the effect of a 'peculiarity' in the original, while 'ashen-speared' has the effect of a 'peculiarity' in English; and 'warlike' is as marking an equivalent as I dare give for ἐϋμμελίω, for fear of disturbing the balance of expression in Homer's sentence. In the fourteenth line, again, I translate χαλκοχιτώνων by 'brazen-coated.' Mr. Newman, meaning to be perfectly literal, translates it by 'brazen-cloaked,' an expression which comes to the

---

[30] Dr. Hawtrey also has translated this passage; but here, he has not, I think, been so successful as in his 'Helen on the walls of Troy.' [Cf. *GBWW*, Vol. 4, pp. 44c–d.]

reader oddly and unnaturally, while Homer's word comes to him quite naturally; but I venture to go as near to a literal rendering as 'brazen-coated,' because a 'coat of brass' is familiar to us all from the Bible, and familiar, too, as distinctly specified in connection with the wearer. Finally, let me further illustrate from the twentieth line the value which I attach, in a question of diction, to the authority of the Bible. The word 'pre-eminent' occurs in that line; I was a little in doubt whether that was not too bookish an expression to be used in rendering Homer, as I can imagine Mr. Newman to have been a little in doubt whether his 'responsively accosted' for ἀμειβόμενος προσέφη was not too bookish an expression. Let us both, I say, consult our Bibles: Mr. Newman will nowhere find it in his Bible that David, for instance, 'responsively accosted Goliath'; but I do find in mine that 'the right hand of the Lord hath the pre-eminence'; and forthwith I use 'pre-eminent' without scruple. My Bibliolatry is perhaps excessive; and no doubt a true poetic feeling is the Homeric translator's best guide in the use of words; but where this feeling does not exist, or is at fault, I think he cannot do better than take for a mechanical guide Cruden's *Concordance*. To be sure, here, as elsewhere, the consulter must know how to consult— must know how very slight a variation of word or circumstance makes the difference between an authority in his favour and an authority which gives him no countenance at all; for instance, the 'Great simpleton!' (for μέγα νήπιος) of Mr. Newman, and the 'Thou fool!' of the Bible are something alike; but 'Thou fool!' is very grand, and 'Great simpleton!' is an atrocity. So, too, Chapman's 'Poor wretched beasts' is pitched many degrees too low; but Shakspeare's 'Poor venomous fool, Be angry and despatch!' * is in the grand style.

---

* *Antony and Cleopatra,* act 5, sc. 2; *GBWW,* Vol. 27, p. 349d.

One more piece of translation and I have done. I will take the passage in which both Chapman and Mr. Newman have already so much excited our astonishment, the passage at the end of the nineteenth book of the *Iliad,* the dialogue between Achilles and his horse Xanthus, after the death of Patroclus. Achilles begins:

'Xanthus and Balius both, ye far-famed
    seed of Podarga!
See that ye bring your master home to the
    host of the Argives
In some other sort than your last, when the
    battle is ended;
And not leave him behind, a corpse on the
    plain, like Patroclus.'
    Then, from beneath the yoke, the fleet
        horse Xanthus addressed him:
Sudden he bowed his head, and all his mane,
    as he bowed it,
Streamed to the ground by the yoke, escaping from under the collar;
And he was given a voice by the white-
    armed Goddess Hera.
    'Truly, yet this time will we save thee,
        mighty Achilles!
But thy day of death is at hand; nor shall
    we be the reason—
No, but the will of heaven, and Fate's invincible power.
For by no slow pace or want of swiftness of
    ours
Did the Trojans obtain to strip the arms
    from Patroclus;
But that prince among Gods, the son of the
    lovely-haired Leto,
Slew him fighting in front of the fray, and
    glorified Hector.
But, for us, we vie in speed with the breath
    of the West-Wind,
Which, men say, is the fleetest of winds; 't is
    thou who art fated
To lie low in death, by the hand of a God
    and a Mortal.'
    Thus far he; and here his voice was
        stopped by the Furies.
Then, with a troubled heart, the swift

Achilles addressed him:
  'Why dost thou prophesy so my death
    to me, Xanthus? It needs not.
I of myself know well, that here I am des-
  tined to perish,
Far from my father and mother dear: for all
  that I will not
Stay this hand from fight, till the Trojans
  are utterly routed.'

So he spake, and drove with a cry his
  steeds into battle.

Here the only particular remark which I will make is, that in the fourth and eighth line the grammar is what I call a loose and idiomatic grammar. In writing a regular and literary style, one would in the fourth line have to repeat before 'leave' the words 'that ye' from the second line, and to insert the word 'do'; and in the eighth line one would not use such an expression as 'he was given a voice.' But I will make one general remark on the character of my own translations, as I have made so many on that of the translations of others. It is, that over the graver passages there is shed an air somewhat too strenuous and severe, by comparison with that lovely ease and sweetness which Homer, for all his noble and masculine way of thinking, never loses.

Here I stop. I have said so much, because I think that the task of translating Homer into English verse both will be re-attempted, and may be re-attempted successfully. There are great works composed of parts so disparate that one translator is not likely to have the requisite gifts for poetically rendering all of them. Such are the works of Shakspeare, and Goethe's *Faust;** and these it is best to attempt to render in prose only. People praise Tieck and Schlegel's version of Shakspeare: I, for my part, would sooner

read Shakspeare in the French prose translation, and that is saying a great deal; but in the German poets' hands Shakspeare so often gets, especially where he is humorous, an air of what the French call *niaiserie!* and can anything be more un-Shakspearian than that? Again; Mr. Hayward's prose translation of the first part of *Faust*—so good that it makes one regret Mr. Hayward should have abandoned the line of translation for a kind of literature which is, to say the least, somewhat slight—is not likely to be surpassed by any translation in verse. But poems like the *Iliad*, which, in the main, are in one manner, may hope to find a poetical translator so gifted and so trained as to be able to learn that one manner, and to reproduce it. Only, the poet who would reproduce this must cultivate in himself a Greek virtue by no means common among the moderns in general, and the English in particular—*moderation*. For Homer has not only the English vigour, he has the Greek grace; and when one observes the boistering, rollicking way in which his English admirers—even men of genius, like the late Professor Wilson—love to talk of Homer and his poetry, one cannot help feeling that there is no very deep community of nature between them and the object of their enthusiasm. 'It is very well, my good friends,' I always imagine Homer saying to them—if he could hear them: 'you do me a great deal of honour, but somehow or other you praise me too like barbarians.' For Homer's grandeur is not the mixed and turbid grandeur of the great poets of the north, of the authors of *Othello†* and *Faust;* it is a perfect, a lovely grandeur. Certainly his poetry has all the energy and power of the poetry of our ruder climates; but it has, besides, the pure lines of an Ionian horizon, the liquid clearness of an Ionian sky.

---

* *GBWW,* Vol. 47.

† *GBWW,* Vol. 27, pp. 205–43.

The Time Machine

H. G. Wells

Editor's Introduction

In the course of his immensely successful career as a novelist, social critic, and historian, H. G. Wells (1866–1946) wrote widely read books about the present and about the past. But it was as a prophet of the future that he enjoyed his greatest vogue, especially in the kind of writing we now know as science fiction, of which he was an early and original practitioner.

The Time Machine was first published in 1895, when Wells was twenty-nine. Its immediate popularity was the first piece of good fortune in a life marked till then by drabness and disappointment. Born in England at Bromley, Kent, the son of a small shopkeeper whose wife had been a lady's maid, Wells had grown up under the continual threat of poverty, which denied him, among other things, the education his talents deserved. Apprenticed at fourteen to a draper, he had disliked his position so much that he ran away, becoming in fitful succession a druggist's assistant, a draper again, and finally an usher (i.e., an assistant teacher) in a grammar school. There he had been able to read and had found time to prepare himself sufficiently so that he won a scholarship to study biology at what became the Royal College of Science in London, from which he proceeded to take a degree at London University in 1888. But matters had gone indifferently for him since then. He was an obscure science teacher, in poor health, who had made an unhappy marriage, when in the midst of grinding out articles on scientific subjects for popular periodicals he wrote *The Time Machine,* and his luck suddenly changed.

For the next thirty years and more he was one of the most popular of living authors, with an international reputation. A series of further science fantasies followed *The Time Machine* in rapid succession. Among these were *The Island of Doctor Moreau* (1896), *The Invisible Man* (1897), *The War of the Worlds* (1898), and *The First Men in the Moon* (1901). Wells then became interested in social questions and proclaimed a fervent belief in the possibilities of human progress with *Mankind in the Making* (1903) and *A Modern Utopia* (1905); he also became an active socialist, joining the Fabian Society. At about the same time, he began to write novels, some of which, such as *Kipps* (1905), *Tono-Bungay* (1909), and *The History of Mr. Polly* (1910), were of genuine if minor distinction, while others, like *Ann Veronica* (1909), *The New Machiavelli* (1911), and *Marriage* (1912), were little more than fictionalized social tracts. And later, after the First World War, he turned to study of the past, producing in *The Outline of History* (1920) one of the great best sellers of the day.

Not that he was any mere pleaser of crowds. Wells was always a man of ideas, or at least of causes, and as he wrote history less for its own sake than for certain lessons it seemed to offer his own age, so he wrote fiction in order to say the things he wished to say about the world and humankind. He regarded himself as a journalist, not as an artist, which he scorned to be. "To you literature like painting is an end," he once wrote Henry James; "to me literature like architecture is a means, it has a use."

His concerns—socialism, evolution, the status of women, and so forth—were those of his time. Bernard Shaw, for one, shared many of his views and argued for them in his own writings. Not all of his contemporaries, certainly neither G. K. Chesterton nor Hilaire Belloc, could believe, as Wells tended to believe, that, in the words of Beatrice Webb, "it was by science, and by science alone, that all human misery would be ultimately swept away." But even Wells had doubts about this, and as his life wore on, his hope of a future that might someday "bring all men together into one planetary community" was gradually mingled with pessimism, a *fin-de-siècle* sense of decaying civilization, what Henry James called "the imagination of disaster," of an end toward which humanity seemed headed. Indeed, this mood became pronounced in Wells after the First World War, and with the Second, when he was very old, he despaired entirely of man's survival.

While some of what he wrote is now forgotten, and much of the rest is seldom read, his science stories, at least, continue to be interesting. Several of his works, including *The Time Machine,* have been made into movies, and *The War of the Worlds* was once adapted for radio by Orson Welles with such persuasiveness that it threw the listening audience into a panic, especially in New Jersey, where the Martians were reported to have landed. It is remembered that the man who wrote that story three-quarters of a century ago was prescient about space travel and that he foresaw, too, such modern developments as television, motion pictures, airplanes (and air war), prefabricated houses, and air-conditioned cities.

Granting, however, that he made good guesses about such things as these, it is clear that Wells's real gift was an extraordinary imagination that could combine wholly disparate elements—for instance, a *machine* that could move through *time.* He had also a knack of perspective, an ability to show the reverse of what he seemed to see. It is such a perspective, in *The Time Machine,* that allows him to tell us something about human life as it is with the illusion that we are looking at what it may be some two or ten or twenty thousand years hence. It is such a device, in the same story, with its description of the world's last twilight, that makes suddenly real the infinite, cold silence in which the planet earth revolves.

The Time Machine

H. G. Wells

Chapter one

The Time Traveller (for so it will be convenient to speak of him) was expounding a recondite matter to us. His grey eyes shone and twinkled, and his usually pale face was flushed and animated. The fire burned brightly, and the soft radiance of the incandescent lights in the lilies of silver caught the bubbles that flashed and passed in our glasses. Our chairs, being his patents, embraced and caressed us rather than submitted to be sat upon, and there was that luxurious after-dinner atmosphere when thought runs gracefully free of the trammels of precision. And he put it to us in this way—marking the points with a lean forefinger—as we sat and lazily admired his earnestness over this new paradox (as we thought it) and his fecundity.

'You must follow me carefully. I shall have to controvert one or two ideas that are almost universally accepted. The geometry, for instance, they taught you at school is founded on a misconception.'

'Is not that rather a large thing to expect us to begin upon?' said Filby, an argumentative person with red hair.

'I do not mean to ask you to accept anything without reasonable ground for it. You will soon admit as much as I need from you. You know of course that a mathematical line, a line of thickness *nil*, has no real existence. They taught you that? Neither has a mathematical plane. These things are mere abstractions.'

'That is all right,' said the Psychologist.

'Nor, having only length, breadth, and thickness, can a cube have a real existence.'

'There I object,' said Filby. 'Of course a solid body may exist. All real things—'

'So most people think. But wait a moment. Can an *instantaneous* cube exist?'

'Don't follow you,' said Filby.

'Can a cube that does not last for any time at all, have a real existence?'

Filby became pensive. 'Clearly,' the Time Traveller proceeded, 'any real body must have extension in four directions: it must have length, breadth, thickness, and—duration. But through a natural infirmity of the flesh, which I will explain to you in a moment, we incline to overlook this fact. There are really four dimensions, three which we call the three planes of Space, and a fourth, Time. There is, however, a tendency to draw an unreal distinction between the former three dimensions and the latter, because it happens that our consciousness moves intermittently in one direction along the latter from the beginning to the end of our lives.'

'That,' said a very young man, making spasmodic efforts to relight his cigar over the lamp, 'that . . . very clear indeed.'

'Now, it is very remarkable that this is so extensively overlooked,' continued the Time Traveller, with a slight accession of cheerfulness. 'Really this is what is meant by the Fourth Dimension, though some people who talk about the Fourth Dimension do not know they mean it. It is only another way of looking at time. *There is no difference between Time and any of the three dimensions of Space except that our con-*

sciousness moves along it. But some foolish people have got hold of the wrong side of that idea. You have all heard what they have to say about this Fourth Dimension?'

'*I* have not,' said the Provincial Mayor.

'It is simply this. That Space, as our mathematicians have it, is spoken of as having three dimensions, which one may call Length, Breadth, and Thickness, and is always definable by reference to three planes, each at right angles to the others. But some philosophical people have been asking why *three* dimensions particularly—why not another direction at right angles to the other three?—and have even tried to construct a Four-Dimension geometry. Professor Simon Newcomb was expounding this to the New York Mathematical Society only a month or so ago. You know how on a flat surface, which has only two dimensions, we can represent a figure of a three-dimensional solid, and similarly they think that by models of three dimensions they could represent one of four—if they could master the perspective of the thing. See?'

'I think so,' murmured the Provincial Mayor; and, knitting his brows, he lapsed into an introspective state, his lips moving as one who repeats mystic words. 'Yes, I think I see it now,' he said after some time, brightening in a quite transitory manner.

'Well, I do not mind telling you I have been at work upon this geometry of Four Dimensions for some time. Some of my results are curious. For instance, here is a portrait of a man at eight years old, another at fifteen, another at seventeen, another at twenty-three, and so on. All these are evidently sections, as it were, Three-Dimensional representations of his Four-Dimensioned being, which is a fixed and unalterable thing.

'Scientific people,' proceeded the Time Traveller, after the pause required for the proper assimilation of this, 'know very well that Time is only a kind of Space. Here is a popular scientific diagram, a weather record. This line I trace with my finger shows the movement of the barometer. Yes-

terday it was so high, yesterday night it fell, then this morning it rose again, and so gently upward to here. Surely the mercury did not trace this line in any of the dimensions of Space generally recognized? But certainly it traced such a line, and that line, therefore, we must conclude was along the Time-Dimension.'

'But,' said the Medical Man, staring hard at a coal in the fire, 'if Time is really only a fourth dimension of Space, why is it, and why has it always been, regarded as something different? And why cannot we move in Time as we move about in the other dimensions of Space?'

The Time Traveller smiled. 'Are you sure we can move freely in Space? Right and left we can go, backward and forward freely enough, and men always have done so. I admit we move freely in two dimensions. But how about up and down? Gravitation limits us there.'

'Not exactly,' said the Medical Man. 'There are balloons.'

'But before the balloons, save for spasmodic jumping and the inequalities of the surface, man had no freedom of vertical movement.'

'Still they could move a little up and down,' said the Medical Man.

'Easier, far easier down than up.'

'And you cannot move at all in Time; you cannot get away from the present moment.'

'My dear sir, that is just where you are wrong. That is just where the whole world has gone wrong. We are always getting away from the present moment. Our mental existences, which are immaterial and have no dimensions, are passing along the Time-Dimension with a uniform velocity from the cradle to the grave. Just as we should travel *down* if we began our existence fifty miles above the earth's surface.'

'But the great difficulty is this,' interrupted the Psychologist. 'You *can* move about in all directions of Space, but you cannot move about in Time.'

'That is the germ of my great discovery.

But you are wrong to say that we cannot move about in Time. For instance, if I am recalling an incident very vividly I go back to the instant of its occurrence: I become absent-minded, as you say. I jump back for a moment. Of course we have no means of staying back for any length of Time, any more than a savage or an animal has of staying six feet above the ground. But a civilized man is better off than the savage in this respect. He can go up against gravitation in a balloon, and why should he not hope that ultimately he may be able to stop or accelerate his drift along the Time-Dimension, or even turn about and travel the other way?'

'Oh, *this*,' began Filby, 'is all—'

'Why not?' said the Time Traveller.

'It's against reason,' said Filby.

'What reason?' said the Time Traveller.

'You can show black is white by argument,' said Filby, 'but you will never convince me.'

'Possibly not,' said the Time Traveller. 'But now you begin to see the object of my investigations into the geometry of Four Dimensions. Long ago I had a vague inkling of a machine—'

'To travel through Time!' exclaimed the Very Young Man.

'That shall travel indifferently in any direction of Space and Time, as the driver determines.'

Filby contented himself with laughter.

'But I have experimental verification,' said the Time Traveller.

'It would be remarkably convenient for the historian,' the Psychologist suggested. 'One might travel back and verify the accepted account of the Battle of Hastings, for instance!'

'Don't you think you would attract attention?' said the Medical Man. 'Our ancestors had no great tolerance for anachronisms.'

'One might get one's Greek from the very lips of Homer and Plato,' the Very Young Man thought.

'In which case they would certainly plough you for the Little-go. The German scholars have improved Greek so much.'

'Then there is the future,' said the Very Young Man. 'Just think! One might invest all one's money, leave it to accumulate at interest, and hurry on ahead!'

'To discover a society,' said I, 'erected on a strictly communistic basis.'

'Of all the wild extravagant theories!' began the Psychologist.

'Yes, so it seemed to me, and so I never talked of it until—'

'Experimental verification!' cried I. 'You are going to verify *that*?'

'The experiment!' cried Filby, who was getting brain-weary.

'Let's see your experiment anyhow,' said the Psychologist, 'though it's all humbug, you know.'

The Time Traveller smiled round at us. Then, still smiling faintly, and with his hands deep in his trousers pockets, he walked slowly out of the room, and we heard his slippers shuffling down the long passage to his laboratory.

The Psychologist looked at us. 'I wonder what he's got?'

'Some sleight-of-hand trick or other,' said the Medical Man, and Filby tried to tell us about a conjurer he had seen at Burslem; but before he had finished his preface the Time Traveller came back, and Filby's anecdote collapsed.

The thing the Time Traveller held in his hand was a glittering metallic framework, scarcely larger than a small clock, and very delicately made. There was ivory in it, and some transparent crystalline substance. And now I must be explicit, for this that follows—unless his explanation is to be accepted—is an absolutely unaccountable thing. He took one of the small octagonal tables that were scattered about the room and set it in front of the fire, with two legs on the hearthrug. On this table he placed the mechanism. Then he drew up a chair and sat down. The only other object on the table was a small shaded lamp, the bright light of which fell upon the model. There were also perhaps a dozen candles about,

two in brass candlesticks upon the mantel and several in sconces, so that the room was brilliantly illuminated. I sat in a low arm-chair nearest the fire, and I drew this forward so as to be almost between the Time Traveller and the fire-place. Filby sat behind him, looking over his shoulder. The Medical Man and the Provincial Mayor watched him in profile from the right, the Psychologist from the left. The Very Young Man stood behind the Psychologist. We were all on the alert. It appears incredible to me that any kind of trick, however subtly conceived and however adroitly done, could have been played upon us under these conditions.

The Time Traveller looked at us, and then at the mechanism. 'Well?' said the Psychologist.

'This little affair,' said the Time Traveller, resting his elbows upon the table and pressing his hands together above the apparatus, 'is only a model. It is my plan for a machine to travel through time. You will notice that it looks singularly askew, and that there is an odd twinkling appearance about this bar, as though it was in some way unreal.' He pointed to the part with his finger. 'Also, here is one little white lever, and here is another.'

The Medical Man got up out of his chair and peered into the thing. 'It's beautifully made,' he said.

'It took two years to make,' retorted the Time Traveller. Then, when we had all imitated the action of the Medical Man, he said: 'Now I want you clearly to understand that this lever, being pressed over, sends the machine gliding into the future, and this other reverses the motion. This saddle represents the seat of a time traveller. Presently I am going to press the lever, and off the machine will go. It will vanish, pass into future Time, and disappear. Have a good look at the thing. Look at the table too, and satisfy yourselves there is no trickery. I don't want to waste this model, and then be told I'm a quack.'

There was a minute's pause perhaps. The Psychologist seemed about to speak to me but changed his mind. Then the Time Traveller put forth his finger towards the lever. 'No,' he said suddenly. 'Lend me your hand.' And turning to the Psychologist, he took that individual's hand in his own and told him to put out his forefinger. So that it was the Psychologist himself who sent forth the model Time Machine on its interminable voyage. We all saw the lever turn. I am absolutely certain there was no trickery. There was a breath of wind, and the lamp flame jumped. One of the candles on the mantel was blown out, and the little machine suddenly swung round, became indistinct, was seen as a ghost for a second perhaps, as an eddy of faintly glittering brass and ivory; and it was gone—vanished! Save for the lamp, the table was bare.

Everyone was silent for a minute. Then Filby said he was damned.

The Psychologist recovered from his stupor and suddenly looked under the table. At that the Time Traveller laughed cheerfully. 'Well?' he said, with a reminiscence of the Psychologist. Then, getting up, he went to the tobacco jar on the mantel and with his back to us began to fill his pipe.

We stared at each other. 'Look here,' said the Medical Man, 'are you in earnest about this? Do you seriously believe that that machine has travelled into Time?'

'Certainly,' said the Time Traveller, stooping to light a spill at the fire. Then he turned, lighting his pipe, to look at the Psychologist's face. (The Psychologist, to show that he was not unhinged, helped himself to a cigar and tried to light it uncut.) 'What is more, I have a big machine nearly finished in there'—he indicated the laboratory—'and when that is put together I mean to have a journey on my own account.'

'You mean to say that that machine has travelled into the future?' said Filby.

'Into the future or the past—I don't, for certain, know which.'

After an interval the Psychologist had an

inspiration. 'It must have gone into the past if it has gone anywhere,' he said.

'Why?' said the Time Traveller.

'Because I presume that it has not moved in space, and if it travelled into the future it would still be here all this time, since it must have travelled through this time.'

'But,' I said, 'if it travelled into the past it would have been visible when we came first into this room; and last Thursday when we were here; and the Thursday before that; and so forth!'

'Serious objections,' remarked the Provincial Mayor, with an air of impartiality, turning towards the Time Traveller.

'Not a bit,' said the Time Traveller, and, to the Psychologist: 'You think. *You* can explain that. It's presentation below the threshold, you know, diluted presentation.'

'Of course,' said the Psychologist, and reassured us. 'That's a simple point of psychology. I should have thought of it. It's plain enough, and helps the paradox delightfully. We cannot see it, nor can we appreciate this machine, any more than we can the spoke of a wheel spinning, or a bullet flying through the air. If it is travelling through time fifty times or a hundred times faster than we are, if it gets through a minute while we get through a second, the impression it creates will of course be only one-fiftieth or one-hundredth of what it would make if it were not travelling in Time. That's plain enough.' He passed his hand through the space in which the machine had been. 'You see?' he said, laughing.

We sat and stared at the vacant table for a minute or so. Then the Time Traveller asked us what we thought of it all.

'It sounds plausible enough to-night,' said the Medical Man, 'but wait until to-morrow. Wait for the common sense of the morning.'

'Would you like to see the Time Machine itself?' asked the Time Traveller. And therewith, taking the lamp in his hand, he led the way down the long, draughty corridor to his laboratory. I remember vividly the flickering light, his queer, broad head in silhouette, the dance of the shadows, how we all followed him, puzzled but incredulous, and how there in the laboratory we beheld a larger edition of the little mechanism which we had seen vanish from before our eyes. Parts were of nickel, parts of ivory, parts had certainly been filed or sawn out of rock crystal. The thing was generally complete, but the twisted crystalline bars lay unfinished upon the bench beside some sheets of drawings, and I took one up for a better look at it. Quartz it seemed to be.

'Look here,' said the Medical Man, 'are you perfectly serious? Or is this a trick—like that ghost you showed us last Christmas?'

'Upon that machine,' said the Time Traveller, holding the lamp aloft, 'I intend to explore Time. Is that plain? I was never more serious in my life.'

None of us quite knew how to take it.

I caught Filby's eye over the shoulder of the Medical Man, and he winked at me solemnly.

Chapter two

I think that at that time none of us quite believed in the Time Machine. The fact is, the Time Traveller was one of those men who are too clever to be believed: you never felt that you saw all round him; you always suspected some subtle reserve, some ingenuity in ambush, behind his lucid frankness. Had Filby shown the model and explained the matter in the Time Traveller's words, we should have shown *him* far less scepticism. For we should have perceived his motives; a pork butcher could understand Filby. But the Time Traveller had more than a touch of whim among his elements, and we distrusted him. Things that would have made the fame of a less clever man seemed tricks in his hands. It is a mistake to do things too easily. The serious people who took him seriously never felt quite sure of his deportment; they were somehow aware that trusting their reputations for judgment with him was like furnishing a nursery with egg-shell china. So I don't think any of us said very much about time travelling in the interval between that Thursday and the next, though its odd potentialities ran, no doubt, in most of our minds: its plausibility, that is, its practical incredibleness, the curious possibilities of anachronism and of utter confusion it suggested. For my own part, I was particularly preoccupied with the trick of the model. That I remember discussing with the Medical Man, whom I met on Friday at the Linnaean. He said he had seen a similar thing at Tübingen and laid considerable stress on the blowing out of the candle. But how the trick was done he could not explain.

The next Thursday I went again to Richmond—I suppose I was one of the Time Traveller's most constant guests—and, arriving late, found four or five men already assembled in his drawing-room. The Medical Man was standing before the fire with a sheet of paper in one hand and his watch in the other. I looked round for the Time Traveller, and—'It's half-past seven now,' said the Medical Man. 'I suppose we'd better have dinner?'

'Where's——?' said I, naming our host.

'You've just come? It's rather odd. He's unavoidably detained. He asks me in this note to lead off with dinner at seven if he's not back. Says he'll explain when he comes.'

'It seems a pity to let the dinner spoil,' said the Editor of a well-known daily paper, and thereupon the Doctor rang the bell.

The Psychologist was the only person besides the Doctor and myself who had attended the previous dinner. The other men were Blank, the Editor aforementioned, a certain journalist, and another—a quiet, shy man with a beard—whom I didn't know, and who, as far as my observation went, never opened his mouth all the evening. There was some speculation at the dinner-table about the Time Traveller's absence, and I suggested time travelling, in a half-jocular spirit. The Editor wanted that explained to him, and the Psychologist volunteered a wooden account of the 'ingenious paradox and trick' we had witnessed that day week. He was in the midst of his exposition when the door from the corridor opened slowly and without noise. I was facing the door and saw it first. 'Hallo!' I said. 'At last!' And the door opened wider, and the Time Traveller stood before us. I gave a cry of surprise. 'Good heavens! man, what's the matter?' cried the Medical Man, who saw him next. And the whole tableful turned towards the door.

He was in an amazing plight. His coat was dusty and dirty, and smeared with green down the sleeves; his hair disordered, and as it seemed to me greyer—either with dust and dirt or because its colour had actually faded. His face was ghastly pale; his chin had a brown cut on it—a cut half healed; his expression was haggard and drawn, as by intense suffering. For a moment he hesitated in the doorway, as if he had been dazzled by the light. Then he came into the room. He walked with just such a limp as I have seen in footsore tramps. We stared at him in silence, expecting him to speak.

He said not a word but came painfully to the table and made a motion towards the wine. The Editor filled a glass of champagne and pushed it towards him. He drained it, and it seemed to do him good: for he looked round the table, and the ghost of his old smile flickered across his face. 'What on earth have you been up to, man?' said the Doctor. The Time Traveller did not seem to hear. 'Don't let me disturb you,' he said, with a certain faltering articulation. 'I'm all right.' He stopped, held out his glass for more, and took it off at a draught. 'That's good,' he said. His eyes grew brighter, and a faint colour came into his cheeks. His glance flickered over our faces with a certain dull approval and then went round the warm and comfortable room. Then he spoke again, still as it were feeling his way among his words. 'I'm going to wash and dress, and then I'll come down and explain things. . . . Save me some of that mutton. I'm starving for a bit of meat.'

He looked across at the Editor, who was a rare visitor, and hoped he was all right. The Editor began a question. 'Tell you presently,' said the Time Traveller. 'I'm— funny! Be all right in a minute.'

He put down his glass and walked towards the staircase door. Again I remarked his lameness and the soft padding sound of his footfall, and standing up in my place, I saw his feet as he went out. He had nothing on them but a pair of tattered, blood-stained socks. Then the door closed upon him. I had half a mind to follow, till I remembered how he detested any fuss about himself. For a minute, perhaps, my mind was wool-gathering. Then, 'Remarkable Behaviour of an Eminent Scientist,' I heard the Editor say, thinking (after his wont) in headlines. And this brought my attention back to the bright dinner-table.

'What's the game?' said the Journalist. 'Has he been doing the Amateur Cadger? I don't follow.' I met the eye of the Psychologist and read my own interpretation in his face. I thought of the Time Traveller limping painfully upstairs. I don't think any one else had noticed his lameness.

The first to recover completely from this surprise was the Medical Man, who rang the bell—the Time Traveller hated to have servants waiting at dinner—for a hot plate. At that the Editor turned to his knife and fork with a grunt, and the Silent Man followed suit. The dinner was resumed. Conversation was exclamatory for a little while, with gaps of wonderment, and then the Editor got fervent in his curiosity. 'Does our friend eke out his modest income with a crossing? or has he his Nebuchadnezzar phases?' he inquired. 'I feel assured it's this business of the Time Machine,' I said, and took up the Psychologist's account of our previous meeting. The new guests were frankly incredulous. The Editor raised ob-

jections. 'What *was* this time travelling? A man couldn't cover himself with dust by rolling in a paradox, could he?' And then, as the idea came home to him, he resorted to caricature. Hadn't they any clothes-brushes in the Future? The Journalist, too, would not believe at any price and joined the Editor in the easy work of heaping ridicule on the whole thing. They were both the new kind of journalist—very joyous, irreverent young men. 'Our Special Correspondent in the Day after Tomorrow reports,' the Journalist was saying—or rather shouting—when the Time Traveller came back. He was dressed in ordinary evening clothes, and nothing save his haggard look remained of the change that had startled me.

'I say,' said the Editor hilariously, 'these chaps here say you have been travelling into the middle of next week!! Tell us all about little Rosebery, will you? What will you take for the lot?'

The Time Traveller came to the place reserved for him without a word. He smiled quietly, in his old way. 'Where's my mutton?' he said. 'What a treat it is to stick a fork into meat again!'

'Story!' cried the Editor.

'Story be damned!' said the Time Traveller. 'I want something to eat. I won't say a word until I get some peptone into my arteries. Thanks. And the salt.'

'One word,' said I. 'Have you been time travelling?'

'Yes,' said the Time Traveller, with his mouth full, nodding his head.

'I'd give a shilling a line for a verbatim note,' said the Editor. The Time Traveller pushed his glass towards the Silent Man and rang it with his fingernail; at which the Silent Man, who had been staring at his face, started convulsively, and poured him wine. The rest of the dinner was uncomfortable. For my own part, sudden questions kept on rising to my lips, and I dare say it was the same with the others. The Journalist tried to relieve the tension by telling anecdotes of Hettie Potter. The

Time Traveller devoted his attention to his dinner and displayed the appetite of a tramp. The Medical Man smoked a cigarette and watched the Time Traveller through his eyelashes. The Silent Man seemed even more clumsy than usual and drank champagne with regularity and determination out of sheer nervousness. At last the Time Traveller pushed his plate away and looked round us. 'I suppose I must apologize,' he said. 'I was simply starving. I've had a most amazing time.' He reached out his hand for a cigar and cut the end. 'But come into the smoking-room. It's too long a story to tell over greasy plates.' And ringing the bell in passing, he led the way into the adjoining room.

'You have told Blank, and Dash, and Chose about the machine?' he said to me, leaning back in his easy-chair and naming the three new guests.

'But the thing's a mere paradox,' said the Editor.

'I can't argue to-night. I don't mind telling you the story, but I can't argue. I will,' he went on, 'tell you the story of what has happened to me, if you like, but you must refrain from interruptions. I want to tell it. Badly. Most of it will sound like lying. So be it! It's true—every word of it, all the same. I was in my laboratory at four o'clock, and since then . . . I've lived eight days . . . such days as no human being ever lived before! I'm nearly worn out, but I shan't sleep till I've told this thing over to you. Then I shall go to bed. But no interruptions! Is it agreed?'

'Agreed,' said the Editor, and the rest of us echoed 'Agreed.' And with that the Time Traveller began his story as I have set it forth. He sat back in his chair at first and spoke like a weary man. Afterwards he got more animated. In writing it down I feel with only too much keenness the inadequacy of pen and ink—and, above all, my own inadequacy—to express its quality. You read, I will suppose, attentively enough; but you cannot see the speaker's white, sincere face in the bright circle of the little lamp nor hear the intonation of his voice. You cannot know how his expression followed the turns of his story! Most of us hearers were in shadow, for the candles in the smoking-room had not been lighted, and only the face of the Journalist and the legs of the Silent Man from the knees downward were illuminated. At first we glanced now and again at each other. After a time we ceased to do that and looked only at the Time Traveller's face.

Chapter three

'I told some of you last Thursday of the principles of the Time Machine and showed you the actual thing itself, incomplete in the workshop. There it is now, a little travel-worn, truly; and one of the ivory bars is cracked, and a brass rail bent; but the rest of it's sound enough. I expected to finish it on Friday, but on Friday, when the putting together was nearly done, I found that one of the nickel bars was exactly one inch too short, and this I had to get remade; so that the thing was not complete until this morning. It was at ten o'clock to-day that the first of all Time Machines began its career. I gave it a last tap, tried all the screws again, put one more drop of oil on the quartz rod, and sat myself in the saddle. I suppose a suicide who holds a pistol to his skull feels much the same wonder at what will come next as I felt then. I took the starting lever in one hand and the stopping one in the other, pressed the first, and almost immediately the second. I seemed to reel; I felt a nightmare sensation of falling; and, looking round, I saw the laboratory exactly as before. Had anything happened? For a moment I suspected that my intellect had tricked me. Then I noted the clock. A moment before, as it seemed, it had stood at a minute or so past ten; now it was nearly half-past three!

'I drew a breath, set my teeth, gripped

the starting lever with both hands, and went off with a thud. The laboratory got hazy and went dark. Mrs. Watchett came in and walked, apparently without seeing me, towards the garden door. I suppose it took her a minute or so to traverse the place, but to me she seemed to shoot across the room like a rocket. I pressed the lever over to its extreme position. The night came like the turning out of a lamp, and in another moment came to-morrow. The laboratory grew faint and hazy, then fainter and ever fainter. To-morrow night came black, then day again, night again, day again, faster and faster still. An eddying murmur filled my ears, and a strange, dumb confusedness descended on my mind.

'I am afraid I cannot convey the peculiar sensations of time travelling. They are excessively unpleasant. There is a feeling exactly like that one has upon a switchback—of a helpless headlong motion! I felt the same horrible anticipation, too, of an imminent smash. As I put on pace, night followed day like the flapping of a black wing. The dim suggestion of the laboratory seemed presently to fall away from me, and I saw the sun hopping swiftly across the sky, leaping it every minute, and every minute marking a day. I suppose the laboratory had been destroyed, and I had come into the open air. I had a dim impression of scaffolding, but I was already going too fast to be conscious of any moving things. The slowest snail that ever crawled dashed by too fast for me. The twinkling succession of darkness and light was excessively painful to the eye. Then, in the intermittent darknesses, I saw the moon spinning swiftly through her quarters from new to full and had a faint glimpse of the circling stars. Presently, as I went on, still gaining velocity, the palpitation of night and day merged into one continuous greyness; the sky took on a wonderful deepness of blue, a splendid luminous colour like that of early twilight; the jerking sun became a streak of fire, a brilliant arch, in space; the moon a fainter fluctuating band; and I could see

nothing of the stars, save now and then a brighter circle flickering in the blue.

'The landscape was misty and vague. I was still on the hill-side upon which this house now stands, and the shoulder rose above me grey and dim. I saw trees growing and changing like puffs of vapour, now brown, now green; they grew, spread, shivered, and passed away. I saw huge buildings rise up faint and fair, and pass like dreams. The whole surface of the earth seemed changed—melting and flowing under my eyes. The little hands upon the dials that registered my speed raced round faster and faster. Presently I noted that the sun belt swayed up and down, from solstice to solstice, in a minute or less, and that consequently my pace was over a year a minute; and minute by minute the white snow flashed across the world, and vanished, and was followed by the bright, brief green of spring.

'The unpleasant sensations of the start were less poignant now. They merged at last into a kind of hysterical exhilaration. I remarked indeed a clumsy swaying of the machine, for which I was unable to account. But my mind was too confused to attend to it, so with a kind of madness growing upon me, I flung myself into futurity. At first I scarce thought of stopping, scarce thought of anything but these new sensations. But presently a fresh series of impressions grew up in my mind—a certain curiosity and therewith a certain dread—until at last they took complete possession of me. What strange developments of humanity, what wonderful advances upon our rudimentary civilization, I thought, might not appear when I came to look nearly into the dim elusive world that raced and fluctuated before my eyes! I saw great and splendid architecture rising about me, more massive than any buildings of our own time, and yet, as it seemed, built of glimmer and mist. I saw a richer green flow up the hill-side, and remain there without any wintry intermission. Even through the veil of my confusion the earth seemed very fair. And so my mind came round to the business of stopping.

'The peculiar risk lay in the possibility of my finding some substance in the space which I, or the machine, occupied. So long as I travelled at a high velocity through time, this scarcely mattered; I was, so to speak, attenuated—was slipping like a vapour through the interstices of intervening substances! But to come to a stop involved the jamming of myself, molecule by molecule, into whatever lay in my way; meant bringing my atoms into such intimate contact with those of the obstacle that a profound chemical reaction—possibly a far-reaching explosion—would result, and blow myself and my apparatus out of all possible dimensions—into the Unknown. This possibility had occurred to me again and again while I was making the machine, but then I had cheerfully accepted it as an unavoidable risk—one of the risks a man has got to take! Now the risk was inevitable, I no longer saw it in the same cheerful light. The fact is that, insensibly, the absolute strangeness of everything, the sickly jarring and swaying of the machine, above all, the feeling of prolonged falling, had absolutely upset my nerve. I told myself that I could never stop, and with a gust of petulance I resolved to stop forthwith. Like an impatient fool, I lugged over the lever, and incontinently the thing went reeling over, and I was flung headlong through the air.

'There was the sound of a clap of thunder in my ears. I may have been stunned for a moment. A pitiless hail was hissing round me, and I was sitting on soft turf in front of the overset machine. Everything still seemed grey, but presently I remarked that the confusion in my ears was gone. I looked round me. I was on what seemed to be a little lawn in a garden, surrounded by rhododendron bushes, and I noticed that their mauve and purple blossoms were dropping in a shower under the beating of the hailstones. The rebounding, dancing hail hung in a cloud over the machine and drove along the ground like smoke. In a moment

I was wet to the skin. "Fine hospitality," said I, "to a man who has travelled innumerable years to see you."

'Presently I thought what a fool I was to get wet. I stood up and looked round me. A colossal figure, carved apparently in some white stone, loomed indistinctly beyond the rhododendrons through the hazy downpour. But all else of the world was invisible.

'My sensations would be hard to describe. As the columns of hail grew thinner, I saw the white figure more distinctly. It was very large, for a silver birch-tree touched its shoulder. It was of white marble, in shape something like a winged sphinx, but the wings, instead of being carried vertically at the sides, were spread so that it seemed to hover. The pedestal, it appeared to me, was of bronze and was thick with verdigris. It chanced that the face was towards me; the sightless eyes seemed to watch me; there was the faint shadow of a smile on the lips. It was greatly weather-worn, and that imparted an unpleasant suggestion of disease. I stood looking at it for a little space—half a minute, perhaps, or half an hour. It seemed to advance and to recede as the hail drove before it denser or thinner. At last I tore my eyes from it for a moment and saw that the hail curtain had worn threadbare, and that the sky was lightening with the promise of the sun.

'I looked up again at the crouching white shape, and the full temerity of my voyage came suddenly upon me. What might appear when that hazy curtain was altogether withdrawn? What might not have happened to men? What if cruelty had grown into a common passion? What if in this interval the race had lost its manliness and had developed into something inhuman, unsympathetic, and overwhelmingly powerful? I might seem some old-world savage animal, only the more dreadful and disgusting for our common likeness—a foul creature to be incontinently slain.

'Already I saw other vast shapes—huge buildings with intricate parapets and tall columns, with a wooded hill-side dimly

creeping in upon me through the lessening storm. I was seized with a panic fear. I turned frantically to the Time Machine and strove hard to readjust it. As I did so the shafts of the sun smote through the thunderstorm. The grey downpour was swept aside and vanished like the trailing garments of a ghost. Above me, in the intense blue of the summer sky, some faint brown shreds of cloud whirled into nothingness. The great buildings about me stood out clear and distinct, shining with the wet of the thunderstorm, and picked out in white by the unmelted hailstones piled along their courses. I felt naked in a strange world. I felt as perhaps a bird may feel in the clear air, knowing the hawk wings above and will swoop. My fear grew to frenzy. I took a breathing space, set my teeth, and again grappled fiercely, wrist and knee, with the machine. It gave under my desperate onset and turned over. It struck my chin violently. One hand on the saddle, the other on the lever, I stood panting heavily in attitude to mount again.

'But with this recovery of a prompt retreat my courage recovered. I looked more curiously and less fearfully at this world of the remote future. In a circular opening, high up in the wall of the nearer house, I saw a group of figures clad in rich soft robes. They had seen me, and their faces were directed towards me.

'Then I heard voices approaching me. Coming through the bushes by the White Sphinx were the heads and shoulders of men running. One of these emerged in a pathway leading straight to the little lawn upon which I stood with my machine. He was a slight creature—perhaps four feet high—clad in a purple tunic, girdled at the waist with a leather belt. Sandals or buskins—I could not clearly distinguish which—were on his feet; his legs were bare to the knees, and his head was bare. Noticing that, I noticed for the first time how warm the air was.

'He struck me as being a very beautiful and graceful creature, but indescribably frail. His flushed face reminded me of the more beautiful kind of consumptive—that hectic beauty of which we used to hear so much. At the sight of him I suddenly regained confidence. I took my hands from the machine.

Chapter four

'In another moment we were standing face to face, I and this fragile thing out of futurity. He came straight up to me and laughed into my eyes. The absence from his bearing of any sign of fear struck me at once. Then he turned to the two others who were following him and spoke to them in a strange and very sweet and liquid tongue.

'There were others coming, and presently a little group of perhaps eight or ten of these exquisite creatures were about me. One of them addressed me. It came into my head, oddly enough, that my voice was too harsh and deep for them. So I shook my head, and, pointing to my ears, shook it again. He came a step forward, hesitated, and then touched my hand. Then I felt other soft little tentacles upon my back and shoulders. They wanted to make sure I was real. There was nothing in this at all alarming. Indeed, there was something in these pretty little people that inspired confidence—a graceful gentleness, a certain childlike ease. And besides, they looked so frail that I could fancy myself flinging the whole dozen of them about like nine-pins. But I made a sudden motion to warn them when I saw their little pink hands feeling at the Time Machine. Happily then, when it was not too late, I thought of a danger I had hitherto forgotten, and reaching over the bars of the machine I unscrewed the little levers that would set it in motion and put these in my pocket. Then I turned again to see what I could do in the way of communication.

'And then, looking more nearly into their features, I saw some further peculiarities in their Dresden-china type of prettiness. Their hair, which was uniformly curly, came to a sharp end at the neck and cheek; there was not the faintest suggestion of it on the face, and their ears were singularly minute. The mouths were small, with bright red, rather thin lips, and the little chins ran to a point. The eyes were large and mild; and—this may seem egotism on my part—I fancied even that there was a certain lack of the interest I might have expected in them.

'As they made no effort to communicate with me but simply stood round me smiling and speaking in soft cooing notes to each other, I began the conversation. I pointed to the Time Machine and to myself. Then hesitating for a moment how to express time, I pointed to the sun. At once a quaintly pretty little figure in chequered purple and white followed my gesture, and then astonished me by imitating the sound of thunder.

'For a moment I was staggered, though the import of his gesture was plain enough. The question had come into my mind abruptly: were these creatures fools? You may hardly understand how it took me. You see I had always anticipated that the people of the year Eight Hundred and Two Thousand odd would be incredibly in front of us in knowledge, art, everything. Then one of them suddenly asked me a question that showed him to be on the intellectual level of one of our five-year-old children— asked me, in fact, if I had come from the sun in a thunderstorm! It let loose the judgment I had suspended upon their clothes, their frail light limbs, and fragile features. A flow of disappointment rushed across my mind. For a moment I felt that I had built the Time Machine in vain.

'I nodded, pointed to the sun, and gave them such a vivid rendering of a thunder-clap as startled them. They all withdrew a pace or so and bowed. Then came one laughing towards me, carrying a chain of beautiful flowers altogether new to me, and put it about my neck. The idea was received with melodious applause; and presently they were all running to and fro for flowers, and laughingly flinging them upon me until I was almost smothered with blossom. You who have never seen the like can scarcely imagine what delicate and wonderful flowers countless years of culture had created. Then someone suggested that their plaything should be exhibited in the nearest building, and so I was led past the sphinx of white marble, which had seemed to watch me all the while with a smile at my astonishment, towards a vast grey edifice of fretted stone. As I went with them the memory of my confident anticipations of a profoundly grave and intellectual posterity came, with irresistible merriment, to my mind.

'The building had a huge entry and was altogether of colossal dimensions. I was naturally most occupied with the growing crowd of little people, and with the big open portals that yawned before me shadowy and mysterious. My general impression of the world I saw over their heads was a tangled waste of beautiful bushes and flowers, a long-neglected and yet weedless garden. I saw a number of tall spikes of strange white flowers, measuring a foot perhaps across the spread of the waxen petals. They grew scattered, as if wild, among the variegated shrubs, but, as I say, I did not examine them closely at this time. The Time Machine was left deserted on the turf among the rhododendrons.

'The arch of the doorway was richly carved, but naturally I did not observe the carving very narrowly, though I fancied I saw suggestions of old Phoenician decorations as I passed through, and it struck me that they were very badly broken and weather-worn. Several more brightly clad people met me in the doorway, and so we entered, I, dressed in dingy nineteenth-century garments, looking grotesque enough, garlanded with flowers, and surrounded by an eddying mass of bright, soft-coloured robes and shining white limbs, in a melodious whirl of laughter and laughing speech.

'The big doorway opened into a proportionately great hall hung with brown. The roof was in shadow, and the windows, partially glazed with coloured glass and partially unglazed, admitted a tempered light. The floor was made up of huge blocks of some very hard white metal, not plates nor slabs—blocks, and it was so much worn, as I judged by the going to and fro of past generations, as to be deeply channeled along the more frequented ways. Transverse to the length were innumerable tables made of slabs of polished stone, raised perhaps a foot from the floor, and upon these were heaps of fruits. Some I recognized as a kind of hypertrophied raspberry and orange, but for the most part they were strange.

'Between the tables was scattered a great number of cushions. Upon these my conductors seated themselves, signing for me to do likewise. With a pretty absence of ceremony they began to eat the fruit with their hands, flinging peel and stalks, and so forth, into the round openings in the sides of the tables. I was not loath to follow their example, for I felt thirsty and hungry. As I did so I surveyed the hall at my leisure.

'And perhaps the thing that struck me most was its dilapidated look. The stained-glass windows, which displayed only a geometrical pattern, were broken in many places, and the curtains that hung across the lower end were thick with dust. And it caught my eye that the corner of the marble table near me was fractured. Nevertheless, the general effect was extremely rich and picturesque. There were, perhaps, a couple of hundred people dining in the hall, and most of them, seated as near to me as they could come, were watching me with interest, their little eyes shining over the fruit they were eating. All were clad in the same soft, and yet strong, silky material.

'Fruit, by the by, was all their diet. These people of the remote future were strict vegetarians, and while I was with them, in spite of some carnal cravings, I had to be frugivorous also. Indeed, I found afterwards that horses, cattle, sheep, dogs, had followed the Ichthyosaurus into extinction. But the fruits were very delightful; one, in particular, that seemed to be in season all the time I was there—a floury thing in a three-sided husk—was especially good, and I made it my staple. At first I was puzzled by all these strange fruits, and by the strange flowers I saw, but later I began to perceive their import.

'However, I am telling you of my fruit dinner in the distant future now. So soon as my appetite was a little checked, I determined to make a resolute attempt to learn the speech of these new men of mine. Clearly that was the next thing to do. The fruits seemed a convenient thing to begin upon, and holding one of these up I began a series of interrogative sounds and gestures. I had some considerable difficulty in conveying my meaning. At first my efforts met with a stare of surprise or inextinguishable laughter, but presently a fair-haired little creature seemed to grasp my intention and repeated a name. They had to chatter and explain the business at great length to each other, and my first attempts to make the exquisite little sounds of their language caused an immense amount of amusement. However, I felt like a school-master amidst children, and persisted, and presently I had a score of noun substantives at least at my command; and then I got to demonstrative pronouns, and even the verb "to eat." But it was slow work, and the little people soon tired and wanted to get away from my interrogations, so I determined, rather of necessity, to let them give their lessons in little doses when they felt inclined. And very little doses I found they were before long, for I never met people more indolent or more easily fatigued.

'A queer thing I soon discovered about my little hosts, and that was their lack of interest. They would come to me with eager cries of astonishment, like children, but like children they would soon stop examining me and wander away after some other toy.

The dinner and my conversational beginnings ended, I noted for the first time that almost all those who had surrounded me at first were gone. It is odd, too, how speedily I came to disregard these little people. I went out through the portal into the sunlit world again as soon as my hunger was satisfied. I was continually meeting more of these men of the future, who would follow me a little distance, chatter and laugh about me, and, having smiled and gesticulated in a friendly way, leave me again to my own devices.

'The calm of evening was upon the world as I emerged from the great hall, and the scene was lit by the warm glow of the setting sun. At first things were very confusing. Everything was so entirely different from the world I had known—even the flowers. The big building I had left was situated on the slope of a broad river valley, but the Thames had shifted perhaps a mile from its present position. I resolved to mount to the summit of a crest, perhaps a mile and a half away, from which I could get a wider view of this our planet in the year Eight Hundred and Two Thousand Seven Hundred and One A.D. For that, I should explain, was the date the little dials of my machine recorded.

'As I walked I was watchful for every impression that could possibly help to explain the condition of ruinous splendour in which I found the world—for ruinous it was. A little way up the hill, for instance, was a great heap of granite, bound together by masses of aluminium, a vast labyrinth of precipitous walls and crumbled heaps, amidst which were thick heaps of very beautiful pagoda-like plants—nettles possibly—but wonderfully tinted with brown about the leaves, and incapable of stinging. It was evidently the derelict remains of some vast structure, to what end built I could not determine. It was here that I was destined, at a later date, to have a very strange experience—the first intimation of a still stranger discovery—but of that I will speak in its proper place.

'Looking round with a sudden thought, from a terrace on which I rested for a while, I realized that there were no small houses to be seen. Apparently the single house, and possibly even the household, had vanished. Here and there among the greenery were palace-like buildings, but the house and the cottage, which form such characteristic features of our own English landscape, had disappeared.

' "Communism," said I to myself.

'And on the heels of that came another thought. I looked at the half-dozen little figures that were following me. Then, in a flash, I perceived that all had the same form of costume, the same soft hairless visage, and the same girlish rotundity of limb. It may seem strange, perhaps, that I had not noticed this before. But everything was so strange. Now, I saw the fact plainly enough. In costume, and in all the differences of texture and bearing that now mark off the sexes from each other, these people of the future were alike. And the children seemed to my eyes to be but the miniatures of their parents. I judged, then, that the children of that time were extremely precocious, physically at least, and I found afterwards abundant verification of my opinion.

'Seeing the ease and security in which these people were living, I felt that this close resemblance of the sexes was after all what one would expect; for the strength of a man and the softness of a woman, the institution of the family, and the differentiation of occupations are mere militant necessities of an age of physical force; where population is balanced and abundant, much child-bearing becomes an evil rather than a blessing to the State; where violence comes but rarely and offspring are secure, there is less necessity—indeed there is no necessity—for an efficient family, and the specialization of the sexes with reference to their children's needs disappears. We see some beginnings of this even in our own time, and in this future age it was complete. This, I must remind you, was my speculation at the time. Later, I was to appreciate how far it fell short of the reality.

'While I was musing upon these things, my attention was attracted by a pretty little structure, like a well under a cupola. I thought in a transitory way of the oddness of wells still existing and then resumed the thread of my speculations. There were no large buildings towards the top of the hill, and as my walking powers were evidently miraculous, I was presently left alone for the first time. With a strange sense of freedom and adventure I pushed on up to the crest.

'There I found a seat of some yellow metal that I did not recognize, corroded in places with a kind of pinkish rust half smothered in soft moss, the arm-rests cast and filed into the resemblance of griffins' heads. I sat down on it, and I surveyed the broad view of our old world under the sunset of that long day. It was as sweet and fair a view as I have ever seen. The sun had already gone below the horizon, and the west was flaming gold, touched with some horizontal bars of purple and crimson. Below was the valley of the Thames, in which the river lay like a band of burnished steel. I have already spoken of the great palaces dotted about among the variegated greenery, some in ruins and some still occupied. Here and there rose a white or silvery figure in the waste garden of the earth, here and there came the sharp vertical line of some cupola or obelisk. There were no hedges, no signs of proprietary rights, no evidences of agriculture; the whole earth had become a garden.

'So watching, I began to put my interpretation upon the things I had seen, and as it shaped itself to me that evening, my interpretation was something in this way. (Afterwards I found I had got only a half-truth—or only a glimpse of one facet of the truth.)

'It seemed to me that I had happened upon humanity upon the wane. The ruddy sunset set me thinking of the sunset of mankind. For the first time I began to realize an odd consequence of the social effort in which we are at present engaged. And yet, come to think, it is a logical consequence enough. Strength is the outcome of need; security sets a premium on feebleness. The work of ameliorating the conditions of life—the true civilizing process that makes life more and more secure—had gone steadily on to a climax. One triumph of a united humanity over Nature had followed another. Things that are now mere dreams had become projects deliberately put in hand and carried forward. And the harvest was what I saw!

'After all, the sanitation and the agriculture of to-day are still in the rudimentary stage. The science of our time has attacked but a little department of the field of human disease, but, even so, it spreads its operations very steadily and persistently. Our agriculture and horticulture destroy a weed just here and there and cultivate perhaps a score or so of wholesome plants, leaving the greater number to fight out a balance as they can. We improve our favourite plants and animals—and how few they are —gradually by selective breeding; now a new and better peach, now a seedless grape, now a sweeter and larger flower, now a more convenient breed of cattle. We improve them gradually, because our ideals are vague and tentative, and our knowledge is very limited; because Nature, too, is shy and slow in our clumsy hands. Some day all this will be better organized, and still better. That is the drift of the current in spite of the eddies. The whole world will be intelligent, educated, and co-operating; things will move faster and faster towards the subjugation of Nature. In the end, wisely and carefully we shall readjust the balance of animal and vegetable life to suit our human needs.

'This adjustment, I say, must have been done, and done well; done indeed for all Time, in the space of Time across which my machine had leaped. The air was free from gnats, the earth from weeds or fungi; everywhere were fruits and sweet and delightful flowers; brilliant butterflies flew hither and thither. The ideal of preventive medicine was attained. Diseases had been stamped out. I saw no evidence of any contagious diseases during all my stay. And I shall have to tell you later that even the processes of putrefaction and decay had been profoundly affected by these changes.

'Social triumphs, too, had been effected. I saw mankind housed in splendid shelters, gloriously clothed, and as yet I had found them engaged in no toil. There were no signs of struggle, neither social nor economical struggle. The shop, the advertisement, traffic, all that commerce which constitutes the body of our world, was gone. It was natural on that golden evening that I should jump at the idea of a social paradise. The difficulty of increasing population had been met, I guessed, and population had ceased to increase.

'But with this change in condition comes inevitably adaptations to the change. What, unless biological science is a mass of errors, is the cause of human intelligence and vigour? Hardship and freedom: conditions under which the active, strong, and subtle survive, and the weaker go to the wall; conditions that put a premium upon the loyal alliance of capable men, upon self-restraint, patience, and decision. And the institution of the family, and the emotions that arise therein, the fierce jealousy, the tenderness for offspring, parental self-devotion, all found their justification and support in the imminent dangers of the young. *Now,* where are these imminent dangers? There is a sentiment arising, and it will grow, against connubial jealousy, against fierce maternity, against passion of all sorts; unnecessary things now, and things that make us uncomfortable, savage survivals, discords in a refined and pleasant life.

'I thought of the physical slightness of the people, their lack of intelligence, and those big abundant ruins, and it strength-ened my belief in a perfect conquest of Nature. For after the battle comes Quiet. Humanity had been strong, energetic, and intelligent, and had used all its abundant vitality to alter the conditions under which it lived. And now came the reaction of the altered conditions.

'Under the new conditions of perfect comfort and security, that restless energy, that with us is strength, would become weakness. Even in our own time certain tendencies and desires, once necessary to survival, are a constant source of failure. Physical courage and the love of battle, for instance, are no great help—may even be hindrances—to a civilized man. And in a state of physical balance and security, power, intellectual as well as physical, would be out of place. For countless years I judged there had been no danger of war or solitary violence, no danger from wild beasts, no wasting disease to require strength of constitution, no need of toil. For such a life, what we should call the weak are as well equipped as the strong, are indeed no longer weak. Better equipped indeed they are, for the strong would be fretted by an energy for which there was no outlet. No doubt the exquisite beauty of the buildings I saw was the outcome of the last surgings of the now purposeless energy of mankind before it settled down into perfect harmony with the conditions under which it lived—the flourish of that triumph which began the last great peace. This has ever been the fate of energy in security; it takes to art and to eroticism, and then come languor and decay.

'Even this artistic impetus would at last die away—had almost died in the Time I saw. To adorn themselves with flowers, to dance, to sing in the sunlight: so much was left of the artistic spirit, and no more. Even that would fade in the end into a contented inactivity. We are kept keen on the grindstone of pain and necessity, and, it seemed to me, that here was that hateful grindstone broken at last!

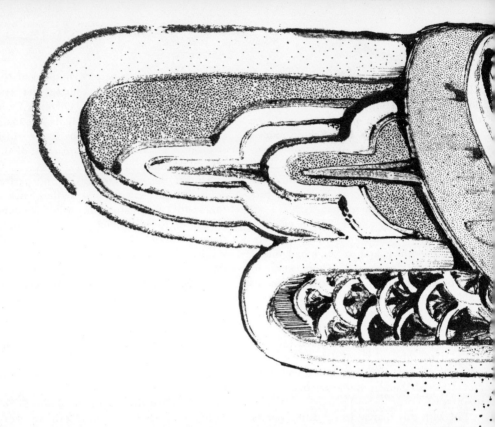

'As I stood there in the gathering dark I thought that in this simple explanation I had mastered the problem of the world—mastered the whole secret of these delicious people. Possibly the checks they had devised for the increase of population had succeeded too well, and their numbers had rather diminished than kept stationary. That would account for the abandoned ruins. Very simple was my explanation, and plausible enough—as most wrong theories are!

Chapter five

'As I stood there musing over this too perfect triumph of man, the full moon, yellow and gibbous, came up out of an overflow of silver light in the north-east. The bright little figures ceased to move about below, a noiseless owl flitted by, and I shivered with the chill of the night. I determined to descend and find where I could sleep.

'I looked for the building I knew. Then my eye travelled along to the figure of the White Sphinx upon the pedestal of bronze, growing distinct as the light of the rising moon grew brighter. I could see the silver birch against it. There was the tangle of rhododendron bushes, black in the pale light, and there was the little lawn. I looked at the lawn again. A queer doubt chilled my complacency. "No," said I stoutly to myself, "that was not the lawn."

'But it *was* the lawn. For the white leprous face of the sphinx was towards it. Can you imagine what I felt as this conviction came home to me? But you cannot. The Time Machine was gone!

'At once, like a lash across the face, came the possibility of losing my own age, of being left helpless in this strange new world. The bare thought of it was an actual physical sensation. I could feel it grip me at the throat and stop my breathing. In another

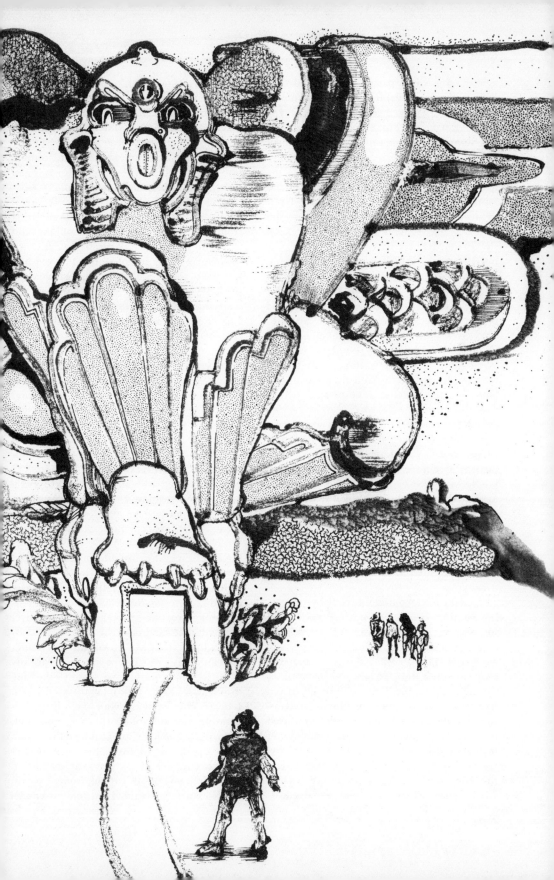

moment I was in a passion of fear and running with great leaping strides down the slope. Once I fell headlong and cut my face; I lost no time in stanching the blood but jumped up and ran on, with a warm trickle down my cheek and chin. All the time I ran I was saying to myself: "They have moved it a little, pushed it under the bushes out of the way." Nevertheless, I ran with all my might. All the time, with the certainty that sometimes comes with excessive dread, I knew that such assurance was folly, knew instinctively that the machine was removed out of my reach. My breath came with pain. I suppose I covered the whole distance from the hill crest to the little lawn, two miles perhaps, in ten minutes. And I am not a young man. I cursed aloud, as I ran, at my confident folly in leaving the machine, wasting good breath thereby. I cried aloud, and none answered. Not a creature seemed to be stirring in that moonlit world.

'When I reached the lawn my worst fears were realized. Not a trace of the thing was to be seen. I felt faint and cold when I faced the empty space among the black tangle of bushes. I ran round it furiously, as if the thing might be hidden in a corner, and then stopped abruptly, with my hands clutching my hair. Above me towered the sphinx, upon the bronze pedestal, white, shining, leprous, in the light of the rising moon. It seemed to smile in mockery of my dismay.

'I might have consoled myself by imagining the little people had put the mechanism in some shelter for me, had I not felt assured of their physical and intellectual inadequacy. That is what dismayed me: the sense of some hitherto unsuspected power, through whose intervention my invention had vanished. Yet, for one thing I felt assured: unless some other age had produced its exact duplicate, the machine could not have moved in time. The attachment of the levers—I will show you the method later—prevented anyone from tampering with it in that way when they were removed. It

had moved, and was hid, only in space. But then, where could it be?

'I think I must have had a kind of frenzy. I remember running violently in and out among the moonlit bushes all round the sphinx, and startling some white animal that, in the dim light, I took for a small deer. I remember, too, late that night, beating the bushes with my clenched fist until my knuckles were gashed and bleeding from the broken twigs. Then, sobbing and raving in my anguish of mind, I went down to the great building of stone. The big hall was dark, silent, and deserted. I slipped on the uneven floor and fell over one of the malachite tables, almost breaking my shin. I lit a match and went on past the dusty curtains, of which I have told you.

'There I found a second great hall covered with cushions, upon which, perhaps, a score or so of the little people were sleeping. I have no doubt they found my second appearance strange enough, coming suddenly out of the quiet darkness with inarticulate noises and the splutter and flare of a match. For they had forgotten about matches. "Where is my Time Machine?" I began, bawling like an angry child, laying hands upon them and shaking them up together. It must have been very queer to them. Some laughed; most of them looked sorely frightened. When I saw them standing round me, it came into my head that I was doing as foolish a thing as it was possible for me to do under the circumstances, in trying to revive the sensation of fear. For, reasoning from their daylight behaviour, I thought that fear must be forgotten.

'Abruptly, I dashed down the match and, knocking one of the people over in my course, went blundering across the big dining-hall again, out under the moonlight. I heard cries of terror and their little feet running and stumbling this way and that. I do not remember all I did as the moon crept up the sky. I suppose it was the unexpected nature of my loss that maddened me. I felt hopelessly cut off from my own kind—a strange animal in an unknown world. I must have raved to and fro, screaming and crying upon God and Fate. I have a memory of horrible fatigue, as the long night of despair wore away; of looking in this impossible place and that; of groping among moonlit ruins and touching strange creatures in the black shadows; at last, of lying on the ground near the sphinx and weeping with absolute wretchedness. I had nothing left but misery. Then I slept, and when I woke again it was full day, and a couple of sparrows were hopping round me on the turf within reach of my arm.

'I sat up in the freshness of the morning, trying to remember how I had got there, and why I had such a profound sense of desertion and despair. Then things came clear in my mind. With the plain, reasonable daylight, I could look my circumstances fairly in the face. I saw the wild folly of my frenzy overnight, and I could reason with myself. "Suppose the worst?" I said. "Suppose the machine altogether lost—perhaps destroyed? It behooves me to be calm and patient, to learn the way of the people, to get a clear idea of the method of my loss, and the means of getting materials and tools; so that in the end, perhaps, I may make another." That would be my only hope, perhaps, but better than despair. And, after all, it was a beautiful and curious world.

'But probably, the machine had only been taken away. Still, I must be calm and patient, find its hiding-place, and recover it by force or cunning. And with that I scrambled to my feet and looked about me, wondering where I could bathe. I felt weary, stiff, and travel-soiled. The freshness of the morning made me desire an equal freshness. I had exhausted my emotion. Indeed, as I went about my business, I found myself wondering at my intense excitement overnight. I made a careful examination of the ground about the little lawn. I wasted some time in futile questionings, conveyed, as well as I was able, to such of the little people as came by. They all failed to understand my gestures; some were simply stolid,

some thought it was a jest and laughed at me. I had the hardest task in the world to keep my hands off their pretty laughing faces. It was a foolish impulse, but the devil begotten of fear and blind anger was ill curbed and still eager to take advantage of my perplexity. The turf gave better counsel. I found a groove ripped in it, about midway between the pedestal of the sphinx and the marks of my feet where, on arrival, I had struggled with the overturned machine. There were other signs of removal about, with queer narrow footprints like those I could imagine made by a sloth. This directed my closer attention to the pedestal. It was, as I think I have said, of bronze. It was not a mere block, but highly decorated with deep framed panels on either side. I went and rapped at these. The pedestal was hollow. Examining the panels with care I found them discontinuous with the frames. There were no handles or keyholes, but possibly the panels, if they were doors, as I supposed, opened from within. One thing was clear enough to my mind. It took no very great mental effort to infer that my Time Machine was inside that pedestal. But how it got there was a different problem.

'I saw the heads of two orange-clad people coming through the bushes and under some blossom-covered apple-trees towards me. I turned smiling to them and beckoned them to me. They came, and then, pointing to the bronze pedestal, I tried to intimate my wish to open it. But at my first gesture towards this they behaved very oddly. I don't know how to convey their expression to you. Suppose you were to use a grossly improper gesture to a delicate-minded woman—it is how she would look. They went off as if they had received the last possible insult. I tried a sweet-looking little chap in white next, with exactly the same result. Somehow, his manner made me feel ashamed of myself. But, as you know, I wanted the Time Machine, and I tried him once more. As he turned off, like the others, my temper got the better of me. In three strides I was after him, had him by the loose part of his robe round the neck, and began dragging him towards the sphinx. Then I saw the horror and repugnance of his face, and all of a sudden I let him go.

'But I was not beaten yet. I banged with my fist at the bronze panels, I thought I heard something stir inside—to be explicit, I thought I heard a sound like a chuckle—but I must have been mistaken. Then I got a big pebble from the river and came and hammered till I had flattened a coil in the decorations, and the verdigris came off in powdery flakes. The delicate little people must have heard me hammering in gusty outbreaks a mile away on either hand, but nothing came of it. I saw a crowd of them upon the slopes, looking furtively at me. At last, hot and tired, I sat down to watch the place. But I was too restless to watch long; I am too Occidental for a long vigil. I could work at a problem for years, but to wait inactive for twenty-four hours—that is another matter.

'I got up after a time and began walking aimlessly through the bushes towards the hill again. "Patience," said I to myself. "If you want your machine again you must leave that sphinx alone. If they mean to take your machine away, it's little good your wrecking their bronze panels, and if they don't, you will get it back as soon as you can ask for it. To sit among all those unknown things before a puzzle like that is hopeless. That way lies monomania. Face this world. Learn its ways, watch it, be careful of too hasty guesses at its meaning. In the end you will find clues to it all." Then suddenly the humour of the situation came into my mind: the thought of the years I had spent in study and toil to get into the future age, and now my passion of anxiety to get out of it. I had made myself the most complicated and the most hopeless trap that ever a man devised. Although it was at my own expense, I could not help myself. I laughed aloud.

'Going through the big palace, it seemed to me that the little people avoided me. It may have been my fancy, or it may have had

something to do with my hammering at the gates of bronze. Yet I felt tolerably sure of the avoidance. I was careful, however, to show no concern and to abstain from any pursuit of them, and in the course of a day or two things got back to the old footing. I made what progress I could in the language, and in addition I pushed my explorations here and there. Either I missed some subtle point, or their language was excessively simple—almost exclusively composed of concrete substantives and verbs. There seemed to be few, if any, abstract terms, or little use of figurative language. Their sentences were usually simple and of two words, and I failed to convey or understand any but the simplest propositions. I determined to put the thought of my Time Machine and the mystery of the bronze doors under the sphinx as much as possible in a corner of memory, until my growing knowledge would lead me back to them in a natural way. Yet a certain feeling, you may understand, tethered me in a circle of a few miles round the point of my arrival.

'So far as I could see, all the world displayed the same exuberant richness as the Thames valley. From every hill I climbed I saw the same abundance of splendid buildings, endlessly varied in material and style, the same clustering thickets of evergreens, the same blossom-laden trees and tree-ferns. Here and there water shone like silver, and beyond, the land rose into blue undulating hills and so faded into the serenity of the sky. A peculiar feature, which presently attracted my attention, was the presence of certain circular wells, several, as it seemed to me, of a very great depth. One lay by the path up the hill, which I had followed during my first walk. Like the others, it was rimmed with bronze, curiously wrought, and protected by a little cupola from the rain. Sitting by the side of these wells, and peering down into the shafted darkness, I could see no gleam of water, nor could I start any reflection with a lighted match. But in all of them I heard a certain sound: a thud—thud—thud, like the beating of some big engine; and I discovered, from the flaring of my matches, that a steady current of air set down the shafts. Further, I threw a scrap of paper into the throat of one, and, instead of fluttering slowly down, it was at once sucked swiftly out of sight.

'After a time, too, I came to connect these wells with tall towers standing here and there upon the slopes; for above them there was often just such a flicker in the air as one sees on a hot day above a sun-scorched beach. Putting things together, I reached a strong suggestion of an extensive system of subterranean ventilation, whose true import it was difficult to imagine. I was at first inclined to associate it with the sanitary apparatus of these people. It was an obvious conclusion, but it was absolutely wrong.

'And here I must admit that I learned very little of drains and bells and modes of conveyance, and the like conveniences, during my time in this real future. In some of these visions of Utopias and coming times which I have read, there is a vast amount of detail about building, and social arrangements, and so forth. But while such details are easy enough to obtain when the whole world is contained in one's imagination, they are altogether inaccessible to a real traveller amid such realities as I found here. Conceive the tale of London which a Negro, fresh from Central Africa, would take back to his tribe! What would he know of railway companies, of social movements, of telephone and telegraph wires, of the Parcels Delivery Company, and postal orders and the like? Yet we, at least, should be willing enough to explain these things to him! And even of what he knew, how much could he make his untravelled friend either apprehend or believe? Then, think how narrow the gap between a Negro and a white man of our own times, and how wide the interval between myself and these of the Golden Age! I was sensible of much which was unseen, and which contributed to my comfort; but save for a general impression of automatic organization, I fear I can convey very little of the difference to your mind.

'In the matter of sepulture, for instance, I could see no signs of crematoria nor anything suggestive of tombs. But it occurred to me that, possibly, there might be cemeteries (or crematoria) somewhere beyond the range of my explorings. This, again, was a question I deliberately put to myself, and my curiosity was at first entirely defeated upon the point. The thing puzzled me, and I was led to make a further remark, which puzzled me still more: that aged and infirm among this people there were none.

'I must confess that my satisfaction with my first theories of an automatic civilization and a decadent humanity did not long endure. Yet I could think of no other. Let me put my difficulties. The several big palaces I had explored were mere living places, great dining-halls and sleeping apartments. I could find no machinery, no appliances of any kind. Yet these people were clothed in pleasant fabrics that must at times need renewal, and their sandals, though undecorated, were fairly complex specimens of metalwork. Somehow such things must be made. And the little people displayed no vestige of a creative tendency. There were no shops, no workshops, no sign of importations among them. They spent all their time in playing gently, in bathing in the river, in making love in a half-playful fashion, in eating fruit and sleeping. I could not see how things were kept going.

'Then again, about the Time Machine: something, I knew not what, had taken it into the hollow pedestal of the White Sphinx. *Why?* For the life of me I could not imagine. Those waterless wells, too, those flickering pillars. I felt I lacked a clue. I felt—how shall I put it? Suppose you found an inscription, with sentences here and there in excellent plain English, and interpolated therewith, others made up of words, of letters even, absolutely unknown to you? Well, on the third day of my visit, that was how the world of Eight Hundred and Two Thousand Seven Hundred and One presented itself to me!

'That day, too, I made a friend—of a sort. It happened that, as I was watching some of the little people bathing in a shallow, one of them was seized with cramp and began drifting downstream. The main current ran rather swiftly, but not too strongly for even a moderate swimmer. It will give you an idea, therefore, of the strange deficiency in these creatures, when I tell you that none made the slightest attempt to rescue the weakly crying little thing which was drowning before their eyes. When I realized this, I hurriedly slipped off my clothes, and, wading in at a point lower down, I caught the poor mite and drew her safe to land. A little rubbing of the limbs soon brought her round, and I had the satisfaction of seeing she was all right before I left her. I had got to such a low estimate of her kind that I did not expect any gratitude from her. In that, however, I was wrong.

'This happened in the morning. In the afternoon I met my little woman, as I believe it was, as I was returning towards my centre from an exploration, and she received me with cries of delight and presented me with a big garland of flowers—evidently made for me and me alone. The thing took my imagination. Very possibly I had been feeling desolate. At any rate I did my best to display my appreciation of the gift. We were soon seated together in a little stone arbour, engaged in conversation, chiefly of smiles. The creature's friendliness affected me exactly as a child's might have done. We passed each other flowers and she kissed my hands. I did the same to hers. Then I tried to talk and found that her name was Weena, which, though I don't know what it meant, somehow seemed appropriate enough. That was the beginning of a queer friendship which lasted a week, and ended—as I will tell you!

'She was exactly like a child. She wanted to be with me always. She tried to follow me everywhere, and on my next journey out and about it went to my heart to tire her down and leave her at last, exhausted and calling after me rather plaintively. But the problems of the world had to be mastered. I had not, I said to myself, come into the future to carry on a miniature flirtation. Yet her distress when I left her was very great, her expostulations at the parting were sometimes frantic, and I think, altogether, I had as much trouble as comfort from her devotion. Nevertheless she was, somehow, a very great comfort. I thought it was mere childish affection that made her cling to me. Until it was too late, I did not clearly know what I had inflicted upon her when I left her. Nor until it was too late did I clearly understand what she was to me. For, by merely seeming fond of me, and showing in her weak, futile way that she cared for me, the little doll of a creature presently gave my return to the neighbourhood of the White Sphinx almost the feeling of coming home; and I would watch for her tiny figure of white and gold so soon as I came over the hill.

'It was from her, too, that I learned that fear had not yet left the world. She was fearless enough in the daylight, and she had the oddest confidence in me; for once, in a foolish moment, I made threatening grimaces at her, and she simply laughed at them. But she dreaded the dark, dreaded shadows, dreaded black things. Darkness to her was the one thing dreadful. It was a singularly passionate emotion, and it set me thinking and observing. I discovered then, among other things, that these little people gathered into the great houses after dark and slept in droves. To enter upon them without a light was to put them into a tumult of apprehension. I never found one out of doors, or one sleeping alone within doors, after dark. Yet I was still such a blockhead that I missed the lesson of that fear, and in spite of Weena's distress I insisted upon sleeping away from these slumbering multitudes.

'It troubled her greatly, but in the end

her odd affection for me triumphed, and for five of the nights of our acquaintance, including the last night of all, she slept with her head pillowed on my arm. But my story slips away from me as I speak of her. It must have been the night before her rescue that I was awakened about dawn, I had been restless, dreaming most disagreeably that I was drowned, and that sea-anemones were feeling over my face with their soft palps. I woke with a start, and with an odd fancy that some greyish animal had just rushed out of the chamber. I tried to get to sleep again, but I felt restless and uncomfortable. It was that dim grey hour when things are just creeping out of darkness, when everything is colourless and clear cut, and yet unreal. I got up, and went down into the great hall, and so out upon the flagstones in front of the palace. I thought I would make a virtue of necessity and see the sunrise.

'The moon was setting, and the dying moonlight and the first pallor of dawn were mingled in a ghastly half-light. The bushes were inky black, the ground a sombre grey, the sky colourless and cheerless. And up the hill I thought I could see ghosts. There several times, as I scanned the slope, I saw white figures. Twice I fancied I saw a solitary white, ape-like creature running rather quickly up the hill, and once near the ruins I saw a leash of them carrying some dark body. They moved hastily. I did not see what became of them. It seemed that they vanished among the bushes. The dawn was still indistinct, you must understand. I was feeling that chill, uncertain, early-morning feeling you may have known. I doubted my eyes.

'As the eastern sky grew brighter, and the light of the day came on and its vivid colouring returned upon the world once more, I scanned the view keenly. But I saw no vestige of my white figures. They were mere creatures of the half-light. "They must have been ghosts," I said; "I wonder whence they dated." For a queer notion of Grant Allen's came into my head and

amused me. If each generation die and leave ghosts, he argued, the world at last will get over-crowded with them. On that theory they would have grown innumerable some Eight Hundred Thousand Years hence, and it was no great wonder to see four at once. But the jest was unsatisfying, and I was thinking of these figures all the morning, until Weena's rescue drove them out of my head. I associated them in some undefinite way with the white animal I had startled in my first passionate search for the Time Machine. But Weena was a pleasant substitute. Yet all the same, they were soon destined to take far deadlier possession of my mind.

'I think I have said how much hotter than our own was the weather of this Golden Age. I cannot account for it. It may be that the sun was hotter, or the earth nearer the sun. It is usual to assume that the sun will go on cooling steadily in the future. But people, unfamiliar with such speculations as those of the younger Darwin, forget that the planets must ultimately fall back one by one into the parent body. As these catastrophes occur, the sun will blaze with renewed energy; and it may be that some inner planet had suffered this fate. Whatever the reason, the fact remains that the sun was very much hotter than we know it.

'Well one very hot morning—my fourth, I think—as I was seeking shelter from the heat and glare in a colossal ruin near the great house where I slept and fed, there happened this strange thing: Clambering among these heaps of masonry, I found a narrow gallery, whose end and side windows were blocked by fallen masses of stone. By contrast with the brilliancy outside, it seemed at first impenetrably dark to me. I entered it groping, for the change from light to blackness made spots of colour swim before me. Suddenly I halted spellbound. A pair of eyes, luminous by reflection against the daylight without, was watching me out of the darkness.

'The old instinctive dread of wild beasts came upon me. I clenched my hands and steadfastly looked into the glaring eyeballs. I was afraid to turn. Then the thought of the absolute security in which humanity appeared to be living came to my mind. And then I remembered that strange terror of the dark. Overcoming my fear to some extent, I advanced a step and spoke. I will admit that my voice was harsh and ill-controlled. I put out my hand and touched something soft. At once the eyes darted sideways, and something white ran past me. I turned with my heart in my mouth and saw a queer little ape-like figure, its head held down in a peculiar manner, running across the sunlit space behind me. It blundered against a block of granite, staggered aside, and in a moment was hidden in a black shadow beneath another pile of ruined masonry.

'My impression of it is, of course, imperfect; but I know it was a dull white and had strange large greyish-red eyes; also that there was flaxen hair on its head and down its back. But, as I say, it went too fast for me to see distinctly. I cannot even say whether it ran on all-fours, or only with its forearms held very low. After an instant's pause I followed it into the second heap of ruins. I could not find it at first; but, after a time in the profound obscurity, I came upon one of those round well-like openings of which I have told you, half closed by a fallen pillar. A sudden thought came to me. Could this Thing have vanished down the shaft? I lit a match, and, looking down, I saw a small, white, moving creature, with large bright eyes which regarded me steadfastly as it retreated. It made me shudder. It was so like a human spider! It was clambering down the wall, and now I saw for the first time a number of metal foot and hand rests forming a kind of ladder down the shaft. Then the light burned my fingers and fell out of my hand, going out as it dropped, and when I had lit another the little monster had disappeared.

'I do not know how long I sat peering down that well. It was not for some time that I could succeed in persuading myself that the thing I had seen was human. But, gradually, the truth dawned on me: that Man had not remained one species but had differentiated into two distinct animals: that my graceful children of the Upper-world were not the sole descendants of our generation, but that this bleached, obscene, nocturnal Thing, which had flashed before me, was also heir to all the ages.

'I thought of the flickering pillars and of my theory of an underground ventilation. I began to suspect their true import. And what, I wondered, was this Lemur doing in my scheme of a perfectly balanced organization? How was it related to the indolent serenity of the beautiful Upper-worlders? And what was hidden down there, at the foot of that shaft? I sat upon the edge of the well telling myself that, at any rate, there was nothing to fear, and that there I must descend for the solution of my difficulties. And withal I was absolutely afraid to go! As I hesitated, two of the beautiful Upper-world people came running in their amorous sport across the daylight in the shadow. The male pursued the female, flinging flowers at her as he ran.

'They seemed distressed to find me, my arm against the overturned pillar, peering down the well. Apparently it was considered bad form to remark these apertures; for when I pointed to this one, and tried to frame a question about it in their tongue, they were still more visibly distressed and turned away. But they were interested by my matches, and I struck some to amuse them. I tried them again about the well, and again I failed. So presently I left them, meaning to go back to Weena and see what I could get from her. But my mind was already in revolution; my guesses and impressions were slipping and sliding to a new adjustment. I had now a clue to the import of these wells, to the ventilating towers, to the mystery of the ghosts; to say nothing of a hint at the meaning of the bronze gates and the fate of the Time Machine! And very vaguely there came a suggestion towards the solution of the economic problem that had puzzled me.

'Here was the new view. Plainly, this second species of Man was subterranean. There were three circumstances in particular which made me think that its rare emergence above ground was the outcome of a long-continued underground look common in most animals that live largely in the dark—the white fish of the Kentucky caves, for instance. Then, those large eyes, with that capacity for reflecting light, are common features of nocturnal things—witness the owl and the cat. And last of all, that evident confusion in the sunshine, that hasty yet fumbling awkward flight towards dark shadow, and that peculiar carriage of the head while in the light—all reinforced the theory of an extreme sensitiveness of the retina.

'Beneath my feet, then, the earth must be tunnelled enormously, and these tunnellings were the habitat of the new race. The presence of ventilating shafts and wells along the hill slopes—everywhere, in fact, except along the river valley—showed how universal were its ramifications. What so natural, then, as to assume that it was in this artificial Under-world that such work as was necessary to the comfort of the daylight race was done? The notion was so plausible that I at once accepted it and went on to assume the how of this splitting of the human species. I dare say you will anticipate the shape of my theory; though, for myself, I very soon felt that it fell far short of the truth.

'At first, proceeding from the problems of our own age, it seemed clear as daylight to me that the gradual widening of the present merely temporary and social difference between the Capitalist and the Labourer was the key to the whole position. No doubt it will seem grotesque enough to you—and wildly incredible!—and yet even now there are existing circumstances to point that way. There is a tendency to uti-lize underground space for the less ornamental purposes of civilization; there is the Metropolitan Railway in London, for instance, there are new electric railways, there are subways, there are underground workrooms and restaurants, and they increase and multiply. Evidently, I thought, this tendency had increased till Industry had gradually lost its birthright in the sky. I mean that it had gone deeper and deeper into larger and ever larger underground factories, spending a still-increasing amount of its time therein, till, in the end—! Even now, does not an East-end worker live in such artificial conditions as practically to be cut off from the natural surface of the earth?

'Again, the exclusive tendency of richer people—due, no doubt, to the increasing refinement of their education, and the widening gulf between them and the rude violence of the poor—is already leading to the closing, in their interest, of considerable portions of the surface of the land. About London, for instance, perhaps half the prettier country is shut in against intrusion. And this same widening gulf—which is due to the length and expense of the higher educational process and the increased facilities for and temptations towards refined habits on the part of the rich—will make that exchange between class and class, that promotion by intermarriage which at present retards the splitting of our species along lines of social stratification, less and less frequent. So, in the end, above ground you must have the Haves, pursuing pleasure and comfort and beauty, and below ground the Have-nots, the Workers getting continually adapted to the conditions of their labour. Once they were there, they would no doubt have to pay rent, and not a little of it, for the ventilation of their caverns; and if they refused, they would starve or be suffocated for arrears. Such of them as were so constituted as to be miserable and rebellious would die; and, in the end, the balance being permanent, the survivors would become as well adapted to the conditions of underground life, and as happy in their way, as the Upper-world people were to theirs. As it seemed to me, the refined beauty and the etiolated pallor followed naturally enough.

'The great triumph of Humanity I had dreamed of took a different shape in my mind. It had been no such triumph of moral education and general co-operation as I had imagined. Instead, I saw a real aristocracy, armed with a perfected science and working to a logical conclusion the industrial system of to-day. Its triumph had not been simply a triumph over Nature, but a triumph over Nature and the fellow-man. This, I must warn you, was my theory at the time. I had no convenient cicerone in the pattern of the Utopian books. My explanation may be absolutely wrong. I still think it is the most plausible one. But even on this supposition the balanced civilization that was at last attained must have long since passed its zenith and was now far fallen into decay. The too-perfect security of the Upper-worlders had led them to a slow movement of degeneration, to a general dwindling in size, strength, and intelligence. That I could see clearly enough already. What had happened to the Under-grounders I did not yet suspect; but from what I had seen of the Morlocks—that, by the by, was the name by which these creatures were called—I could imagine that the modification of the human type was even far more profound than among the "Eloi," the beautiful race that I already knew.

'Then came troublesome doubts. Why had the Morlocks taken my Time Machine? For I felt sure it was they who had taken it. Why, too, if the Eloi were masters, could they not restore the machine to me? And why were they so terribly afraid of the dark? I proceeded, as I have said, to question Weena about this Under-world, but here again I was disappointed. At first she would not understand my questions, and presently she refused to answer them. She shivered as though the topic was unendurable. And when I pressed her, perhaps a little harshly, she burst into tears. They were the only tears, except my own, I ever saw in that Golden Age. When I saw them I ceased abruptly to trouble about the Morlocks and was only concerned in banishing these signs of the human inheritance from Weena's eyes. And very soon she was smiling and clapping her hands, while I solemnly burned a match.

Chapter six

'It may seem odd to you, but it was two days before I could follow up the new-found clue in what was manifestly the proper way. I felt a peculiar shrinking from those pallid bodies. They were just the half-bleached colour of the worms and things one sees preserved in spirit in a zoological museum. And they were filthily cold to the touch. Probably my shrinking was largely due to the sympathetic influence of the Eloi, whose disgust of the Morlocks I now began to appreciate.

'The next night I did not sleep well. Probably my health was a little disordered. I was oppressed with perplexity and doubt. Once or twice I had a feeling of intense fear for which I could perceive no definite reason. I remember creeping noiselessly into the great hall where the little people were sleeping in the moonlight—that night Weena was among them—and feeling reassured by their presence. It occurred to me even then, that in the course of a few days the moon must pass through its last quarter, and the nights grow dark, when the appearances of these unpleasant creatures from below, these whitened Lemurs, this new vermin that had replaced the old, might be more abundant. And on both these days I had the restless feeling of one who shirks an inevitable duty. I felt assured that the Time Machine was only to be recovered by boldly penetrating these underground mysteries. Yet I could not face the mystery. If only I had had a companion it would have been different. But I was so horribly alone, and even to clamber down into the darkness of the well appalled me. I don't know if you will understand my feeling, but I never felt quite safe at my back.

'It was this restlessness, this insecurity, perhaps, that drove me further and further afield in my exploring expeditions. Going to the south-westward towards the rising country that is now called Combe Wood, I observed far off, in the direction of nineteenth-century Banstead, a vast green structure, different in character from any I had hitherto seen. It was larger than the largest of the palaces or ruins I knew, and the façade had an Oriental look: the face of it having the lustre, as well as the pale-green tint, a kind of bluish-green, of a certain type of Chinese porcelain. This difference in aspect suggested a difference in use, and I was minded to push on and explore. But the day was growing late, and I had come upon the sight of the place after a long and tiring circuit; so I resolved to hold over the adventure for the following day, and I returned to the welcome and the caresses of little Weena. But next morning I perceived clearly enough that my curiosity regarding the Palace of Green Porcelain was a piece of self-deception, to enable me to shirk, by another day, an experience I dreaded. I resolved I would make the descent without further waste of time and started out in the early morning towards a well near the ruins of granite and aluminium.

'Little Weena ran with me. She danced beside me to the well, but when she saw me lean over the mouth and look downward, she seemed strangely disconcerted, "Good-bye, little Weena," I said, kissing her; and then, putting her down, I began to feel over the parapet for the climbing hooks. Rather hastily, I may as well confess, for I feared my courage might leak away! At first she watched me in amazement. Then she gave a most piteous cry, and, running to me, she began to pull at me with her little hands.

I think her opposition nerved me rather to proceed. I shook her off, perhaps a little roughly, and in another moment I was in the throat of the well. I saw her agonized face over the parapet and smiled to reassure her. Then I had to look down at the unstable hooks to which I clung.

'I had to clamber down a shaft of perhaps two hundred yards. The descent was effected by means of metallic bars projecting from the sides of the well, and these being adapted to the needs of a creature much smaller and lighter than myself, I was speedily cramped and fatigued by the descent. And not simply fatigued! One of the bars bent suddenly under my weight and almost swung me off into the blackness beneath. For a moment I hung by one hand, and after that experience I did not dare to rest again. Though my arms and back were presently acutely painful, I went on clambering down the sheer descent with as quick a motion as possible. Glancing upward, I saw the aperture, a small blue disk, in which a star was visible, while little Weena's head showed as a round black projection. The thudding sound of a machine below grew louder and more oppressive. Everything save that little disk was profoundly dark, and when I looked up again Weena had disappeared.

'I was in an agony of discomfort. I had some thought of trying to go up the shaft again, and leave the Under-world alone. But even while I turned this over in my mind I continued to descend. At last, with intense relief, I saw dimly coming up, a foot to the right of me, a slender loophole in the wall. Swinging myself in, I found it was the aperture of a narrow horizontal tunnel in which I could lie down and rest. It was not too soon. My arms ached, my back was cramped, and I was trembling with the prolonged terror of a fall. Besides this, the unbroken darkness had had a distressing effect upon my eyes. The air was full of the throb and hum of machinery pumping air down the shaft.

'I do not know how long I lay. I was

roused by a soft hand touching my face. Starting up in the darkness I snatched at my matches and, hastily striking one, I saw three stooping white creatures similar to the one I had seen above ground in the ruin, hastily retreating before the light. Living, as they did, in what appeared to me impenetrable darkness, their eyes were abnormally large and sensitive, just as are the pupils of the abysmal fishes, and they reflected the light in the same way. I have no doubt they could see me in that rayless obscurity, and they did not seem to have any fear of me apart from the light. But, so soon as I struck a match in order to see them, they fled incontinently, vanishing into dark gutters and tunnels, from which their eyes glared at me in the strangest fashion.

'I tried to call to them, but the language they had was apparently different from that of the Over-world people; so that I was needs left to my own unaided efforts, and the thought of flight before exploration was even then in my mind. But I said to myself, "You are in for it now," and, feeling my way along the tunnel, I found the noise of machinery grow louder. Presently the walls fell away from me, and I came to a large open space and, striking another match, saw that I had entered a vast arched cavern, which stretched into utter darkness beyond the range of my light. The view I had of it was as much as one could see in the burning of a match.

'Necessarily my memory is vague. Great shapes like big machines rose out of the dimness and cast grotesque black shadows, in which dim spectral Morlocks sheltered from the glare. The place, by the by, was very stuffy and oppressive, and the faint halitus of freshly shed blood was in the air. Some way down the central vista was a little table of white metal, laid with what seemed a meal. The Morlocks at any rate were carnivorous! Even at the time, I remember wondering what large animal could have survived to furnish the red joint I saw. It was all very indistinct: the heavy smell, the big unmeaning shapes, the obscene

figures lurking in the shadows, and only waiting for the darkness to come at me again! Then the match burned down, and stung my fingers, and fell, a wriggling red spot in the blackness.

'I have thought since how particularly ill-equipped I was for such an experience. When I had started with the Time Machine, I had started with the absurd assumption that the men of the Future would certainly be infinitely ahead of ourselves in all their appliances. I had come without arms, without medicine, without anything to smoke—at times I missed tobacco frightfully—even without enough matches. If only I had thought of a Kodak! I could have flashed that glimpse of the Underworld in a second and examined it at leisure. But, as it was, I stood there with only the weapons and the powers that Nature had endowed me with—hands, feet, and teeth; these, and four safety-matches that still remained to me.

'I was afraid to push my way in among all this machinery in the dark, and it was only with my last glimpse of light I discovered that my store of matches had run low. It had never occurred to me until that moment that there was any need to economize them, and I had wasted almost half the box in astonishing the Upper-worlders, to whom fire was a novelty. Now, as I say, I had four left, and while I stood in the dark, a hand touched mine, lank fingers came feeling over my face, and I was sensible of a peculiar unpleasant odour. I fancied I heard the breathing of a crowd of those dreadful little beings about me. I felt the box of matches in my hand being gently disengaged, and other hands behind me plucking at my clothing. The sense of these unseen creatures examining me was indescribably unpleasant. The sudden realization of my ignorance of their ways of thinking and doing came home to me very vividly in the darkness. I shouted at them as loudly as I could. They started away, and then I could feel them approaching me again. They clutched at me more boldly, whispering odd sounds to each other. I shivered violently and shouted again—rather discordantly. This time they were not so seriously alarmed, and they made a queer laughing noise as they came back at me. I will confess I was horribly frightened. I determined to strike another match and escape under the protection of its glare. I did so, and eking out the flicker with a scrap of paper from my pocket, I made good my retreat to the narrow tunnel. But I had scarce entered this when my light was blown out, and in the blackness I could hear the Morlocks rustling like wind among leaves, and pattering like the rain, as they hurried after me.

'In a moment I was clutched by several hands, and there was no mistaking that they were trying to haul me back. I struck another light and waved it in their dazzled faces. You can scarce imagine how nauseatingly inhuman they looked—those pale, chinless faces and great, lidless, pinkish-grey eyes!—as they stared in their blindness and bewilderment. But I did not stay to look, I promise you: I retreated again, and when my second match had ended, I struck my third. It had almost burned through when I reached the opening into the shaft. I lay down on the edge, for the throb of the great pump below made me giddy. Then I felt sideways for the projecting hooks, and, as I did so, my feet were grasped from behind, and I was violently tugged backward. I lit my last match . . . and it incontinently went out. But I had my hand on the climbing bars now, and, kicking violently, I disengaged myself from the clutches of the Morlocks and was speedily clambering up the shaft, while they stayed peering and blinking up at me: all but one little wretch who followed me for some way, and well-nigh secured my boot as a trophy.

'That climb seemed interminable to me. With the last twenty or thirty feet of it a deadly nausea came upon me. I had the greatest difficulty in keeping my hold. The last few yards was a frightful struggle against this faintness. Several times my head swam, and I felt all the sensations of falling. At last, however, I got over the well-mouth somehow and staggered out of the ruin into the blinding sunlight. I fell upon my face. Even the soil smelt sweet and clean. Then I remember Weena kissing my hands and ears, and the voices of others among the Eloi. Then, for a time, I was insensible.

Chapter seven

'Now, indeed, I seemed in a worse case than before. Hitherto, except during my night's anguish at the loss of the Time Machine, I had felt a sustaining hope of ultimate escape, but that hope was staggered by these new discoveries. Hitherto I had merely thought myself impeded by the childish simplicity of the little people, and by some unknown forces which I had only to understand to overcome; but there was an altogether new element in the sickening quality of the Morlocks—a something inhuman and malign. Instinctively I loathed them. Before, I had felt as a man might feel who had fallen into a pit: my concern was with the pit and how to get out of it. Now I felt like a beast in a trap, whose enemy would come upon him soon.

'The enemy I dreaded may surprise you. It was the darkness of the new moon. Weena had put this into my head by some at first incomprehensible remarks about the Dark Nights. It was not now such a very difficult problem to guess what the coming Dark Nights might mean. The moon was on the wane: each night there was a longer interval of darkness. And I now understood to some slight degree at least the reason of the fear of the little Upper-world people for the dark. I wondered vaguely what foul villainy it might be that the Morlocks did under the new moon. I felt pretty sure now that my second hypothesis was all wrong. The Upper-world people might once have been the favoured aristocracy, and the Morlocks their mechanical servants: but that had long since passed away. The two species that had resulted from the evolution of man were sliding down towards, or had already arrived at, an altogether new relationship. The Eloi, like the Carlovingian kings, had decayed to a mere beautiful futility. They still possessed the earth on sufferance: since the Morlocks, subterranean for innumerable generations, had come at last to find the daylit surface intolerable. And the Morlocks made their garments, I inferred, and maintained them in their habitual needs, perhaps through the survival of an old habit of service. They did it as a standing horse paws with his foot, or as a man enjoys killing animals in sport: because ancient and departed necessities had impressed it on the organism. But, clearly, the old order was already in part reversed. The Nemesis of the delicate ones was creeping on apace. Ages ago, thousands of generations ago, man had thrust his brother man out of the ease and the sunshine. And now that brother was coming back—changed! Already the Eloi had begun to learn one old lesson anew. They were becoming reacquainted with Fear. And suddenly there came into my head the memory of the meat I had seen in the Under-world. It seemed odd how it floated into my mind: not stirred up as it were by the current of my meditations, but coming in almost like a question from outside. I tried to recall the form of it. I had a vague sense of something familiar, but I could not tell what it was at the time.

'Still, however helpless the little people in the presence of their mysterious Fear, I was differently constituted. I came out of this age of ours, this ripe prime of the human race, when Fear does not paralyse and mystery has lost its terrors. I at least would defend myself. Without further delay I determined to make myself arms and a fastness where I might sleep. With that refuge as a base, I could face this strange world with some of that confidence I had

lost in realizing to what creatures night by night I lay exposed. I felt I could never sleep again until my bed was secure from them. I shuddered with horror to think how they must already have examined me.

'I wandered during the afternoon along the valley of the Thames but found nothing that commended itself to my mind as inaccessible. All the buildings and trees seemed easily practicable to such dexterous climbers as the Morlocks, to judge by their wells, must be. Then the tall pinnacles of the Palace of Green Porcelain and the polished gleam of its walls came back to my memory; and in the evening, taking Weena like a child upon my shoulder, I went up the hills towards the south-west. The distance, I had reckoned, was seven or eight miles, but it must have been nearer eighteen. I had first seen the place on a moist afternoon when distances are deceptively diminished. In addition, the heel of one of my shoes was loose, and a nail was working through the sole—they were comfortable old shoes I wore about indoors—so that I was lame. And it was already long past sunset when I came in sight of the palace, silhouetted black against the pale yellow of the sky.

'Weena had been hugely delighted when I began to carry her, but after a time she desired me to let her down and ran along by the side of me, occasionally darting off on either hand to pick flowers to stick in my pockets. My pockets had always puzzled Weena, but at the last she had concluded that they were an eccentric kind of vase for floral decoration. At least she utilized them for that purpose. And that reminds me! In changing my jacket I found . . .'

The Time Traveller paused, put his hand into his pocket, and silently placed two withered flowers, not unlike very large white mallows, upon the little table. Then he resumed his narrative.

'As the hush of evening crept over the world and we proceeded over the hill crest towards Wimbledon, Weena grew tired and wanted to return to the house of grey stone.

But I pointed out the distant pinnacles of the Palace of Green Porcelain to her and contrived to make her understand that we were seeking a refuge there from her Fear. You know that great pause that comes upon things before the dusk? Even the breeze stops in the trees. To me there is always an air of expectation about that evening stillness. The sky was clear, remote, and empty save for a few horizontal bars far down in the sunset. Well, that night the expectation took the colour of my fears. In that darkling calm my senses seemed preternaturally sharpened. I fancied I could even feel the hollowness of the ground beneath my feet: could, indeed, almost see through it the Morlocks on their anthill going hither and thither and waiting for the dark. In my excitement I fancied that they would receive my invasion of their burrows as a declaration of war. And why had they taken my Time Machine?

'So we went on in the quiet, and the twilight deepened into night. The clear blue of the distance faded, and one star after another came out. The ground grew dim and the trees black. Weena's fears and her fatigue grew upon her. I took her in my arms and talked to her and caressed her. Then, as the darkness grew deeper, she put her arms round my neck and, closing her eyes, tightly pressed her face against my shoulder. So we went down a long slope into a valley, and there in the dimness I almost walked into a little river. This I waded and went up the opposite side of the valley, past a number of sleeping houses, and by a statue—a Faun, or some such figure, *minus* the head. Here too were acacias. So far I had seen nothing of the Morlocks, but it was yet early in the night, and the darker hours before the old moon rose were still to come.

'From the brow of the next hill I saw a thick wood spreading wide and black before me. I hesitated at this. I could see no end to it, either to the right or the left. Feeling tired—my feet, in particular, were very sore—I carefully lowered Weena from my shoulder as I halted and sat down upon the turf. I could no longer see the Palace of Green Porcelain, and I was in doubt of my direction. I looked into the thickness of the wood and thought of what it might hide. Under that dense tangle of branches one would be out of sight of the stars. Even were there no other lurking danger—a danger I did not care to let my imagination loose upon—there would still be all the roots to stumble over and the tree-boles to strike against.

'I was very tired, too, after the excitements of the day; so I decided that I would not face it but would pass the night upon the open hill.

'Weena, I was glad to find, was fast asleep. I carefully wrapped her in my jacket and sat down beside her to wait for the moonrise. The hill-side was quiet and deserted, but from the black of the wood there came now and then a stir of living things. Above me shone the stars, for the night was very clear. I felt a certain sense of friendly comfort in their twinkling. All the old constellations had gone from the sky, however: that slow movement which is imperceptible in a hundred human lifetimes had long since rearranged them in unfamiliar groupings. But the Milky Way, it seemed to me, was still the same tattered streamer of star-dust as of yore. Southward (as I judged it) was a very bright red star that was new to me; it was even more splendid than our own green Sirius. And amid all these scintillating points of light one bright planet shone kindly and steadily like the face of an old friend.

'Looking at these stars suddenly dwarfed my own troubles and all the gravities of terrestrial life. I thought of their unfathomable distance, and the slow inevitable drift of their movements out of the unknown past into the unknown future. I thought of the great precessional cycle that the pole of the earth describes. Only forty times had that silent revolution occurred during all the years that I had traversed. And during these few revolutions all the activity, all the traditions, the complex organizations, the nations, languages, literatures, aspirations, even the mere memory of Man as I knew him, had been swept out of existence. Instead were these frail creatures who had forgotten their high ancestry, and the white Things of which I went in terror. Then I thought of the Great Fear that was between the two species, and for the first time, with a sudden shiver, came the clear knowledge of what the meat I had seen might be. Yet it was too horrible! I looked at little Weena sleeping beside me, her face white and starlike under the stars, and forthwith dismissed the thought.

'Through that long night I held my mind off the Morlocks as well as I could and whiled away the time by trying to fancy I could find signs of the old constellations in the new confusion. The sky kept very clear, except for a hazy cloud or so. No doubt I dozed at times. Then, as my vigil wore on, came a faintness in the eastward sky, like the reflection of some colourless fire, and the old moon rose, thin and peaked and white. And close behind, and overtaking it, and overflowing it, the dawn came, pale at first, and then growing pink and warm. No Morlocks had approached us. Indeed, I had seen none upon the hill that night. And in the confidence of renewed day it almost seemed to me that my fear had been unreasonable. I stood up and found my foot with the loose heel swollen at the ankle and painful under the heel; so I sat down again, took off my shoes, and flung them away.

'I awakened Weena, and we went down into the wood, now green and pleasant instead of black and forbidding. We found some fruit wherewith to break our fast. We soon met others of the dainty ones, laughing and dancing in the sunlight as though there was no such thing in nature as the night. And then I thought once more of the meat that I had seen. I felt assured now of what it was, and from the bottom of my heart I pitied this last feeble rill from the great flood of humanity. Clearly, at some time in the Long-Ago of human decay the Morlocks' food had run short. Possibly they had lived on rats and such-like vermin. Even now man is far less discriminating and exclusive in his food than he was—far less than any monkey. His prejudice against human flesh is no deep-seated instinct. And so these inhuman sons of men—! I tried to look at the thing in a scientific spirit. After all, they were less human and more remote than our cannibal ancestors of three or four thousand years ago. And the intelligence that would have made this state of things a torment had gone. Why should I trouble myself? These Eloi were mere fatted cattle, which the ant-like Morlocks preserved and preyed upon—probably saw to the breeding of. And there was Weena dancing at my side!

'Then I tried to preserve myself from the horror that was coming upon me, by regarding it as a rigorous punishment of human selfishness. Man had been content to live in ease and delight upon the labours of his fellow-man, had taken Necessity as his watchword and excuse, and in the fullness of time Necessity had come home to him. I even tried a Carlyle-like scorn of this wretched aristocracy in decay. But this attitude of mind was impossible. However great their intellectual degradation, the Eloi had kept too much of the human form not to claim my sympathy, and to make me perforce a sharer in their degradation and their Fear.

'I had at that time very vague ideas as to the course I should pursue. My first was to secure some safe place of refuge, and to make myself such arms of metal or stone as I could contrive. That necessity was immediate. In the next place, I hoped to procure some means of fire, so that I should have the weapon of a torch at hand, for nothing, I knew, would be more efficient against these Morlocks. Then I wanted to arrange some contrivance to break open the doors of bronze under the White Sphinx. I had in mind a battering-ram. I had a persuasion that if I could enter those doors and carry a blaze of light before me I should discover the Time Machine and escape. I could not imagine the Morlocks were strong enough to move it far away. Weena I had resolved to bring with me to our own time. And turning such schemes over in my mind I pursued our way towards the building which my fancy had chosen as our dwelling.

Chapter eight

'I found the Palace of Green Porcelain, when we approached it about noon, deserted and falling into ruin. Only ragged vestiges of glass remained in its windows, and great sheets of the green facing had fallen away from the corroded metallic framework. It lay very high upon a turfy down, and looking north-eastward before I entered it, I was surprised to see a large estuary, or even creek, where I judged Wandsworth and Battersea must once have been. I thought then—though I never followed up the thought—of what might have happened, or might be happening, to the living things in the sea.

'The material of the Palace proved on examination to be indeed porcelain, and along the face of it I saw an inscription in some unknown character. I thought, rather foolishly, that Weena might help me to interpret this, but I only learned that the bare idea of writing had never entered her head. She always seemed to me, I fancy, more human than she was, perhaps because her affection was so human.

'Within the big valves of the door—which were open and broken—we found, instead of the customary hall, a long gallery lit by many side windows. At the first glance I was reminded of a museum. The tiled floor was thick with dust, and a remarkable array of miscellaneous objects was shrouded in the same grey covering. Then I perceived, standing strange and gaunt in the centre of the hall, what was clearly the lower part of a huge skeleton. I recognized by the oblique feet that it was some extinct creature after the fashion of the Megatherium. The skull and the upper bones lay be-

side it in the thick dust, and in one place, where rain-water had dropped through a leak in the roof, the thing itself had been worn away. Further in the gallery was the huge skeleton barrel of a Brontosaurus. My museum hypothesis was confirmed. Going towards the side I found what appeared to be sloping shelves, and clearing away the thick dust, I found the old familiar glass cases of our own time. But they must have been air-tight to judge from the fair preservation of some of their contents.

'Clearly we stood among the ruins of some latter-day South Kensington! Here, apparently, was the Palaeontological Section, and a very splendid array of fossils it must have been, though the inevitable process of decay that had been staved off for a time, and had, through the extinction of bacteria and fungi, lost ninety-nine hundredths of its force, was nevertheless, with extreme sureness if with extreme slowness, at work again upon all its treasures. Here and there I found traces of the little people in the shape of rare fossils broken to pieces or threaded in strings upon reeds. And the cases had in some instances been bodily removed—by the Morlocks as I judged. The place was very silent. The thick dust deadened our footsteps. Weena, who had been rolling a sea-urchin down the sloping glass of a case, presently came, as I stared about me, and very quietly took my hand and stood beside me.

'And at first I was so much surprised by this ancient monument of an intellectual age, that I gave no thought to the possibilities it presented. Even my preoccupation about the Time Machine receded a little from my mind.

'To judge from the size of the place, this

Palace of Green Porcelain had a great deal more in it than a Gallery of Palaeontology; possibly historical galleries; it might be, even a library! To me, at least in my present circumstances, these would · be vastly more interesting than this spectacle of old-time geology in decay. Exploring, I found another short gallery running transversely to the first. This appeared to be devoted to minerals, and the sight of a block of sulphur set my mind running on gunpowder. But I could find no saltpeter; indeed, no nitrates of any kind. Doubtless they had deliquesced ages ago. Yet the sulphur hung in my mind and set up a train of thinking. As for the rest of the contents of that gallery, though on the whole they were the best preserved of all I saw, I had little interest. I am no specialist in mineralogy, and I went on down a very ruinous aisle running parallel to the

first hall I had entered. Apparently this section had been devoted to natural history, but everything had long since passed out of recognition. A few shrivelled and blackened vestiges of what had once been stuffed animals, desiccated mummies in jars that had once held spirit, a brown dust of departed plants: that was all! I was sorry for that, because I should have been glad to trace the patent readjustments by which the conquest of animated nature had been attained. Then we came to a gallery of simply colossal proportions, but singularly ill-lit, the floor of it running downward at a slight angle from the end at which I entered. At intervals white globes hung from the ceiling—many of them cracked and smashed—which suggested that originally the place had been artificially lit. Here I was more in my element, for rising on either side of me were the huge bulks of big machines, all greatly corroded and many broken down, but some still fairly complete. You know I have a certain weakness for mechanism, and I was inclined to linger among these; the more so as for the most part they had the interest of puzzles, and I could make only the vaguest guesses at what they were for. I fancied that if I could solve their puzzles I should find myself in possession of powers that might be of use against the Morlocks.

'Suddenly Weena came very close to my side. So suddenly that she startled me. Had it not been for her I do not think I should have noticed that the floor of the gallery sloped at all.[1] The end I had come in at was quite above ground and was lit by rare slit-like windows. As you went down the length, the ground came up against these windows, until at last there was a pit like the "area" of a London house before each, and only a narrow line of daylight at the top. I went slowly along, puzzling about the machines, and had been too intent upon them to notice the gradual diminution of the light, until Weena's increasing apprehensions drew my attention. Then I saw that the gallery ran down at last into a thick darkness. I hesitated, and then, as I looked round me, I saw that the dust was less abundant and its surface less even. Further away towards the dimness, it appeared to be broken by a number of small narrow footprints. My sense of the immediate presence of the Morlocks revived at that. I felt that I was wasting my time in this academic examination of machinery. I called to mind that it was already far advanced in the afternoon, and that I had still no weapon, no refuge, and no means of making a fire. And then down in the remote blackness of the gallery I heard a peculiar pattering, and the same odd noises I had heard down the well.

'I took Weena's hand. Then, struck with a sudden idea, I left her and turned to a machine from which projected a lever not unlike those in a signal-box. Clambering upon the stand, and grasping this lever in my hands, I put all my weight upon it sideways. Suddenly Weena, deserted in the central aisle, began to whimper. I had judged the strength of the lever pretty correctly, for it snapped after a minute's strain, and I rejoined her with a mace in my hand more than sufficient, I judged, for any Morlock skull I might encounter. And I longed very much to kill a Morlock or so. Very inhuman, you may think, to want to go killing one's own descendants! But it was impossible, somehow, to feel any humanity in the things. Only my disinclination to leave Weena, and a persuasion that if I began to slake my thirst for murder my Time Machine might suffer, restrained me from going straight down the gallery and killing the brutes I heard.

'Well, mace in one hand and Weena in the other, I went out of that gallery and into another and still larger one, which at the first glance reminded me of a military chapel hung with tattered flags. The brown and charred rags that hung from the sides of it, I presently recognized as the decaying vestiges of books. They had long since dropped to pieces, and every semblance of print had left them. But here and there were warped boards and cracked metallic clasps that told the tale well enough. Had I been a literary man I might, perhaps, have moralized upon the futility of all ambition. But as it was, the thing that struck me with keenest force was the enormous waste of labour to which this sombre wilderness of rotting paper testified. At the time I will confess that I thought chiefly of the *Philosophical Transactions* and my own seventeen papers upon physical optics.

'Then, going up a broad staircase, we came to what may once have been a gallery of technical chemistry. And here I had not a little hope of useful discoveries. Except at one end where the roof had collapsed,

---

[1] It may be, of course, that the floor did not slope, but that the museum was built into the side of a hill.—Ed.

this gallery was well preserved. I went eagerly to every unbroken case. And at last, in one of the really air-tight cases, I found a box of matches. Very eagerly I tried them. They were perfectly good. They were not even damp. I turned to Weena. "Dance," I cried to her in her own tongue. For now I had a weapon indeed against the horrible creatures we feared. And so, in that derelict museum, upon the thick soft carpeting of dust, to Weena's huge delight, I solemnly performed a kind of composite dance, whistling *The Land of the Leal* as cheerfully as I could. In part it was a modest *cancan,* in part a step-dance, in part a skirt-dance (so far as my tail-coat permitted), and in part original. For I am naturally inventive, as you know.

'Now, I still think that for this box of matches to have escaped the wear of time for immemorial years was a most strange, as for me it was a most fortunate thing. Yet, oddly enough, I found a far unlikelier substance, and that was camphor. I found it in a sealed jar, that by chance, I supposed, had been really hermetically sealed. I fancied at first that it was paraffin wax and smashed the glass accordingly. But the odour of camphor was unmistakable. In the universal decay this volatile substance had chanced to survive, perhaps through many thousands of centuries. It reminded me of a sepia painting I had once seen done from the ink of a fossil Belemnite that must have perished and became fossilized millions of years ago. I was about to throw it away, but I remembered that it was inflammable and burned with a good bright flame—was, in fact, an excellent candle—and I put it in my pocket. I found no explosives, however, nor any means of breaking down the bronze doors. As yet my iron crowbar was the most helpful thing I had chanced upon. Nevertheless I left that gallery greatly elated.

'I cannot tell you all the story of that long afternoon. It would require a great effort of memory to recall my explorations in at all the proper order. I remember a long gallery of rusting stands of arms, and how I hesitated between my crowbar and a hatchet or a sword. I could not carry both, however, and my bar of iron promised best against the bronze gates. There were numbers of guns, pistols, and rifles. The most were masses of rust, but many were of some new metal, and still fairly sound. But any cartridges or powder there may once have been had rotted into dust. One corner I saw was charred and shattered; perhaps, I thought, by an explosion among the specimens. In another place was a vast array of idols—Polynesian, Mexican, Grecian, Phoenician, every country on earth, I should think. And here, yielding to an irresistible impulse, I wrote my name upon the nose of a steatite monster from South America that particularly took my fancy.

'As the evening drew on, my interest waned. I went through gallery after gallery, dusty, silent, often ruinous, the exhibits sometimes mere heaps of rust and lignite, sometimes fresher. In one place I suddenly found myself near the model of a tin-mine, and then by the merest accident I discovered, in an air-tight case, two dynamite cartridges! I shouted "Eureka!" and smashed the case with joy. Then came a doubt. I hesitated. Then, selecting a little side gallery, I made my essay. I never felt such a disappointment as I did in waiting five, ten, fifteen minutes for an explosion that never came. Of course the things were dummies, as I might have guessed from their presence. I really believe that, had they not been so, I should have rushed off incontinently and blown Sphinx, bronze doors, and (as it proved) my chances of finding the Time Machine, all together into nonexistence.

'It was after that, I think, that we came to a little open court within the palace. It was turfed, and had three fruit-trees. So we rested and refreshed ourselves. Towards sunset I began to consider our position. Night was creeping upon us, and my inaccessible hiding-place had still to be found. But that troubled me very little now. I had in my possession a thing that was, perhaps, the best of all defences against the Morlocks—I had matches! I had the camphor in my pocket, too, if a blaze were needed. It seemed to me that the best thing we could do would be to pass the night in the open, protected by a fire. In the morning there was the getting of the Time Machine. Towards that, as yet, I had only my iron mace. But now, with my growing knowledge, I felt very differently towards those bronze doors. Up to this, I had refrained from forcing them, largely because of the mystery on the other side. They had never impressed me as being very strong, and I hoped to find my bar of iron not altogether inadequate for the work.

Chapter nine

'We emerged from the palace while the sun was still in part above the horizon. I was determined to reach the White Sphinx early the next morning, and ere the dusk I purposed pushing through the woods that had stopped me on the previous journey. My plan was to go as far as possible that night, and then, building a fire, to sleep in the protection of its glare. Accordingly, as we went along I gathered any sticks or dried grass I saw and presently had my arms full of such litter. Thus loaded, our progress was slower than I had anticipated, and besides Weena was tired. And I began to suffer from sleepiness too; so that it was full night before we reached the wood. Upon the shrubby hill of its edge Weena would have stopped, fearing the darkness before us; but a singular sense of impending calamity, that should indeed have served me as a warning, drove me onward. I had been without sleep for a night and two days, and I was feverish and irritable. I felt sleep coming upon me, and the Morlocks with it.

'While we hesitated, among the black bushes behind us, and dim against their blackness, I saw three crouching figures. There was scrub and long grass all about us, and I did not feel safe from their insidious approach. The forest, I calculated, was rather less than a mile across. If we could get through it to the bare hill-side, there, as it seemed to me, was an altogether safer resting-place; I thought that with my matches and my camphor I could contrive to keep my path illuminated through the woods. Yet it was evident that if I was to flourish matches with my hands I should have to abandon my firewood; so, rather reluctantly, I put it down. And then it came into my head that I would amaze our friends behind by lighting it. I was to discover the atrocious folly of this proceeding, but it came to my mind as an ingenious move for covering our retreat.

'I don't know if you have ever thought what a rare thing flame must be in the absence of man and in a temperate climate. The sun's heat is rarely strong enough to burn, even when it is focused by dewdrops, as is sometimes the case in more tropical districts. Lightning may blast and blacken, but it rarely gives rise to widespread fire. Decaying vegetation may occasionally smoulder with the heat of its fermentation, but this rarely results in flame. In this decadence, too, the art of fire-making had been forgotten on the earth. The red tongues that went licking up my heap of wood were an altogether new and strange thing to Weena.

'She wanted to run to it and play with it. I believe she would have cast herself into it had I not restrained her. But I caught her up and, in spite of her struggles, plunged boldly before me into the wood. For a little way the glare of my fire lit the path. Looking back presently I could see, through the crowded stems, that from my heap of sticks the blaze had spread to some bushes adjacent, and a curved line of fire was creeping up the grass of the hill. I laughed at that, and turned again to the dark trees before me. It was very black, and Weena clung to me convulsively, but there was still, as my eyes grew accustomed to the darkness, sufficient light for me to avoid the stems. Overhead it was simply black, except where a gap of remote blue sky shone down upon us here and there. I struck none of my matches because I had no hand free. Upon my left arm I carried my little one, in my right hand I had my iron bar.

'For some way I heard nothing but the crackling twigs under my feet, the faint rustle of the breeze above, and my own breathing and the throb of the blood-vessels in my ears. Then I seemed to know of a pattering about me. I pushed on grimly. The pattering grew more distinct, and then I caught the same queer sound and voices I had heard in the Under-world. There were evidently several of the Morlocks, and they were closing in upon me. Indeed, in another minute I felt a tug at my coat, then something at my arm. And Weena shivered violently and became quite still.

'It was time for a match. But to get one I must put her down. I did so, and, as I fumbled with my pocket, a struggle began in the darkness about my knees, perfectly silent on her part and with the same peculiar cooing sounds from the Morlocks. Soft little hands, too, were creeping over my coat and back, touching even my neck. Then the match scratched and fizzed. I held it flaring and saw the white backs of the Morlocks in flight amid the trees. I hastily took a lump of camphor from my pocket and prepared to light it as soon as the match should wane. Then I looked at Weena. She was lying clutching my feet and quite motionless, with her face to the ground. With a sudden fright I stooped to her. She seemed scarcely to breathe. I lit the block of camphor and flung it to the ground, and as it split and flared up and drove back the Morlocks and the shadows, I knelt down and lifted her. The wood behind seemed full of the stir and murmur of a great company!

'She seemed to have fainted. I put her carefully upon my shoulder and rose to push on, and then there came a horrible realization. In maneuvering with my matches and Weena, I had turned myself about several times, and now I had not the faintest idea in what direction lay my path. For all I knew, I might be facing back towards the Palace of Green Porcelain. I found myself in a cold sweat. I had to think rapidly what to do. I determined to build a fire and encamp where we were. I put Weena, still motionless, down upon a turfy bole, and very hastily, as my first lump of camphor waned, I began collecting sticks and leaves. Here and there out of the darkness round me the Morlocks' eyes shone like carbuncles.

'The camphor flickered and went out. I lit a match, and as I did so, two white forms that had been approaching Weena dashed hastily away. One was so blinded by the light that he came straight for me, and I felt his bones grind under the blow of my fist. He gave a whoop of dismay, staggered a little way, and fell down. I lit another piece of camphor and went on gathering my bonfire. Presently I noticed how dry was some of the foliage above me, for since my arrival on the Time Machine, a matter of a week, no rain had fallen. So, instead of casting about among the trees for fallen twigs, I began leaping up and dragging down branches. Very soon I had a choking smoky fire of green wood and dry sticks and could economize my camphor. Then I turned to where Weena lay beside my iron mace. I tried what I could to revive her, but she lay like one dead. I could not even satisfy myself whether or not she breathed.

'Now, the smoke of the fire beat over towards me, and it must have made me heavy of a sudden. Moreover, the vapour of camphor was in the air. My fire would not need replenishing for an hour or so. I felt very weary after my exertion and sat down. The wood, too, was full of a slumbrous murmur that I did not understand. I seemed just to nod and open my eyes. But all was dark, and the Morlocks had their hands upon me. Flinging off their clinging fingers I hastily felt in my pocket for the match-box, and—it had gone! Then they gripped and closed with me again. In a moment I knew what

had happened. I had slept, and my fire had gone out, and the bitterness of death came over my soul. The forest seemed full of the smell of burning wood. I was caught by the neck, by the hair, by the arms, and pulled down. It was indescribably horrible in the darkness to feel all those soft creatures heaped upon me. I felt as if I was in a monstrous spider's web. I was overpowered and went down. I felt little teeth nipping at my neck. I rolled over, and as I did so my hand came against my iron lever. It gave me strength. I struggled up, shaking the human rats from me, and, holding the bar short, I thrust where I judged their faces might be. I could feel the succulent giving of flesh and bone under my blows, and for a moment I was free.

'The strange exultation that so often seems to accompany hard fighting came upon me. I knew that both I and Weena were lost, but I determined to make the Morlocks pay for their meat. I stood with my back to a tree, swinging the iron bar before me. The whole wood was full of the stir and cries of them. A minute passed. Their voices seemed to rise to a higher pitch of excitement, and their movements grew faster. Yet none came within reach. I stood glaring at the blackness. Then suddenly came hope. What if the Morlocks were afraid? And close on the heels of that came a strange thing. The darkness seemed to grow luminous. Very dimly I began to see the Morlocks about me—three battered at my feet—and then I recognized, with incredulous surprise, that the others were running, in an incessant stream, as it seemed, from behind me, and away through the wood in front. And their backs seemed no longer white, but reddish. As I stood agape, I saw a little spark go drifting across the gap of starlight between the branches and vanish. And at that I understood the smell of burning wood, the slumbrous murmur that was growing now into a gusty roar, the red glow, and the Morlocks' flight.

'Stepping out from behind my tree and looking back, I saw, through the black pillars of the nearer trees, the flames of the burning forest. It was my first fire coming after me. With that I looked for Weena, but she was gone. The hissing and crackling behind me, the explosive thud as each fresh tree burst into flame, left little time for reflection. My iron bar still gripped, I followed in the Morlocks' path. It was a close race. Once the flames crept forward so swiftly on my right as I ran that I was outflanked and had to strike off to the left. But at last I emerged upon a small open space, and as I did so, a Morlock came blundering towards me, and past me, and went on straight into the fire!

'And now I was to see the most weird and horrible thing, I think, of all that I beheld in that future age. This whole space was as bright as day with the reflection of the fire. In the centre was a hillock or tumulus, surmounted by a scorched hawthorn. Beyond this was another arm of the burning forest, with yellow tongues already writhing from it, completely encircling the space with a fence of fire. Upon the hill-side were some thirty or forty Morlocks, dazzled by the light and heat, and blundering hither and thither against each other in their bewilderment. At first I did not realize their blindness, and struck furiously at them with my bar, in a frenzy of fear, as they approached me, killing one and crippling several more. But when I had watched the gestures of one of them groping under the hawthorn against the red sky, and heard their moans, I was assured of their absolute helplessness and misery in the glare, and I struck no more of them.

'Yet every now and then one would come straight towards me, setting loose a quivering horror that made me quick to elude him. At one time the flames died down somewhat, and I feared the foul creatures would presently be able to see me. I was thinking of beginning the fight by killing some of them before this should happen; but the fire burst out again brightly, and I stayed my hand. I walked about the hill among them and avoided them, looking for some trace of Weena. But Weena was gone.

At last I sat down on the summit of the hillock and watched these strange incredible company of blind things groping to and fro, and making uncanny noises to each other, as the glare of the fire beat on them. The coiling uprush of smoke streamed across the sky, and through the rare tatters of that red canopy, remote as though they belonged to another universe, shone the little stars. Two or three Morlocks came blundering into me, and I drove them off with blows of my fists, trembling as I did so.

'For the most part of that night I was persuaded it was a nightmare. I bit myself and screamed in a passionate desire to awake. I beat the ground with my hands, and got up and sat down again, and wandered here and there, and again sat down. Then I would fall to rubbing my eyes and calling upon God to let me awake. Thrice I saw Morlocks put their heads down in a kind of agony and rush into the flames. But, at last, above the subsiding red of the fire, above the streaming masses of black smoke and the whitening and blackening tree stumps, and the diminishing numbers of these dim creatures, came the white light of the day.

'I searched again for traces of Weena, but there were none. It was plain that they had left her poor little body in the forest.

I cannot describe how it relieved me to think that it had escaped the awful fate to which it seemed destined. As I thought of that, I was almost moved to begin a massacre of the helpless abominations about me, but I contained myself. The hillock, as I have said, was a kind of island in the forest. From its summit I could now make out through a haze of smoke the Palace of Green Porcelain, and from that I could get my bearings for the White Sphinx. And so, leaving the remnant of these damned souls still going hither and thither and moaning, as the day grew clearer, I tied some grass about my feet and limped on across smoking ashes and among black stems, that still pulsated internally with fire, towards the hiding-place of the Time Machine. I walked slowly, for I was almost exhausted, as well as lame, and I felt the intensest wretchedness for the horrible death of little Weena. It seemed an overwhelming calamity. Now, in this old familiar room, it is more like the sorrow of a dream than an actual loss. But that morning it left me absolutely lonely again—terribly alone. I began to think of this house of mine, of this fireside, of some of you, and with such thoughts came a longing that was pain.

'But, as I walked over the smoking ashes under the bright morning sky, I made a discovery. In my trouser pocket were still some loose matches. The box must have leaked before it was lost.

Chapter ten

'About eight or nine in the morning I came to the same seat of yellow metal from which I had viewed the world upon the evening of my arrival. I thought of my hasty conclusions upon that evening and could not refrain from laughing bitterly at my confidence. Here was the same beautiful scene, the same abundant foliage, the same splendid palaces and magnificent ruins, the same silver river running between its fertile banks. The gay robes of the beautiful people moved hither and thither among the trees. Some were bathing in exactly the place where I had saved Weena, and that suddenly gave me a keen stab of pain. And like blots upon the landscape rose the cupolas above the ways to the Under-world. I understood now what all the beauty of the Over-world people covered. Very pleasant was their day, as pleasant as the day of the cattle in the field. Like the cattle, they knew of no enemies and provided against no needs. And their end was the same.

'I grieved to think how brief the dream of the human intellect had been. It had committed suicide. It had set itself steadfastly towards comfort and ease, a balanced society with security and permanency as its watchword, it had attained its hopes—to come to this at last. Once, life and property must have reached almost absolute safety. The rich had been assured of his wealth and comfort, the toiler assured of his life and work. No doubt in that perfect world there had been no unemployed problem, no social question left unsolved. And a great quiet had followed.

'It is a law of nature we overlook, that intellectual versatility is the compensation for change, danger, and trouble. An animal perfectly in harmony with its environment is a perfect mechanism. Nature never appeals to intelligence until habit and instinct are useless. There is no intelligence where there is no change and no need of change. Only those animals partake of intelligence that have to meet a huge variety of needs and dangers.

'So, as I see it, the Upper-world man had drifted towards his feeble prettiness, and the Under-world to mere mechanical industry. But that perfect state had lacked one thing even for mechanical perfection—absolute permanency. Apparently as time went on, the feeding of the Under-world, however it was effected, had become disjointed. Mother Necessity, who had been staved off for a few thousand years, came back again, and she began below. The Under-world being in contact with machinery, which, however perfect, still needs some little thought outside habit, had probably retained perforce rather more initiative, if less of every other human character, than the Upper. And when other meat failed them, they turned to what old habit had hitherto forbidden. So I say I saw it in my last view of the world of Eight Hundred and Two Thousand Seven Hundred and One. It may be as wrong an explanation as mortal wit could invent. It is how the thing shaped itself to me, and as that I give it to you.

'After the fatigues, excitements, and terrors of the past days, and in spite of my grief, this seat and the tranquil view and the warm sunlight were very pleasant. I was very tired and sleepy, and soon my theorizing passed into dozing. Catching myself at that, I took my own hint, and spreading myself out upon the turf I had a long and refreshing sleep.

'I awoke a little before sunsetting. I now felt safe against being caught napping by the Morlocks, and, stretching myself, I came on down the hill towards the White Sphinx. I had my crowbar in one hand, and the other hand played with the matches in my pocket.

'And now came a most unexpected thing. As I approached the pedestal of the sphinx I found the bronze valves were open. They had slid down into grooves.

'At that I stopped short before them, hesitating to enter.

'Within was a small apartment, and on a raised place in the corner of this was the Time Machine. I had the small levers in my pocket. So here, after all my elaborate preparations for the siege of the White Sphinx, was a meek surrender. I threw my iron bar away, almost sorry not to use it.

'A sudden thought came into my head as I stooped towards the portal. For once, at least, I grasped the mental operations of the Morlocks. Suppressing a strong inclination to laugh, I stepped through the bronze frame and up to the Time Machine. I was surprised to find it had been carefully oiled and cleaned. I have suspected since that the Morlocks had even partially taken it to pieces while trying in their dim way to grasp its purpose.

'Now as I stood and examined it, finding a pleasure in the mere touch of the contrivance, the thing I had expected happened.

The bronze panels suddenly slid up and struck the frame with a clang. I was in the dark—trapped. So the Morlocks thought. At that I chuckled gleefully.

'I could already hear their murmuring laughter as they came towards me. Very calmly I tried to strike the match. I had only to fix on the levers and depart then like a ghost. But I had overlooked one little thing. The matches were of that abominable kind that light only on the box.

'You may imagine how all my calm vanished. The little brutes were close upon me. One touched me. I made a sweeping blow in the dark at them with the levers and began to scramble into the saddle of the machine. Then came one hand upon me and then another. Then I had simply to fight against their persistent fingers for my levers and at the same time feel for the studs over which these fitted. Once, indeed, they almost got away from me. As it slipped from my hand, I had to butt in the dark with my head—I could hear the Morlock's skull ring—to recover it. It was a nearer thing than the fight in the forest, I think, this last scramble.

'But at last the lever was fixed and pulled over. The clinging hands slipped from me. The darkness presently fell from my eyes. I found myself in the same grey light and tumult I have already described.

Chapter eleven

'I have already told you of the sickness and confusion that comes with time travelling. And this time I was not seated properly in the saddle, but sideways and in an unstable fashion. For an indefinite time I clung to the machine as it swayed and vibrated, quite unheeding how I went, and when I brought myself to look at the dials again I was amazed to find where I had arrived. One dial records days, and another thousands of days, another millions of days, and another thousands of millions. Now, instead of reversing the levers, I had pulled them over so as to go forward with them, and when I came to look at these indicators I found that the thousands hand was sweeping round as fast as the seconds hand of a watch—into futurity.

'As I drove on, a peculiar change crept over the appearance of things. The palpitating greyness grew darker; then—though I was still travelling with prodigious velocity—the blinking succession of day and night, which was usually indicative of a slower pace, returned, and grew more and more marked. This puzzled me very much at first. The alternations of night and day grew slower and slower, and so did the passage of the sun across the sky, until they seemed to stretch through centuries. At last a steady twilight brooded over the earth, a twilight only broken now and then when a comet glared across the darkling sky. The band of light that had indicated the sun had long since disappeared; for the sun had ceased to set—it simply rose and fell in the west and grew ever broader and more red. All trace of the moon had vanished. The circling of the stars, growing slower and slower, had given place to creeping points of light. At last, some time before I stopped, the sun, red and very large, halted motionless upon the horizon, a vast dome glowing with a dull heat, and now and then suffering a momentary extinction. At one time it had for a little while glowed more brilliantly again, but it speedily reverted to its sullen red heat. I perceived by this slowing down of its rising and setting that the work of the tidal drag was done. The earth had come to rest with one face to the sun, even as in our own time the moon faces the earth. Very cautiously, for I remembered my former headlong fall, I began to reverse my motion. Slower and slower went the circling hands until the thousands one seemed motionless and the daily one was no longer a mere mist upon its scale. Still slower, until the dim outlines of a desolate beach grew visible.

'I stopped very gently and sat upon the Time Machine, looking round. The sky was no longer blue. North-eastward it was inky black, and out of the blackness shone brightly and steadily the pale white stars. Overhead it was a deep Indian red and starless, and south-eastward it grew brighter to a glowing scarlet where, cut by the horizon, lay the huge hull of the sun, red and motionless. The rocks about me were of a harsh reddish colour, and all the trace of life that I could see at first was the intensely green vegetation that covered every projecting point on their south-eastern face. It was the same rich green that one sees on forest moss or on the lichen in caves: plants which like these grow in a perpetual twilight.

'The machine was standing on a sloping beach. The sea stretched away to the south-west, to rise into a sharp bright horizon against the wan sky. There were no breakers and no waves, for not a breath of wind was stirring. Only a slight oily swell rose and fell like a gentle breathing and showed that the eternal sea was still moving and living. And along the margin where the water sometimes broke was a thick incrustation of salt—pink under the lurid sky. There was a sense of oppression in my head, and I noticed that I was breathing very fast. The sensation reminded me of my only experience of mountaineering, and from that I judged the air to be more rarefied than it is now.

'Far away up the desolate slope I heard a harsh scream and saw a thing like a huge white butterfly go slanting and fluttering up into the sky and, circling, disappear over some low hillocks beyond. The sound of its voice was so dismal that I shivered and seated myself more firmly upon the machine. Looking round me again, I saw that, quite near, what I had taken to be a reddish mass of rock was moving slowly towards me. Then I saw the thing was really a monstrous crab-like creature. Can you imagine

a crab as large as yonder table, with its many legs moving slowly and uncertainly, its big claws swaying, its long antennae, like carters' whips, waving and feeling, and its stalked eyes gleaming at you on either side of its metallic front? Its back was corrugated and ornamented with ungainly bosses, and a greenish incrustation blotched it here and there. I could see the many palps of its complicated mouth flickering and feeling as it moved.

'As I stared at this sinister apparition crawling towards me, I felt a tickling on my cheek as though a fly had lighted there. I tried to brush it away with my hand, but in a moment it returned, and almost immediately came another by my ear. I struck at this and caught something thread-like. It was drawn swiftly out of my hand. With a frightful qualm, I turned, and I saw that I had grasped the antenna of another monster crab that stood just behind me. Its evil eyes were wriggling on their stalks, its mouth was all alive with appetite, and its vast ungainly claws, smeared with an algal slime, were descending upon me. In a moment my hand was on the lever, and I had placed a month between myself and these monsters. But I was still on the same beach, and I saw them distinctly now as soon as I stopped. Dozens of them seemed to be crawling here and there, in the sombre light, among the foliated sheets of intense green.

'I cannot convey the sense of abominable desolation that hung over the world. The red eastern sky, the northward blackness, the salt Dead Sea, the stony beach crawling with these foul, slow-stirring monsters, the uniform poisonous-looking green of the lichenous plants, the thin air that hurts one's lungs: all contributed to an appalling effect. I moved on a hundred years and there was the same red sun—a little larger, a little duller—the same dying sea, the same chill air, and the same crowd of earthly crustacea creeping in and out among the green weed and the red rocks. And in the westward sky, I saw a curved pale line like a vast new moon.

'So I travelled, stopping ever and again, in great strides of a thousand years or more, drawn on by the mystery of the earth's fate, watching with a strange fascination the sun grow larger and duller in the westward sky, and the life of the old earth ebb away. At last, more than thirty millions years hence, the huge red-hot dome of the sun had come to obscure nearly a tenth part of the darkling heavens. Then I stopped once more, for the crawling multitude of crabs had disappeared, and the red beach, save for its livid green liverworts and lichens, seemed lifeless. And now it was flecked with white. A bitter cold assailed me. Rare white flakes ever and again came eddying down. To the north-eastward, the glare of snow lay under the starlight of the sable sky, and I could see an undulating crest of hillocks pinkish white. There were fringes of ice along the sea margin, with drifting masses further out; but the main expanse of that salt ocean, all bloody under the eternal sunset, was still unfrozen.

'I looked about me to see if any traces of animal life remained. A certain indefinable apprehension still kept me in the saddle of the machine. But I saw nothing moving, in earth or sky or sea. The green slime on the rocks alone testified that life was not extinct. A shallow sandbank had appeared in the sea, and the water had receded from the beach. I fancied I saw some black object flopping about upon this bank, but it became motionless as I looked at it, and I judged that my eye had been deceived, and that the black object was merely a rock. The stars in the sky were intensely bright and seemed to me to twinkle very little.

"Suddenly I noticed that the circular westward outline of the sun had changed; that a concavity, a bay, had appeared in the curve. I saw this grow larger. For a minute perhaps I stared aghast at this blackness that was creeping over the day, and then I realized that an eclipse was be-

ginning. Either the moon or the planet Mercury was passing across the sun's disk. Naturally, at first I took it to be the moon, but there is much to incline me to believe that what I really saw was the transit of an inner planet passing very near to the earth.

'The darkness grew apace; a cold wind began to blow in freshening gusts from the east, and the showering white flakes in the air increased in number. From the edge of the sea came a ripple and whisper. Beyond these lifeless sounds the world was silent. Silent? It would be hard to convey the stillness of it. All the sounds of man, the bleating of sheep, the cries of birds, the hum of insects, the stir that makes the background of our lives—all that was over. As the darkness thickened, the eddying flakes grew more abundant, dancing before my eyes; and the cold of the air more intense. At last, one by one, swiftly, one after the other, the white peaks of the distant hills vanished into blackness. The breeze rose to a moaning wind. I saw the black central shadow of the eclipse sweeping towards me. In another moment the pale stars alone were visible. All else was rayless obscurity. The sky was absolutely black.

'A horror of this great darkness came on me. The cold, that smote to my marrow, and the pain I felt in breathing, overcame me. I shivered, and a deadly nausea seized me. Then like a red-hot bow in the sky appeared the edge of the sun. I got off the machine to recover myself. I felt giddy and incapable of facing the return journey. As I stood sick and confused I saw again the moving thing upon the shoal—there was no mistake now that it was a moving thing—against the red water of the sea. It was a round thing, the size of a football perhaps, or, it may be, bigger, and tentacles trailed down from it; it seemed black against the weltering blood-red water, and it was hopping fitfully about. Then I felt I was fainting. But a terrible dread of lying helpless in that remote and awful twilight sustained me while I clambered upon the saddle.

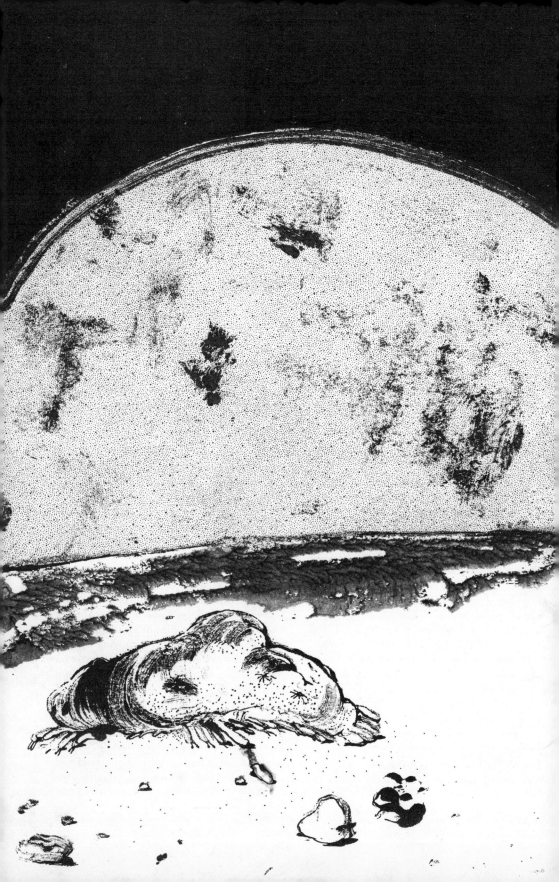

Chapter twelve

'So I came back. For a long time I must have been insensible upon the machine. The blinking succession of the days and nights was resumed, the sun got golden again, the sky blue. I breathed with greater freedom. The fluctuating contours of the land ebbed and flowed. The hands spun backward upon the dials. At last I saw again the dim shadows of houses, the evidences of decadent humanity. These, too, changed and passed, and others came. Presently, when the million dial was at zero, I slackened speed. I began to recognize our own petty and familiar architecture, the thousands hand ran back to the starting-point, the night and day flapped slower and slower. Then the old walls of the laboratory came round me. Very gently, now, I slowed the mechanism down.

'I saw one little thing that seemed odd to me. I think I have told you that when I set out, before my velocity became very high, Mrs. Watchett had walked across the room, travelling, as it seemed to me, like a rocket. As I returned, I passed again across that minute when she traversed the laboratory. But now her every motion appeared to be the exact inversion of her previous ones. The door at the lower end opened, and she glided quietly up the laboratory, back foremost, and disappeared behind the door by which she had previously entered. Just before that I seemed to see Hillyer for a moment; but he passed like a flash.

'Then I stopped the machine and saw about me again the old familiar laboratory, my tools, my appliances just as I had left them. I got off the thing very shakily and sat down upon my bench. For several minutes I trembled violently. Then I became calmer. Around me was my old workshop again, exactly as it had been. I might have slept there, and the whole thing have been a dream.

'And yet, not exactly! The thing had started from the south-east corner of the laboratory. It had come to rest again in the north-west, against the wall where you saw it. That gives you the exact distance from my little lawn to the pedestal of the White Sphinx, into which the Morlocks had carried my machine.

'For a time my brain went stagnant. Presently I got up and came through the passage here, limping, because my heel was still painful, and feeling sorely begrimed. I saw the *Pall Mall Gazette* on the table by the door. I found the date was indeed to-day and, looking at the timepiece, saw the hour was almost eight o'clock. I heard your voices and the clatter of plates. I hesitated —I felt so sick and weak. Then I sniffed good wholesome meat and opened the door on you. You know the rest. I washed, and dined, and now I am telling you the story.

'I know,' he said, after a pause, 'that all this will be absolutely incredible to you. To me one incredible thing is that I am here to-night in this old familiar room looking into your friendly faces and telling you these strange adventures.'

He looked at the Medical Man. 'No. I cannot expect you to believe it. Take it as a lie—or a prophecy. Say I dreamed it in the workshop. Consider I have been speculating upon the destinies of our race until I have hatched this fiction. Treat my assertion of its truth as a mere stroke of art to enhance its interest. And taking it as a story, what do you think of it?'

He took up his pipe and began, in his old accustomed manner, to tap with it nervously upon the bars of the grate. There was a momentary stillness. Then chairs began to creak and shoes to scrape upon the carpet. I took my eyes off the Time Traveller's face and looked round at his audience. They were in the dark, and little spots of colour swam before them. The Medical Man seemed absorbed in the contemplation of our host. The Editor was looking hard at the end of his cigar—the sixth. The Journalist fumbled for his watch. The others, as far as I remember, were motionless.

The Editor stood up with a sigh. 'What a pity it is you're not a writer of stories!' he

said, putting his hand on the Time Traveller's shoulder.

'You don't believe it?'

'Well—'

'I thought not.'

The Time Traveller turned to us. 'Where
are the matches?' he said. He lit one and
spoke over his pipe, puffing. 'To tell you
the truth . . . I hardly believe it myself. . . .
And yet . . .'

His eye fell with a mute inquiry upon the
withered white flowers upon the little table.
Then he turned over the hand holding his
pipe, and I saw he was looking at some
half-healed scars on his knuckles.

The Medical Man rose, came to the lamp,
and examined the flowers. 'The gynaece-
um's odd,' he said. The Psychologist leant
forward to see, holding out his hand for a
specimen.

'I'm hanged if it isn't a quarter to
one,' said the Journalist. 'How shall we
get home?'

'Plenty of cabs at the station,' said the
Psychologist.

'It's a curious thing,' said the Medical
Man, 'but I certainly don't know the natural
order of these flowers. May I have them?'

The Time Traveller hesitated. Then suddenly: 'Certainly not.'

'Where did you really get them?' said the
Medical Man.

The Time Traveller put his hand to his
head. He spoke like one who was trying to
keep hold of an idea that eluded him. 'They
were put into my pocket by Weena, when
I travelled into Time.' He stared round the
room. 'I'm damned if it isn't all going. This
room and you and the atmosphere of every
day is too much for my memory. Did I ever
make a Time Machine, or a model of a
Time Machine? Or is it all only a dream?
They say life is a dream, a precious poor
dream at times—but I can't stand another
that won't fit. It's madness. And where did
the dream come from? . . . I must look at
that machine. If there *is* one!'

He caught up the lamp swiftly and carried it, flaring red, through the door into the
corridor. We followed him. There in the
flickering light of the lamp was the machine
sure enough, squat, ugly, and askew; a
thing of brass, ebony, ivory, and translucent
glimmering quartz. Solid to the touch—for
I put out my hand and felt the rail of it—
and with brown spots and smears upon the
ivory and bits of grass and moss upon the
lower parts, and one rail bent awry.

The Time Traveller put the lamp down
on the bench and ran his hand along the
damaged rail. 'It's all right now,' he said.
'The story I told you was true. I'm sorry to
have brought you out here in the cold.' He
took up the lamp, and, in an absolute silence, we returned to the smoking-room.

He came into the hall with us and helped
the Editor on with his coat. The Medical
Man looked into his face and, with a certain
hesitation, told him he was suffering from
overwork, at which he laughed hugely. I
remember him standing in the open doorway, bawling good night.

I shared a cab with the Editor. He
thought the tale a 'gaudy lie.' For my own
part I was unable to come to a conclusion.
The story was so fantastic and incredible,
the telling so credible and sober. I lay
awake most of the night thinking about it.
I determined to go next day and see the
Time Traveller again. I was told he was in
the laboratory, and being on easy terms in
the house, I went up to him. The laboratory, however, was empty. I stared for a
minute at the Time Machine and put out
my hand and touched the lever. At that the
squat substantial-looking mass swayed like
a bough shaken by the wind. Its instability
startled me extremely, and I had a queer
reminiscence of the childish days when I
used to be forbidden to meddle. I came
back through the corridor. The Time Traveller met me in the smoking-room. He was
coming from the house. He had a small
camera under one arm and a knapsack under the other. He laughed when he saw me,
and gave me an elbow to shake. 'I'm frightfully busy,' said he, 'with that thing in
there.'

'But is it not some hoax?' I said. 'Do you really travel through time?'

'Really and truly I do.' And he looked frankly into my eyes. He hesitated. His eye wandered about the room. 'I only want half an hour,' he said. 'I know why you came, and it's awfully good of you. There's some magazines here. If you'll stop to lunch I'll prove you this time travelling up to the hilt, specimen and all. If you'll forgive my leaving you now?'

I consented, hardly comprehending then the full import of his words, and he nodded and went on down the corridor. I heard the door of the laboratory slam, seated myself in a chair, and took up a daily paper. What

was he going to do before lunch-time? Then suddenly I was reminded by an advertisement that I had promised to meet Richardson, the publisher, at two. I looked at my watch and saw that I could barely save that engagement. I got up and went down the passage to tell the Time Traveller.

As I took hold of the handle of the door I heard an exclamation, oddly truncated at the end, and a click and a thud. A gust of air whirled round me as I opened the door, and from within came the sound of broken glass falling on the floor. The Time Traveller was not there. I seemed to see a ghostly, indistinct figure sitting in a whirling mass of black and brass for a moment—a figure so transparent that the bench behind with its sheets of drawings was absolutely distinct; but this phantasm vanished as I rubbed my eyes. The Time Machine had gone. Save for a subsiding stir of dust, the further end of the laboratory was empty. A pane of the skylight had, apparently, just been blown in.

I felt an unreasonable amazement. I knew that something strange had happened, and for the moment could not distinguish what the strange thing might be. As I stood staring, the door into the garden opened, and the man-servant appeared.

We looked at each other. Then ideas began to come. 'Has Mr. ——— gone out that way?' said I.

'No, sir. No one has come out this way. I was expecting to find him here.'

At that I understood. At the risk of disappointing Richardson I stayed on, waiting for the Time Traveller; waiting for the second, perhaps still stranger story, and the specimens and photographs he would bring with him. But I am beginning now to fear that I must wait a lifetime. The Time Traveller vanished three years ago. And, as everybody knows now, he has never returned.

Epilogue

One cannot choose but wonder. Will he ever return? It may be that he swept back into the past and fell among the blood-drinking, hairy savages of the Age of Unpolished Stone; into the abysses of the Cretaceous Sea; or among the grotesque saurians, the huge reptilian brutes of the Jurassic times. He may even now—if I may use the phrase—be wandering on some plesiosaurus-haunted Oolitic coral reef, or beside the lonely saline lakes of the Triassic Age. Or did he go forward, into one of the nearer ages, in which men are still men, but with the riddles of our own time answered and its wearisome problems solved? Into the manhood of the race: for I, for my own part, cannot think that these latter days of weak experiment, fragmentary theory, and mutual discord are indeed man's culminating time! I say, for my own part. He, I know—for the question had been discussed among us long before the Time Machine was made—thought but cheerlessly of the Advancement of Mankind and saw in the growing pile of civilization only a foolish heaping that must inevitably fall back upon and destroy its makers in the end. If that is so, it remains for us to live as though it were not so. But to me the future is still black and blank—is a vast ignorance, lit at a few casual places by the memory of his story. And I have by me, for my comfort, two strange white flowers—shrivelled now, and brown and flat and brittle—to witness that even when mind and strength had gone, gratitude and a mutual tenderness still lived on in the heart of man.

NOTE TO THE READER

The highly original conception that underlies *The Time Machine* should not be allowed to obscure the fact that Wells was working with ideas that have their own tradition. Something of this may be gathered by consulting Chapter 93 of the *Syntopicon* on TIME, especially section 3b: The reality of the past and the future in relation to the existence of the present; and section 6f: Knowledge of the future: the truth of propositions about future contingents; the probability of predictions. Reference may be made also to PROGRESS 3c: Man's progressive conquest of the forces of nature through science and invention.

For still other relevant writings, *see,* in Vol. 8 of *GGB,* Sir Arthur Eddington, "The Running-Down of the Universe," pp. 561–80; Sir James Jeans, "Beginnings and Endings," pp. 581–96; and Loren Eiseley, "On Time," pp. 120–29.

PICTURE CREDITS

*Key to abbreviations used to indicate location of pictures on page: r.—right; l.—left; t.—top; b.—bottom; *—courtesy. Abbreviations are combined to describe unusual placement.*

The type for this book was set primarily by SSPA Typesetting, Inc., Carmel, Indiana, and the book was printed and bound by Kingsport Press, Inc., Kingsport, Tennessee.

GB

Authors

in Great Books of the Western World

Homer

Aeschylus

Sophocles

Herodotus

Euripides

Thucydides

Hippocrates

Aristophanes

Plato

Aristotle

Euclid

Archimedes

Apollonius

Lucretius

Virgil

Plutarch

Tacitus

Epictetus

Nicomachus

Ptolemy

Marcus Aurelius

Galen

Plotinus

Augustine

Thomas Aquinas

Dante

Chaucer

Machiavelli

Copernicus

Rabelais

Montaigne

Gilbert

Cervantes

Francis Bacon

Galileo

Shakespeare

Kepler